FINITE MATHEMATICS

James Stewart, Ph.D.
Professor of Mathematics, McMaster University

Thomas M.K. Davison, Ph.D.
Professor of Mathematics, McMaster University

O. Michael G. Hamilton, M.Sc.
Department Head, Ridley College, St. Catharines

James Laxton, M.Sc.
Delta Secondary School, Hamilton

M. Patricia Lenz, M.Sc.
Department Head, St. John's College, Brantford

Consultant
John Carter, M.Sc.
Department Head, North Toronto Collegiate Institute, Toronto

McGraw-Hill Ryerson Limited

Toronto   Montreal   New York   Auckland   Bogotá   Cairo   Caracas   Hamburg   Lisbon
London   Madrid   Mexico   Milan   New Delhi   Panama   Paris   San Juan
São Paulo   Singapore   Sydney   Tokyo

FINITE MATHEMATICS

Copyright © McGraw-Hill Ryerson Limited, 1988

ISBN 0-07-549600-3

 234567890 BP 7654321098

Printed and bound in Canada

Cover and Text Design by Daniel Kewley

Technical Illustrations by Sam Graphics Inc. and Warren Macdonald

Canadian Cataloguing in Publication Data

Main entry under title:

Finite mathematics

(The McGraw-Hill Ryerson mathematics program)
ISBN 0-07-549600-3

1. Mathematics – 1961-   . I. Stewart, James.
II. Series.

QA39.2.F566 1988   510   C88-093594-4

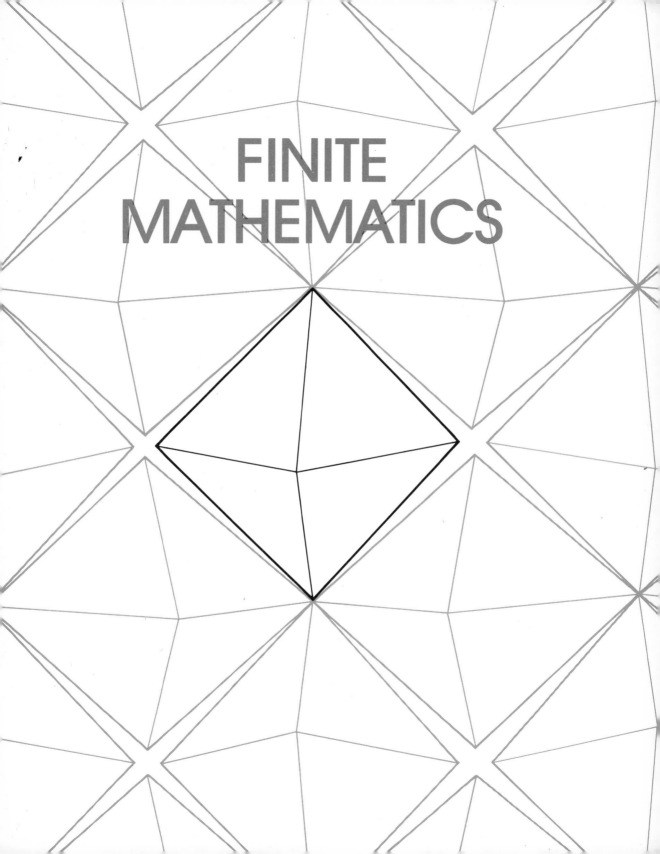

FINITE
MATHEMATICS

THE McGRAW-HILL RYERSON
MATHEMATICS PROGRAM

LIFE MATH 1
LIFE MATH 2
LIFE MATH 3

INTERMEDIATE MATHEMATICS 1
INTERMEDIATE MATHEMATICS 2
INTERMEDIATE MATHEMATICS 3

TEACHER'S EDITION FOR:
INTERMEDIATE MATHEMATICS 1
INTERMEDIATE MATHEMATICS 2
INTERMEDIATE MATHEMATICS 3

BLACKLINE MASTERS FOR:
INTERMEDIATE MATHEMATICS 1
INTERMEDIATE MATHEMATICS 2

APPLIED MATHEMATICS 9
APPLIED MATHEMATICS 10
APPLIED MATHEMATICS 11
APPLIED MATHEMATICS 12

TEACHER'S EDITION FOR:
APPLIED MATHEMATICS 9

TEACHER'S GUIDES FOR:
AM 10
AM 11
AM 12

FOUNDATIONS OF MATHEMATICS 9
FOUNDATIONS OF MATHEMATICS 10
FOUNDATIONS OF MATHEMATICS 11
FOUNDATIONS OF MATHEMATICS 12

TEACHER'S EDITION FOR:
FOUNDATIONS OF MATHEMATICS 9

TEACHER'S GUIDE FOR:
FM 10
FM 11
FM 12

FINITE MATHEMATICS
ALGEBRA AND GEOMETRY
CALCULUS

TABLE
OF
CONTENTS

PREFACE

This textbook on Finite Mathematics is part of a three-volume series, also including books on Calculus and Algebra and Geometry, for courses that represent the culmination of a high school mathematics program.

MATHEMATICAL MODELLING

One of the principal themes of Finite Mathematics is the construction of mathematical models of physical and social situations. Among the diverse applications that we include in this book are the following:
- Matrix multiplication is used to study the networking patterns involved in transportation problems.
- The hypergeometric distribution is used in estimating the population of an endangered species.
- The normal distribution is applied in weighing the advantages of manufacturing in space.
- The sum of an arithmetico-geometric series is used to determine the actual cost of a loan in today's dollars.
- Markov chains are applied to predict long-term trends in consumer buying.

PROBLEM SOLVING EMPHASIS

Our educational philosophy has been strongly influenced by the books of George Polya and the lectures of both Polya and Gabor Szego at Stanford University. They consistently introduced a topic by relating it to something concrete or familiar. In this spirit, we have tried to motivate new topics by relating mathematical concepts to the students' experience.

The influence of Polya's work on problem-solving can be seen throughout the book. The Review and Preview to Chapter 1 gives an introduction to some of the problem-solving strategies that he has explained at greater length in his books *How to Solve It, Mathematical Discovery*, and *Mathematics and Plausible Reasoning*. When these strategies occur in examples, we highlight their use with margin captions.

In addition to the graded exercise sets, we have included special problems, called PROBLEMS PLUS, that require a higher level of problem-solving skill.

ORDER OF TOPICS

We have chosen to present the topics in an order that we think is pedagogically preferable, starting with combinatorics and using it in the binomial theorem, series, and probability and statistics, and concluding with linear algebra. However, it is certainly possible to start with the linear algebra (Chapters 8-10) by leaving the material on markov chains in Sections 8.4 and 8.5 to be integrated into Chapter 5. We also note that Chapter 4 can be covered anytime after Chapter 3.

Sections that are labelled optional in the curriculum for the Ontario Academic Course in Finite Mathematics have been indicated by an asterisk. Enrichment topics that go beyond this curriculum are indicated by double asterisks.

TWENTIETH-CENTURY MATHEMATICIANS

Many people have the mistaken impression that all of mathematics was done centuries ago. To show that mathematics is still very much alive and is still being created, we have included biographies of five contemporary mathematicians whose work involves Finite Mathematics: George Polya, Persi Diaconis, Albert Tucker, Herbert Robbins, and Ronald Graham.

ACKNOWLEDGMENTS

In addition to the reviewers listed earlier and our consultant John Carter, who attended all our authors' meetings, we wish to thank our teaching colleagues for their valuable advice, the editorial and production staff at McGraw-Hill Ryerson for a superb job, and those close to us who understandingly put up with the long hours that we devoted to this project.

James Stewart
Thomas M.K. Davison
O. Michael G. Hamilton
James Laxton
M. Patricia Lenz

CREDITS

pp. 29, 111, 258, 336, 505; Birkhauser Boston: Cambridge, MA.
p. 29; photo: Ken Regan
p. 111; photo: Stella Polya
p. 111; quote: Princeton University Press: Princeton, N.J.
p. 149; cartoon by: Andrejs Dunkels, © 1979 National Council of Teachers
of Mathematics. Used by permission.
p. 199; Canadian Press
p. 258; photo: Herbert Robbins
p. 265; The Globe and Mail, Toronto
p. 336; photo: Stanford University
p. 505; photo: Albert Tucker

CHAPTER 1

PERMUTATIONS

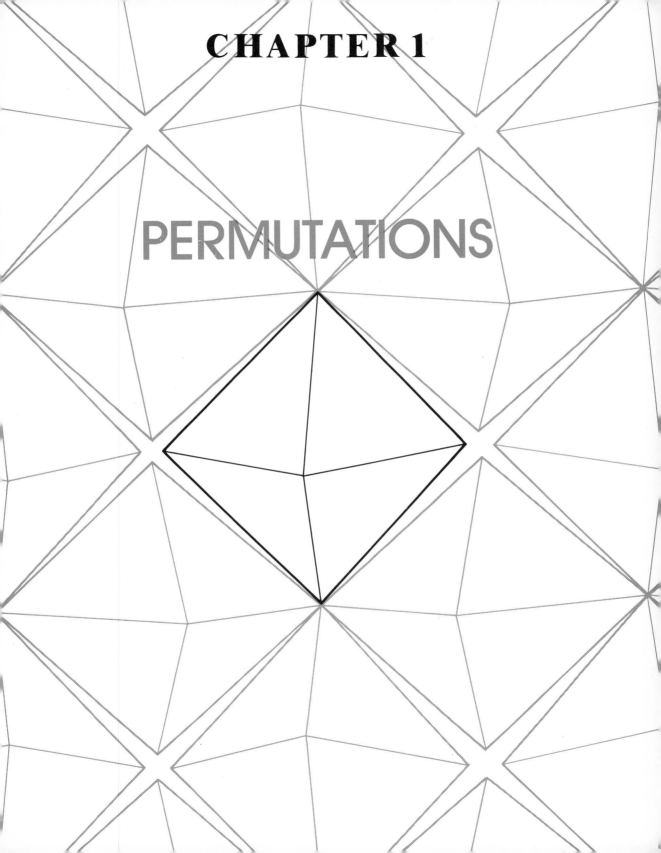

REVIEW AND PREVIEW TO
CHAPTER 1

Problem Solving

There are no hard and fast rules that will ensure success in solving problems. However, it is possible to outline some general steps in the problem-solving process and to give some principles that may be useful in the solution of certain problems. These steps and principles are just common sense made explicit. They have been adapted from George Polya's book *How to Solve It*.

1. **UNDERSTAND THE PROBLEM.** The first step is to read the problem and make sure that you understand it clearly. Ask yourself the following questions:

> *What is the unknown?*
> *What are the given quantities?*
> *What are the given conditions?*

For many problems it is useful to

> *draw a diagram*

and identify the given and required quantities on the diagram.

Usually it is necessary to

> *introduce suitable notation.*

In choosing symbols for the unknown quantities we often use letters such as a, b, c, ..., m, n, ..., x, y, ... , but in some cases it helps to use initials as suggestive symbols, for instance, V for volume, t for time.

2. **THINK OF A PLAN.** Find a connection between the given information and the unknown that will enable you to calculate the unknown. If you do not see the connection immediately, the following ideas may be helpful in devising a plan.

(a) *Try to recognize something familiar.*   Relate the given situation to previous knowledge. Look at the unknown and try to recall a more familiar problem having a similar unknown.

(b) *Try to recognize patterns.*   Some problems are solved by recognizing that some kind of pattern is occurring. The pattern could be geometric, or numerical, or algebraic. If you can see regularity or repetition in a problem, then you might be able to guess what the continuing pattern is, and then prove it.

(c) *Use analogy.*   Try to think of an analogous problem, that is, a similar and related problem, but one that is easier than the original problem. If you can solve the similar, simpler problem, then it might give you the clues you need to solve the original, more difficult one. For instance, if a problem involves very large numbers, you could first try a similar problem with smaller numbers. Or if the problem is in three-dimensional geometry, you could look for a similar problem in two-dimensional geometry. Or if the problem you start with is a general one, you could first try a special case.

(d) *Introduce something extra.*   It may sometimes be necessary to introduce something new, an auxiliary aid, to help make the connection between the given and the unknown. For instance, in geometry the auxiliary aid could be a new line drawn in a diagram. In algebra it could be a new unknown that is related to the original unknown.

(e) *Take cases.*   You may sometimes have to split a problem into several cases and give a different argument for each of the cases.

(f) *Work backwards.*   Sometimes it is useful to imagine that your problem is solved and work backwards, step by step, till you arrive at the given data. Then you may be able to reverse your steps and thereby construct a solution to the original problem.

(g) *Use indirect reasoning.*   Sometimes it is appropriate to attack a problem indirectly. For instance, in a counting argument it might be best to count the total number of objects and subtract the number of objects that do *not* have the required property. Another example of indirect reasoning is *proof by contradiction* in which we assume that the desired conclusion is false and eventually arrive at a contradiction.

(h) *Use mathematical induction.*   In proving statements that involve a positive integer n, it is frequently helpful to use the Principle of Mathematical Induction, which is discussed in Section 4.7.

3. **CARRY OUT THE PLAN.** In Step 2 a plan was devised. In carrying out that plan you have to check each stage of the plan and write the details that prove that each stage is correct.

4. **LOOK BACK.** Having completed your solution, it is wise to look back over it, partly to see if there are errors in the solution, and partly to see if there is an easier way to solve the problem. Another reason for looking back is that it will familiarize you with the method of solution and this may be useful for solving a future problem. Descartes said, ''Every problem that I solved became a rule which I then used in solving other problems.''

Example Find the final digit in the number 7^{366}.

Solution First, notice that 7^{366} is a very large number—far too large to be found on a calculator. Therefore, we attack this problem by first looking at analogous problems. A similar, but simpler, problem would be to find the final digit in 7^6 or 7^{19}. In fact, let us start with the exponents, 1, 2, 3, ... and see what happens.

ANALOGY

Number	Final Digit
7^1	7
7^2	9
7^3	3
7^4	1
7^5	7
7^6	9
7^7	3
7^8	1
:	:

PATTERN

By now you can see a pattern. The final digits occur in a cycle with length 4: 7, 9, 3, 1, 7, 9, 3, 1, 7, 9, 3, 1, ... Which number occurs in the 366th position? If we divide 366 by 4, the remainder is 2. So the final digit is the second number in the cycle, namely 9.

The final digit in the number 7^{366} is 9.

EXERCISE 1

1. Find the final digit in the number $(75\ 923)^{413}$.

2. Find the number of solutions of the equation $3x + 4y = 229$ if x and y must be positive integers.

3. Find all positive integers n such that $3^n + 1$ is divisible by 5.

4. The perimeter of a right triangle is 60 cm and the altitude perpendicular to the hypotenuse is 12 cm. Find the lengths of the three sides of the triangle.

5. Prove that at any party there are two people who know the same number of people. (Assume that if A knows B, then B knows A. Hint: use indirect reasoning.)

INTRODUCTION

The ability to count possibilities is useful in a wide range of occupations and hobbies. A worker in the city's traffic department is investigating the routes from one point to another within the city. A computer programmer is planning the paths a user might take through an adventure game program, given a series of exciting options. A physicist is studying the physical properties of a new material by examining the possibilities for its molecular structure. All of these use techniques from the branch of mathematics called *combinatorics*.

Of more immediate interest is the fact that many problems in probability and statistics (Chapters 5–7) require counting the number of possibilities in a given situation. For example, calculating the likelihood of winning in a game of craps requires counting the number of ways of rolling a 7 or an 11 with two dice. In addition, some of the theory developed for these purposes is helpful in developing a formula for the expansion of binomial expressions (Chapter 3).

1.1   COUNTING PRINCIPLES

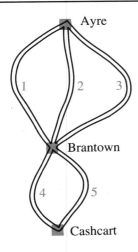

Suppose that Ayre, Brantown, and Cashcart are three towns. If there are three roads from Ayre to Brantown and two roads from Brantown to Cashcart, how many routes are there from Ayre to Cashcart passing through Brantown?

If the roads are numbered as in the diagram at the left, then we can identify the various routes as follows:

$$1–4 \quad 1–5 \quad 2–4 \quad 2–5 \quad 3–4 \quad 3–5$$

So, there are six routes.

We could also use a tree diagram to show the six routes.

Ayre to Brantown	Brantown to Cashcart
1	4
	5
2	4
	5
3	4
	5

Similarly, if there were *m* roads from Ayre to Brantown and *n* roads from Brantown to Cashcart, by visualizing either the roads themselves or a tree diagram, we can see that the number of routes from Ayre to Cashcart via Brantown would be *mn*.

The reasoning used in this situation is called the Fundamental Counting Principle, also called the Rule of Product.

The Fundamental Counting Principle

If a first action can be performed in m ways and a second action can be performed in n ways then these two actions can be performed, in this order, in mn ways.

Example 1 At a private school, students wear school uniforms. Each student must wear either a white dress shirt, a blue dress shirt, or a white golf shirt. Students must also wear dress pants in grey, black, navy, or white. How many variations are there of this uniform?

Solution *First action:* selecting a type of shirt
A shirt can be selected in three ways (white dress shirt, blue dress shirt, white golf shirt).

Second action: picking a type of pants
Pants can be selected in four ways (grey, black, navy, or white).

By the Fundamental Counting Principle, a complete uniform (shirt and pants) can be selected in

$$3 \times 4 = 12 \text{ ways}$$

So, there are 12 variations of this uniform.

```
shirt        pants

             grey
white        black
dress        navy
             white

             grey
blue         black
dress        navy
             white

             grey
white        black
golf         navy
             white
```

When there are *several* actions involved, the Fundamental Counting Principle can be extended as follows:

If a first action can be performed in a ways, a second action in b ways, a third in c ways, ... and so on, then all of the actions can be performed together, in this order, in $a \times b \times c \times \ldots$ ways.

Example 2 A new rule regarding footwear is introduced for the uniform described in Example 1. It states that:
"Students must wear only black or blue shoes in a loafer or laced-up style; socks must be black, navy, white, grey, or light blue."
Now, how many different styles of uniform are possible?

Solution *First action:* picking a (type of) shirt
It is possible to select a shirt in three ways.

Second action: picking pants
It is possible to select pants in four ways.

Third action: picking shoes

Shoes may be selected in four ways (black loafers, black laced-up, navy loafers, navy laced-up).

Fourth action: picking socks

Socks may be selected in five ways (five different colours).

A complete uniform, including footwear, can be selected in

$$3 \times 4 \times 4 \times 5 = 240 \text{ ways}$$

So, now there are 240 variations on the uniform.

Using a tree diagram for this situation is awkward because so many levels are needed.

Example 3   Tim tosses four coins, one after the other.
  (a)   Draw a tree diagram to illustrate the results of this activity.
  (b)   *Count* the number of possible results by using the tree diagram.
  (c)   Use the Fundamental Counting Principle to *calculate* the number of possible results.

Solution   (a)   When Tim tosses a coin, either a head or a tail will show on its upper face. We use H to represent "head" and T to represent "tail."

| 1st
Coin | 2nd
Coin | 3rd
Coin | 4th
Coin |

  (b)   There are 16 "branches" in the tree diagram representing the 16 possible results of Tim's activity.
  (c)   Using the Fundamental Counting Principle, we find that the number of possible results is

$$2 \times 2 \times 2 \times 2 = 16$$

If we are interested in having one *or* the other of two actions occur, we use another counting principle.

Rule of Sum

If one action can be performed in *m* ways and another action can be performed in *n* ways and the first and second action cannot be performed at the same time, then there are $m + n$ ways in which either the first action or the second action can be performed.

Example 4   In a deck of cards the *major suits* are hearts and spades. How many ways are there to select a card in a major suit which is either a red face card or a black ace?

Solution   ***First action:***   selecting a red face card in a major suit
There are three such cards (jack, queen, and king of hearts).

Second action: selecting the ace of spades (only black ace in a major suit)
There is only one such card (in a standard deck).

A standard deck of cards has 52 cards divided into four suits, clubs, hearts, diamonds, and spades. Each suit includes 2, 3, ..., 10, jack, queen, king, and ace.

Because these actions cannot be performed at the same time (it is impossible to pick a red face card which is the ace of spades), the Rule of Sum applies.

So, by the Rule of Sum, there are

$$3 + 1 = 4 \text{ ways}$$

of selecting, from a major suit, either a red face card or a black ace.

EXERCISE 1.1

A **1.**   For each situation described, indicate which rule applies in determining the number of possibilities: the Rule of Product or the Rule of Sum.
   (a)   rolling a sum of either four or seven with two dice
   (b)   selecting a dress, hat, and purse to wear to a wedding
   (c)   making a sandwich with ham or salami, hot or sweet mustard on white, whole wheat, or rye bread
   (d)   picking a horse in either the first or second race at Dashing Downs Raceway
   (e)   buying a car with or without air conditioning, automatic transmission, stereo tape deck, and power windows.

B 2. When Jill is purchasing her first new car, she is given a choice of two upholstery materials (cloth and leather) and four colours (black, ivory, grey, and blue).
   (a) Draw a tree diagram for this situation.
   (b) How many different choices does she have?

3. Show with a tree diagram the number of methods of travelling from Toronto to Vancouver via Calgary, if you can go from Toronto to Calgary by either plane or train and from Calgary to Vancouver by bus, plane, or train.

4. An all-star baseball team has a roster of seven pitchers and three catchers. How many pairs of pitcher and catcher can the manager select from this roster?

5. (a) If repetition of digits is allowed, how many two-digit numbers can be formed using the digits 1, 2, 3, 4, and 5?
   (b) How many numbers consisting of two *different* digits can be formed by using these same digits?

6. Darla's Diner offers the following menu:

Main Course	Dessert	Beverage
chicken	cheesecake	coffee
ham	ice cream	tea
steak	muffin	milk
roast pork		juice
hamburger		

In how many ways can a customer order a meal consisting of one choice from each category?

7. (a) Draw a tree diagram to show win-loss possibilities for one of the teams in a best-two-of-three playoff series.
   (b) Using the tree diagram, count the number of ways a team could win the series despite losing one game.

8. Larry prefers classical music but he also enjoys country and western songs. His friend Lee has a collection of record albums including 35 classical albums, 20 rock, and 12 country and western. In how many ways can Lee select one album that will match Larry's musical tastes?

9. A team of students for the county computer programming contest will be chosen according to the following rules: one student from Grade 9 or 10, two students from Grade 11, and one student from Grade 12. At St. Lawrence High this year there are five interested students in Grade 9, two in Grade 10, two in Grade 11, and four in Grade 12. How many different teams could be formed?

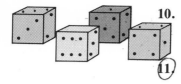

10. Four dice of different colours are rolled. We then examine the uppermost faces of the dice. How many possible configurations are there? | 296

11. In her third year of high school, Maria will definitely study English, Physics, Biology, and Mathematics. She will pick her other three courses from the following list: Data Processing, Dramatic Arts, Instrumental Music, French, Italian, German, Spanish, Keyboarding, and Accounting. How many different course programs are available to her if she wants to take one business subject, one arts course, and one second language?

12. New houses in a subdivision are available in three-, four-, and five-bedroom models, which may be built with six different exterior finishes, with or without a swimming pool. How many distinct selections can be made by the customer?

13. A combination lock has 60 different positions. To open the lock you move to a certain number in the clockwise direction, then to a number in the counterclockwise direction, and finally to a third number in the clockwise direction. If consecutive numbers in the combination cannot be the same, how many different combinations are there?

14. (a) In how many ways can a queen be picked from a deck of cards?
    (b) In how many ways can a diamond be selected from a deck of cards?
    (c) In how many ways can either a queen or a diamond be chosen from a deck of cards?
    (d) Does the Rule of Sum apply in 14(c)? Explain why or why not.

C 15. There are 1500 students in Dunesville High School. Each student requires a lock for a personal locker. The school provides a standard brand of lock for all students. If the locks are to operate the same way as those described in Question 13, what is the smallest number of positions that must be in the lock to give each student a unique combination?

16. (a) Draw a tree diagram representing the makeup (boy, girl) of a family with three children.
    (b) Using the tree diagram, count the number of variations with exactly two girls.
    (c) How many different families have either a boy as eldest or boys as eldest and middle children?
    (d) Does the Rule of Sum apply in 16(c)? Explain.

1.2   FACTORIAL NOTATION

In combinatorics questions we will often multiply consecutive numbers such as the following:

$$7 \times 6 \times 5 \times 4 \times 3 \times 2 \times 1$$

To work more easily with such calculations we introduce a new notation.

For a natural number n,

$$\textbf{\textit{n}}! = n \times (n-1) \times (n-2) \times \ldots \times 3 \times 2 \times 1$$

This is read as **n factorial.**

Example 1 Calculate each of the following:
(a) 4!   (b) 9!   (c) 1!

Solution (a) $4! = 4 \times 3 \times 2 \times 1 = 24$

(b) $9! = 9 \times 8 \times 7 \times 6 \times 5 \times 4 \times 3 \times 2 \times 1 = 362\ 880$

(c) $1! = 1$

Your calculator may have a key that performs this operation. If so, consult the manual to see how to use this key.

Example 2 Evaluate each expression.

(a) $\dfrac{8!}{6!}$ (b) $\dfrac{75!}{71!}$ (c) $\dfrac{17!}{15!2!}$

Solution (a) $8! = 8 \times 7 \times 6 \times 5 \times 4 \times 3 \times 2 \times 1 = 40\ 320$
$6! = 6 \times 5 \times 4 \times 3 \times 2 \times 1 = 720$

so, $\dfrac{8!}{6!} = \dfrac{40\ 320}{720} = 56$

For such large numbers a calculator is definitely handy.

What is the largest number n for which *your* calculator can find $n!$ accurately?

(b) But 75! and 71! are too large for any calculator to handle accurately. So we make use of the definition of the factorial operation to simplify our task.

$$\frac{75!}{71!} = \frac{75 \times 74 \times 73 \times 72 \times \cancel{(71 \times 70 \times \ldots \times 3 \times 2 \times 1)}}{\cancel{(71 \times 70 \times \ldots \times 3 \times 2 \times 1)}}$$

$$= 75 \times 74 \times 73 \times 72$$
$$= 29\ 170\ 800$$

More briefly

$$\frac{17!}{15!2!} = \frac{17 \times 16 \times 15!}{15!2!}$$

(c) $\dfrac{17!}{15!2!} = \dfrac{17 \times 16 \times \cancel{15 \times 14 \times \ldots 3 \times 2 \times 1}}{\cancel{(15 \times 14 \times \ldots 3 \times 2 \times 1)} \times (2 \times 1)}$

$$= \frac{17 \times 16}{2 \times 1}$$

$$= 17 \times 8$$

$$= 136$$

For a reason that will not be obvious until Section 1.3, we define $0! = 1$.

Example 3   Simplify each expression.

(a) $(n+2)(n+1)!$ (b) $\dfrac{(n+1)!}{(n-1)!}$

Solution   (a) $(n+2)(n+1)! = (n+2)[(n+1)n(n-1)(n-2) \ldots 3 \times 2 \times 1]$
                            $= (n+2)!$

(b) $\dfrac{(n+1)!}{(n-1)!} = \dfrac{(n+1)n\cancel{(n-1)(n-2)} \ldots \times \cancel{3 \times 2 \times 1}}{\cancel{(n-1)(n-2)} \ldots \times \cancel{3 \times 2 \times 1}}$

$$= (n+1)n \quad \text{or} \quad n^2 + n$$

EXERCISE 1.2

A 1. Can the factorial operation be defined for negative integers? Explain your answer.

2. Match each expression on the left with an equivalent expression on the right.

(a) $\dfrac{14!}{13!}$ (i) 10 100

(b) $\dfrac{52!}{51!}$ (ii) 6!

(c) $\dfrac{101!}{99!}$ (iii) 52

(d) $20 \times 19!$ (iv) 10!

(e) $90 \times 8!$ (v) 14

(f) $30 \times 4!$ (vi) 20!

B 3. Find the value for each expression.

(a) $\dfrac{8!}{5!}$ (b) $\dfrac{19!}{13!}$

(c) $\dfrac{21!}{17!4!}$ (d) $\dfrac{9!}{7!2!}$

(e) $\dfrac{155!}{152!}$ (f) $\dfrac{93!}{89!4!}$

4. Evaluate each of the expressions, using the definition of the factorial operation to simplify the work.

(a) $\dfrac{10!}{5!}$

(b) $\dfrac{21!}{14!}$

(c) $\dfrac{9!}{3!6!}$

(d) $\dfrac{12!}{8!4!}$

(e) $\dfrac{7!}{2!5!} + \dfrac{7!}{4!3!}$

(f) $\dfrac{15!}{9!6!} + \dfrac{15!}{10!5!}$

(g) $2 \times \dfrac{5!}{3!2!}$

(h) $3 \times \dfrac{11!}{7!4!}$

5. Repeat Question 4 using the ! key on a calculator wherever possible.

6. On the assembly line at Micro Manufacturing, six-digit serial numbers are assigned to products according to the following regulations: only the digits 4 to 9 are used; no digit may be used twice in the same serial number.

   (a) Use the Fundamental Counting Principle to calculate the number of possible serial numbers under this system. (Hint: The first action is picking the first digit of the serial number, the second action, the second digit and so on.)

   (b) Write this answer using factorial notation.

7. In rearranging the letters of a word such as KETCHUP, the number of possibilities for the first letter is seven because any one of the seven letters is eligible. For the second letter, there are only six possibilities because the letter used first will not be reused.

   Write the number of arrangements of the letters of the word KETCHUP using factorial notation.

8. Simplify, $n \in W$.

   (a) $n(n - 1)!$

   (b) $n!(n + 1)$

   (c) $(n - 1)!(n^2 + n)$

   (d) $n!(n^2 + 3n + 2)$

   (e) $\dfrac{n!}{(n - 2)!}$

   (f) $\dfrac{(n + 2)!}{(n - 1)!}$

C 9. Solve for n, $n \in W$.

   (a) $\dfrac{(n + 1)!}{n!} = 9$

   (b) $\dfrac{n!}{(n - 2)!} = 20$

   (c) $\dfrac{3(n + 1)!}{(n - 1)!} = 126$

   (d) $\dfrac{2n!}{(n-3)!} = 84n$

1.3 PERMUTATIONS: ARRANGEMENTS OF DISTINCT OBJECTS

In arranging seven students to sit in the front row for a class picture, the photographer first puts the three girls to the right and the four boys to the left. He is not pleased with this setup. Then he tries mixing boys and girls, starting with Leo at the far left. He feels this is still not quite right. Then he rearranges the group so that the tallest, Dorinka, is at the left with the shortest, Shawn, at the right. Still he is not satisfied! How many possible arrangements of the seven students are there?

In order to apply the Fundamental Counting Principle, we reason as follows:

The positions for the students can be illustrated by using a series of seven boxes.

7 6 5 4 3 2 1

In the position at the far left, there are seven possibilities because any student could be put there. In the next position there are six possibilities because the student in the first position cannot also be in the second position. This reasoning continues so that there are

$$7 \times 6 \times 5 \times 4 \times 3 \times 2 \times 1 = 5040 \text{ ways}$$

of arranging these students.

> A **permutation of n (distinct) objects** is an arrangement of all of the objects *in a definite order*.
> The total number of such permutations is denoted by $P(n, n)$.

Note that, by the Fundamental Counting Principle, $P(n, n) = n!$

Example 1   A choir has learned eight songs for its spring concert. In how many different ways can the director arrange these songs to form the concert program?

Solution   There are eight items (the songs) to be arranged, so there are

$$P(8, 8) = 8!$$
$$= 8 \times 7 \times 6 \times 5 \times 4 \times 3 \times 2 \times 1$$
$$= 40\ 320 \text{ ways}$$

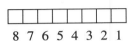

of arranging these songs for the concert program.

Sometimes we arrange only *some* of the objects being considered, as the next example illustrates.

Example 2   An investment club with five members wants to select a president and a vice-president. In how many ways can this be done?

Solution   By the Fundamental Counting Principle, they can be selected in

$$5 \times 4 = 20 \text{ ways}$$

A **permutation of *n* (distinct) objects taken *r* at a time** is an arrangement of *r* of the *n* objects *in a definite order*. The total number of such arrangements is denoted by **$P(n, r)$**.

Such arrangements may also be referred to as ***r*-arrangements** and their number denoted by $_nP_r$ or $n_{(r)}$.

In general, to form an arrangement of *r* objects selected from a set of *n* objects, the first object can be selected in *n* ways. The second object can then be selected in $n - 1$ ways; the third in $n - 2$ ways and so on, so that the *r*th object can be selected in $n - (r - 1)$, or $n - r + 1$ ways.

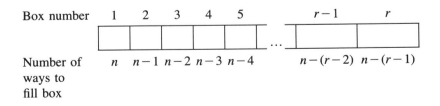

Thus, by the Fundamental Counting Principle,

$$P(n, r) = n(n-1)(n-2)(n-3) \ldots (n-r+1)$$

Factorial notation allows us to express this formula more briefly:

$$P(n,r) = n(n-1)(n-2)(n-3) \dots (n-r+1) \times \frac{(n-r)(n-r-1) \dots 3 \times 2 \times 1}{(n-r)(n-r-1) \dots 3 \times 2 \times 1}$$

$$= \frac{n(n-1)(n-2)(n-3) \dots (n-r+1) \times (n-r)(n-r-1) \dots 3 \times 2 \times 1}{(n-r)(n-r-1) \dots 3 \times 2 \times 1}$$

$$= \frac{n!}{(n-r)!}$$

So,
$$\boxed{P(n,r) = \frac{n!}{(n-r)!}}$$

Example 3   Evaluate each expression.

(a) $P(8,3)$ (b) $P(6,6)$

Solution (a) $P(8,3) = \dfrac{8!}{(8-3)!} = \dfrac{8!}{5!} = 8 \times 7 \times 6 = 336$

(b) $P(6,6) = \dfrac{6!}{(6-6)!} = \dfrac{6!}{0!}$

but $0! = 1$ by definition,

so the number of arrangements of 6 out of a set of 6 objects is 6!, or 720, just as we expected from the Fundamental Counting Principle. This, in fact, is why 0! is defined as 1.

In the following examples we calculate the number of permutations possible when specific conditions must be met.

Example 4   (a) Find the number of permutations of the letters of the word DIPLOMA for which the letter L remains in the middle position.

(b) How many ways are there of arranging the letters of DIPLOMA so that the letters O and I are together?

Solution   The technique of filling boxes, as used in the class photo example, is helpful in dealing with variations of straightforward permutation situations.

(a) We use seven boxes with L in the middle position.

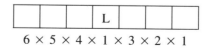

$$6 \times 5 \times 4 \times 1 \times 3 \times 2 \times 1$$

Then the middle box can be filled only with the L, that is, in one way, while the other six letters can be arranged freely.

So there are $1 \times P(6,6) = 1 \times 6! = 720$ ways of arranging the letters of DIPLOMA with the L in the middle.

(b) Because the O and I must always be together, the list of valid arrangements includes D<u>IO</u>PLMA and DPL<u>IO</u>MA but not D<u>I</u>PO<u>L</u>MA. So we treat O and I as a single unit. Thus, in this situation, we need only *six* boxes.

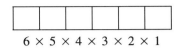

$$6 \times 5 \times 4 \times 3 \times 2 \times 1$$

However, for every arrangement including the pair OI there is a different arrangement with IO. So, the number of arrangements of the letters of DIPLOMA with O and I together is

$$2 \times P(6,6) = 2 \times 6! = 1440$$

Example 5   At a used car lot, six cars for sale are to be parked side-by-side. In how many different ways can this be done if:
(a) the one (and only) car with a sunroof must be at the right end of the line?
(b) the three black cars must be together?

Solution   (a) The various orders of the cars could appeal in different ways to customers, so the order is significant.

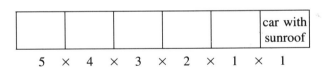

$$5 \quad \times \quad 4 \quad \times \quad 3 \quad \times \quad 2 \quad \times \quad 1 \quad \times \quad 1$$

The number of different ways the cars could be parked is

$$1 \times P(5,5) = 1 \times 5! = 120$$

(b) The three black cars are considered as one unit, so there are four items to be arranged. There are 3! ways of arranging the black cars within the one unit.

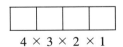

$$4 \times 3 \times 2 \times 1$$

So, there are

$$
\begin{aligned}
3! \times P(4,4) &= 3! \times 4! \\
&= (3 \times 2 \times 1) \times (4 \times 3 \times 2 \times 1) \\
&= 144 \text{ ways}
\end{aligned}
$$

of parking the cars with the three black cars together.

EXERCISE 1.3

B **1.** Evaluate each expression.
  (a) $P(5,3)$ (b) $P(9,5)$
  (c) $P(11,7)$ (d) $P(6,3)$
  (e) $P(8,4)$ (f) $P(10,8)$

2. Your calculator may have a key for calculating $P(n,r)$. Consult the manual to see how to use this key. (Remember the alternate notations, $_nP_r$ and $n_{(r)}$, either of which might appear on the key.) Repeat the calculations for Question 1 by using this key.

3. A ship carries four signal flags of different colours. How many different signals can be sent by hoisting these flags on the ship's flagpole in various orders?

4. How many three-digit numbers can be made from the digits 1 to 5 if:
  (a) repetition of digits is not allowed?
  (b) repetition of digits is allowed?
  (c) no repetition is allowed and the number must be greater than 500? List all numbers fitting this description.
  (d) repetition is allowed and the number must be less than 300?

5. In how many ways can a chairman, treasurer, and secretary be selected from a Board of Directors with eight members?

6. The manager of a baseball team has picked the nine players for the starting line-up. In how many ways can he set the batting order so that the pitcher bats last?

7. If 1000 people enter a contest in which there is a first prize, a second prize, and a third prize, in how many ways could the prizes be given?

8. Emilio has picked up his textbooks for the seven courses he will study this year. In how many ways can he arrange them on his bookshelf if he wants to keep the French and German texts side by side?

9. Twelve different portraits are in the Ling family's collection.
  (a) In how many ways could five of them be hung in a row on the living room wall?
  (b) If Grandma Ling's picture must be included and must be hung in the middle of the group of five, how many different arrangements are there?

10. In how many ways can three different awards be distributed among 20 students in the following situations?
  (a) No student may receive more than one award.
  (b) There is no limit on the number of awards won by one student.

11. Show that the number of three-letter "words" that can be formed from the word CAMPGROUND is the same as the number of permutations of the letters of GROUND.

12. Find the number of ways of arranging the letters of MATCHING if:
    (a) there are no restrictions;
    (b) the first letter must be M;
    (c) the odd-numbered positions must remain unchanged;
    (d) the arrangement must end with NG.

13. Suggest why the format for standard Ontario licence plates was changed from three letters followed by three numbers to the reverse, that is, three numbers followed by three letters.

C 14. (a) Evaluate each pair of expressions.
       (i) $P(5, 2)$ $P(5, 3)$ 5·4·2
       (ii) $P(8, 3)$ $P(8, 5)$
       (iii) $P(12, 7)$ $P(12, 5)$
    (b) Using the results from (a), verify for each pair of expressions
        that $P(n, n-r) = \dfrac{(n-r)!}{r!}P(n, r)$.

        For example, show that $P(5, 5-3) = \dfrac{(5-3)!}{3!}P(5, 3)$.

    (c) Find the value for each expression using the given information.
        (i) If $P(11, 4) = 7920$, find $P(11, 7)$.
        (ii) If $P(9, 5) = 15\,120$, find $P(9, 4)$.

15. Solve for n, $n \in W$.
    (a) $7P(n, 3) = 6P(n+1, 3)$ (b) $3P(n, 4) = P(n-1, 5)$

16. For natural numbers n and r with $n > r$
    (a) prove that $P(n, n) = P(n, r)P(n-r, n-r)$;
    (b) prove that $P(n, r+1) = (n-r)P(n, r)$

PROBLEMS PLUS

Dominoes

The game of dominoes involves pieces with zero to six dots on each half. The dominoes are to be matched end-to-end so that the matching ends have an equal number of dots. If all 28 dominoes in the set of dominoes are on the table, in how many ways is it possible to select a matched pair?

1.4 ARRANGEMENTS OF OBJECTS WHEN SOME ARE ALIKE

Example 1 How many permutations are there of the letters in each word:
(a) ROAM?   (b) ROOM?

Solution (a) The number of permutations of the letters in ROAM is

$$P(4,4) = 4 \times 3 \times 2 \times 1 = 24$$

ROOM
ROMO
RMOO
OROM
ORMO
OORM
OOMR
OMRO
OMOR
MOOR
MORO
MROO

(b) If we apply the technique from (a) to this situation, the answer would again be 24 permutations. But if we list all the permutations of R, O, O, and M, as shown at the left, we find only 12 arrangements!

The difficulty here is that two of the letters in the word ROOM are *indistinguishable*. By writing the two O's in two colours we can see the additional possibilities:

RO O M	R O OM
ROM O	R O MO
RMO O	R O MOO
OR O M	O O ROM
ORM O	O O RMO
⋮	⋮

Since two arrangements such as RO O M and R O OM would be the same without the colours, we counted twice as many arrangements as there really are. So we must divide by 2 to take care of this.

Thus, the number of permutations of the word ROOM is

$$\frac{4!}{2} = 12$$

Example 2 Seven sheets of coloured paper are on Shannon's desk. If there are four sheets of blue paper, and one each of red, yellow, and green paper, in how many ways can she stack the paper when she tidies her desk?

Solution If each sheet of paper were of a different colour, there would be 7! arrangements.

For now we represent the different coloured sheets as follows:
R for red, Y for yellow, G for green, and B_1, B_2, B_3, B_4 for the four sheets of blue paper

The eight different arrangements

$B_1B_2B_3B_4RYG$ $B_1B_2B_4B_3RYG$ $B_1B_4B_2B_3RYG$ $B_4B_1B_2B_3RYG$
$B_1B_3B_2B_4RYG$ $B_3B_1B_2B_4RYG$ $B_2B_1B_3B_4RYG$ $B_2B_1B_4B_3RYG$

(as well as several other arrangements) would look the same without the numbers because only the four indistinguishable blue sheets have been moved. There are 4! = 24 ways of arranging the blue sheets; thus in counting the 7! arrangements we counted 24 times as many different stacks as there really are. So we must divide 7! by 4! to find the actual number of such stacks of paper.

Thus, the number of ways in which the paper could be stacked is

$$\frac{7!}{4!} = \frac{7 \times 6 \times 5 \times 4!}{4!}$$

$$= 7 \times 6 \times 5$$

$$= 210$$

Example 3   In how many ways can the letters of the word MINIMUM be arranged?

Solution   If the seven letters of the word MINIMUM were all different, then there would be 7! permutations. Let us label the three M's with numbers to distinguish between them. The six different arrangements

$$M_1INIM_2UM_3 \qquad M_1INIM_3UM_2 \qquad M_3INIM_1UM_2$$
$$M_3INIM_2UM_1 \qquad M_2INIM_1UM_3 \qquad M_2INIM_3UM_1$$

would look the same without the numbers because only the 3 indistinguishable M's have been rearranged. There are 3! = 6 ways of arranging the M's; thus in counting the 7! arrangements we counted six times as many permutations as there really are. So we must divide 7! by 3!.

By the same reasoning, we must divide by 2! to account for the two I's. So, the number of arrangements of the letters of the word MINIMUM is

$$\frac{7!}{3!2!} = \frac{7 \times 6 \times 5 \times 4 \times 3!}{3! \times (2 \times 1)}$$

$$= \frac{7 \times 6 \times 5 \times 4}{2}$$

$$= 420$$

The same reasoning used in Example 3 gives us the following general principle.

> The number of permutations of n objects, of which a objects are alike, another b objects are alike, another c objects are alike, and so on is
>
> $$\frac{n!}{a!b!c! \dots}$$

EXERCISE 1.4

A 1. Identify the indistinguishable items in each situation. (Class discussion of various interpretations of the given information would be useful.)
   (a) The letters of the word LETTUCE are rearranged.
   (b) Several copies of textbooks for the Grade 9 and Grade 10 Math courses are lined up on a shelf.
   (c) At a buffet table, there are four pieces of cheesecake, two dishes of chocolate mousse, and three chocolate eclairs.
   (d) The digits 4, 5, 6 are used, twice each, to create six-digit numbers.

B. 2. In how many ways can the letters of each word be arranged?
   (a) MAXIMUM   (b) CANADA
   (c) SASKATCHEWAN   (d) INTERESTING
   (e) UNINTERESTING   (f) MISSISSAUGA

   3. List all five-digit numbers that can be formed by using two 4's and three 6's.

   4. How many seven-digit integers are there which include
   (a) two 3's, three 2's, and two 8's?
   (b) four 3's and three 4's?

   5. A man bought two vanilla ice cream cones, three chocolate cones, four strawberry cones, and one pistachio cone for his ten children. In how many ways can he distribute the flavours among the children?

   6. A coin is tossed nine times. In how many ways could the results be six heads and three tails?

   7. Anya is starting out on her evening run. Her route always takes her eight blocks east and five blocks north to her grandmother's apartment building. But she likes to vary the path she follows. How many different possibilities does she have?
   [Hint: Consider the permutations of 13 letters, 8E's and 5 N's.]

   8. How many numbers greater than 300 000 are there using only the digits 1, 1, 1, 2, 2, 3?

   9. Yurak is shelving books in a display in the school library. He has four different books with three copies of each. In how many ways can he arrange the books on the shelf for display?

   10. A developer will build 12 houses on the same side of Costly Court in a new subdivision. If he has room for two houses modeled on Plan A, four modeled on Plan B, and six modeled on Plan C, in how many different ways can he arrange the houses on the street?

11. Emily's minor soccer team played a total of 14 games in the season. Their record was eight wins, four losses, and two ties. In how many orders could this have happened?

12. (a) How many permutations are there of the letters of the word BASKETBALL?

    (b) How many of the arrangements begin with K?

    (c) How many of the arrangements start with a B?

    (d) In how many of the arrangements would the two L's be together?

C 13. In how many ways can the letters of the word SECTION be arranged if the consonants must always be in the order in which they occur in the word itself?

14. A soap company will give away a million dollars to anyone who guesses the order into which they have rearranged the letters of the word SUPERCLEANER. Each entry must be in a separate envelope. How much would it cost you in postage to submit all possible entries?

15. In how many ways can 12 basketball players be assigned to
    (a) six double rooms?   (b) four triple rooms?

1.5 PROBLEM SOLVING WITH PERMUTATIONS

We have developed a formula for calculating the number of permutations of r out of a group of n objects. But we have also worked with several situations where the formula alone is not sufficient to count the items. First, a problem must be analysed to determine the specific conditions involved. Based on the insights gained, it may or may not appear wise to simply apply the formula. Illustration of the situation with boxes as introduced in Section 1.3 may be helpful in reaching the solution.

In this section we deal with several more variations on the straightforward permutations problems. It is useful to apply some of the problem-solving principles discussed in the Review and Preview to this chapter.

Example 1   Find the number of seating arrangements of eight basketball players on a bench if either the one centre or both of the two forwards must sit at the end where the coach always sits.

Solution   There are two different cases to be considered here. *Either* the centre sits at the end by the coach *or* both forwards sit at the end. These two cases cannot both happen at the same time (the centre *and* the two forwards could not all sit beside the coach at once), so the Rule of Sum introduced in Section 1.1 applies in this situation.

According to the Rule of Sum, once we calculate the number of possibilities for each of these situations, we must add these results to find the total number of possibilities.

TAKE CASES

Case 1: the centre sits beside the coach

Once the centre is seated by the coach there are seven other players to be arranged, so the number of seating arrangements is

Coach	Centre							
1	7	6	5	4	3	2	1	

$$1 \times P(7,7) = 1 \times 7!$$
$$= 5040$$

Case 2: both forwards sit next to the coach

Treating the forwards as one unit, we seat them beside the coach, then arrange the other six players, and, finally, multiply by 2 to account for the arrangements of the two forwards.

Coach	Two Forwards						
1	6	5	4	3	2	1	

The number of seating arrangements is

$$1 \times P(6,6) \times 2 = 6! \times 2$$
$$= 1440$$

So, by the Rule of Sum, there are $5040 + 1440 = 6480$ seating arrangements on the bench.   ◇

Example 2   René reaches into his gym bag for a pair of running shoes. If there are seven different pairs of shoes loose in the bag, in how many ways can he pick two shoes that do not match?

Solution   This situation can be best handled indirectly. If we find the total number of possible pairings of the 14 shoes, then subtract the number of matched pairs, we have the number of unmatched pairs.

INDIRECT REASONING

By the Fundamental Counting Principle, there are

$$14 \times 13 = 182 \text{ ways}$$

of selecting a "pair" of shoes.

There are seven pairs of matched shoes; in picking out each matched pair, the shoes could be selected in two different orders. So, there are

$$7 \times 2 = 14 \text{ ways}$$

of selecting a matched pair.

Thus, there are $182 - 14 = 168$ ways of picking an unmatched pair of shoes.   ◇

Example 3   The six members of the yearbook staff sit around the circular table in their office. How many different seating arrangements are there of this group of people?

Solution   If the staff were sitting in a line there would be 6! = 720 possible arrangements (and little communication).

DRAW A
DIAGRAM

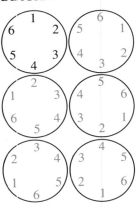

   Because they are in a circle there is some duplication. Only the positions of the members relative to each other are really significant. If each person moves one place to the right the arrangement would not be considered different because of the closed circle, even though it would be different in the line setup.

   To deal with this, we fix the position of one of the people, then consider all possible arrangements. So the number of permutations is only

$$1 \times 5! = 120$$

   The following exercise includes questions dealing with situations similar to those discussed in the examples, as well as with other variations of permutation questions.

EXERCISE 1.5

B **1.**   Twelve football players stand in a circular huddle. How many different arrangements of the players are there?

2.   How many "words" can be formed using all of the letters of the word SHRINKS if S must be directly in front of H?

3.   In how many ways can eight test questions be arranged so that the easiest and most difficult do not immediately follow one another?

4.   How many four-digit numbers are there with the following restrictions?
(a)   using the digits 1 to 8
(b)   using the digits 0 to 7
(c)   using only odd digits
(d)   the number is odd
(e)   the number is even

5.   How many three-digit numbers can be formed using only the numbers 1 to 7 if the number 2 must be included?

6.   The Greek alphabet contains 24 letters. How many different Greek-letter fraternity names can be formed using either two or three letters? (Repetitions are allowed.)

7.   In how many ways can 11 players be seated on the team bench so that Joey and Jill are not seated next to each other?

8. A ship carries four signal flags of different colours. How many different signals could be sent using at least two flags for each signal?

9. How many natural numbers less than 10 000 include at least one 9?

10. In how many ways can the six members of the hockey team line up at the blue line so that the two defencemen are not side by side?

11. Anwar is stringing wooden beads on a leather thong. He has 12 beads of various sizes and will tie a knot in the thong when he has put them all onto it. How many different necklaces could he make? [Hint: Does the exact opposite order of beads produce a different necklace?]

12. The original cast recording of a rock opera is a four-album set. In how many ways can the eight sides be played so that at least one side is played out of its correct order?

13. How many arrangements of the word ALGORITHM begin with a vowel and end with a consonant?

C 14. In how many ways can four men and four women be seated around a circular table if each man must be flanked by two women? [Hint: Arrange the men first, then the women.]

15. How many three-letter arrangements are there of the letters taken from the word SILLY? [Hint: Consider cases with and without two L's.]

16. In how many ways can you form a three-digit number using only the digits of the number 21 150?

17. Calculate the number of permutations of the word CALENDAR in which C and A are together but N and D are not.

1.6 REVIEW EXERCISE

1. Explain why it makes sense to define 0! as 1.

2. Explain why $P(n, n) = n!$

3. Evaluate each expression.
   (a) $P(5, 1)$ (b) $P(8, 0)$ (c) $(5 - 5)!$ (d) $P(3, 3)$

4. Draw a tree diagram to show the possible orders for playing three record albums.

5. Evaluate each expression.
   (a) $P(6, 4)$ (b) $P(8, 5)$

   (c) $3!P(4, 2)$ (d) $\dfrac{9!}{5!4!} \times \dfrac{5 \times 4!}{3!2!}$

6. If the call letters of any Canadian television station must begin with the letter C, how many different stations could be named using three letters? What if four letters are allowed?

7. A series of history books has volumes A to G. In how many ways can these be arranged on a bookshelf so that they are *not* in order?

8. How many arrangements are there of the letters for each word given?
   (a) FRIENDS   (b) REHEARSAL   (c) BELLEVILLE

9. When Julia's parents return from Jamaica, they will give her a bracelet made of eight different sea shells with no visible clasp. How many different bracelets could have been made with these same shells? Why is the information about the clasp relevant?

10. In how many ways can seven people line up, single file, at the Capitol Theatre box office to purchase tickets for the Chinese Acrobats Show?

11. There are five speakers scheduled for a seminar on careers. How many different orders of speaking are possible if
    (a) there are no special conditions?
    (b) the marine biologist must speak first so that she can get back to her lab?
    (c) the electrical engineer and machinist are to speak one after the other?
    (d) the lawyer and paralegal are not to follow one another in the program?

12. Prove each statement for natural numbers n and r.
    (a) $P(n, 2) + P(n+1, 2) = 2n^2$.
    (b) $P(n, r) = P(n, 2)P(n-2, r-2)$

13. Solve the expression for $n \in N$.

$$P(2n+4, 3) = \frac{2}{3}P(n+4, 4)$$

PROBLEMS PLUS

Anagram codes

In scientific and political circles during the Middle Ages, anagrams were often used to encode key information related to a scientific discovery or political intrigue. Christian Huygens cleverly arranged the following message when he discovered the rings of Saturn:

annulo cingitur tenui, plano, musquam cohaerente, ad eclipticam inclinato. (Surrounded by a thin ring, flat, suspended nowhere, inclined to the ecliptic.) His anagram was as follows:

aaaaaaa ccccc d eeeee g h iiiiiii llll mmm nnnnnnnn oooo pp q rr s ttttt uuuuu

In order to decipher the message, some scholars attempted trial-and-error methods. How many possible ways could the letters of this anagram be arranged?

1.7 CHAPTER 1 TEST

1. Evaluate the expression.
$$3! - 2 \times 4! + P(7,0) - P(3,3) + 0!$$

2. Students can travel to and from school by way of the park, the library, or the variety store. For example, they can go to school by way of the park and return by way of the library. Draw a tree diagram to show the possible routes taken to and from school on one day.

3. How many three-letter "words" can be formed from the letters of the word SHORTEN with no letter repeated?

4. In how many ways can the eight members of the board of directors of Pride International Corp. be seated around the round table in the board room?

5. At the opening assembly of the school year, the music students are to perform. The Senior Band knows seven pieces but the Junior Band knows only two so far, and the students of the Vocal Music class know three songs. Each group is to perform one piece.
(a) If the Junior Band must play first, followed by the Vocal Music students, and then the Senior Band, how many different programs are possible?
(b) If the groups may play in any order, how many possible programs would there be?

6. How many different arrangements of the word SUCCESS are there if
(a) there are no restrictions?
(b) the two vowels must be together?

7. How many odd four-digit numbers, all of the digits different, can be formed from the digits 0 to 7, if there must be a 4 in the number?

8. Five boats of various types are to be docked in the five slips at a small marina.
(a) In how many ways can they be docked so that the powerboat is at the end nearest the boathouse?
(b) In how many ways can they be located so that the two sailboats are at the extreme ends of the marina?
(c) In how many ways can they be located so that *either* the powerboat is nearest the boathouse *or* the sailboats are at the extreme ends?

TWENTIETH CENTURY MATHEMATICIANS

Dr. Ronald L. Graham, head of the Mathematical Studies Center at Bell Laboratories in Murray Hill, New Jersey, has been described as one of the world's leading *combinatorial* mathematicians. For the past twenty years he has faced and solved mathematical problems that arise in the telephone industry: the need to accurately transmit millions of telephone calls through cables, microwaves, and satellites.

A remarkably prolific mathematician, he publishes more than a dozen papers a year. He is also a talented and dedicated juggler and has been president of the International Jugglers Association.

During the Apollo moon program, NASA needed to evaluate mission schedules so that the three astronauts aboard a spacecraft could find the time to perform all the necessary tasks: experiments, eating and sleeping, and managing their spacecraft. The number of ways to allot these tasks was astronomical—too vast even for a computer to sort out—and NASA officials were concerned about wasting valuable time through inefficient scheduling. Graham, using his knowledge of *worst case analysis* was able to reassure the agency that their methods were yielding answers within a few percentage points of the theoretically best possible solutions.

Dr. Graham is convinced that all mathematics is related to the real world: "Is mathematics a creation of the human mind or is it really out there? I happen to believe it is there, it was always there and would be there without us. Our job is to discover, not to create. But the act of discovery is a creative act."

According to Dr. Graham, mathematics is the study of order, and therefore he is interested in a subject called Ramsey theory which implies that, in Dr. Graham's words, "Complete disorder is impossible. There is always structure somewhere." The following is a simple prediction of Ramsey theory. If two people are selected from any group, they will either know each other or be strangers. In any group of at least six people, there will be three people who all know each other or are all strangers. In any group of at least eighteen people, there will be four people who are mutual friends, or mutual strangers. How big a group is required so that it will always be possible to find five mutual friends or five mutual strangers? Nobody knows yet! But Dr. Graham is working on it.

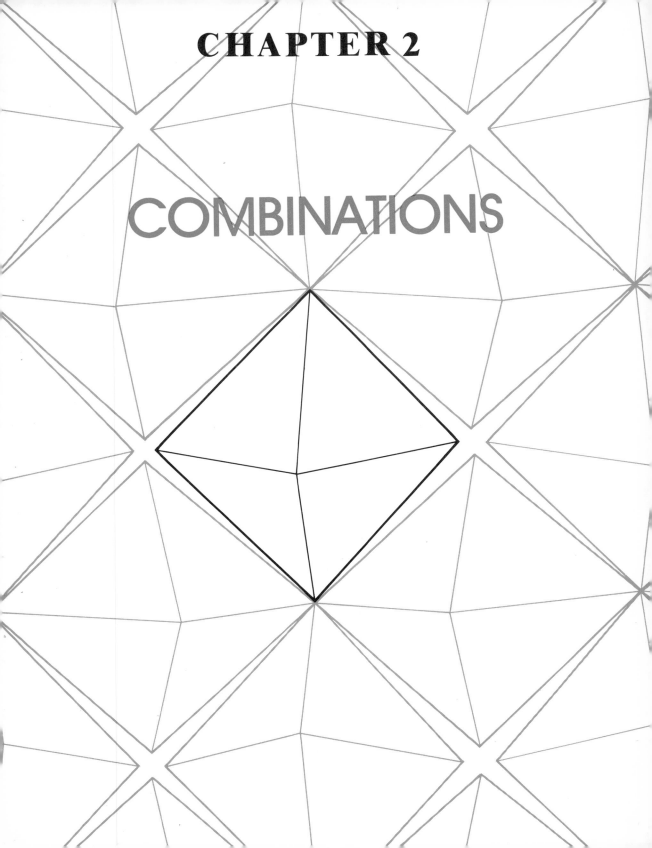

CHAPTER 2

COMBINATIONS

REVIEW AND PREVIEW TO
CHAPTER 2

EXERCISE 1   **Multiplying Rational Expressions**

Express the following as rational expressions in lowest terms. Assume that all variables are restricted so that no denominator is equal to zero.

1. (a) $\dfrac{m}{3n} \times \dfrac{3m}{n}$
(b) $\dfrac{x-y}{6} \times \dfrac{3}{x-y}$

(c) $\dfrac{x^3}{y^4} \times \dfrac{y^6}{x^5}$
(d) $\dfrac{(x+2)(x+3)}{(x-1)(x+2)} \times \dfrac{(x-1)}{(x+4)}$

(e) $\dfrac{(x-3)(x-2)}{(x-7)(x-3)} \times \dfrac{(x+5)(x-7)}{(x-2)(x+5)}$
(f) $\dfrac{x(x+y)}{x^2} \times \dfrac{x}{y}$

2. (a) $\dfrac{x^2-6x+5}{x^2+x-2} \times \dfrac{x^2-2x}{4x-20}$
(b) $\dfrac{2x^2+7x-15}{2x^2-3x} \times \dfrac{16x^4-x^2}{4x^2+19x-5}$

(c) $\dfrac{a^2+ab}{a^2-b^2} \times \dfrac{2a^2+3ab-5b^2}{4a^2-25b^2} \times \dfrac{2a^2-5ab}{a^4+a^2b^2}$

EXERCISE 2   **Adding and Subtracting Rational Expressions**

---

1. Add or subtract as indicated.

(a) $\dfrac{x^2+2x-5}{6} - \dfrac{3x+2}{6}$
(b) $\dfrac{2x+3}{x-4} + \dfrac{5x}{x-4}$

2. Find the LCM (Lowest Common Multiple) for each of the following.
(a) 20, 35, and 60
(b) $x+1$ and x^2-1
(c) $2-x$, $2+x$, and $4+4x+x^2$

3. Add or subtract as indicated, then simplify.

(a) $\dfrac{3a}{4} - \dfrac{a}{9} + \dfrac{5a}{6}$
(b) $\dfrac{2}{x} - \dfrac{3+2x}{y}$

(c) $\dfrac{2a-b}{6a} + \dfrac{8a+5b}{9b}$
(d) $\dfrac{x-1}{x+3} - \dfrac{x+2}{x-4}$

(e) $\dfrac{a^2}{a^2+2ab} + \dfrac{ab}{ab-ab^2}$

INTRODUCTION

In the problems of Chapter 1, a change in the order of the items or the actions performed resulted in a new arrangement or permutation and affected the count of the total number of possibilities. In lining up students, or setting up a batting order, or hanging pictures on the wall, order is significant. But this is not always the case. In choosing members of a committee or picking books off a shelf, the order is not of interest. Problems where order is not important are related to the area of mathematics known as *set theory*. In this chapter we study some concepts of set theory and then apply these to counting problems where order is not significant.

2.1 SETS AND SUBSETS

We use the term **set** without giving it a precise definition. It is one of the mathematical terms that is so fundamental that it is difficult to define. We understand it to mean simply a collection of distinct objects. It is common to use uppercase letters, A, B, C, ..., X, Y, Z, to represent sets.

The objects in a set are called its **elements** or **members**. When the elements of a set are listed, they are included in brace brackets, { }, and separated by commas. The *order* of the elements in the list *does not matter*.

For example,

$$A = \{2, 4, 6, 8, 10]$$
or $\quad X = \{\text{red, orange, yellow, green, blue, violet}\}$
or $\quad W = \{0, 1, 2, 3, ...\}$

To denote the number of elements in a set A, we write $n(A)$.

Example 1   Find $n(A)$ for each set A.
(a) $A = \{1, 3, 5, 7, 9, 11\}$
(b) $A = \{\text{Marcel, Mike, Carol, Agnes, Kazuo, Dante, Irina, Martine, Richard, Jimmy, Pam, Mary, Gerard, Pia}\}$

Solution   (a) There are six elements in set A; so $n(A) = 6$.
(b) There are 14 elements in A; so $n(A) = 14$.

A set with no elements is called the **null set** or the **empty set**; it is denoted by $\varnothing$ or { }. What is the value of $n(\varnothing)$?

A set may be related to another set in a variety of different ways:

> If two sets have no elements in common, they are called **disjoint sets**.

For example, the set of horses in the barn and the set of cars in the parking garage are disjoint sets.

> If all the elements of set B are also elements of set A, we say that set B is a **subset** of set A and write $B \subseteq A$, saying B is *contained in A or A contains B*.

According to this, every set is a subset of itself and the null set is a subset of every set. (Explanations of these points are left to the student as an exercise, Question 1 in Exercise 2.1).

Example 2   Describe the relationship between the sets described, using the terms *equal, disjoint, subset.*

(a) N = the set of natural numbers
W = the set of whole numbers

(b) R = the set of colours in a rainbow
B = {grey, black, brown}

(c) D = the set of prime divisors of 34
E = {2, 17}

Solution   (a)   Because all natural numbers are also whole numbers, N is a *subset* of W, that is $N \subseteq W$.

(b)   Because the colours grey, black, and brown are not colours found in a rainbow, the sets R and B are *disjoint*.

(c)   Because the prime divisors of the numbers 34 are exactly 2 and 17, the sets D and E are equal, $D = E$.

All sets in which we are interested, in a particular situation, are subsets of the **universal set** for that situation. We will denote the universal set by S.

For example,

(i)   in considering divisors of a natural number we are concerned only with natural numbers;

(ii)   in considering costs for a new car, we are concerned only with dollar figures with fewer than six digits (probably);

(iii)   in considering colours of ink in a pen to be used to do homework questions, we are concerned only with colours like black, blue, and, maybe, green.

Sometimes the elements of the universal set are obvious because of our understanding of the situation (as in (i)). At other times, some clarification is required; in (ii), we might specify that the car is to be a standard model to guarantee that the cost will not exceed $100 000; in (iii), we might provide a list of colours considered practical for this purpose.

Relationships between sets and their subsets can be illustrated using **Venn diagrams**. In such a diagram we use a rectangle to represent the universal set and closed curves, usually circles, to represent the sets in which we are interested.

Example 3   Represent relationships between the indicated sets using Venn diagrams.

(a) S, the universal set, is the set of integers.

    W is the set of whole numbers.

    N is the set of natural numbers.

(b) S, the universal set, is the set of foods you eat.

    D is the set of your favourite desserts.

    V is the set of your favourite vegetables.

(c) $A =$ the set of letters of our alphabet.

    $N =$ the set of symbols used to write a person's nickname.

Solution   (a)   Because W contains every natural number as well as 0, N is a subset of W.

Note: Venn diagrams are not meant to give information about the size of a set or even of the relative sizes of the sets; so, although $n(W) - n(N) = 1$, this is not reflected in the Venn diagram.

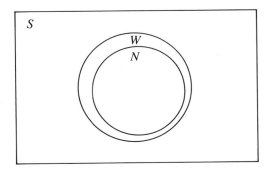

(b)   To construct a mathematical model of a non-mathematical situation, we must often make assumptions. Because your favourite desserts are probably not vegetables, we assume that these sets are disjoint.

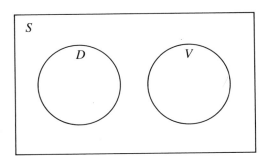

(c)   We use as the universal set a set S containing symbols used in writing, such as letters, numbers, punctuation symbols, and so on. Assuming the alphabet and naming symbols are those we commonly use, and ignoring extremely unusual names, we see that $A = N$.

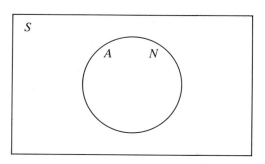

From existing sets it is possible to construct new sets within the universal set in various ways. In a Venn diagram these new sets are indicated by a shaded area.

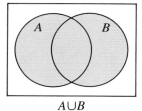

A'

> For a set A, the **complement of** A is the set, denoted A', containing all the elements of the universal set which are not elements of A.

For example, if H is the set of even-numbered houses on Elmwood Avenue, then H' is the set of odd-numbered houses on Elmwood Avenue. Note the assumption that the universal set, S, is the set of *houses* on Elmwood Avenue.

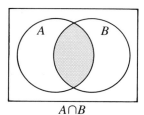

$A \cup B$

> For two sets A and B, the **union of** A **and** B is the set, denoted $A \cup B$, containing all the elements of the universal set which are *either* in a set A *or* in set B *or* in both sets.

For example, if A is the set of students on the dance committee and B is the set of students on the student council executive, then $A \cup B$ is the set of all students who are either on the dance committee or on the student council executive. Note the assumption that the universal set is the set of all students at a particular school.

$A \cap B$

> For two sets A and B, the **intersection of** A **and** B is the set, denoted by $A \cap B$, containing all elements of the universal set, which are *both* in set A and in set B.

For example, if *A* is the set of horses entered in the first race at the county fair and *B* is the set of horses entered in the fifth race, then *A*∩*B* is the set of horses entered in both the first and the fifth races at the fair.

Note the assumption that the universal set is the set of all horses entered in races at the county fair.

Depending on the extent of the information given, a Venn diagram may represent only one of several possibilities in a particular situation. For this reason, Venn diagrams are used only for illustration and not for proof of statements about sets.

Example 4   For the given sets, find *A'*, *B'*, *A*∪*B*, and *A*∩*B*. Draw a Venn diagram for each situation.

(a)   *S* = the set of positive integers less than 20
       A = {4, 5, 6, 7, 8}
       B = the set of prime numbers in *S*

(b)   *S* = the set of face cards in a deck of cards
       A = the set of black cards in *S*
       B = the set of kings in *S*

Solution   (a)   *A'* = {1, 2, 3, 9, 10, 11, 12, 13, 14, 15, 16, 17, 18, 19}

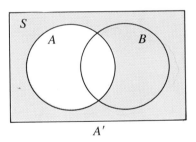

$$A'$$

Because *B* = {2, 3, 5, 7, 11, 13, 17, 19}
B' = {1, 4, 6, 8, 9, 10, 12, 14, 15, 16, 18}

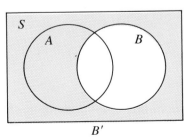

$$B'$$

$A \cup B$ includes all prime numbers less than 20 as well as all elements of A;

so, $A \cup B = \{2, 3, 4, 5, 6, 7, 8, 11, 13, 17, 19\}$

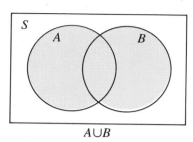

$A \cup B$

$A \cap B$ includes only elements from A which are prime numbers;

so, $A \cap B = \{5, 7\}$

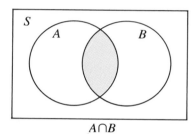

$A \cap B$

(b) $A' =$ the set of red face cards
     $B' =$ the set of jacks and queens

$A \cup B$ includes all black face cards as well as all kings;

so, $A \cup B = \{J\clubsuit, Q\clubsuit, K\clubsuit, J\spadesuit, Q\spadesuit, K\spadesuit, K\diamondsuit, K\heartsuit\}$

$A \cap B$ includes only cards which are both black and king;

so, $A \cap B = \{K\clubsuit, K\spadesuit\}$

EXERCISE 2.1

This question is for class discussion.

A **1.** Explain why each of the following statements is true for any set A.
      (a) $A \subseteq A$ (b) $\varnothing \subseteq A$ (c) $A \subseteq S$

   2. What is the value of $n(\varnothing)$? Why?

B **3.** List the elements of each set described below.
      (a) P, the set of permutations of the letters of the word DEER

      (b) Q, the set of rational numbers $\dfrac{a}{b}$ using only the single digits 2,
          3, and 5 in the numerator and denominator, with $a \neq b$
      (c) R, the set of red face cards in a deck of cards

(d) *T*, the set of textbooks required for the courses in which you are presently enrolled

4. For each set *X*, give the value of *n(X)*.
    (a) *X* is the set of students in your mathematics class.
    (b) *X* is the set of positive, even numbers less than 75.
    (c) *X* is the set of blackboards in your mathematics classroom.
    (d) *X* is the set of tests you have written so far in this course.
    (e) *X* is the set of students in your mathematics class who have at least one part-time job.

5. List all subsets of each set.
    (a) {green}   (b) {*H*, *T*}
    (c) {yes, no, maybe}   (d) {3, 5, 7, 9}

6. Using the results of Question 5, find the number of subsets of a set with the number of elements given.
    (a) 1 element   (b) 2 elements
    (c) 3 elements   (d) 4 elements
    (e) 5 elements   (f) 13 elements
    (g) 105 elements   (h) *n* elements, *n* natural

7. List the complement of each set described for the given universal set.
    (a) *S* = the set of whole numbers less than 25
         F = {2, 3, 5, 10, 15, 20}
    (b) *S* = the set of positive integers
         G = the set of natural numbers greater than 7
    (c) *S* = the set of letters of the alphabet
         C = the set of consonants
    (d) *S* = the set of integers
         B = the set of integers less than 12 or greater than 20

8. Using the terms *equal*, *disjoint*, *subset*, describe the relationship between the given sets. Draw a Venn diagram for each situation.
    (a) *I*, the set of integers
         R, the set of real numbers
    (b) *R*, the set of all rectangles
         C, the set of all circles
    (c) *E*, the set of figures with sides of equal length
         T, the set of equilateral triangles
    (d) *N*, the set of countries in North America
         W, the set of countries in the Third World
    (e) *N*, the set of natural numbers
         P, the set of positive integers

9. (a) Draw Venn diagrams representing all possible relationships between two sets in the same universal set.
    (b) Draw Venn diagrams representing six of the possible relationships between three subsets of the same universal set.

whole number –

10. If Z is a subset of X, but X is not a subset of Y, is it possible that Y and Z are disjoint? Is this the only possibility? Illustrate your answers with examples in the form of Venn diagrams.

11. For S = the set of whole numbers $0 \, 1 \, \cdots$
    A = the set of numbers which are perfect squares $4, 16, 25$
    B = the set of positive even numbers $2 \, 4 \, 6 \, 8 \, 10 \, 12 \, 14$
    describe:
(a) A'	(b) B'	(c) $A \cup B$
(d) $A \cap B$	(e) $A' \cup B'$	(f) $A' \cap B'$
(g) $(A \cup B)'$	(h) $(A \cap B)'$	

12. For S, the set of letters in the word KEYBOARD,
    A, the set of vowels in KEYBOARD,
    B, the set of letters in the word BOARD,
    list:
(a) A'	(b) B'	(c) $A \cup B$
(d) $A \cap B$	(e) $A' \cup B'$	(f) $A' \cap B'$
(g) $(A \cup B)'$	(h) $(A \cap B)'$	

13. (a) Draw two identical Venn diagrams illustrating the situation that $A \subseteq B$, for sets A and B.
    (b) On one of the diagrams drawn in (a), shade $A' \cup B'$. On the other shade $(A \cap B)'$.
    (c) Repeat (a) and (b) for the situation where $A \cap B = \emptyset$, that is, A and B are disjoint sets.

14. (a) Draw two identical Venn diagrams illustrating the situation that $A \subseteq B$, for sets A and B.
    (b) On one of the diagrams drawn in (a), shade $A' \cap B'$. On the other shade $(A \cup B)'$.
    (c) Repeat (a) and (b) for the situation where $A \cap B = \emptyset$, that is, A and B are disjoint sets.

15. Find the indicated values for the given sets.
    (a) S = {red, green, blue, white, gold}
       D = {red, green}
       E = {blue, white, gold}
(i) $n(S)$	(ii) $n(D)$	(iii) $n(E)$
(iv) $n(D')$	(v) $n(E')$	(vi) $n(D \cup E)$ (vii) $n(D \cap E)$
    (b) S = {black, orange, purple, yellow, brown}
       F = {black, brown}
       G = {orange, yellow}
(i) $n(S)$	(ii) $n(F)$	(iii) $n(G)$
(iv) $n(F')$	(v) $n(G')$	(vi) $n(F \cup G)$ (vii) $n(F \cap G)$

(c) S = {white, black, grey, brown, beige}
  H = {white, black, grey}
  J = {white, brown, beige}
  (i) $n(S)$ (ii) $n(H)$ (iii) $n(J)$
  (iv) $n(H')$ (v) $n(J')$ (vi) $n(H \cup J)$ (vii) $n(H \cap J)$

16. (a)   For any set A, $A \cup \varnothing = A$. Why?
   (b)   For any set A, $A \cap \varnothing = \varnothing$. Why?
   (c)   Using the definition of set union, give a simpler expression for $A \cup S$. Give reasons for your answer.
   (d)   Using the definition of set intersection, give a simpler expression for $A \cap S$. Give reasons for your answer.
   (e)   Give a simpler expression for $A \cup A$. Include an explanation for your answer.
   (f)   Give a simpler expression for $A \cap A$. Include an explanation for your answer.
   (g)   Give simpler expressions for $A \cup A'$ and $A \cap A'$. Explain your answers.

C 17.   By examining results for Questions 11 (e)–(h), 12 (e)–(h), 13, and 14, suggest an equivalent expression for these.
   (a) $(A \cup B)'$ (b) $(A \cap B)'$

18.   By examining results for Question 15, suggest a formula for $n(A \cup B)$.

19.   Explain why each of the following statements is true:
   (a)   For any set A, $(A')' = A$.
   (b) $S' = \varnothing$
   (c) $\varnothing' = S$

20.   The tree diagram shown illustrates the number of subsets of a set with two elements, $\{a, b\}$.

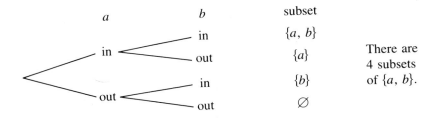

Set up a tree diagram to show the number of subsets of a set with three elements.

2.2 COMBINATIONS: COUNTING THE SUBSETS

There are five students from the school dance committee who will work the cleanup shift after next Friday's dance. In how many ways can a group of three of these students be chosen to clean up the canteen area?

There is a significant difference between this situation and the situations dealt with in Sections 1.3–1.5 of Chapter 1. In this setting the *order* of the students' selection is not important because they will all be doing the same type of job. In the earlier situations, such as choice of president and vice-president for a club, rearranging letters of a word, hoisting signal flags, and lining up books on a shelf, the order of the items is important. However, when some items are indistinguishable, their order becomes irrelevant and that fact suggests a technique for solving the problem about the dance committee workers.

In this situation, the students chosen to clean up the canteen are indistinguishable for they will all do the same job. By the same reasoning, the students not chosen are indistinguishable because none of them will do that job. Thus, the number of ways of choosing the three students is the number of ways of arranging five items with three of one type and two of another type, that is,

$$\frac{5!}{3!2!} = \frac{5 \times 4 \times 3!}{3! \times 2 \times 1} = \frac{5 \times 4}{2} = 10$$

This example suggests a definition to cover situations where the order of the items is not to be considered.

> A **combination of n (distinct) objects taken r at a time** is a selection of r of the n objects *without regard to order*. The total number of combinations of n objects taken r at a time is denoted by $\binom{n}{r}$, read as n choose r.

Alternate notations for $\binom{n}{r}$ include $C(n,r)$ and $_nC_r$. In fact we are forming subsets with r elements chosen from a set of n objects.

Example 1   (a) List all combinations of three out of the four colours: red, blue, white, and green.

(b) Considering the colour combinations as arrangements with indistinguishable elements, check the number of combinations of three out of four items.

Solution   (a)   The only such combinations are:

red, blue, white;

red, blue, green;

red, white, green; and

blue, white, green.

Note: These are all the three-element subsets of the set

{red, blue, white, green}

(b)   Because the order of the three chosen colours is unimportant, they are considered indistinguishable. Thus, the number of combinations of three of this set of four items, $\binom{4}{3}$, is

$$\frac{4!}{3!1!} = \frac{4 \times 3!}{3!} = 4$$

In general, to select a combination of r out of n objects we find the number of arrangements of the objects, $n!$, then divide by both $r!$ and $(n-r)!$ to account for the fact that the order of the items chosen and the items not chosen is not important.

$$\binom{n}{r} = \frac{n!}{r!(n-r)!}$$

An alternate explanation is given by the following reasoning: Once we calculate the number of combinations of r out of n objects, $\binom{n}{r}$, in order to find the number of arrangements, $P(n,r)$, we must arrange the r objects. There are $r!$ ways of doing this.

Thus, $P(n,r) = r!\binom{n}{r}$

So, $\binom{n}{r} = \dfrac{P(n,r)}{r!}$

$$= \frac{n!}{(n-r)!r!}$$

Example 2   Evaluate each expression.

(a) $\binom{12}{5}$ (b) $\binom{7}{7}$ (c) $\binom{6}{3} \times \binom{9}{4}$

Solution (a) Using the formula for $\binom{n}{r}$ with 12 for n and 5 for r,

$$\binom{12}{5} = \frac{12!}{5!(12-5)!}$$
$$= \frac{12!}{5!7!}$$
$$= \frac{12 \times 11 \times 10 \times 9 \times 8}{5 \times 4 \times 3 \times 2 \times 1}$$
$$= 11 \times 9 \times 8$$
$$= 792$$

(b) $\binom{7}{7}$ means the number of ways of selecting all seven of a group of seven objects with order not considered. There is certainly only one way of doing this. Let us check that the formula for $\binom{n}{r}$ indeed gives us this result.

$$\binom{7}{7} = \frac{7!}{7!(7-7)!} = \frac{7!}{7!0!}$$

But $0! = 1$, so $\binom{7}{7} = \frac{7!}{7!} = 1$, just as we had reasoned.

(c) $\binom{6}{3} \times \binom{9}{4} = \frac{6!}{3!3!} \times \frac{9!}{4!5!}$
$$= \frac{6 \times 5 \times 4 \times 3!}{3! \times 3 \times 2} \times \frac{9 \times 8 \times 7 \times 6 \times 5!}{4 \times 3 \times 2 \times 5!}$$
$$= 2520$$

Some situations involve selections of a specified number of items from different collections and thus require repeated use of the formula for $\binom{n}{r}$.

Example 3 A gardener bought five geraniums, three rose bushes, and four evergreen bushes from a nursery that had 14 geraniums, 12 rose bushes, and only five evergreen bushes. How many choices did the gardener have?

Solution Order is not important among the plants chosen.

The number of ways of choosing the geraniums is $\binom{14}{5}$.

The number of ways of choosing the rose bushes is $\binom{12}{3}$.

The number of ways of choosing the evergreens is $\binom{5}{4}$.

Because varying the geranium selection for each different selection of rose bushes and evergreens produces a different choice of plants, the Fundamental Counting Principle shows that the total number of choices is

$$\binom{14}{5} \times \binom{12}{3} \times \binom{5}{4} = \frac{14!}{5!9!} \times \frac{12!}{3!9!} \times \frac{5!}{4!1!}$$

$$= \frac{14 \times 13 \times 12 \times 11 \times 10}{5 \times 4 \times 3 \times 2 \times 1} \times \frac{12 \times 11 \times 10}{3 \times 2 \times 1} \times \frac{5}{1}$$

$$= \frac{14 \times 13 \times 11 \times 12 \times 11 \times 10 \times 5}{3 \times 2}$$

$$= 2\ 202\ 200$$

Using the vocabulary from Section 2.1, we can refer to the combinations of a certain number of items from a collection of items as *subsets* of that *set* of items because order of items in subsets is not important. Thus, for a set with five elements, the number of subsets with two elements is given by $\binom{5}{2} = \frac{5!}{2!3!} = \frac{5 \times 4}{2} = 10.$

To indicate the *size* of the subset considered, the term *r*-**subset** is used to denote a selection of r elements of the set.

Example 4   Find the number of 4-subsets of a set of 11 elements.

Solution   The number of 4-subsets of a set of 11 elements is

$$\binom{11}{4} = \frac{11!}{4!7!} = \frac{11 \times 10 \times 9 \times 8}{4 \times 3 \times 2 \times 1} = \frac{11 \times 10 \times 9}{3} = 330$$

EXERCISE 2.2

A **1.** Explain the key difference between *permutations* of three out of a group of seven objects and *combinations* of three out of a group of seven objects.

2. Which is larger:
   (a) the number of arrangements of five out of nine objects or the number of 5-subsets of a set with nine elements? Why?
   (b) the number of ways of choosing three books from a shelf holding eight different books or the number of possible lists of the first, second, and third most popular books on that shelf? Why?

B **3.** Evaluate each expression.

(a) $\binom{6}{2}$ (b) $\binom{12}{4}$ (c) $\binom{9}{9}$

(d) $\binom{8}{5}$ (e) $\binom{10}{7}$ (f) $\binom{10}{3}$

(g) $\binom{16}{2}$ (h) $\binom{7}{0}$ (i) $\binom{5}{2} \times \binom{4}{2}$

(j) $\binom{7}{5} \times \binom{4}{2}$ (k) $\binom{12}{4} \times \binom{5}{3}$ (l) $\binom{8}{4} \times \binom{5}{2}$

4. Your calculator may have a key for calculating $\binom{n}{r}$. Consult the manual to learn how to use this key. (Remember the alternate notations $_nC_r$ and $C(n, r)$ either of which may appear on this key.) Repeat the calculations for Question 3 using this key.

5. There are 12 volumes of the Encyclopedia Canadiana labelled V.I to V.XII on a shelf. In how many ways can you choose five books from that shelf?

6. A club has 25 members.

(a) In how many ways can a committee of three members be chosen?

(b) In how many ways can the offices of president, secretary, and treasurer be filled?

7. If you are going on a five-day trip, in how many ways can you pick five pairs of socks from a drawer in which there are eight neatly-rolled pairs of socks?

8. Find the number of different five-card hands that could be dealt from a deck of 52 cards.

9. (a) Evaluate each expression.

(i) $\binom{5}{5}$ (ii) $\binom{9}{9}$ (iii) $\binom{11}{11}$ (iv) $\binom{17}{17}$

(b) Based on the results of (a), give a formula for $\binom{n}{n}$, for any natural number n.

(c) Give reasoning why the formula suggested in (b) makes sense.

10. Repeat Question 9 using expressions like $\binom{5}{0}$ to find an expression for $\binom{n}{0}$.

11. (a) Evaluate each expression.

(i) $\binom{5}{1}$ (ii) $\binom{9}{1}$ (iii) $\binom{11}{1}$ (iv) $\binom{17}{1}$

(b) Suggest a formula for $\binom{n}{1}$ for any natural number n.

(c) Why does the formula suggested in (b) make sense?

12. The school gardening club consists of five boys and five girls. How many working groups of four people can be formed with
(a) no restrictions? (b) four boys?
(c) three boys and a girl? (d) two boys and two girls?
(e) a boy and three girls? (f) four girls?

13. Five people go to dinner at a Chinese restaurant. The menu includes 14 dishes in Column A and 10 dishes in Column B. The *dinner for five* consists of three dishes from Column A and two dishes from Column B. How many different *dinners for five* could they choose?

14. In how many ways can the five starting positions on a basketball team be filled from these groups?
(a) ten players who can play any position
(b) two players who play only centre and eight others who play any of the other positions
(c) two centres, four forwards and four others who play guard

15. From a group of 14 Conservatives, 12 Liberals, eight NDP, and two Independent Members of Parliament, how many different committees can be formed consisting of three Conservatives, three Liberals, two NDP, and one Independent member?

16. How many poker hands (five cards) are there with three aces and two kings?

17. How many bridge hands (13 cards) contain five clubs, two hearts, three diamonds, and three spades? (Leave the answer in factorial form.)

18. (a) Evaluate each pair of expressions.

(i) $\binom{9}{6}$ $\binom{9}{3}$

(ii) $\binom{11}{7}$ $\binom{11}{4}$

(iii) $\binom{8}{2}$ $\binom{8}{6}$

(iv) $\binom{10}{1}$ $\binom{10}{9}$

(b) Based on the results of (a), suggest a relationship between $\binom{n}{r}$ and $\binom{n}{n-r}$, for n, r natural numbers.

(c) Explain why the relationship you suggested in (b) makes sense.

19. (a) Show that $\binom{7}{4} = \frac{7}{4}\binom{6}{3}$.

(b) Show that $\binom{10}{6} = \frac{10}{6}\binom{9}{5}$.

(c) Based on the results from (a) and (b), suggest a relationship between $\binom{n+1}{r+1}$ and $\binom{n}{r}$ for n, r natural.

C 20. Solve each equation for n, n a natural number.

(a) $\binom{n}{n-2} = 10$

(b) $4\binom{n}{2} = \binom{n+2}{3}$

(c) $\binom{n+1}{3} = \binom{n}{2}$

(d) $P(n,4) = 60\binom{n-1}{3}$

21. Prove each of the following statements for n, r natural.

(a) $\binom{n}{n} = \binom{n}{0}$

(b) $\binom{n}{r} = \binom{n}{n-r}$

(c) $(r+1)\binom{n+1}{r+1} = (n+1)\binom{n}{r}$

(d) $\binom{n+1}{r} = \binom{n}{r} + \binom{n}{r-1}$

22. How many bridge hands contain exactly five spades? (Leave the answer in factorial form.)

23. In how many ways can 12 prizes be divided equally
    (a) between two people?
    (b) among three people?
    (c) among four people?

2.3 PROBLEM SOLVING WITH COMBINATIONS

As with arrangement problems, there are situations in which various cases must be considered with the result obtained by applying the Rule of Sum (as in Section 1.5, Example 1) and also situations which can be dealt with indirectly (as in Section 1.5, Example 2).

Example 1 A delegation of three people is to be chosen from a group of community volunteers consisting of four lawyers, a minister, and three retail merchants. In how many ways can this group be formed if at least one retailer must be a member of the delegation?

Solution This problem can be dealt with either directly, using separate cases, or indirectly.

TAKE CASES
(DIRECT
REASONING)

To handle it *directly*, we consider three cases: (i) a delegation with exactly one retailer; (ii) a delegation with two retailers; or (iii) a delegation with three retailers.

Case (i): a delegation with one retailer

There are $\binom{3}{1} = 3$ ways of choosing one retailer.

Because there are five other volunteers, there are $\binom{5}{2} = 10$ ways of choosing the other two delegates.

So, there are $3 \times 10 = 30$ ways of forming a delegation including exactly one retailer.

Case (ii):   a delegation with two retailers

There are $\binom{3}{2} = 3$ ways of selecting the two retailers.

Because there are five other volunteers, there are $\binom{5}{1} = 5$ ways of selecting the other delegate.

So, there are $3 \times 5 = 15$ ways of forming a delegation including two retailers.

Case (iii):   a delegation with three retailers

There is $\binom{3}{3} = 1$ way of forming a delegation of only retailers.

Finally, by the Rule of Sum, there are

$$30 + 15 + 1 = 46 \text{ ways}$$

of forming a delegation with at least one retailer.

To handle the problem *indirectly*, we find the total number of three-person delegations without restrictions, then subtract the number of delegations with no retailers.

INDIRECT REASONING

The total number of delegations formed from eight volunteers is

$$
\begin{aligned}
\binom{8}{3} &= \frac{8!}{3!5!} \\
&= \frac{8 \times 7 \times 6 \times 5!}{3 \times 2 \times 5!} \\
&= 56
\end{aligned}
$$

To form a delegation with no retailers involves picking the three delegates from the other five volunteers. There are $\binom{5}{3} = 10$ ways of doing this.

Thus, there are

$$56 - 10 = 46 \text{ ways}$$

of forming a delegation with at least one retailer.

Example 2   Twenty people are to travel in a bus from the airport to the hotel at the resort. The bus is designed for use in a tropical climate; it can carry twelve passengers outside and eight inside. If four of the passengers refuse to travel outside and five will not travel inside, in how many ways can the passengers be seated if the arrangements of passengers inside or outside is not considered except to take into account these wishes?

Solution   We must first seat the "picky passengers," four inside and five outside. There is only one way to do this if the order of seating outside or inside is not considered.

Next, there are 11 passengers still to be seated. There are still seven seats outside and four inside.

There are $\binom{11}{7}$ ways of filling the outside seats and $\binom{4}{4}$ ways of filling the inside seats. So, by the Fundamental Counting Principle, the total number of ways of seating the passengers with the given restrictions is

$$
\begin{aligned}
1 \times \binom{11}{7} \times \binom{4}{4} &= \frac{11!}{7!4!} \times 1 \\
&= \frac{11 \times 10 \times 9 \times 8}{4 \times 3 \times 2} \\
&= 330
\end{aligned}
$$

A school librarian is purchasing books. Altogether there have been requests from staff members for three copies of *Webster's Dictionary*, six copies of *The English Writer's Style Manual*, two copies of *Romeo and Juliet*, and one copy of *The History of Mathematics*. Because of budget restrictions, he may not be able to buy all of these. How many different possible purchases could he make?

The order of the books need not be considered. However this is not a simple combination question. If the librarian is to purchase 11 books, he could include all three copies of the dictionary, all six copies of the style manual, one copy of *Romeo and Juliet*, and the requested copy of *The History of Mathematics*. But, he could also purchase the three dictionaries, the six style manuals, the *other* copy of *Romeo and Juliet*, and the history book without receiving a different selection of books. So each purchase is a *combination* selected from a collection in which *some items are alike*.

To count the possibilities, we consider the number of ways each item could be treated in making the selection:

The purchase might include three, two, one, or no dictionaries. Thus, there are four ways of treating the dictionaries.

It might include six, five, four, three, two, one, or no style manuals; so, there are seven ways of treating the style manuals.

It might include two, one, or no copies of *Romeo and Juliet*. There are three ways of treating *Romeo and Juliet*. And, finally, it might include one or no copies of *The History of Mathematics*, that is, there are two ways of treating this book.

By the Fundamental Counting Principle, there are

$$4 \times 7 \times 3 \times 2 = 168 \text{ ways}$$

of treating the books. However, one of these ways is the choice of no copies of any book. This is not much of a purchase. Thus we disregard this combination to find that the number of different purchases which could be made is

$$168 - 1 = 167$$

In general, to count the number of possible combinations of objects for which some are alike, we use the following formula:

The total number of selections which can be made from p items of one kind, q items of another kind, r items of another kind, and so on, is

$$(p+1)(q+1)(r+1) \ldots -1$$

In Section 2.2, the term r-subset was introduced as an alternative to *combination of r objects* because combinations are simply subsets of the set of items. With this link in mind, the procedure described above can be used to determine the total number of subsets of a set.

A set with n distinct elements has 2^n subsets.

The reasoning for this is as follows:
Because the elements are distinct, use $p = q = r = \ldots = 1$ in the formula above. We do *not* subtract 1 because the choice of no elements at all produces the null set which *is* a subset and must be counted. So, the number of subsets of a set of n elements is

$$\underbrace{2 \times 2 \times 2 \times \ldots \times 2}_{n \text{ times}} = 2^n$$

Example 3   Find the number of subsets of a set with the given number of elements.
(a) 3 elements   (b) 5 elements   (c) 13 elements

Solution   (a) A set with 3 elements has $2^3 = 8$ subsets.
(b) A set with 5 elements has $2^5 = 32$ subsets.
(c) A set with 13 elements has $2^{13} = 8192$ subsets.
Compare these results to those of Exercise 2.1, Question 6 where the answer was based on the pattern observed in the results of 2.1, Question 5.

Example 4   Patti wants to throw coins in the fountain at the mall.

(a) In her pocket she has a penny, a nickel, a dime, and a quarter. How many different sums of money could she throw into the fountain?

(b) How many different sums of money could she throw if she had three more pennies?

Solution   (a) Because she has four types of coins, one of each type, Patti could throw

$$2 \times 2 \times 2 \times 2 - 1 = 16 - 1 = 15$$

different sums of money into the fountain.

(b) The situation is the same as in (a) except that Patti has four of one type of coin. So, she could now throw

$$5 \times 2 \times 2 \times 2 - 1 = 40 - 1 = 39$$

different sums of money into the fountain.

The exercise that follows includes questions dealing with situations similar to those discussed in the examples, as well as other variations of combination (and arrangement) problems.

EXERCISE 2.3

A 1. (a) How many subsets are there for a set with six elements?

(b) How many of the subsets in (a) contain five elements?

2. (a) What is the total number of subsets of a set with n elements?

(b) How many of the subsets from (a) have $n - 1$ elements?

3. In how many ways can a committee of at least one person be formed from seven club members?

B 4. Chang arrives at the giant auction sale late in the afternoon. There are only five items left to be sold. How many different purchases could he make?

5. (a) In how many different ways could a team of three students be chosen from Lin's Finite Mathematics class of 25 students to compete in the County Mathematics Contest?

(b) In how many of these cases would Lin be a member of the team?

(c) In how many of these would Lin *not* be a team member?

6. Twelve dots are on the page of Pierre's dot-to-dot puzzle book. If no three points are collinear, how many straight lines can he form by joining dots? (Recall: Any two points determine a line.)

7. (a) How many different sums of money can be made from a
        $2-bill, a $5-bill, and a $10-bill?
    (b) How many different sums of money can be made from the bills
        in (a) as well as one more $10-bill?
    (c) Why does the situation become much more complicated if
        another $5-bill is added?

8. A committee of students and teachers is being formed to study the
    issue of student parking privileges. Fifteen staff members and 18
    students have expressed an interest in serving on the committee. In
    how many different ways could a five-person committee be formed
    if it must include at least one student and one teacher?

9. In the binary number system which is used in computer operations,
    there are only two digits allowed: 0 and 1.
    (a) How many different binary numbers can be formed using at
        most four binary digits (for example, 0110)?
    (b) If eight binary digits are used (for example, 11001101), how
        many different binary numbers can be formed?
    (c) A *binary code* is a system of binary numbers with a fixed
        number of digits that are used to represent letters, numbers, and
        symbols. To produce enough binary numbers to represent all of
        the letters of our alphabet (both upper- and lower-case), how
        many binary digits must be used?

10. From a deck of 52 cards, how many different four-card hands could
    be dealt which include one card from each suit?

11. The prime factorization of 12 is $2 \times 2 \times 3$. Find the number of
    divisors of 12 other than 1 by finding all combinations of these
    numbers.

12. The prime factorization of 540 is $2 \times 2 \times 3 \times 3 \times 3 \times 5$. Find the
    number of divisors of 540 other than 1.

13. There are 14 teams competing in the Bilton Community Darts
    League. Teams are to be selected for the first and second divisions
    in the upcoming tournament. Each division is to have seven teams.
    If last year's champs, the Arrows, must be in the first division and
    the current league leaders, the Bows, must be in the second division,
    in how many ways can the selection be made?

14. Marla's bag of marbles contains two red, three blue, and five green
    marbles. If she reaches in to pick some without looking, how many
    different selections might she make?

15. A railcar compartment has eight seats; four facing the engine of the
    train and four facing away from the engine. Of eight passengers,
    three prefer to face away from the engine, two prefer to face the

engine, and the others have no preference. In how many ways can the passengers be seated if the order on each side of the car is disregarded?

16. A travel agency has a limited number of six different free pamphlets about the Beetle Islands. The agent tells you to take any that you want, but not more than two of any kind. Assuming that you take at least one pamphlet, how many choices could you make?

17. In Lisa's first-year college program she must take nine courses including at least two science courses. If there are five science courses, three mathematics courses, four language courses, and five business courses from which to choose, how many different academic programs could she follow?

18. The science club members are to work in pairs on an experiment.
   (a) If there are eight members present, in how many ways can the pairs be formed?
   (b) If Louis and Simone will not work together, how many different pairs can be formed?

19. A shelf holds seven mystery novels and eight biographies. Josie chooses *either* a mystery novel *or* a biography. Then Juan is to choose a mystery novel *and* a biography. In which case would Juan have the greater number of choices?

C **20.** For the resort bus discussed in Example 2, how many different seating plans are there if the order of passengers inside and out *is* considered? (Leave your answer in factorial form.)

21. Morse code is used to send messages. Using this code, letters, numbers, and a few other symbols can be transmitted. Each symbol is represented by a series of dots and dashes.
   (a) Suggest why it is sufficient to use at most five dots and/or dashes to represent any symbol.
   (b) Would a maximum of four dots and/or dashes be sufficient?

22. Find the number of divisors of each number.
   (a) 98   (b) 2520

A *composite number* is the product of at least two primes.

23. Find the number of divisors of 1050 that are:
   (a) odd numbers.   (b) even numbers.
   (c) composite numbers.   (d) divisible by 5.

24. (a) Calculate the number of diagonals of a hexagon.
   (b) If a polygon has 35 diagonals, how many sides does it have?

25. Five different signal flags are available to fly on a ship's flagpole. How many different signals can be sent using at least two flags?

26. (a) Draw a tree diagram to illustrate the formula for the number of subsets of a set of *n* elements. [Hint: See Question 20 in Exercise 2.1.]

(b) Draw a tree diagram to illustrate the formula for the number of selections that can be made from p items of one kind, q items of another kind, r items of another kind, and so on.

2.4 PRINCIPLE OF INCLUSION AND EXCLUSION

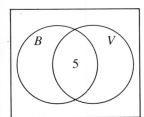

At St. Mary's High School there are twelve players on the school basketball team, and eight players on its volleyball team. How many players could show up at a party for both teams if exactly five students play on both teams?

The Rule of Sum introduced in Section 1.1 does not apply here; simply adding the number of players on the two teams $(12+8)$ gives a result in which the five players who are on both teams have been counted twice. We must subtract five to make up for that. So, the number of players who could show up at the party is

$$12 + 8 - 5 = 15$$

In general, we are counting the number of elements in the union of two sets, such as the set of basketball players and the set of volleyball players. When the sets have common elements (players who play for both teams), these common elements must be subtracted so that they are not counted twice.

Principle of Inclusion and Exclusion (2 sets)

For sets A and B, $n(A \cup B) = n(A) + n(B) - n(A \cap B)$

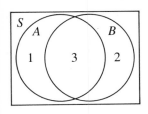

Proof:

Given any element in $A \cup B$, it falls in one of three categories:
1. in A but not in B
2. in B but not in A
3. in both A and B

We count the number of elements in each category. Those in category 3 are exactly the elements of $A \cap B$, so there are $n(A \cap B)$ elements in this category. The number in category 1 is $n(A) - n(A \cap B)$. Similarly, the number in category 2 is $n(B) - n(A \cap B)$. Finally, the number in $A \cup B$ is given by

$$n(A \cup B) = n(A \cap B) + n(A) - n(A \cap B) + n(B) - n(A \cap B)$$
$$= n(A) + n(B) - n(A \cap B)$$

This formula is useful in analysing numerical data such as that gathered in experiments or by polls.

Example 1   A researcher looking for two characteristics known as x and y examines 100 insects. Every insect has x or y or maybe both. But the researcher cannot determine directly whether an insect has characteristic y alone. She finds that 48 insects have x and 23 have both x and y.
(a) How many insects have characteristic y?
(b) How many have only y?

Solution   Let X represent the set of insects with characteristic x and Y the set with characteristic y.

Every insect has x or y or maybe both, so $n(X \cup Y) = 100$. Forty-eight insects have x, so $n(X) = 48$. Twenty-three have both x and y, so $n(X \cap Y) = 23$. The formula reads

$$n(X \cup Y) = n(X) + n(Y) - n(X \cup Y)$$
$$100 = 48 + n(Y) - 23$$

So, $n(Y) = 100 - 48 + 23$
$$= 75$$

(a) Thus, 75 insects have characteristic y.
(b) The number of insects with *only* characteristic y is given by

$$n(Y) - n(X \cap Y) = 75 - 23 = 52$$

So, 52 insects have only characteristic y.

The result for the number of elements in the union of two sets can be extended to deal with three sets as follows:

Principle of Inclusion and Exclusion (3 sets)

For sets A, B, and C,
$$n(A \cup B \cup C) = n(A) + n(B) + n(C)$$
$$- n(A \cap B) - n(A \cap C) - n(B \cap C)$$
$$+ n(A \cap B \cap C)$$

Venn diagrams are helpful in understanding the general formula as well as in sorting out the details in particular situations.

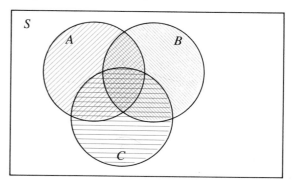

In the Venn diagram shown, each time the elements in a region are counted, the region itself is shaded.

Because A is shaded with ⬚ , B with ⬚ , and C with ⬚ ,

$A \cap B$ is shaded with ⬚ ,

$A \cap C$ is shaded with ⬚ , and

$B \cap C$ is shaded with ⬚ .

Also, $A \cap B \cap C$ is shaded with ⬚

This illustrates that we subtract from $n(A) + n(B) + n(C)$ the number of elements in $A \cap B$, $A \cap C$, and $B \cap C$ because otherwise they are counted twice, as reflected by the shading. It also illustrates that the elements in $A \cap B \cap C$ are at first counted three times. But in subtracting $n(A \cap B)$, $n(A \cap C)$, and $n(B \cap C)$, we also subtract $n(A \cap B \cap C)$ three times, so we must add it again once.

The name of this rule comes from the fact that we *include* all elements in the three sets, *exclude* the elements which are in the intersection of any two of the sets, then *include* the elements in the intersection of all three sets.

This principle can be generalized to count the number of elements in the union of any number of sets.

Example 2   (a)   For sets D, E, and F,
$n(D) = 15$, $n(E) = 12$, $n(F) = 7$, $n(D \cap E \cap F) = 2$,
$n(D \cap E) = 5$, $n(D \cap F) = 4$, $n(E \cap F) = 3$.
Find the number of elements in $D \cup E \cup F$.

(b)   For sets K, L, and M,
$n(K \cup L \cup M) = 97$, $n(K) = 47$, $n(L) = 25$, $n(M) = 30$,
$n(K \cap L) = 3$, $n(K \cap M) = 20$, $n(L \cap M) = 9$.
Find the number of elements in $K \cap L \cap M$.

Solution   (a) $n(D \cup E \cup F) = n(D) + n(E) + n(F) - n(D \cap E) - n(D \cap F) -$
$n(E \cap F) + n(D \cap E \cap F)$
$= 15 + 12 + 7 - 5 - 4 - 3 + 2$
$= 24$

(b) $n(K \cup L \cup M) = n(K) + n(L) + n(M) - n(K \cap L) - n(K \cap M)$
$- n(L \cap M) + n(K \cap L \cap M)$
$97 = 47 + 25 + 30 - 3 - 20 - 9 + n(K \cap L \cap M)$
So, $n(K \cap L \cap M) = 27$.

Example 3 In an advertisement, a firm that manufactures three types of shampoo, Shine, Bubble, and Glory, stated that of 1000 families surveyed,

842 use Shine,
673 use Bubble,
585 use Glory,
600 use both Shine and Bubble,
423 use both Shine and Glory,
322 use both Bubble and Glory, and
265 use all three types.

Show that there is an error in the survey results as reported in the advertisement.

Solution Let S represent the set of families who use Shine, B the set of those who use Bubble, and G the set of those who use Glory.

According to the Principle of Inclusion and Exclusion,

$$n(S \cup B \cup G) = n(S) + n(B) + n(G) - n(S \cap B) - n(S \cap G) - n(B \cap G) + n(S \cap B \cap G)$$

However, $n(S \cup B \cup G) = 1000$, while

$n(S) + n(B) + n(G) - n(S \cap B) - n(S \cap G) - n(B \cap G) + n(S \cap B \cap G)$
$= 842 + 673 + 585 - 600 - 423 - 322 + 265$
$= 1020$

The total surveyed is calculated to be more than 1000; so, there is some error in the reported data.

Depending on the information supplied and the question(s) asked, use of a Venn diagram may be helpful.

Example 4 According to a representative of the Student Services Department at Sir Jonathan Collegiate, of 100 students currently taking OAC courses, the distribution of students in Mathematics courses is as follows: Calculus 52, Algebra/Geometry 38, Finite Mathematics 41, Algebra/Geometry and Finite Mathematics 17, Albegra/Geometry and Calculus 22, Finite Mathematics and Calculus 15, and in all three of the courses, eight students.

(a) Draw a Venn diagram illustrating the data.
(b) How many study only Algebra/Geometry?
(c) How many of the students study Mathematics at the OAC level?

Solution (a) Let C represent the set of OAC students who study Calculus, A the set of those who study Algebra/Geometry, and F the set of those who study Finite Mathematics.

In the area representing the intersection of all three sets, we put 8 because eight students study all three subjects.

In the area $F \cap C$ outside $A \cap F \cap C$, we put $15 - 8 = 7$ to include the students who study Finite Mathematics and Calculus but not Algebra/

Geometry. Similarly, we enter $17 - 8 = 9$ and $22 - 8 = 14$ in appropriate regions. In the area of F outside C and A, we put $41 - 7 - 9 - 8 = 17$ to reflect those who study only Finite Mathematics. Similarly, we put $38 - 14 - 9 - 8 = 7$ and $52 - 14 - 7 - 8 = 23$ in appropriate regions to reflect those who study only Algebra/Geometry and only Calculus.

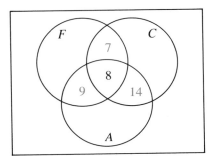 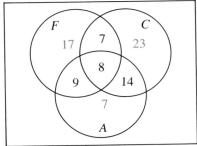

(b) To find the number of students who study only Algebra/Geometry, we locate on the Venn diagram the number in the region representing the part of set A that does not overlap with either set C or set F.

So, seven students study only Algebra/Geometry.

(c) To find the total number of students who study Mathematics at the OAC level, we add the numbers from all distinct regions on the Venn diagram.

Thus, $n(C \cup A \cup F) = 23 + 17 + 7 + 7 + 9 + 14 + 8$
$$= 85$$

So, 85 of the 100 students study Mathematics at the OAC level.

EXERCISE 2.4

A. **1.** Find $n(A \cup B)$ for each pair of sets described.
   (a) $n(A) = 10$, $n(B) = 8$, $n(A \cap B) = 4$
   (b) $n(A) = 7$, $n(B) = 12$, $A \subseteq B$

2. State a formula for finding $n(X \cap Y)$.

3. For disjoint sets P and Q, give formulas for
   (a) $n(P \cup Q)$ (b) $n(P \cap Q)$

4. If $n(D \cup E) = n(D) + n(E)$, how are sets D and E related?

B **5.** (a) For sets X, Y, and Z, given that $n(X) = 5$, $n(Y) = 8$, $n(Z) = 10$, $X \subseteq Y \subseteq Z$, give the value of $n(X \cup Y \cup Z)$.

(b) Illustrate the situation described in (a) with a Venn diagram.

6. Given: $A = \{1, 2, 3\}$
  $B = \{2, 4, 6, 8\}$
  $C = \{2, 3, 5, 7\}$
verify the formula for $n(A \cup B \cup C)$.

7. The Braves junior hockey team has twelve forwards and eight defencemen; there are also two goalkeepers. How many players are on the hockey team if:

(a) no one plays both defence and forward?

(b) three of the players are able to play forward or defence?

8. The Swiss embassy in Ottawa has 65 employees. Of these workers, 47 speak German, 35 speak Italian, and 20 speak both German and Italian. How many embassy employees speak neither German nor Italian? Illustrate the situation with a Venn diagram.

9. A survey of television viewers at A Child's Place Preschool produces the following data:

  60% watch Sesame Street.
  50% watch Captain Kangaroo.
  50% watch Polka Dot Door.
  30% watch Sesame Street and Captain Kangaroo.
  20% watch Captain Kangaroo and Polka Dot Door.
  30% watch Sesame Street and Polka Dot Door.
  10% watch all three shows.

(a) What percentage view at least one of these programs?

(b) What percentage view none of the shows?

(c) What percentage view Sesame Street and Captain Kangaroo but not Polka Dot Door?

(d) What percentage view exactly two of these programs?

10. Ace Electronics, a growing firm, has applied to Doe Insurance Company for a group life insurance policy. The insurance company requests the following data concerning the 1605 employees of Ace: the number who are married, the number who are over 40 years of age, and the number who have passed the required physical examination. The personnel manager from Ace provides the following data:

  715 are married.
  894 are over 40.
  911 have passed the physical.
  352 are married and over 40.
  365 are married and have passed the physical.
  320 are over 40 and have passed the physical.
  209 have passed the physical, are married, and are over 40.

Show that this information is in error. (Illustrate the situation with a Venn diagram and record all your calculations to prove the data error.)

11. Of 1400 students at Tomlintown High, 800 attended the first school dance of the year. The music was not good so only 500 attended the next dance. If 300 attended both dances, how many did not go to either event?

800 - F
500 - S
300 - B

12. The 29 students of Mr. Vicker's class use a variety of forms of transportation to get to school. Twenty of them sometimes arrive at school in a car; 12 bicycle to school at least occasionally; 16 take the bus some days. If four students use all three of these options, six either bicycle or take the bus, ten come by car or bike, and nine arrive by car when they do not come on the bus, how many always use some other type of transportation?

13. Write the Principle of Inclusion and Exclusion for four sets A, B, C, and D.

C **14.** A penny, a nickel, and a dime were tossed together 50 times. The penny came up heads 30 times, the nickel 26, and the dime 24; the penny and the nickel came up heads together 14, the penny and the dime 10, and the nickel and the dime 11. Show that all three came up tails together, at most, five times.

15. In a recent election poll of 193 people, the following information was collected:

140 of those polled were professionals; 84 were under 30 years of age; 133 voted Conservative in the last election; 56 were professionals under 30; 41 of those under 30 voted Conservative; 111 professionals voted Conservative; 36 of the professionals under 30 voted Conservative.

Of those polled, how many non-professionals aged 30 or over did not vote Conservative?

16. In Mrs. Paul's Instrumental Music class, students learn to play only the clarinet, guitar, saxaphone, and trombone. So far this term, no student can play all four; the one who plays three cannot play sax but all those who do play sax also play clarinet. If there are 36 students in the class and the following chart shows the skills of the students, how many students still cannot play any instrument?

saxaphone	— 2 students
clarinet	— 15
guitar	— 16
trombone	— 18
clarinet and guitar	— 4
clarinet and trombone	— 5
guitar and trombone	— 7

PROBLEMS PLUS

Pathways

(a) A rectangle of dimensions $p \times q$ is divided into unit squares. Show that the number of paths from the bottom left corner to the top right corner travelling always up or right is $\binom{p+q}{q}$.

(b) Generalize the result from (a) to a rectangular box of dimensions $p \times q \times r$.

2.5 REVIEW EXERCISE

In solving combinatorics problems, a key skill is the ability to pinpoint the type of problem. Is order important or not? Are some elements alike or are they all distinct? Are we considering subsets of a specific size or of all possible sizes? To help you develop this skill, this exercise includes problems of all types considered in both Chapter 1 and Chapter 2.

1. In each of the following situations, decide whether or not the *order* of the occurrences is significant.
   (a) choosing colours of the shirt, shorts, and socks for a soccer uniform
   (b) putting a set of encyclopedia on a bookshelf
   (c) sending a Morse code signal of dots and dashes
   (d) choosing three volunteers to mow the lawn outside the senior citizens' complex
   (e) rolling two dice, once
   (f) naming members of the tennis team
   (g) choosing the cast for a dramatic production

2. Given universal set $S = \{a, b, c, d, e, g, i, n, o, t, u\}$ and sets $X = \{a, e, i, o, u\}$, $Y = \{a, c, g\}$; list
   (a) X'
   (b) Y'
   (c) $X \cup Y$
   (d) $X \cap Y$

3. Which is smaller:
   (a) $P(7, 4)$ or $\binom{7}{4}$?
   (b) the number of 3-arrangements of 10 objects or the number of 3-subsets of a set containing 10 objects?
   (c) the number of ways of choosing flavours for a triple-scoop ice cream cone or the number of ways of choosing flavours each for single-scoop cones for Tran, Taylor, and Chantal?

4. Evaluate each expression.

(a) $\binom{4}{4}$ (b) $\binom{9}{1}$ (c) $\binom{11}{0}$ (d) $\binom{8}{7}$

5. For sets Q and R, give a formula for $n(Q \cup R)$, if
(a) $Q \cap R = \varnothing$ (b) $Q \cap R \neq \varnothing$

6. (a) List all permutations of the elements of the set $\{+, -, \times\}$.
(b) List all subsets (combinations) of the set $\{+, -, \times\}$.

7. For the set $\{a, s, d, f, g\}$,
(a) list all 2-arrangements of its elements;
(b) list all its 2-subsets.

8. Give the following in factorial notation
(a) the number of arrangements of five objects
(b) the number of 5-arrangements of 12 items
(c) the number of 4-subsets of a set of nine objects

9. Evaluate each expression.

(a) $\binom{9}{6}$ (b) $\binom{10}{2}$ (c) $5!\binom{11}{6}$

(d) $\binom{7}{2}5!$ (e) $\binom{10}{3}\binom{7}{2}\binom{4}{3}\binom{2}{2}$

10. Match each expression (a) – (h) with one equivalent expression from the list below.

$$15, \ 6!, \ P(7,4), \ 4!, \ \binom{8}{5}, \ 9900, \ \binom{7}{4}, \ 28!$$

(a) $12 \times 2!$ (b) $28 \times 27!$ (c) $\dfrac{15!}{14!}$ (d) $\dfrac{100!}{98!}$

(e) $30P(4,4)$ (f) $4!\binom{7}{4}$ (g) $\binom{8}{3}$ (h) $\binom{9}{9}\binom{7}{4}$

11. A contractor needs four carpenters; ten are sent from the union hall. In how many ways can he pick his work crew?

12. Laurie's bedroom has four doors. In how many different ways can she enter, then leave the room?

13. Of the 21 young girls auditioning for the role of Annie, nine were good dancers who could not sing well enough, but five could sing and dance well. Assuming that all girls possessed at least one of these skills, how many girls must have been good singers without dancing skills?

14. There are 16 teams entered in the Theatre Games tournament. In how many ways can first-, second-, and third-place ribbons be awarded to the teams?

15. Seven-year-old Sarah has nine crayons; three blue, one red, two green, and three yellow.
(a) In how many ways can she line up the crayons on her desk?
(b) She is to pick up some of the crayons. How many different choices of *some* crayons could she make?

16. An Austrian village consists of five streets running north and south and three streets running east and west. A tourist sets out from the north-east corner of the village to reach the south-west corner. In how many different ways could the tourist wander these streets if she is always facing south or west?

17. The members of City Council are to vote *yes* or *no* on each of seven issues. In marking a ballot, each councillor has the option of abstaining on as many as six of the issues, but should not abstain in all seven cases. In how many ways can a ballot be marked?

18. Serge is handing out snacks at the day-care centre. There are 15 children. He has seven apples, six oranges, and two boxes of raisins. In how many different ways could the snacks be distributed?

19. There are five different colours available in a fabric that is suitable for a flag. How many different flags of three stripes, all vertical or all horizontal, (tricolours) can be made, assuming that no colour is repeated in a flag?

20. A committee of six is to be chosen from the 25 members of the student council (including the executive) to organize Spirit Week activities. In how many ways can this be done if:
    (a) there are no restrictions?
    (b) there are 14 junior council members and 11 senior members; the committee must include four juniors and two seniors?
    (c) the social director and student council vice-president must be on the committee?
    (d) there must be at least two of the six executive members on the committee?

21. In her repertoire, Esther has seven songs from which she will perform two at each school concert. In how many ways can the programs for three consecutive shows be arranged so that she does not perform the same song two shows in a row?

22. From records at D.D. Collegiate, the following data was collected:
    > 12 students studied Sociology, Economics, and Accounting
    > 27 studied Sociology and Accounting
    > 20 studied Sociology and Economics
    > 21 studied Economics and Accounting
    > 36 studied Sociology
    > 36 studied Economics
    > 58 studied Accounting

    (a) What is the least number of individual student records that were examined?
    Illustrate your answer with a Venn diagram and show all your calculations.
    (b) How many students studied Sociology but neither of the Business subjects?

23. Prove, for n, r natural numbers, that

$$\binom{n}{r} = \frac{n - r + 1}{r}\binom{n}{r-1}$$

24. Solve for $n \in N$.

(a) $5P(n, 3) = 24\binom{n}{4}$

(b) $\frac{3}{2}\binom{n}{3} = \binom{n+1}{2}$

PROBLEMS PLUS

Sieve of Eratosthenes

The Greek mathematician Eratosthenes, in the third century B.C., developed a technique for finding all prime numbers from 1 to n, for any natural number n. His procedure is as follows: from the list of numbers 1, 2, ... , n

 i) First remove all multiples of 2 other than 2,

 ii) then remove all multiples of 3 other than 3,

 iii) then remove all multiples of 5 other than 5 and so on ...

Using the principle of inclusion and exclusion, calculate how many numbers would be left in the list 1, 2, ... , n after these first three steps for each value of n.

(a) $n = 10$

(b) $n = 100$

(c) $n = 1000$

[Hint: Let $A =$ the set of numbers divisible by 2.

$B =$ the set of numbers divisible by 3.

$C =$ the set of numbers divisible by 5.]

PROBLEMS PLUS

Dominoes

Explain why there are 28 dominoes in a set of dominoes.

(See the Problems Plus on page 19.)

2.6 CHAPTER 2 TEST

1. Evaluate the expression.

$$\binom{7}{7} + P(4,4) - \binom{5}{0} + \binom{6}{4} + \binom{4}{1}$$

2. Twelve executives arrive at a meeting. If all shake hands with each other, how many handshakes occur?

3. Jonathan has six close friends. In how many ways can he invite one or more of them to dinner?

4. (a) What is the relationship between $P(n, r)$ and $\binom{n}{r}$?

    (b) Explain the relationship described in (a).

5. On an examination paper are instructions that, in total, seven questions must be completed. If ten questions are given and the first three questions are compulsory, how many selections of questions are possible?

6. In how many ways can a school committee of ten be formed if the committee must include the principal or vice-principal, four teachers from a staff of 71, and five student council members from the council of 21 students? (Leave your answer in factorial notation.)

7. A package of 20 transistors contains fifteen that are perfect and five that are defective. In how many ways can five of these transistors be selected so that at least three are perfect?

8. Data obtained from a survey of families were reported as follows:

    114 eat meat at least once every day
    100 eat bread at least once every day
    70 eat fruit at least once every day
    48 eat meat and bread once a day
    41 eat meat and fruit once a day
    27 eat bread and fruit once a day
    17 eat all three of these foods once a day

    (a) What is the minimum number of families that were surveyed?
    (b) How many of these families did not eat meat on a daily basis?

9. A sign outside a local fast food outlet proclaims
        WE KNOW 256 WAYS TO SAY HAMBURGER!
    Explain this statement.
    [Hint: Think "toppings."]

PROBLEMS PLUS

Five-card poker

In playing poker, the likelihood of being dealt a particular hand depends on the number of ways in which that hand could have been dealt from the 52-card deck. Find the number of ways each hand could be dealt.

(a) No pairs (five different face values, not in sequence, not all cards in the same suit).

(b) One pair (two cards of one face value and three cards of different face values, none matching the pair).

(c) Two pairs (one pair of each of two different face values and a card of a third face value).

(d) Three of a kind (exactly three cards of one face value and two different cards)

(e) Straight (five cards in sequence, but not all of same suit).

(f) Flush (five cards of the same suit but not in sequence).

(g) Full house (three cards of one face value and two cards of another face value).

(h) Four of a kind (four cards of one face value and one other card).

(i) Straight flush (five cards in sequence and of the same suit).

PROBLEMS PLUS

The Pigeonhole Principle

If seven pigeons fly into six pigeonholes, at least one of the pigeonholes will contain two or more pigeons. More generally:

THE PIGEONHOLE PRINCIPLE

If $n + 1$ pigeons are in n pigeonholes, at least one of the pigeonholes will contain two or more pigeons.

This rather obvious result has many interesting consequences.

EXAMPLE 1

Show that in every group of eight people, there are at least two whose birthdays fall on the same day of the week.

Solution

If we let the days of the week correspond to the pigeonholes and the birthdays correspond to the pigeons, then we have seven pigeonholes and eight pigeons. By the Pigeonhole Principle, at least two birthdays fall on the same day of the week.

In general we have:

If there are more than k times as many pigeons as pigeonholes then some pigeonholes must contain at least $k + 1$ pigeons.

EXAMPLE 2

Show that in Ontario there must be at least 33 people with the same number of hairs on their head. (You may assume that the population of Ontario exceeds 8 million, and that no one has more than 250 000 hairs.)

Solution

Using the number of hairs as the pigeonhole we see that there are 250 000 pigeonholes. Now $8\ 000\ 000 = 32 \times 250\ 000$, and there are more than 32 times as many people as pigeonholes, so there must be at least $32 + 1 = 33$ people with the same number of hairs.

We remark that the pigeonhole principle asserts the existence of a pigeonhole with at least $k + 1$ objects in it but gives no method of finding this pigeonhole. In the above example it is impossible to find 33 people sharing that characteristic.

EXAMPLE 3

Let S be a set of 101 natural numbers none of which is greater than 200. Prove that there are $s, t \in S$ with $s \neq t$, and s dividing t.

Solution

The natural numbers which are $\leqslant 200$ may be described as follows:

the odd numbers $\qquad$ $\{1, 3, 5, \ldots, \quad 199\}$ (100 of them)

twice the odd numbers $\qquad$ $\{2, 6, 10, \ldots, 198\}$

four times the odd numbers $\{4, 12, 20, \ldots, 196\}$

eight times the odd numbers $\{8, 24, 40, \ldots, 200\}$

and so on.

We deduce from this that each number $n \leqslant 200$ may be written in the form $n = 2^k j$ where $k \in W$, $j \in N$, j odd. We take the 100 odd numbers $\leqslant 200$ as our pigeonholes and put $s \in S$ in pigeonhole j if $s = 2^k j$ for some $k \in W$.

Now S has 101 elements, so at least two of them must end up in the same pigeonhole. That is: there are $s, t \in S$ with $s < t$, $s = 2^k j$, $t = 2^l j$, j odd, $k < l$. So s divides t.

Exercise

1. Prove that in a crowd of 400 people at least two people celebrate their birthdays on the same day.

2. Prove that in any group of 37 people there are always at least four people who were born in the same month of the year.

3. Given a group of n married women and their husbands, how many people must be chosen from this group of $2n$ people to guarantee the inclusion of a married couple?

4. Prove that if there are five points on the plane with integral coordinates then there is at least one pair of distinct points whose midpoint also has integer coordinates. [Hint: the pigeonholes are (even, even), (even, odd), ...].

5. Prove that if five pins are stuck into a piece of cardboard cut in the form of an equilateral triangle with sides of length two, then at least two of the pins must be within a distance one unit of each other. (Hint: Apply the pigeonhole principle to the four equilateral triangle of side one).

6. Consider six points in the plane, no three of which are collinear. There are 15 line segments connecting the points. Let those segments be coloured in any way by the use of two colours, say blue and green with the entire segment being either blue or green. A triangle connecting three points is chromatic if its sides have the same colour. Prove that no matter how the segments are coloured, it is always possible to find a chromatic triangle.

CHAPTER 3

THE BINOMIAL THEOREM

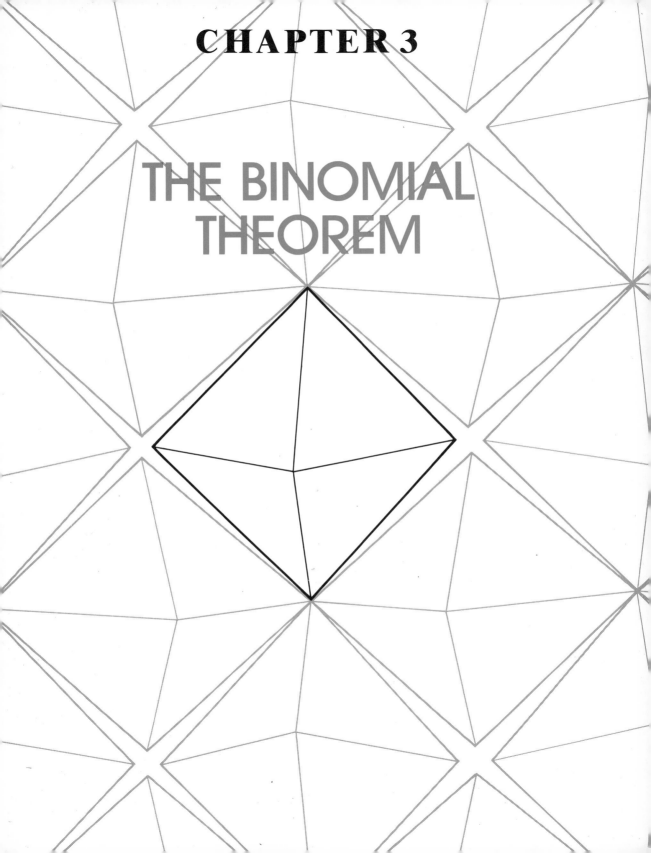

REVIEW AND PREVIEW TO
CHAPTER 3

Sigma Notation

Series can be described using the Greek letter Σ (sigma). For example,

$$3 + 5 + 7 + 9 + 11$$

can be written

$$\sum_{i=1}^{5}(2i + 1)$$

which is read "the sum of $2i + 1$ from $i=1$ to $i=5$"

Example 1   Write $\sum_{i=0}^{4}(2i^2 - i)$ in expanded form.

Solution

$$\sum_{i=0}^{4}(2i^2 - i) = [2(0)^2 - 0] + [2(1)^2 - 1] + [2(2)^2 - 2]$$
$$+ [2(3)^2 - 3] + [2(4)^2 - 4]$$
$$= 0 + 1 + 6 + 15 + 28$$

Example 2   Write $1 + 4 + 9 + \dots + 64$ by using sigma notation.

Solution

$$1 + 4 + 9 + \dots + 64 = (1)^2 + (2)^2 + (3)^2 + \dots + (8)^2$$
$$= \sum_{i=1}^{8} i^2$$

EXERCISE 1

1. Write each of the following in expanded form.

(a) $\sum_{i=1}^{4}(2i - 3)$ (b) $\sum_{i=2}^{6} \dfrac{1}{i+4}$

(c) $\sum_{k=0}^{5} k(k + 1)$ (d) $\sum_{r=0}^{6} 2^{r-1}$

(e) $\sum_{r=0}^{4} \binom{4}{r}$ (f) $\sum_{r=0}^{7}(-1)^r \binom{7}{r}^2$

2. Write each of the following by using sigma notation.
   (a) $1 + 2 + 4 + 8 + 16 + 32 + 64 + 128$
   (b) $3x + 4x + 5x + 6x + 7x$
   (c) $a + a^2 + a^3 + a^4 + a^5 + a^6 + a^7$
   (d) $x - x^2 + x^3 - x^4 + x^5 - x^6$

(e) $\dbinom{7}{0} + \dbinom{7}{1} + \dbinom{7}{2} + \dbinom{7}{3} + \dbinom{7}{4} + \dbinom{7}{5} + \dbinom{7}{6} + \dbinom{7}{7}$

(f) $\dbinom{10}{0}^2 + \dbinom{10}{1}^2 + \dbinom{10}{2}^2 + \cdots + \dbinom{10}{10}^2$

(g) $\dbinom{9}{0} - \dbinom{9}{1} + \dbinom{9}{2} - \dbinom{9}{3} + \cdots - \dbinom{9}{9}$

(h) $\dbinom{n}{0} + \dbinom{n}{1} + \dbinom{n}{2} + \cdots + \dbinom{n}{n}$

(i) $\dbinom{n}{0}^2 - \dbinom{n}{1}^2 + \dbinom{n}{2}^2 - \dbinom{n}{3}^2 + \cdots + (-1)^n\dbinom{n}{n}^2$

Exponents

$$a^m \times a^n = a^{m+n} \qquad \frac{a^m}{a^n} = a^{m-n} \qquad (a^m)^n = a^{mn}$$

$$a^0 = 1 \qquad a^{-1} = \frac{1}{a} \qquad a^{\frac{1}{n}} = \sqrt[n]{a}$$

$$(ab)^n = a^n b^n \qquad \left(\frac{a}{b}\right)^n = \frac{a^n}{b^n} \qquad a^{\frac{m}{n}} = \left(\sqrt[n]{a}\right)^m$$

EXERCISE 2

1. Write an equivalent expression for each of the following. Use negative and/or fractional exponents.

(a) $\dfrac{1}{x}$ (b) $\dfrac{1}{x^2}$ (c) $-\dfrac{1}{x^3}$ (d) $\dfrac{2}{x^2}$

(e) $-\dfrac{3}{x}$ (f) $\sqrt{x}$ (g) $\sqrt{\dfrac{1}{x}}$ (h) $\dfrac{1}{\sqrt[3]{x}}$

2. Use the exponent laws to simplify each of the following.

(a) $(3x^2)^3 \,(x^4)^4$

(b) $(2x^5)\left(-\dfrac{1}{x}\right)^3$

(c) $(-x^2)^7 \left(\sqrt{x}\right)^6$

(d) $x^{2(8-r)} \, x^r$

(e) $a^{11-r}\left(\dfrac{1}{a}\right)^r$

(f) $(2x^2)^{5-r}\left(-\dfrac{1}{x}\right)^r$

(g) $\left(\dfrac{2}{x}\right)^{n-r} (x^2)^r$

(h) $x^{n-r}\left(-\dfrac{1}{x^2}\right)^r$

EXERCISE 3   Expanding

1. Expand and simplify each of the following.

(a) $(2x - 3)^2$

(b) $(x^2 + 3x)^2$

(c) $(x + 1)^3$

(d) $(a^2 - 4)^3$

(e) $(3x - 5)(2x + 5)^2$

(f) $(a + b)(a - b)^3$

(g) $(x - 2)^4$

(h) $(3p + 2q)^2 (5p - 4q)^2$

INTRODUCTION

Very often an idea from one part of mathematics has applications to another. In the first two sections of this chapter, we investigate properties of the numbers $\binom{n}{r}$ by writing them in the form of a triangular array known as Pascal's Triangle. In the remaining sections we see how these concepts can be applied to the expansion of binomials, generalizing to the Binomial Theorem.

3.1 PASCAL'S TRIANGLE

In Chapter 2 we defined the number $\binom{n}{r}$ of r-subsets of a set of n elements, and showed that

$$\binom{n}{r} = \frac{n!}{r!(n-r)!} \quad n, r \in W, r \leqslant n$$

We write these numbers in the following way.

Value of n

0	$\binom{0}{0}$ $r=0$
1	$\binom{1}{0}$ $\binom{1}{1}$ $r=1$
2	$\binom{2}{0}$ $\binom{2}{1}$ $\binom{2}{2}$ $r=2$
3	$\binom{3}{0}$ $\binom{3}{1}$ $\binom{3}{2}$ $\binom{3}{3}$ $r=3$
4	$\binom{4}{0}$ $\binom{4}{1}$ $\binom{4}{2}$ $\binom{4}{3}$ $\binom{4}{4}$ $r=4$
5	$\binom{5}{0}$ $\binom{5}{1}$ $\binom{5}{2}$ $\binom{5}{3}$ $\binom{5}{4}$ $\binom{5}{5}$ $r=5$
6	$\binom{6}{0}$ $\binom{6}{1}$ $\binom{6}{2}$ $\binom{6}{3}$ $\binom{6}{4}$ $\binom{6}{5}$ $\binom{6}{6}$ $r=6$
⋮	⋮

If we evaluate each entry, we obtain the following triangular array of numbers.

Value of n

0				1			
1			1		1		
2			1	2	1		
3		1	3		3	1	
4		1	4	6	4	1	
5	1	5	10		10	5	1
6	1	6	15	20	15	6	1
⋮				⋮			

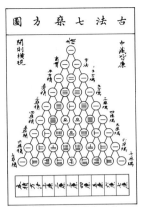

The "Pascal" Triangle as depicted in a Chinese manuscript of 1303.

This array is known as **Pascal's Triangle**. It originated in China about 1100 A.D. but it is called Pascal's Triangle because Blaise Pascal developed and applied many of its properties in the seventeenth century.

This arrangement of the various values of $\binom{n}{r}$ is a convenient way to study the properties introduced in Chapter 2 and to investigate further properties of subsets of sets.

Notice that in any row of Pascal's Triangle, entries equidistant (the same distance) from each end are equal. For example,

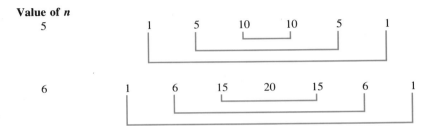

Value of n

5   1   5   10   10   5   1

6   1   6   15   20   15   6   1

That is,

$$\binom{5}{0} = \binom{5}{5} = 1 \qquad \binom{6}{0} = \binom{6}{6} = 1$$

$$\binom{5}{1} = \binom{5}{4} = 5 \quad \text{and} \quad \binom{6}{1} = \binom{6}{5} = 6$$

$$\binom{5}{2} = \binom{5}{3} = 10 \qquad \binom{6}{2} = \binom{6}{4} = 15$$

The generalization of this property is

$$\boxed{\binom{n}{r} = \binom{n}{n-r}}$$

which is easily proved.

Proof

$$\binom{n}{n-r} = \frac{n!}{(n-r)!\,(n-(n-r))!}$$

$$= \frac{n!}{(n-r)!\,r!}$$

$$= \binom{n}{r}$$

Note: This is the relationship suggested in Exercise 2.2, Question 18.

Example 1   To what other expression in the form $\binom{n}{r}$ is each of the following equal?

(a) $\binom{9}{3}$ (b) $\binom{17}{6}$

(c) $\binom{43}{19}$ (d) $\binom{8}{x}$

Solution   (a) In this case $n = 9$ and $r = 3$, so
$$\binom{9}{3} = \binom{9}{9-3} = \binom{9}{6}$$

(b) $\binom{17}{6} = \binom{17}{17-6} = \binom{17}{11}$

(c) $\binom{43}{19} = \binom{43}{43-19} = \binom{43}{24}$

(d) $\binom{8}{x} = \binom{8}{8-x}$

Example 2   The calculations of $\binom{7}{r}$ for $r = 0, 1, 2, 3, \dots , 7$ can be simplified by using this property.

Solution
$$\binom{7}{0} = \frac{7!}{0!\,7!} = 1$$

$$\binom{7}{1} = \frac{7!}{1!\,6!} = 7$$

$$\binom{7}{2} = \frac{7!}{2!\,5!} = \frac{7 \times 6}{2 \times 1} = 21$$

$$\binom{7}{3} = \frac{7!}{3!\,4!} = \frac{7 \times 6 \times 5}{3 \times 2 \times 1} = 35$$

$$\binom{7}{4} = \binom{7}{3} = 35$$

$$\binom{7}{5} = \binom{7}{2} = 21$$

$$\binom{7}{6} = \binom{7}{1} = 7$$

$$\binom{7}{7} = \binom{7}{0} = 1$$

Returning to our study of Pascal's Triangle, we notice that each number in any row can be obtained by adding the numbers to the left and right of it in the row above.

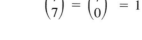

Value of *n*

```
0                                    1

1                                1       1

2                            1       2       1

3                        1       3       3       1

4                    1       4       6       4       1

5                1       5      10      10      5       1

6            1       6      15      20      15      6       1
```

This makes it a simple matter to extend Pascal's Triangle to further rows.

Value of *n*

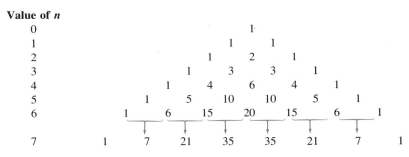

```
0                                    1

1                                1       1

2                            1       2       1

3                        1       3       3       1

4                    1       4       6       4       1

5                1       5      10      10      5       1

6            1       6      15      20      15      6       1

7        1       7      21      35      35      21      7       1
```

These values for $\binom{7}{r}$ $(r = 0, 1, 2, \ldots, 7)$ agree with those calculated in Example 2.

Example 3   (a)   Extend Pascal's Triangle to include the row where $n = 8$ by using the pattern illustrated.

(b)   Check these values by evaluating $\binom{8}{r}$ for $r = 0, 1, 2, \ldots, 8$.

Solution   (a)

Value of *n*

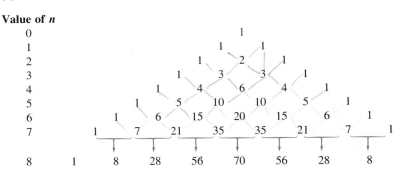

```
0                                        1

1                                    1       1

2                                1       2       1

3                            1       3       3       1

4                        1       4       6       4       1

5                    1       5      10      10      5       1

6                1       6      15      20      15      6       1

7            1       7      21      35      35      21      7       1

8        1       8      28      56      70      56      28      8       1
```

(b) $\dbinom{8}{0} = \dfrac{8!}{0!\,8!} = 1$ $\dbinom{8}{5} = \dbinom{8}{3} = 56$

$\dbinom{8}{1} = \dfrac{8!}{1!\,7!} = 8$ $\dbinom{8}{6} = \dbinom{8}{2} = 28$

$\dbinom{8}{2} = \dfrac{8!}{2!\,6!} = \dfrac{8 \times 7}{2 \times 1} = 28$ $\dbinom{8}{7} = \dbinom{8}{1} = 8$

$\dbinom{8}{3} = \dfrac{8!}{3!\,5!} = \dfrac{8 \times 7 \times 6}{3 \times 2 \times 1} = 56$ $\dbinom{8}{8} = \dbinom{8}{0} = 1$

$\dbinom{8}{4} = \dfrac{8!}{4!\,4!} = \dfrac{8 \times 7 \times 6 \times 5}{4 \times 3 \times 2 \times 1} = 70$ ◇

Now we investigate what property of subsets of sets is suggested by this pattern.

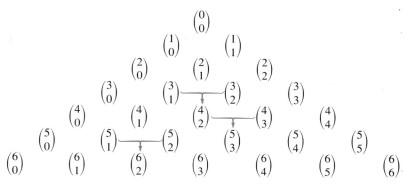

The pattern discovered suggests that

$$\dbinom{3}{1} + \dbinom{3}{2} = \dbinom{4}{2}$$

$$\dbinom{4}{2} + \dbinom{4}{3} = \dbinom{5}{3}$$

$$\dbinom{5}{1} + \dbinom{5}{2} = \dbinom{6}{2}$$

$$\vdots$$

Example 4 What expression in the form $\dbinom{n}{r}$ would we predict to be equal to each of the following?

(a) $\dbinom{7}{4} + \dbinom{7}{5}$

(b) $\dbinom{9}{2} + \dbinom{9}{3}$

(c) $\dbinom{23}{18} + \dbinom{23}{19}$

(d) $\dbinom{64}{30} + \dbinom{64}{29}$

Solution   (a) $\dbinom{7}{4} + \dbinom{7}{5} = \dbinom{8}{5}$

(b) $\dbinom{9}{2} + \dbinom{9}{3} = \dbinom{10}{3}$

(c) $\dbinom{23}{18} + \dbinom{23}{19} = \dbinom{24}{19}$

(d) $\dbinom{64}{30} + \dbinom{64}{29} = \dbinom{65}{30}$

The generalization of this pattern is known as Pascal's Theorem.

PASCAL'S THEOREM

$$\binom{n}{r} + \binom{n}{r+1} = \binom{n+1}{r+1}$$

Proof

$$\binom{n}{r} + \binom{n}{r+1} = \frac{n!}{r!\,(n-r)!} + \frac{n!}{(r+1)!\,[n-(r+1)]!}$$

$$= \frac{n!}{r!\,(n-r)!} + \frac{n!}{(r+1)!\,(n-r-1)!}$$

$$= \frac{n!\,(r+1)}{(r+1)\,r!\,(n-r)!} + \frac{n!\,(n-r)}{(r+1)!\,(n-r)\,(n-r-1)!} \qquad \text{(Common Denominator)}$$

$$= \frac{n!\,(r+1) + n!\,(n-r)}{(r+1)!\,(n-r)!}$$

$$= \frac{n!\,[(r+1) + (n-r)]}{(r+1)!\,(n-r)!} \qquad \text{(Common Factor)}$$

$$= \frac{n!\,(n+1)}{(r+1)!\,(n-r)!}$$

$$= \frac{(n+1)!}{(r+1)!\,(n-r)!}$$

$$= \frac{(n+1)!}{(r+1)!\,[(n+1) - (r+1)]!}$$

$$= \binom{n+1}{r+1}$$

WORKING BACKWARDS

EXERCISE 3.1

A **1.** What other expressions in the form $\binom{n}{r}$ are equal to the following?

(a) $\binom{9}{2}$ (b) $\binom{13}{5}$ (c) $\binom{46}{39}$ (d) $\binom{26}{26}$

2. What expression in the form $\binom{n}{r}$ is equal to each of the following?

(a) $\binom{8}{3} + \binom{8}{4}$

(b) $\binom{17}{6} + \binom{17}{7}$

(c) $\binom{28}{5} + \binom{28}{4}$

(d) $\binom{n-1}{r-1} + \binom{n-1}{r}$

B **3.** In your Finite Mathematics class of 25 students, a committee of five students is to be chosen to determine if there will be a quiz given on this section.

(a) In how many different ways can this committee be chosen?

(b) On how many of these possible committees would you be a member?

(c) On how many of these possible committees would you not be a member?

(d) How does this relate to Pascal's Theorem?

4. Repeat Question 3, assuming that there are n students in your class and a committee of r students, $r \leq n$, is to be chosen.

5. Make a copy of Pascal's Triangle to include the rows where $n = 0$ through $n = 12$. Keep this handy as it will be useful in the questions that follow and in future sections.

There are many other patterns that arise from Pascal's Triangle. The following questions are designed to help you discover some of these patterns.

6. (a) Add the numbers in each row of Pascal's Triangle and complete a chart similar to the one given.

n	Sum of the Numbers in the Row	
0	1	= 1
1	1 + 1	= 2
2	1 + 2 + 1	= 4
⋮	⋮	
6		

(b) What would you predict to be the sum of the numbers in the row where $n = 7$? Check your prediction.

(c) Use your results from parts (a) and (b) to evaluate the following.

(i) $\binom{8}{0} + \binom{8}{1} + \binom{8}{2} + \binom{8}{3} + \binom{8}{4} + \binom{8}{5} + \binom{8}{6}$
$+ \binom{8}{7} + \binom{8}{8}$

(ii) $\binom{9}{0} + \binom{9}{1} + \binom{9}{2} + \ldots + \binom{9}{9}$

(iii) $\sum_{r=0}^{10} \binom{10}{r}$

(d) Generalize your results to find an expression for $\sum_{r=0}^{n} \binom{n}{r}$.

7. Using your results from Question 6, what is the total number of subsets of a set containing 7 elements? n elements?

8. The set of all possible subsets of a set is called the **power set** of that set. If the power set of a set contains 256 elements, how many elements are in the set?

9. If $\binom{n}{0} + \binom{n}{1} + \binom{n}{2} + \ldots + \binom{n}{n} = 128$ find n.

10. If $\sum_{r=0}^{n} \binom{n}{r} = 512$ find n.

11. (a) Add the squares of the numbers in each row of Pascal's Triangle and complete a chart similar to the one given.

n	Sum of the Squares of the Numbers in the Row	
0	1^2	$= 1$
1	$1^2 + 1^2$	$= 2$
2	$1^2 + 2^2 + 1^2$	$= 6$
.	.	
.	.	
.	.	
5		

(b) Locate these numbers in Pascal's Triangle.

(c) What would you predict to be the sum of the squares of the numbers in the row where $n = 6$? Check your prediction.

(d) What other expression in the form $\binom{n}{r}$ does each of the following equal?

(i) $\binom{2}{0}^2 + \binom{2}{1}^2 + \binom{2}{2}^2$

(ii) $\binom{3}{0}^2 + \binom{3}{1}^2 + \binom{3}{2}^2 + \binom{3}{3}^2$

(iii) $\binom{4}{0}^2 + \binom{4}{1}^2 + \binom{4}{2}^2 + \binom{4}{3}^2 + \binom{4}{4}^2$

(iv) $\sum_{r=0}^{5} \binom{5}{r}^2$

(v) $\displaystyle\sum_{r=0}^{6}\binom{6}{r}^{2}$

(e) Generalize your result to find a simpler expression for

$$\binom{n}{0}^{2}+\binom{n}{1}^{2}+\binom{n}{2}^{2}+\ldots+\binom{n}{n}^{2}$$

(f) Write the expression in part (e) by using sigma notation.

12. (a) In a Finite Mathematics class there are n girls and n boys. One-half of the students are to be chosen to take part in a survey on student behavior in the school halls. In how many possible ways can these students be chosen?

(b) How many of these choices would contain no girls, one girl, two girls, three girls, ..., n girls?

(c) Write an equation relating parts (a) and (b).

(d) Use the fact that $\binom{n}{r}=\binom{n}{n-r}$ to rewrite your equation in part (c).

13. In each row of Pascal's Triangle, alternate the signs of each entry; the first positive, the second negative, the third positive, the fourth negative, and so on.

(a) Find the sum of the new elements in each row and complete a chart similar to the one given.

n	Sum of the Numbers in the Row (Alternate Signs Assumed)	
0	1	$=1$
1	$1-1$	$=0$
2	$1-2+1$	$=0$
⋮	⋮	
6		

(b) What would you predict to be the sum of the numbers in the row where $n=7$? Check your prediction.

(c) Use your results from parts (a) and (b) to evaluate

(i) $\binom{8}{0}-\binom{8}{1}+\binom{8}{2}-\binom{8}{3}+\binom{8}{4}-\binom{8}{5}+\binom{8}{6}$
$-\binom{8}{7}+\binom{8}{8}$

(ii) $\displaystyle\sum_{r=0}^{9}(-1)^{r}\binom{9}{r}$

Note: The use of $(-1)^{r}$ in the sigma notation has the effect of alternating the signs of the terms in the expansion. The terms will be positive when $r=0,2,4,6,8$ and negative when $r=1,3,5,7,9$.

(d) Generalize your results to find an expression for

$$\binom{n}{0} - \binom{n}{1} + \binom{n}{2} - \ldots + (-1)^n\binom{n}{n}$$

[Note: There are two cases to consider.]

14. A different way of writing the numbers in Pascal's Triangle is to position the first entries in the rows in a column, the second entries in the rows in another column, and so on.

r	0	1	2	3	4	5	6	...
n								
0	1							
1	1	1						
2	1	2	1					
3	1	3	3	1				
4								
5								
6								
⋮								

Extend a chart similar to the one given through nine rows. Make reference to this chart when answering Questions 15 and 17.

15. Quarters can be arranged in the shape of an equilateral triangle as shown.

The first contains one quarter, the second contains three quarters, the third, six quarters, and so on.

(a) How many quarters do the fourth, fifth, and sixth contain?

(b) Such numbers are called **triangular numbers**. [Note: The *n*th triangular number is the sum of the first *n* natural numbers.] Locate the triangular numbers in the version of Pascal's Triangle you made in Question 14.

(c) Express each of the first six triangular numbers in the form $\binom{n}{r}$.

(d) Predict expressions, in the form $\binom{n}{r}$, for the seventh and eighth triangular numbers. Check your predictions.

(e) Generalize your results to find an expression for the *n*th triangular number.

16. Use your results from Question 15 to find the sum of
    (a) the first 100 natural numbers.
    (b) the first 1000 natural numbers.
    (c) the numbers from 150 to 250 inclusive.

17. Tennis balls can be arranged in the shape of a tetrahedron as shown.

The first contains one tennis ball, the second contains four tennis balls, the third, ten, and so on.
    (a) How many tennis balls do the fourth, fifth, and sixth contain?
    (b) Such numbers are called **tetrahedral numbers**. Locate the tetrahedral numbers in the version of Pascal's Triangle you made in Question 14.
    (c) Express each of the first six tetrahedral numbers in the form $\binom{n}{r}$.
    (d) Predict an expression in the form $\binom{n}{r}$ for the seventh and eighth tetrahedral numbers. Check your predictions.
    (e) Generalize your results to find an expression for the nth tetrahedral number.

3.2 PROBLEM SOLVING WITH PASCAL'S TRIANGLE

An interesting physical illustration of Pascal's Triangle is the fountain shown. The water overflows from each basin on two sides. Determine the number of distinct paths of water leading to each basin.

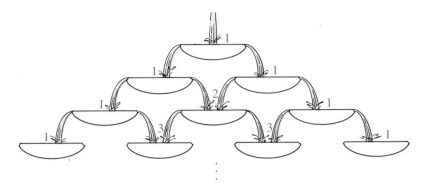

There is precisely one path to the basin on the first (top) level. Similarly, there is one path leading to each of the basins on the second level. On the third level, the outside basins each has one path leading to it, whereas, the middle basin has two paths because both basins on the second level overflow into it. On the fourth level, the outside basins both have one path leading to them. However, water overflows into the basins in the middle from the basins on the third level to the immediate right and left. The number of paths to one of these basins on level four will be the sum of the number of paths leading into the basins overflowing into it; that is, $1 + 2 = 3$ paths. On a level further down, the number of paths leading to any one basin will be the sum of the number of paths to the basins overflowing into it. Proceeding in this fashion, we obtain the numbers in Pascal's Triangle.

$$
\begin{array}{ccccccccccc}
 & & & & & 1 & & & & & \\
 & & & & 1 & & 1 & & & & \\
 & & & 1 & & 2 & & 1 & & & \\
 & & 1 & & 3 & & 3 & & 1 & & \\
 & 1 & & 4 & & 6 & & 4 & & 1 & \\
1 & & 5 & & 10 & & 10 & & 5 & & 1 \\
 & & & & & \vdots & & & & & \\
\end{array}
$$

Each number indicates the number of paths to the basin that would be located at that position in the fountain.

There are many different situations where this kind of pathfinding occurs.

Example 1 George Polya was a mathematician and mathematics teacher. He was dedicated to the problem-solving approach in the teaching of mathematics. In his words, "There, you may experience the tension and enjoy the triumph of discovery."

In the arrangement of letters given, starting from the top we proceed to the row below by moving diagonally to the immediate right or left. How many different paths will spell the name George Polya?

```
                        G
                   E         E
              O         O         O
         R         R         R         R
              G         G         G
                   E         E
                        P
                   O         O
              L         L         L
                   Y         Y
                        A
```

Solution We determine the number of paths leading to each letter in the arrangement.

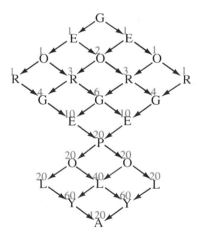

Completing this, we see there are 120 ways to reach the bottom; therefore, there are 120 different paths that will spell George Polya.

Example 2 A six-square by six-square gameboard is shown. A checker is placed at the second position in the bottom row. You are allowed to move the checker one square diagonally up (either left or right) at any one time. How many different ways are there to get to the opposite side of the board?

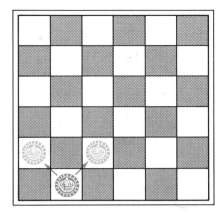

Solution We determine the number of paths leading to each square on the gameboard.

Blank squares have no paths leading to them. There are five ways to reach the top left corner, nine ways to reach the third position in the top row, and five ways to reach the fifth position in the top row. Therefore, there are 5 + 9 + 5 = 19 ways to reach the opposite side of the gameboard.

A useful and surprising application of Pascal's Triangle is in the expansion of binomials.

In your previous mathematical experience, when confronted with an expression like $(a+b)^2$, the instructions would usually read, "Expand and collect the like terms" or "Expand and simplify."

$$\begin{aligned} (a+b)^2 &= (a+b)(a+b) \\ &= a^2 + ab + ba + b^2 \\ &= a^2 + 2ab + b^2 \end{aligned}$$

For higher powers of $a+b$, like $(a+b)^3$, the expansion would proceed in the following way.

$$\begin{aligned}(a+b)^3 &= (a+b)\,(a+b)^2 \\ &= (a+b)\,(a^2\ +\ 2ab\ +\ b^2) \\ &= a^3\ +\ 2a^2b\ +\ ab^2\ +\ a^2b\ +\ 2ab^2\ +\ b^3 \\ &= a^3\ +\ 3a^2b\ +\ 3ab^2\ +\ b^3\end{aligned}$$

Similarly, $(a+b)^4$ would be expanded

$$\begin{aligned}(a+b)^4 &= (a+b)\,(a+b)^3 \\ &= (a+b)\,(a^3\ +\ 3a^2b\ +\ 3ab^2\ +\ b^3) \\ &= a^4\ +\ 3a^3b\ +\ 3a^2b^2\ +\ ab^3\ +\ a^3b\ +\ 3a^2b^2\ +\ 3ab^3\ +\ b^4 \\ &= a^4\ +\ 4a^3b\ +\ 6a^2b^2\ +\ 4ab^3\ +\ b^4\end{aligned}$$

Unfortunately, the use of this method to expand $(a+b)^{12}$ requires the previous expansion of $(a+b)^{11}$, which in turn requires knowing the expansion of $(a+b)^{10}$, and so on.

To discover how Pascal's Triangle can be useful, let us summarize the expansions we have already determined in this section. $(a+b)^0$ and $(a+b)^1$ are also included.

Value of n	$(a+b)^n$	
0	$(a+b)^0 =$	1
1	$(a+b)^1 =$	$a\ +\ b$
2	$(a+b)^2 =$	$a^2\ +\ 2ab\ +\ b^2$
3	$(a+b)^3 =$	$a^3\ +\ 3a^2b\ +\ 3ab^2\ +\ b^3$
4	$(a+b)^4 =$	$a^4\ +\ 4a^3b\ +\ 6a^2b^2\ +\ 4ab^3\ +\ b^4$

First, notice that all expansions proceed in decreasing powers of a and increasing powers of b, their exponents always adding to the exponent on the binomial. Second, the coefficients are precisely the numbers in Pascal's Triangle.

$$\begin{array}{ccccccccccc} & & & & & 1 & & & & & \\ & & & & 1 & & 1 & & & & \\ & & & 1 & & 2 & & 1 & & & \\ & & 1 & & 3 & & 3 & & 1 & & \\ & 1 & & 4 & & 6 & & 4 & & 1 & \end{array}$$

Example 3 (a) Use Pascal's Triangle to determine the expansions of $(a+b)^5$ and $(a+b)^6$.

(b) Check these results by expanding.

Solution (a) Extending Pascal's Triangle for $n=5$ and $n=6$, we obtain the following.

Value of *n*

0							1						
1						1		1					
2					1		2		1				
3				1		3		3		1			
4			1		4		6		4		1		
5		1		5		10		10		5		1	
6	1		6		15		20		15		6		1

Proceeding with decreasing powers of *a* and increasing powers of *b*, we get

$$(a+b)^5 = 1a^5 + 5a^4b + 10a^3b^2 + 10a^2b^3 + 5ab^4 + 1b^5$$

and

$$(a+b)^6 = 1a^6 + 6a^5b + 15a^4b^2 + 20a^3b^3 + 15a^2b^4$$
$$+ 6ab^5 + 1b^6$$

(b) Check.

$$(a+b)^5 = (a+b)(a+b)^4$$
$$= (a+b)(a^4 + 4a^3b + 6a^2b^2 + 4ab^3 + b^4)$$
$$= a^5 + 4a^4b + 6a^3b^2 + 4a^2b^3 + ab^4 + a^4b + 4a^3b^2$$
$$+ 6a^2b^3 + 4ab^4 + b^5$$
$$= a^5 + 5a^4b + 10a^3b^2 + 10a^2b^3 + 5ab^4 + b^5$$

$$(a+b)^6 = (a+b)(a+b)^5$$
$$= (a+b)(a^5 + 5a^4b + 10a^3b^2 + 10a^2b^3 + 5ab^4 + b^5)$$
$$= a^6 + 5a^5b + 10a^4b^2 + 10a^3b^3 + 5a^2b^4 + ab^5$$
$$+ a^5b + 5a^4b^2 + 10a^3b^3 + 10a^2b^4 + 5ab^5 + b^6$$
$$= a^6 + 6a^5b + 15a^4b^2 + 20a^3b^3 + 15a^2b^4 + 6ab^5 + b^6$$

EXERCISE 3.2

B **1.** In the arrangement of the letters given, starting from the top we proceed to the row below by moving diagonally to the immediate right or left. How many different paths will spell each of the following names?

(a) PASCAL

(b) BLAISE

```
                    B
              L        L
          A        A        A
      I        I        I        I
          S        S        S
              E        E
```

(c) EULER

```
                    E
              U        U
                    L
              E        E
                    R
```

(d) Your last name if the letters are placed in an arrangement similar to part (a).

2. Consider the five-square by five-square gameboard given.

A checker is positioned in the middle of the bottom row. The checker is allowed to move one square at a time, diagonally left or right, to the row above. How many different paths will lead to each of the positions in the top row?

3. Repeat Question 2 for a checker positioned in the bottom left corner.

4. In Question 2, assume the checker is allowed to move one square diagonally left or right or straight forward. How many different paths will lead to each of the positions in the top row?

5. Consider a six-square by six-square gameboard. Your piece is in the bottom row and the opponent's piece is indicated by X.

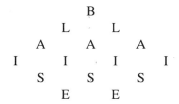

The opponent's piece does not move. Your piece is allowed to move one square at a time diagonally left or right, unless the opponent's piece is in the way. In that case, your piece is allowed to jump over the opponent's piece to the square two rows away. How many different paths will lead to each position in the top row?

6. A store is located six blocks east and four blocks south of your house. If you are allowed to walk only east or south, how many different paths lead from your house to the store?

7. Using the copy of Pascal's Triangle you completed in Exercise 3.1, Question 5, expand each of the following.
(a) $(a+b)^9$
(b) $(a+b)^{10}$
(c) $(a+b)^{11}$

8. Using the $\binom{n}{r}$ representation for the numbers in Pascal's Triangle, write an expression for each of the following.
(a) $(a+b)^3$
(b) $(a+b)^4$
(c) $(a+b)^5$

9. Using the pattern illustrated in Question 8, predict a formula for the expansion of $(a+b)^n$. This formula is known as the **Binomial Theorem** and will be proved in the next section.

PROBLEMS PLUS

Squares in Pascal's Triangle are shown in the diagram.

Discover and prove a formula for the sums of the numbers inside an $n \times n$ square.

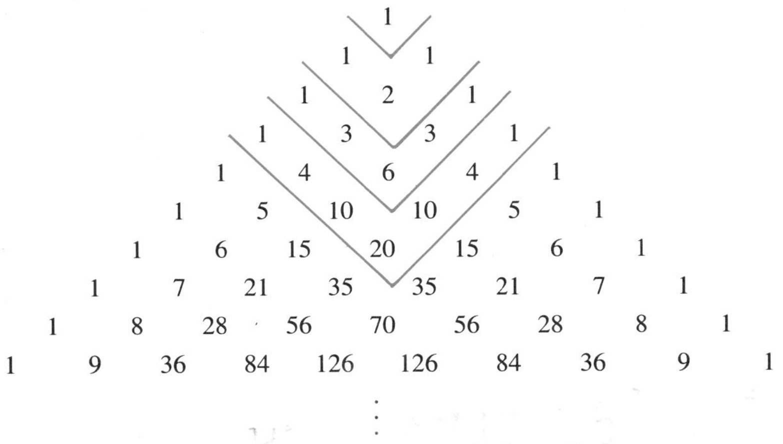

3.3 THE BINOMIAL THEOREM

In Section 3.2 we saw how Pascal's Triangle can be used in the expansion of binomials of the form $(a+b)^2$, $(a+b)^3$, $(a+b)^4$, and so on. The generalization of this result is known as

---

The Binomial Theorem

$$(a+b)^n = \binom{n}{0}a^n + \binom{n}{1}a^{n-1}b + \binom{n}{2}a^{n-2}b^2 + \ldots + \binom{n}{r}a^{n-r}b^r + \ldots + \binom{n}{n}b^n$$

Before proving the Binomial Theorem, we consider the following way of looking at these expansions.

$$(a+b)^2 = (a+b)\,(a+b)$$
$$= aa + ab + ba + bb$$

We obtain each term by choosing a letter (either a or b) from each of the two factors $(a+b)$ and then multiplying the two chosen letters. In the expansion, a^2 appears only once (aa), ab appears twice (ab, ba), and b^2 appears once (bb).

$$(a+b)^3 = (a+b)\,(a+b)\,(a+b)$$
$$= (a+b)\,(aa + ab + ba + bb)$$
$$= aaa + aab + aba + abb + baa + bab + bba + bbb$$

Again, we obtain each term by choosing a letter (either a or b) from each of the three factors $(a+b)$ and then multiplying the three chosen letters. In the expansion, a^3 appears only once (aaa), a^2b appears three times (aab, aba, baa), ab^2 appears three times (abb, bab, bba), and b^3 appears only once (bbb).

Note that we can select either no b's, one b, two b's, or three b's. If we select no b's, we can do this in $\binom{3}{0} = 1$ way. If we select one b, we can do this in $\binom{3}{1} = 3$ ways. If we select two b's, we can do this in $\binom{3}{2} = 3$ ways. If we select three b's, we can do this in $\binom{3}{3} = 1$ way.

We now use this reasoning to expand $(a+b)^4$.

$$(a+b)^4 = (a+b)\,(a+b)\,(a+b)\,(a+b)$$

We obtain each term by choosing a letter (either a or b) from each of the four factors $(a+b)$. If we choose no b's, we can do this in $\binom{4}{0} = 1$ way. If we choose one b, we can do this in $\binom{4}{1} = 4$ ways.

If we choose two b's, we can do this in $\binom{4}{2} = 6$ ways. If we choose three b's, we can do this in $\binom{4}{3} = 4$ ways. If we choose four b's, we can do this in $\binom{4}{4} = 1$ way.

Therefore

$$(a+b)^4 = \overset{\text{no } b\text{'s}}{\binom{4}{0}a^4} + \overset{1\ b}{\binom{4}{1}a^3b} + \overset{2\ b\text{'s}}{\binom{4}{2}a^2b^2} + \overset{3\ b\text{'s}}{\binom{4}{3}ab^3} + \overset{4\ b\text{'s}}{\binom{4}{4}b^4}$$

$$= a^4 + 4a^3b + 6a^2b^2 + 4ab^3 + b^4$$

We are now prepared to prove the Binomial Theorem.

Proof

$$(a+b)^n = (a+b)\,(a+b)\,(a+b)\,\ldots\,(a+b)$$

We obtain each term by choosing a letter (either a or b) from each of the n factors $(a+b)$ and then multiplying the n chosen letters. If we choose no b's, this can be done in $\binom{n}{0} = 1$ way and a^n will appear only once in the expansion. If we choose one b, this can be done in $\binom{n}{1} = n$ ways and $a^{n-1}b$ will appear n times in the expansion. If we choose two b's, this can be done in $\binom{n}{2}$ ways and $a^{n-2}b^2$ will appear $\binom{n}{2}$ times in the expansion. Continuing in this fashion, if we choose r b's, this can be done in $\binom{n}{r}$ ways and $a^{n-r}b^r$ will appear $\binom{n}{r}$ times in the expansion.

Therefore,

$$(a+b)^n = \binom{n}{0}a^n + \binom{n}{1}a^{n-1}b + \binom{n}{2}a^{n-2}b^2 + \ldots + \binom{n}{r}a^{n-r}b^r + \ldots + \binom{n}{n}b^n$$

Example 1   Expand $(a+b)^7$ using the Binomial Theorem.

Solution

$$(a+b)^7 = \binom{7}{0}a^7 + \binom{7}{1}a^6b + \binom{7}{2}a^5b^2 + \binom{7}{3}a^4b^3$$

$$+ \binom{7}{4}a^3b^4 + \binom{7}{5}a^2b^5 + \binom{7}{6}ab^6 + \binom{7}{7}b^7$$

$$= a^7 + 7a^6b + 21a^5b^2 + 35\,a^4b^3 + 35a^3b^4$$

$$+ 21a^2b^5 + 7ab^6 + b^7$$

Example 2 Expand $(x - 2)^6$.

Solution Use the binomial expansion for $(a + b)^n$ where $a = x, b = -2, n = 6$:

$$(x - 2)^6 = \left(x + (-2) \right)^6$$

$$= \binom{6}{0}x^6 + \binom{6}{1}x^5(-2) + \binom{6}{2}x^4(-2)^2 + \binom{6}{3}x^3(-2)^3$$

$$+ \binom{6}{4}x^2(-2)^4 + \binom{6}{5}x(-2)^5 + \binom{6}{6}(-2)^6$$

$$= x^6 + 6x^5(-2) + 15x^4(4) + 20x^3(-8)$$
$$+ 15x^2(16) + 6x(-32) + 64$$
$$= x^6 - 12x^5 + 60x^4 - 160x^3 + 240x^2 - 192x + 64$$

Example 3 Use the Binomial Theorem to find the first four terms in the expansion of $\left(2x - \dfrac{1}{x} \right)^9$.

Solution

$$\left(2x - \frac{1}{x} \right)^9 = \left(2x + \left(-\frac{1}{x} \right) \right)^9$$

$$= \binom{9}{0}(2x)^9 + \binom{9}{1}(2x)^8\left(-\frac{1}{x} \right) + \binom{9}{2}(2x)^7\left(-\frac{1}{x} \right)^2$$

$$+ \binom{9}{3}(2x)^6\left(-\frac{1}{x} \right)^3 + \cdots$$

$$= 512x^9 + 9(256x^8)\left(-\frac{1}{x} \right) + 36(128x^7)\left(\frac{1}{x^2} \right)$$

$$+ 84(64x^6)\left(-\frac{1}{x^3} \right) + \cdots$$

$$= 512x^9 - 2304x^7 + 4608x^5 - 5376x^3 + \cdots$$

Example 4 Use the Binomial Theorem and the identity $(1 + 1)^n = 2^n$ to prove

$$\binom{n}{0} + \binom{n}{1} + \binom{n}{2} + \cdots + \binom{n}{n} = 2^n$$

Solution

$$2^n = (1 + 1)^n$$

$$= \binom{n}{0}1^n + \binom{n}{1}1^{n-1}1 + \binom{n}{2}1^{n-2}1^2 + \cdots + \binom{n}{n}1^n$$

$$= \binom{n}{0} + \binom{n}{1} + \binom{n}{2} + \cdots + \binom{n}{n}$$

Note: This is the property investigated in Exercise 3.1, Question 6(d), that is, the total number of subsets of a set is 2^n, where n is the number of elements in the set.

EXERCISE 3.3

A **1.** Without simplifying, state the terms in the expansion of each of the following.
(a) $(a+b)^5$
(b) $(x+y)^3$
(c) $\left(\dfrac{1}{4} + \dfrac{3}{4}\right)^4$

2. If the numerical coefficients are disregarded, terms of the following form will appear in the expansion of $(a+b)^9$. State the value of the exponent k in each case.
(a) a^3b^k
(b) a^kb^8
(c) a^9b^k
(d) $a^{k+1}b^k$

3. State the numerical coefficient, in the form $\begin{pmatrix}n\\r\end{pmatrix}$, for each of the following terms in the expansion of $(a+b)^{11}$.
(a) a^9b^2
(b) a^3b^8
(c) a^{11}
(d) $a^{11-r}b^r$

4. Express each of the following in the form $(a+b)^n$.
(a) $\begin{pmatrix}4\\0\end{pmatrix}a^4 + \begin{pmatrix}4\\1\end{pmatrix}a^3b + \begin{pmatrix}4\\2\end{pmatrix}a^2b^2 + \begin{pmatrix}4\\3\end{pmatrix}ab^3 + \begin{pmatrix}4\\4\end{pmatrix}b^4$
(b) $\begin{pmatrix}6\\0\end{pmatrix}(x^2)^6 + \begin{pmatrix}6\\1\end{pmatrix}(x^2)^5\left(\dfrac{1}{x}\right) + \begin{pmatrix}6\\2\end{pmatrix}(x^2)^4\left(\dfrac{1}{x}\right)^2 + \ldots + \begin{pmatrix}6\\6\end{pmatrix}\left(\dfrac{1}{x}\right)^6$
(c) $\begin{pmatrix}5\\0\end{pmatrix}(-3)^5 + \begin{pmatrix}5\\1\end{pmatrix}(-3)^4(2) + \begin{pmatrix}5\\2\end{pmatrix}(-3)^3(2)^2 + \begin{pmatrix}5\\3\end{pmatrix}(-3)^2(2)^3$
$+ \begin{pmatrix}5\\4\end{pmatrix}(-3)(2)^4 + \begin{pmatrix}5\\5\end{pmatrix}(2)^5$

B **5.** Expand and simplify each of the following.
(a) $(2a + b)^3$ (b) $(a - 2b)^4$
(c) $(1 - x)^5$ (d) $(1 + x^2)^6$
(e) $\left(1 + \dfrac{1}{x}\right)^4$ (f) $\left(x - \dfrac{1}{x}\right)^5$

6. Expand and simplify each of the following.
(a) $\left(x - \dfrac{2}{x^2}\right)^5$ (b) $\left(2x^3 + \sqrt{y}\right)^4$
(c) $\left(a^2 + \dfrac{3b}{a}\right)^4$ (d) $\left(\sqrt{x} - \dfrac{2}{\sqrt{x}}\right)^6$

7. Find the first four terms in the expansion of each of the following.
   (a) $(a+b)^{10}$

   (b) $(1 - x^2)^{12}$

   (c) $\left(x^2 + \dfrac{2}{x^2}\right)^9$

   (d) $\left(2x - \dfrac{3}{x^2}\right)^8$

   (e) $\left(x^3 - \dfrac{2}{x^2}\right)^6$

   (f) $\left(x + \sqrt{x^3}\right)^{11}$

8. Evaluate each of the following.
   (a) $\binom{5}{0}\left(\dfrac{1}{3}\right)^5 + \binom{5}{1}\left(\dfrac{1}{3}\right)^4\left(\dfrac{2}{3}\right) + \binom{5}{2}\left(\dfrac{1}{3}\right)^3\left(\dfrac{2}{3}\right)^2 + \binom{5}{3}\left(\dfrac{1}{3}\right)^2\left(\dfrac{2}{3}\right)^3$

   $+ \binom{5}{4}\left(\dfrac{1}{3}\right)\left(\dfrac{2}{3}\right)^4 + \binom{5}{5}\left(\dfrac{2}{3}\right)^5$

   (b) $\binom{4}{0}2^4 + \binom{4}{1}2^3(-1) + \binom{4}{2}2^2(-1)^2 + \binom{4}{3}2(-1)^3$

   $+ \binom{4}{4}(-1)^4$

   (c) $\binom{3}{0}1^3 + \binom{3}{1}1^2(-3) + \binom{3}{2}1(-3)^2 + \binom{3}{3}(-3)^3$

9. Write the Binomial Theorem by using sigma notation.

10. In probability theory, we are frequently asked to find the terms in the expansions of binomials like $\left(\frac{1}{2} + \frac{1}{2}\right)^5$.
    (a) Find the value of each term in the expansion of $\left(\frac{1}{2} + \frac{1}{2}\right)^5$.
    (b) What is the sum of these terms? Explain.
    (c) On a graph, label the horizontal axis "term number" and the vertical axis "value of the term." Plot the terms in the expansion $\left(\frac{1}{2} + \frac{1}{2}\right)^5$.

11. Repeat Question 10 using $(0.2 + 0.8)^4$.

12. Use the binomial expansion of $(a+b)^n$ and the identity $(1 - 1)^n = 0$ to prove
    $$\binom{n}{0} - \binom{n}{1} + \binom{n}{2} - \dots + (-1)^n\binom{n}{n} = 0, n \neq 0$$
    Note: This is the property investigated in Exercise 3.1, Question 13.

13. Using sigma notation, write the equation in Question 12.

C 14. In the expansion of $(1 + x)^n$, the first three terms are $1 - 18 + 144$. Find the values of x and n.

15. In the expansion of $(1 + ax)^n$, the first three terms are $1 + \frac{5}{3}x + \frac{10}{9}x^2$. Find the value of a and n.

16. The polynomial $(p + q)^9$ is expanded in decreasing powers of p. The second and third terms have equal values, where p and q are positive numbers whose sum is one. What is the value of p?

3.4   THE GENERAL TERM

If we expand $(a+b)^5$ using the Binomial Theorem, we obtain

$$(a+b)^5 = \binom{5}{0}a^5 + \binom{5}{1}a^4b + \binom{5}{2}a^3b^2 + \binom{5}{3}a^2b^3 + \binom{5}{4}ab^4 + \binom{5}{5}b^5$$

$$\quad\; t_1 \qquad\qquad t_2 \qquad\qquad t_3 \qquad\qquad t_4 \qquad\qquad t_5 \qquad\qquad t_6$$

This expansion contains six terms.

The first term, or t_1, occurs when no b's are chosen; $r=0$.

The second term, or t_2, occurs when one b is chosen; $r=1$.

$$\vdots$$

The sixth term, or t_6, occurs when five b's are chosen; $r=5$.

Example 1   How many terms are there in the expansions of the following?
(a) $(a+b)^{13}$
(b) $\left(2x - \dfrac{3}{x}\right)^{20}$

14

Solution   (a)   There are 14 terms: one for each value of $r=0, 1, 2, \ldots, 13$.
(b)   There are 21 terms: one for each value of $r=0, 1, 2, \ldots, 20$.

Example 2   In the expansion of $\left(3x - \dfrac{y}{2}\right)^{14}$, what value for r is used to determine each of the following terms?
(a)   fourth term
(b)   7th term
(c) t_{10}
(d)   the middle term

6
$6\,7\,2$
$6\,44\, y^6$
$144\, x^6$

Solution   (a)   The fourth term occurs when $r=3$.
(b)   The seventh term occurs when $r=6$.
(c) t_{10} occurs when $r=9$.
(d)   There are 15 terms in the expansion. The 8th term is the middle term. Therefore, $r=7$, is used to determine the middle term.

Example 3   Find t_5 in the expansion of $\left(x^2 - \dfrac{1}{x}\right)^{10}$.

Solution   Use the binomial expansion of $(a+b)^n$ where $a = x^2$, $b = -\dfrac{1}{x}$, $n = 10$.

To find t_5, $r=4$.

$$t_5 = \binom{10}{4}(x^2)^{10-4}\left(-\frac{1}{x}\right)^4$$

$$= 210x^{12}\left(\frac{1}{x^4}\right)$$

$$= 210x^8$$

In general, in the expansion of $(a+b)^n$,

$$(a+b)^n = \binom{n}{0}a^n + \binom{n}{1}a^{n-1}b + \binom{n}{2}a^{n-2}b^2 + \ldots + \binom{n}{r}a^{n-r}b^r + \ldots + \binom{n}{n}b^n$$

$$\underset{t_1}{} \qquad \underset{t_2}{} \qquad \underset{t_3}{} \qquad\qquad \underset{t_{r+1}}{} \qquad\qquad \underset{t_{n+1}}{}$$

there are $n+1$ terms.

The **general term** in the expansion of $(a+b)^n$ is

$$t_{r+1} = \binom{n}{r}a^{n-r}b^r$$

Note that this is the $(r+1)$st term.

Example 4 Find the general term in the expansion of $(x^2 + 1)^7$.

Solution
$$t_{r+1} = \binom{7}{r}(x^2)^{7-r}(1)^r$$
$$= \binom{7}{r}x^{14-2r}$$

Example 5 Find the general term in the expansion of $\left(2x^2 - \dfrac{1}{x}\right)^{10}$.

Solution Since $-\dfrac{1}{x} = -x^{-1}$,

$$t_{r+1} = \binom{10}{r}(2x^2)^{10-r}(-x^{-1})^r$$
$$= \binom{10}{r}2^{10-r}x^{20-2r}(-1)^r x^{-r}$$
$$= \binom{10}{r}(-1)^r 2^{10-r}x^{20-3r}$$

Once the *general term* of any expansion has been found, it is a simple matter to find any *particular term*.

Example 6 In the expansion of $\left(x - \dfrac{3}{x^2}\right)^9$, find the following.

(a) the general term
(b) the term containing x^6
(c) the constant term (the term containing x^0)
(d) the coefficient of the term containing x^2

Solution (a) Since $-\dfrac{3}{x^2} = -3x^{-2}$,

$$t_{r+1} = \binom{9}{r}x^{9-r}(-3x^{-2})^r$$
$$= \binom{9}{r}x^{9-r}(-3)^r x^{-2r}$$
$$= \binom{9}{r}(-3)^r x^{9-3r}$$

(b) For the term containing x^6,

$$9 - 3r = 6$$
$$r = 1$$

Therefore, the term containing x^6 is

$$t_2 = \binom{9}{1}(-3)^1 x^6$$
$$= 9(-3)x^6$$
$$= -27x^6$$

(c) The constant term is the term containing x^0.

$$9 - 3r = 0$$
$$r = 3$$

Therefore, the constant term is

$$t_4 = \binom{9}{3}(-3)^3 x^0$$
$$= 84(-27)$$
$$= -2268$$

(d) For the term containing x^2,

$$9 - 3r = 2$$
$$r = \tfrac{7}{3}$$

Since r can only take on values 0, 1, 2, ... , 9, there is no term containing x^2; therefore its coefficient is 0.

EXERCISE 3.4

A **1.** How many terms are there in the expansion of each of the following?

(a) $(a+b)^9$

(b) $\left(1 + \dfrac{1}{x^2}\right)^{18}$

(c) $(2x - 5y)^{33}$

(d) $(p + q)^n$

2. State the value for r in the expansion of $\left(x^2 - \dfrac{4}{y}\right)^{12}$ needed to find the required term.

(a) t_1

(b) t_6

(c) t_{14}

(d) 9th term

(e) t_k

(f) the middle term

3. State, in unsimplified form, the general term in the expansion of each of the following.

(a) $(x + y)^7$

(b) $(p + q)^{13}$

(c) $(1 - x)^{11}$

(d) $\left(x - \dfrac{1}{x}\right)^{12}$

B **4.** Find the indicated term in the expansion of each of the following.

(a) $\left(x^2 + \dfrac{x}{2}\right)^7$ $\qquad$ t_3

(b) $(a + b)^{10}$ $\qquad$ t_6

(c) $\left(\dfrac{x}{2} - \dfrac{2}{x}\right)^{12}$ $\qquad$ 11th term

(d) $\left(x^2 + \dfrac{1}{x}\right)^9$ $\qquad$ t_5

(e) $\left(\dfrac{3}{4} + \dfrac{1}{4}\right)^6$ $\qquad$ 4th term

(f) $(2x - y)^8$ $\qquad$ the middle term

5. Find the general term, in simplified form, in the expansion of each of the following.

(a) $(a + b)^{11}$ $\qquad\qquad$ (b) $(x^2 - x)^{10}$

(c) $\left(a - \dfrac{1}{a}\right)^{13}$ $\qquad\qquad$ (d) $\left(x^2 + \dfrac{1}{x}\right)^7$

(e) $\left(2x - \sqrt{x}\right)^9$ $\qquad\qquad$ (f) $\left(\dfrac{5}{6} + \dfrac{1}{6}\right)^5$

(g) $(0.3 + 0.7)^8$ $\qquad\qquad$ (h) $\left(\dfrac{1}{2} + \dfrac{1}{2}\right)^6$

6. In the expansion of $\left(x - \dfrac{1}{x}\right)^6$, find the following.

(a) the term containing x^4
(b) the term containing x^{-2}

7. In the expansion of $\left(2x + \dfrac{1}{x^2}\right)^8$, find the following.

(a) the coefficient of the term containing x^{-4}
(b) the coefficient of the term containing x^{-8}

8. Find the constant term in the expansion of $\left(x^3 + \dfrac{3}{x^3}\right)^6$.

9. In the expansion of $\left(a - \dfrac{1}{a^2}\right)^9$, find the following.

(a) the coefficient of the term containing a^3
(b) the coefficient of the term containing a^{-6}
(c) the coefficient of the term containing a^{11}

10. In the expansion of $\left(y^2 + \dfrac{1}{y}\right)^5$, find the following.

(a) the term containing y
(b) the term containing y^{-8}

C **11.** If $x + \dfrac{1}{x} = 10$ find the value of $x^3 + \dfrac{1}{x^3}$.

*3.5 PROBLEM SOLVING WITH THE BINOMIAL THEOREM

In this section we consider binomial expansions of the form $(a+b)^n(c+d)^m$ and relate these expansions to some of the properties in Exercise 3.1.

Example 1   Expand $(x^2 + 2)\left(x + \dfrac{1}{x}\right)^5$ and collect the like terms.

Solution   First, we use the Binomial Theorem to find the six terms in the expansion of $\left(x + \dfrac{1}{x}\right)^5$.

Next, each of the six terms is multiplied by x^2 and by 2.
Finally, we add the like terms.

$$(x^2 + 2)\left(x + \frac{1}{x}\right)^5 = (x^2 + 2)\left[\binom{5}{0}x^5 + \binom{5}{1}x^4\left(\frac{1}{x}\right) + \binom{5}{2}x^3\left(\frac{1}{x}\right)^2\right.$$

$$\left. + \binom{5}{3}x^2\left(\frac{1}{x}\right)^3 + \binom{5}{4}x\left(\frac{1}{x}\right)^4 + \binom{5}{5}\left(\frac{1}{x}\right)^5\right]$$

$$= (x^2 + 2)\left(x^5 + 5x^3 + 10x + \frac{10}{x} + \frac{5}{x^3} + \frac{1}{x^5}\right)$$

$$= x^7 + 5x^5 + 10x^3 + 10x + \frac{5}{x} + \frac{1}{x^3} + 2x^5$$

$$+ 10x^3 + 20x + \frac{20}{x} + \frac{10}{x^3} + \frac{2}{x^5}$$

$$= x^7 + 7x^5 + 20x^3 + 30x + \frac{25}{x} + \frac{11}{x^3} + \frac{2}{x^5} \quad \diamondsuit$$

Example 2   Find the first three terms in the expansion of $(x + 1)^5 (x - 2)^6$.

Solution   We use the Binomial Theorem to expand each of the binomials in the question. Since we are interested only in the first three terms, we need to find, at most, three terms in the expansion of these binomials.

$$(x + 1)^5 (x - 2)^6 = \left[\binom{5}{0}x^5 + \binom{5}{1}x^4(1) + \binom{5}{2}x^3(1)^2 + \ldots\right] \times$$

$$\left[\binom{6}{0}x^6 + \binom{6}{1}x^5(-2) + \binom{6}{2}x^4(-2)^2 + \ldots\right]$$

$$= (x^5 + 5x^4 + 10x^3 + \ldots)(x^6 - 12x^5 + 60x^4 - \ldots)$$

$$= x^{11} - 12x^{10} + 60x^9 - \ldots$$

$$+ 5x^{10} - 60x^9 + 300x^8 - \ldots$$

$$+ 10x^9 - 120x^8 + 600x^7 - \ldots$$

$$= x^{11} - 7x^{10} + 10x^9 + \ldots$$

Example 3   In the expansion of $(x^2 - 1)^8 (x + 2)^7$ find the term containing x^8.

Solution   Unlike Example 2, we are not sure which terms or how many terms are actually needed. Rather than finding all the terms, we proceed in the following way.

First, we find the general term in the expansion of each binomial.
    For $(x^2 - 1)^8$, the general term is

$$t_{r+1} = \binom{8}{r}(x^2)^{8-r}(-1)^r$$
$$= \binom{8}{r}(-1)^r x^{16-2r} \qquad\qquad 0 \leqslant r \leqslant 8$$

For $(x + 2)^7$, the general term is

$$t_{s+1} = \binom{7}{s}x^{7-s}(2)^s \qquad\qquad 0 \leqslant s \leqslant 7$$

Note: We use different variables, r and s, for each general term.

The unsimplified terms in the expansion of $(x^2 - 1)^8 (x + 2)^7$ are calculated by multiplying each term of $(x^2 - 1)^8$ with each term of $(x + 2)^7$.
Therefore, each term is of the form

$$\left[\binom{8}{r}(-1)^r x^{16-2r}\right]\left[\binom{7}{s}(2)^s x^{7-s}\right]$$
$$= \binom{8}{r}\binom{7}{s}(-1)^r (2)^s \, x^{23-2r-s}$$

For the terms containing x^8,

$$23 - 2r - s = 8$$
$$2r + s = 15$$

We look for integral solutions to this equation, where $0 \leqslant r \leqslant 8$ and $0 \leqslant s \leqslant 7$. By trial and error we find the four solutions.

$$r = 4 \text{ and } s = 7$$
$$r = 5 \text{ and } s = 5$$
$$r = 6 \text{ and } s = 3$$
$$r = 7 \text{ and } s = 1$$

Therefore, in the unsimplified expansion of $(x^2 - 1)^8 (x + 2)^7$ there are four terms containing x^8.

When $r = 4$ and $s = 7$,

$$\binom{8}{r}\binom{7}{s}(-1)^r(2)^s x^{23-2r-s} = \binom{8}{4}\binom{7}{7}(-1)^4 (2)^7 \, x^8$$
$$= 70 \,(1)\,(1)\,(128)\, x^8$$
$$= 8960 \, x^8$$

When $r = 5$ and $s = 5$,

$$\binom{8}{r}\binom{7}{s}(-1)^r(2)^s x^{23-2r-s} = \binom{8}{5}\binom{7}{5}(-1)^5(2)^5 x^8$$
$$= 56\,(21)\,(-1)\,(32)\,x^8$$
$$= -37632\,x^8$$

When $r = 6$ and $s = 3$,

$$\binom{8}{r}\binom{7}{s}(-1)^r(2)^s x^{23-2r-s} = \binom{8}{6}\binom{7}{3}(-1)^6(2)^3 x^8$$
$$= 28\,(35)\,(1)\,(8)\,x^8$$
$$= 7840\,x^8$$

When $r = 7$ and $s = 1$,

$$\binom{8}{r}\binom{7}{s}(-1)^r(2)^s x^{23-2r-s} = \binom{8}{7}\binom{7}{1}(-1)^7(2)^1 x^8$$
$$= 8\,(7)\,(-1)\,(2)\,x^8$$
$$= -112\,x^8$$

The term containing x^8 is the sum of these four terms, $-20944\,x^8$.

Example 4   Use the Binomial Theorem and the identity
$(1 + x)^n (1 + x)^n = (1 + x)^{2n}$ to prove

$$\binom{n}{0}^2 + \binom{n}{1}^2 + \binom{n}{2}^2 + \ldots + \binom{n}{r}^2 + \ldots + \binom{n}{n}^2 = \binom{2n}{n}$$

In sigma notation,

$$\sum_{r=0}^{n}\binom{n}{r}^2 = \binom{2n}{n}$$

Note: This is the property investigated in Exercise 3.1, Question 11.

Solution   We find the coefficient of x^n in the expansion of each side of the identity
$(1 + x)^n (1 + x)^n = (1 + x)^{2n}$.

In the expansion of $(1 + x)^{2n}$, the general term is

$$t_{r+1} = \binom{2n}{r}(1)^{2n-r}x^r$$
$$= \binom{2n}{r}x^r$$

For the term containing x^n, $r = n$, and the coefficient of this term
is $\binom{2n}{n}$.

The general term in the expansion of the first $(1 + x)^n$ is

$$t_{r+1} = \binom{n}{r}(1)^{n-r}x^r$$
$$= \binom{n}{r}x^r$$

The general term in the expansion of the second $(1 + x)^n$ is

$$t_{s+1} = \binom{n}{s}(1)^{n-s}x^s$$
$$= \binom{n}{s}x^s$$

Each term in the expansion of $(1 + x)^n(1 + x)^n$ will be of the form

$$\binom{n}{r}x^r\binom{n}{s}x^s \quad \text{or} \quad \binom{n}{r}\binom{n}{s}x^{r+s}$$

For the terms containing, x^n, $r + s = n$; $0 \leqslant r, s \leqslant n$.

There are $n+1$ solutions to this equation.

$$r = 0 \text{ and } s = n$$
$$r = 1 \text{ and } s = n-1$$
$$r = 2 \text{ and } s = n-2$$
$$\vdots$$
$$r = n \text{ and } s = 0$$

Therefore, there are $n + 1$ terms containing x^n. Their coefficients are

$r = 0, s = n$ $\qquad \binom{n}{0}\binom{n}{n} = \binom{n}{0}^2$ $\quad \left[\text{Recall: } \binom{n}{r} = \binom{n}{n-r} \right]$

$r = 1, s = n-1$ $\qquad \binom{n}{1}\binom{n}{n-1} = \binom{n}{1}^2$

$r = 2, s = n-2$ $\qquad \binom{n}{2}\binom{n}{n-2} = \binom{n}{2}^2$

$$\vdots \qquad\qquad\qquad \vdots$$

$r = r, s = n-r$ $\qquad \binom{n}{r}\binom{n}{n-r} = \binom{n}{r}^2$

$$\vdots \qquad\qquad\qquad \vdots$$

$r = n, s = 0$ $\qquad \binom{n}{n}\binom{n}{0} = \binom{n}{n}^2$

Adding these, we obtain the coefficient of x^n.

$$\binom{n}{0}^2 + \binom{n}{1}^2 + \binom{n}{2}^2 + \ldots + \binom{n}{r}^2 + \ldots + \binom{n}{n}^2$$

Since the expansions of $(1 + x)^{2n}$ and $(1 + x)^n (1 + x)^n$ are equal, the coefficients of x^n are the same. Therefore,

$$\binom{n}{0}^2 + \binom{n}{1}^2 + \binom{n}{2}^2 + \ldots + \binom{n}{r}^2 + \ldots + \binom{n}{n}^2 = \binom{2n}{n}$$

EXERCISE 3.5

B **1.** Expand $(x - 2)(2x + 1)^3$.

2. Expand $\left(\dfrac{a}{2} + 1\right)(2a + 1)^4$.

3. Expand $(x^2 + 1)\left(x - \dfrac{1}{x}\right)^4$.

4. Find the first three terms in the expansion of $(x - 1)^7 (x + 2)^9$.

5. Find the first three terms in the expansion of $(1 - a^2)^5 (1 + a^2)^{10}$.

6. Find the first three terms in the expansion of $(x^2 - 1)^7 (x^2 + 1)^8$.

7. In the expansion of $(x^2 - 1)^6 (x + 2)^9$, find the term containing x^5.

8. In the expansion of $(x^2 - 1)^5 (1 + x)^8$, find the term containing x.

9. In the expansion of $(a + 1)^7 (a - 1)^7$, find the term containing a^8. [Look for an easier method.]

C **10.** Expand $(a + b + c)^4$. Hint: Write $(a + b + c)$ in the form $(a + (b + c))$.

11. Find the coefficient of x^5 in the expansion of $(1 + 2x - x^2)^4$.

12. In a History class, there are m girls and n boys. A committee of k students is to be chosen, where $k \leqslant m$ and $k \leqslant n$.
(a) In how many ways can this committee be chosen?
(b) How many of these committees contain no girls, one girl, two girls, ... , k girls?
(c) Write an equation relating parts (a) and (b).
(d) Use the Binomial Theorem and the identity $(1 + x)^m (1 + x)^n = (1 + x)^{m+n}$ to prove

$$\binom{m}{0}\binom{n}{k} + \binom{m}{1}\binom{n}{k-1} + \binom{m}{2}\binom{n}{k-2} + \ldots + \binom{m}{k}\binom{n}{0}$$
$$= \binom{m+n}{k}$$

Hint: Determine the coefficient of x^k in the expansion of each side of the given identity.

Note: Example 4 in this section is a special case of this property, where m, n, and k are all equal to n.

3.6 REVIEW EXERCISE

1. To what other expression in the form $\binom{n}{r}$ is each of the following equal?

   (a) $\binom{9}{5}$

   (b) $\binom{18}{5} + \binom{18}{6}$

   (c) $\binom{100}{50} + \binom{100}{49}$

   (d) $\binom{n-1}{k} + \binom{n-1}{k-1}$

2. Use the properties of Pascal's Triangle to evaluate the following.

   (a) $\binom{5}{0} + \binom{5}{1} + \binom{5}{2} + \binom{5}{3} + \binom{5}{4} + \binom{5}{5}$

   (b) $\binom{6}{0} - \binom{6}{1} + \binom{6}{2} - \binom{6}{3} + \binom{6}{4} - \binom{6}{5} + \binom{6}{6}$

   (c) $\binom{4}{0}^2 + \binom{4}{1}^2 + \binom{4}{2}^2 + \binom{4}{3}^2 + \binom{4}{4}^2$

3. How many terms are there in the expansion of each of the following?

   (a) $(a+b)^{12}$

   (b) $\left(2x - \dfrac{1}{x}\right)^{10}$

4. If the numerical coefficients are disregarded, terms of the following form appear in the expansion of $(x + y)^{11}$. State the value of k in each case.

   (a) $x^2 y^k$

   (b) $x^k y^{11}$

   (c) $x^{2k+2} y^k$

5. Find, in unsimplified form, the general term in the expansion of each of the following.

   (a) $\left(2x^2 - \dfrac{3}{x}\right)^{10}$

   (b) $\left(\dfrac{1}{a^2} + a^2\right)^{19}$

6. Evaluate $\binom{1999}{1998} + \binom{1999}{1997}$.

7. (a) If $\binom{n}{0} + \binom{n}{1} + \binom{n}{2} + \ldots + \binom{n}{n} = 64$, find n.

   (b) If $\displaystyle\sum_{r=0}^{n} \binom{n}{r} = 256$, find n.

8. If $\binom{n}{0}^2 + \binom{n}{1}^2 + \binom{n}{2}^2 + \ldots + \binom{n}{n}^2 = 70$, find n.

9. If $\displaystyle\sum_{r=0}^{n} (-1)^r \binom{n}{r} = 1$, find n.

10. Find the total number of subsets of a set containing nine elements.

11. You and 12 other students try out for the team of three students who are to be chosen to write the upcoming mathematics contest.
(a) In how many ways can the team be chosen?
(b) On how many of these teams are you a member?
(c) On how many of these teams are you not a member?

12. In the arrangement of the letters given, starting from the top, one proceeds to the row below by moving diagonally to the immediate right or left. How many different paths will spell each of the following words?
(a) BINOMIAL

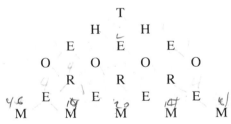

```
                    B
              I           I
         N        N        N
      O       O       O       O
         M       M       M
            I       I
             A
            L       L
```

(b) THEOREM

```
                    T
              H          H
          E       E          E
      O       O       O       O
          R       R       R
       E      E       E       E
      M       M       M       M       M
```

13. A seven-square by seven-square gameboard is shown.

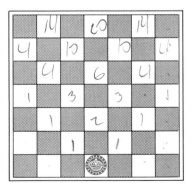

A checker is positioned in the middle of the bottom row. The checker is allowed to move one square at a time, diagonally left or right, to the row above. After six moves, the checker will be in the top row. How many different paths will lead to the top row?

14. Jessica lives six blocks north and four blocks west of her school. There are 200 school days and Jessica is never absent. Is it possible for her to take a different path to school every day, assuming she walks only south and east?

15. Expand and simplify each of the following.

    (a) $\left(2x - \dfrac{1}{x}\right)^6$ (b) $\left(x^2 + \dfrac{1}{x^2}\right)^4$

    (c) $\left(a - \dfrac{2}{b}\right)^5$ (d) $\left(\dfrac{x}{2} + \dfrac{4}{\sqrt{x}}\right)^3$

16. Find the first three terms in the expansion of each of the following.

    (a) $\left(x - \dfrac{1}{x}\right)^8$ (b) $\left(a^2 + \dfrac{1}{a^2}\right)^7$

    (c) $\left(x - \dfrac{2}{x^2}\right)^6$

17. Find the general term, in simplified form, in the expansion of each of the following.

    (a) $(a+b)^{12}$ (b) $(x^2 - x)^7$

    (c) $\left(x - \dfrac{1}{x^2}\right)^{13}$ (d) $\left(\dfrac{2}{x} + \dfrac{\sqrt{x}}{2}\right)^6$

18. In the expansion of $(x^2 - x)^8$, find the coefficient of x^8.

19. In the expansion of $\left(x - \dfrac{1}{x}\right)^{10}$, find the following.

    (a) the term containing x^6
    (b) the constant term

20. In the expansion of $\left(x^2 + \dfrac{1}{x}\right)^7$, find the following.

    (a) the coefficient of the term containing x^2
    (b) the coefficient of the term containing x^7

21. In the expansion of $\left(\dfrac{2}{3} + \dfrac{1}{3}\right)^5$, find the fourth term.

22. If $a+b = -2$, evaluate $\displaystyle\sum_{r=0}^{6} \binom{6}{r} a^{6-r}b^r$.

23. (a) Find the value of each term in the expansion of $(0.8 + 0.2)^4$.
    (b) What is the sum of these terms?
    (c) On a graph, label the horizontal axis "term number" and the vertical axis "value of the term." Plot the terms in the expansion of $(0.8 + 0.2)^4$.

24. In the expansion of $(1 + bx)^n$ the first three terms are $1 - 3x + \frac{15}{4}x^2$. Find b and n.

25. In the expansion of $(1 + x^2)(1 + x)^8$, find the first three terms.

26. In the expansion of $(1 - x)^2(1 + x)^3$, find the first three terms.

27. In the expansion of $(x - 1)^5 \left(1 - \dfrac{1}{x}\right)^4$, find the coefficient of x^3.

28. (a) Use the Binomial Theorem to prove
$$\binom{n}{0} - 3\binom{n}{1} + 9\binom{n}{2} - 27\binom{n}{3} + \ldots + (-3)^n\binom{n}{n} = (-2)^n$$
Hint: Express the left side in the form $(a+b)^n$ for some values of a and b.

    (b) Write the equation in part (a) using sigma notation.

3.7 CHAPTER 3 TEST

1. Use a property of Pascal's Triangle to simplify, then evaluate, each of the following.

    (a) $\binom{19}{3} + \binom{19}{2}$

    (b) $\binom{11}{0} - \binom{11}{1} + \binom{11}{2} - \binom{11}{3} + \ldots - \binom{11}{11}$

    (c) $\displaystyle\sum_{r=0}^{8} \binom{8}{r}$

    (d) $\binom{5}{0}^2 + \binom{5}{1}^2 + \binom{5}{2}^2 + \binom{5}{3}^2 + \binom{5}{4}^2 + \binom{5}{5}^2$

2. Find the sum of the natural numbers from 200 to 300 inclusive.

3. In the arrangement of letters given, starting from the top we proceed to the row below by moving diagonally to the immediate right or left. How many different paths will spell the word WEEKEND?

```
              W
           E     E
        E     E     E
           K     K
        E     E     E
     N     N     N     N
        D     D     D
```

4. Write $\binom{n}{0}^2 - \binom{n}{1}^2 + \binom{n}{2}^2 - \binom{n}{3}^2 + \ldots + (-1)^n\binom{n}{n}^2$ by using sigma notation.

5. Expand and simplify each of the following.

    (a) $\left(x - \dfrac{1}{x}\right)^5$ (b) $\left(2a^2 + \dfrac{1}{a^2}\right)^4$

6. Find the first three terms in the expansion of $\left(x^2 - 3\sqrt{x}\right)^{10}$.

7. If $a + b = -1$, evaluate $\displaystyle\sum_{r=0}^{100} \binom{100}{r} a^{100-r}b^r$.

8. Find the fourth term in the expansion of $\left(\frac{1}{5} + \frac{4}{5}\right)^4$.

9. In the expansion of $\left(2x - \frac{1}{x}\right)^8$ find the following.

   (a) the general term (in simplified form)
   (b) the coefficient of the term containing x^4

10. In the expansion of $\left(x^2 + \frac{1}{\sqrt{x}}\right)^{10}$ find the following.

    (a) the general term (in simplified form)
    (b) the constant term

11. In the expansion of $(x - 1)^4 \left(x^2 + \frac{1}{x}\right)^5$ find the term containing x^4.

12. (a) Use the Binomial Theorem to prove
    $$\binom{n}{0} + 2\binom{n}{1} + 4\binom{n}{2} + 8\binom{n}{3} + \ldots + 2^n\binom{n}{n} = 3^n$$
    Hint: Express the left side in the form $(a+b)^n$ for some values of a and b.

    (b) Write the equation in part (a) using sigma notation.

PROBLEMS PLUS

In the arrangement of letters given, one may move horizontally or vertically to any adjacent letter. How many different paths spell the word PROBLEM.

```
                        P
                    P   R   P
                P   R   O   R   P
            P   R   O   B   O   R   P
        P   R   O   B   L   B   O   R   P
    P   R   O   B   L   E   L   B   O   R   P
P   R   O   B   L   E   M   E   L   B   O   R   P
    P   R   O   B   L   E   L   B   O   R   P
        P   R   O   B   L   B   O   R   P
            P   R   O   B   O   R   P
                P   R   O   R   P
                    P   R   P
                        P
```

TWENTIETH CENTURY MATHEMATICIANS

Professor George Polya was born in Hungary in 1887 and died in California in 1985. He spent 26 years of his life in Switzerland and 46 years in the USA mainly at Stanford University. His book *Problems And Theorems in Analysis* written with G. Szegö extends his problem solving motif into the university curriculum.

He is well known for his book *How To Solve It* which has been translated into 15 languages. The phrases ''in the Polya style'' and ''the Polya method'' are known to mathematics teachers everywhere. In the book he popularized the use of *heuristics*, ''serving to find out'' as a method and process of problem solving.

Polya said that Euler (1707–1783), author of 70 volumes of mathematics in Latin, German, and French, was unique among great mathematicians because he explained how he found his results. Polya often said to students and colleagues, ''Yes, I see that your proof is correct— but how did you discover it?''

In the preface to *How To Solve It* he writes, ''A great discovery solves a great problem but there is a grain of discovery in the solution of any problem. Your problem may be modest; but if it challenges your curiosity and brings into play your inventive faculties, and if you solve it by your own means, you may experience the tension and enjoy the triumph of discovery.''

Polya came to mathematics by a round-about route. He first studied law, then languages and literature in which he earned a teacher's certificate. He then continued into philosophy and physics. Eventually he chose mathematics because, in his words, ''I am not good enough for physics and am too good for philosophy'' and mathematics is between the two subjects.

PROBLEMS PLUS

In Pascal's Triangle, we call the diagonals slanting down to the right *streets*, and the diagonals slanting down to the left *avenues*.

(a) Find the sum of the first five numbers in the third avenue.

(b) Locate this number in the triangle.

(c) Using $\binom{n}{r}$ notation, write an equation relating (a) to (b).

(d) Repeat (a), (b), and (c) for the first six numbers in the third avenue.

(e) Predict and prove a general result for summing numbers on the third avenue of Pascal's Triangle.

(f) Predict and prove a general result for summing numbers on the nth avenue of Pascal's Triangle.

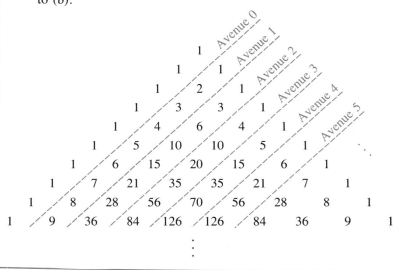

CHAPTER 4

FINITE SERIES

REVIEW AND PREVIEW TO
CHAPTER 4

SEQUENCES

List
General Term
Function Value

A **sequence** is an ordered list of numbers. Alternatively, a sequence is a function whose domain is a subset of the natural numbers. There are a number of ways of describing a sequence:

(i) 1, 3, 5, 7, 9, 11, ...

(ii) $t_n = 2n - 1$ $n \in N$

(iii) $f(n) = 2n - 1$ $n \in N$

Arithmetic Sequences

Sequences such as 1, 3, 5, 7, ... where the difference between consecutive terms is constant are called **arithmetic sequences**. The general arithmetic sequence is

$$a, a + d, a + 2d, a + 3d, \ldots$$

where a is the **first term**, and d is the **common difference**. The nth term is given by

$$t_n = a + (n-1)d, \, n \in N$$

EXERCISE 1

1. Find the first five terms for the following arithmetic sequences; find the relevant a, d.
   (a) $t_n = 3n + 2$ (b) $f(n) = 7 - 2n$
   (c) 1, 4, 7, ...   (d) 3, -1, -5, ...

2. Two of the terms of an arithmetic sequence are given. Find the general term.
   (a) $t_1 = 5, t_2 = 125$ (b) $t_3 = 2, t_5 = 3$
   (c) $t_{10} = 0, t_{19} = 9$ (d) $t_4 = -9, t_7 = -21$

3. The sum of the first two terms of an arithmetic sequence is 12, and the sum of the first three terms is also 12. Find the first term and the common difference.

Geometric Sequences

Sequences such as 3, 6, 12, 24, 48, ... where the ratio of consecutive terms is constant are called **geometric sequences**. The general geometric sequence is

$$a, ar, ar^2, ar^3, \ldots$$

where a is the **first term** and r is the **common ratio**. The general term is

$$t_n = ar^{n-1}, n \in N$$

Example In a geometric sequence $t_3 = 75$ and $t_6 = 9375$. Find t_n.

Solution Since $t_6 = ar^5$, and $t_3 = ar^2$, by division we have $\dfrac{t_6}{t_3} = \dfrac{ar^5}{ar^2}$.

So $\dfrac{t_6}{t_3} = r^3$

But $\dfrac{t_6}{t_3} = \dfrac{9375}{75} = 125$

So we see that $r^3 = 125$, and thus $r = 5$.
From this we have $75 = t_3 = a(5)^2$, so $a = 3$. Hence the general term t_n is given by $t_n = 3(5)^{n-1}$.

EXERCISE 2

1. Find the first five terms for the following geometric sequences; find the values of a, r.
   (a) 1, 2, 4, 8, ...
   (b) $f(n) = 3 \times 2^{n-1}$
   (c) $t_n = 2(3)^n$
   (d) $1, \frac{1}{3}, \frac{1}{9}, \frac{1}{27}, \ldots$

2. Two of the terms of a geometric sequence are given. Find the general term.
   (a) $t_1 = 5, t_{10} = 2560$
   (b) $t_2 = 15, t_5 = 405$
   (c) $t_4 = -7, t_7 = \frac{1}{49}$
   (d) $t_5 = 1875, t_7 = 46\,875$

3. The product of the first two terms of a geometric sequence is 27, and the product of the first three terms is also 27. Find a, r.

4. The sequence $t_1, t_2, t_3, \ldots$ is *both* a geometric sequence *and* an arithmetic sequence. Moreover $t_1 = 10$. Find t_n.

Recursion Formulas

We may describe the pattern of an arithmetic sequence $t_1, t_2, \ldots$ symbolically as follows.

The first term is a so $t_1 = a$, the common difference is d so $t_{n+1} - t_n = d$. We write this as a **recursion formula**.

General Arithmetic
Sequence

$t_1 = a$

$t_{n+1} = t_n + d \qquad n \in N$

Example   Given that $t_1 = 3$, and $t_{n+1} = t_n - 1$, find t_2, t_3, t_4.

Solution
$$t_2 = t_1 - 1 = 3 - 1 = 2$$
$$t_3 = t_2 - 1 = 2 - 1 = 1$$
$$t_4 = t_3 - 1 = 1 - 1 = 0$$

A recursion formula for the geometric sequence with first term a and common ratio r is

General Geometric Sequence
$$t_1 = a$$
$$t_{n+1} = rt_n \qquad n \in N$$

Example   Given that $t_1 = 2$ and $t_{n+1} = 3t_n$, find t_2, t_3, t_4.

Solution
$$t_2 = 3t_1 = 3 \times 2 = 6$$
$$t_3 = 3t_2 = 3 \times 6 = 18$$
$$t_4 = 3t_3 = 3 \times 18 = 54$$

In the preceding examples t_{n+1} was evaluated in terms of constants and t_n. This need not be the case for recursion formulas in general.

An Arithmetico-Geometric Sequence

Example   Suppose $t_1 = 1$, $t_2 = 10$, and $t_{n+2} = 10t_{n+1} - 25t_n$, $n \in N$. Find t_3, t_4, t_5.

Solution
$$t_3 = 10t_2 - 25t_1 = 10 \times 10 - 25 \times 1 = 75$$
$$t_4 = 10t_3 - 25t_2 = 10 \times 75 - 25 \times 10 = 500$$
$$t_5 = 10t_4 - 25t_3 = 10 \times 500 - 25 \times 75 = 3125$$

EXERCISE 3

1. Find t_5 given that

(a) $t_1 = 4$, $t_{n+1} = 6 + t_n$ (b) $t_1 = 7$, $t_{n+1} = \frac{1}{3} t_n$

2. Find t_5 given that $t_1 = 1$, $t_2 = 1$, $t_{n+2} = 6t_{n+1} - 9t_n$.

Present Value

If P is invested now for n interest periods (also called conversion periods) at a rate of i per interest period, then the future amount A is given by

$$A = P(1+i)^n$$

So $\quad P = \dfrac{A}{(1+i)^n}$

and we conclude that P is the *present value* of the amount A in these conditions.

Example   What principal invested now, at 10 percent per annum compounded semi-annually, will produce an amount of $9000 for the purchase of a new car in three years? That is, find the present value of $9000.

Solution   Let the principal be denoted by P (in dollars). Since interest is compounded semi-annually for three years there are six interest periods, and since the annual interest rate is 10% the semi-annual interest rate is 5%, so $i = 0.05$.

Hence, by the formula with $A = 9000$, $n = 6$, $i = 0.05$ we have

$$P = \frac{9000}{(1 + 0.05)^6} \doteq 6715.94$$

So $6715.94 must be invested now.

EXERCISE 4

1. Find the present value of $1000 due in three years at 12% per annum if the interest is compounded
    (a) monthly   (b) quarterly
    (c) semi-annually   (d) annually

2. Mr. and Mrs. Conrad have sold their condominium for $170 000 and moved into an apartment closer to their jobs. Twelve years from now when they retire they would like to have $300 000 for the purchase of a retirement home. How much of the $170 000 should they invest in bonds which pay 11 percent per annum compounded semi-annually in order to have $300 000 in 12 years?

PROBLEMS PLUS

The angles of a pentagon form an arithmetic sequence. Prove that one of the angles must be 108°.

PROBLEMS PLUS

Three numbers a, b, c, (none zero) form an arithmetic sequence. Decreasing a by 1 or increasing c by 2 results in a geometric sequence. Find b.

INTRODUCTION

In this chapter we study series; in particular we concentrate on several special, yet important, series: arithmetic, geometric (both finite and infinite), and arithmetico-geometric. We show how these are applicable in mathematical models. We conclude with a discussion of the principle of mathematical induction, with emphasis on its use in summing series.

4.1 SERIES AND SIGMA NOTATION

A **series** is the sum of the terms of a sequence. For example, 1, 3, 5, 7 is a sequence of odd numbers and

$$1 + 3 + 5 + 7$$

is the corresponding series.

Given the sequence $t_1, t_2, t_3, \ldots, t_n, \ldots$ the **nth partial sum** of the corresponding series is

$$S_n = t_1 + t_2 + \ldots + t_n.$$

Thus S_n is the sum of the first n terms of the sequence.

Example 1 Given the sequence whose general term t_n is equal to $2n - 1$, evaluate S_1, S_2, S_3, and S_4.

Solution In order to evaluate S_1, S_2, S_3, S_4 we need to evaluate t_1, t_2, t_3, t_4 first.

Thus, $t_1 = 2(1) - 1 = 1$
$t_2 = 2(2) - 1 = 3$
$t_3 = 2(3) - 1 = 5$
$t_4 = 2(4) - 1 = 7$

So, $S_1 = t_1 \qquad\qquad = 1 \qquad\qquad = 1$
$S_2 = t_1 + t_2 \qquad = 1 + 3 \qquad = 4$
$S_3 = t_1 + t_2 + t_3 \quad = 1 + 3 + 5 \quad = 9$
$S_4 = t_1 + t_2 + t_3 + t_4 = 1 + 3 + 5 + 7 = 16$

We can abbreviate the expression for S_n by using **sigma notation**:

$$S_n = t_1 + t_2 + \ldots + t_n = \sum_{i=1}^{n} t_i$$

Thus, in Example 1 we have

$$S_4 = 1 + 3 + 5 + 7 = \sum_{i=1}^{4} (2i - 1)$$

since $t_i = 2i - 1$ for $i = 1, 2, 3, 4$.

More generally, to indicate the sum of the terms of a sequence, t_1, t_2, t_3, ... from the mth term up to and including the nth term (where

$m \leq n$) we write

$$t_m + t_{m+1} + \ldots + t_{n-1} + t_n = \sum_{i=m}^{n} t_i$$

Often i, j, k are used for summation indices.

The letter i is called the **index of summation** and the numbers m and n are called the **lower and upper limits of summation**.

Example 2   Write the following in sigma notation:

(a) $1 + 2 + 3 + 4 + 5 + 6 + 7 + 8 + 9 + 10$

(b) $1 + \frac{1}{2} + \frac{1}{3} + \frac{1}{4} + \frac{1}{5} + \frac{1}{6} + \frac{1}{7} + \frac{1}{8} + \frac{1}{9} + \frac{1}{10}$

(c) $1 - \frac{1}{2} + \frac{1}{3} - \frac{1}{4} + \frac{1}{5} - \frac{1}{6} + \frac{1}{7} - \frac{1}{8} + \frac{1}{9} - \frac{1}{10}$

Solution   (a) In words this says: add the first 10 natural numbers. So translated into sigma notation:

$$1 + 2 + \ldots + 10 = \sum_{i=1}^{10} i$$

(b) We see that the denominators are the first 10 natural numbers in increasing order, so we have

$$1 + \frac{1}{2} + \frac{1}{3} + \ldots + \frac{1}{10} = \sum_{i=1}^{10} \frac{1}{i}$$

(c) The denominators are still the first 10 natural numbers. Writing the sum as

$$\frac{1}{1} + \frac{-1}{2} + \frac{1}{3} + \frac{-1}{4} + \frac{1}{5} + \frac{-1}{6} + \frac{1}{7} + \frac{-1}{8} + \frac{1}{9} + \frac{-1}{10}$$

we see that the numerators are

$$1, -1, 1, -1, 1, -1, 1, -1, 1, -1$$

This pattern of alternating of sign may be achieved by recognizing that

$$(-1)^n = 1 \quad \text{if} \quad n \text{ is even,}$$
$$(-1)^n = -1 \quad \text{if} \quad n \text{ is odd.}$$

So the sequence of numerators may be written

$$(-1)^0, (-1)^1, (-1)^2, \ldots, (-1)^9$$

Hence, the ith term of the series is $t_i = \dfrac{(-1)^{i-1}}{i}$

So,

$$1 - \frac{1}{2} + \frac{1}{3} - \ldots - \frac{1}{10} = \sum_{i=1}^{10} \frac{(-1)^{i-1}}{i}$$

Properties of Sums

If we expand $\displaystyle\sum_{i=1}^{7} 2$ we obtain

$$\sum_{i=1}^{7} 2 = 2 + 2 + 2 + 2 + 2 + 2 + 2$$
$$= 7 \times 2$$

This corresponds to a general property of sums:

> I   Let c be a constant, and $n \in N$. Then
>
> $$\sum_{i=1}^{n} c = nc$$

Proofs of this property and the following properties are requested in Exercise 4.1.

Next, consider $\displaystyle\sum_{i=1}^{4} 5t_i$. This, written explicitly, is

$$\sum_{i=1}^{4} 5t_i = 5t_1 + 5t_2 + 5t_3 + 5t_4$$
$$= 5(t_1 + t_2 + t_3 + t_4)$$
$$= 5 \sum_{i=1}^{4} t_i$$

In general, we have:

> II   Let c be a constant, and m, n natural numbers with $m \leqslant n$. Let $t_1, t_2, \ldots$ be a sequence. Then
>
> $$\sum_{i=m}^{n} ct_i = c \sum_{i=m}^{n} t_i$$

Example 3   Suppose $\displaystyle\sum_{i=4}^{17} t_i = 12$. Evaluate $\displaystyle\sum_{i=4}^{17} 11t_i$.

Solution
$$\sum_{i=4}^{17} 11t_i = 11 \sum_{i=4}^{17} t_i \qquad \text{(Property II)}$$
$$= 11 \times 12$$

So $$\sum_{i=4}^{17} 11t_i = 132$$

If we write out $\displaystyle\sum_{i=3}^{6} (i + i^2)$ we obtain

$$\sum_{i=3}^{6} (i+i^2) = (3+3^2) + (4+4^2) + (5+5^2) + (6+6^2)$$

$$= 3 + 4 + 5 + 6 + 3^2 + 4^2 + 5^2 + 6^2$$

$$= \sum_{i=3}^{6} i + \sum_{i=3}^{6} i^2$$

This property, too, is common to all sums of this form.

III   Let t_1, t_2, t_3, ... and u_1, u_2, u_3, ... be sequences, and let m, n be natural numbers with $m \leqslant n$. Then

$$\sum_{i=m}^{n} (t_i + u_i) = \sum_{i=m}^{n} t_i + \sum_{i=m}^{n} u_i$$

Example 4   Suppose $\sum_{i=4}^{16} t_i = 163$ and $\sum_{i=4}^{16} u_i = -48$. Evaluate the following

(a) $\sum_{i=4}^{16} (t_i + u_i)$ (b) $\sum_{i=4}^{16} (2t_i - 5u_i)$

Solution   (a)   Using Property III with $m = 4$, $n = 16$, we get

$$\sum_{i=4}^{16} (t_i + u_i) = \sum_{i=4}^{16} t_i + \sum_{i=4}^{16} u_i$$

$$= 163 + (-48)$$

So, $\sum_{i=4}^{16} (t_i + u_i) = 115$

(b)   Using Property III with $m = 4$, $n = 16$ and sequences $2t_1, 2t_2, 2t_3, ...$ and $-5u_1, -5u_2, -5u_3, ...$ we may expand

$$\sum_{i=4}^{16} (2t_i - 5u_i) = \sum_{i=4}^{16} 2t_i + \sum_{i=4}^{16} -5u_i$$

Now, by Property II

$$\sum_{i=4}^{16} 2t_i = 2\sum_{i=4}^{16} t_i, \text{ and}$$

$$\sum_{i=4}^{16} -5u_i = -5\sum_{i=4}^{16} u_i$$

So $\sum_{i=4}^{16} (2t_i - 5u_i) = 2\sum_{i=4}^{16} t_i - 5\sum_{i=4}^{16} u_i$

$$= 2 \times 163 - 5 \times (-48)$$

Thus, $\sum_{i=4}^{16} (2t_i - 5u_i) = 566$

The final property of sums that we state arises from the following type of situation:

$$t_5 + t_6 + t_7 + t_8 + t_9 = (t_5 + t_6) + (t_7 + t_8 + t_9)$$

IV Let $t_1, t_2, \ldots$ be a sequence. Let m, n, p be natural numbers with $m < n < p$. Then

$$\sum_{i=m}^{p} t_i = \sum_{i=m}^{n} t_i + \sum_{i=n+1}^{p} t_i$$

EXERCISE 4.1

A **1.** Which of the following is an abbreviation for $1 + k + k^2 + \ldots + k^{12}$?

(a) $\displaystyle\sum_{i=1}^{12} k^i$

(b) $\displaystyle\sum_{i=1}^{13} k^{i-1}$

(c) $\displaystyle\sum_{i=1}^{13} i^k$

(d) $\displaystyle\sum_{k=1}^{13} k^{k-1}$

2. Suppose $t_n = n + 2$ for all $n \in N$. Evaluate.

(a) $\displaystyle\sum_{i=7}^{7} t_i$

(b) $\displaystyle\sum_{j=8}^{8} t_{j-2}$

(c) $\displaystyle\sum_{k=17}^{17} t_{k-16}$

3. Which of the following can be written as a single sum?

(a) $\displaystyle\sum_{i=3}^{5} t_i + \sum_{i=6}^{9} t_i$

(b) $\displaystyle\sum_{i=3}^{5} t_i + \sum_{i=5}^{8} t_i$

B **4.** Write the following summations in expanded form. Do not simplify.

(a) $\displaystyle\sum_{i=1}^{5} i$

(b) $\displaystyle\sum_{i=2}^{4} (i^2 - 6)$

(c) $\displaystyle\sum_{i=5}^{8} (i - 6)$

(d) $\displaystyle\sum_{i=2}^{7} \left(7 - \frac{4}{i^2}\right)$

5. Write the following explicitly but do not simplify.

(a) $\displaystyle\sum_{i=10}^{12} \binom{12}{i}$

(b) $\displaystyle\sum_{i=1}^{7} t_{2i-1}$

(c) $\displaystyle\sum_{i=1}^{6} t_{7-i}$

(d) $\displaystyle\sum_{i=4}^{9} \frac{1}{i-3}$

6. Using sigma notation, write the following with the lower limit equal to 1.

(a) $1 + 4 + 9 + 16 + 25 + 36 + 49$

(b) $1^3 + 2^3 + 3^3 + 4^3 + 5^3 + 6^3 + 7^3 + 8^3 + 9^3$

(c) $1 + \dfrac{1}{2} + \dfrac{1}{4} + \dfrac{1}{8} + \dfrac{1}{16} + \dfrac{1}{32} + \dfrac{1}{64}$

(d) $\dfrac{1}{11} + \dfrac{1}{12} + \dfrac{1}{13} + \dfrac{1}{14} + \dfrac{1}{15} + \dfrac{1}{16} + \dfrac{1}{17} + \dfrac{1}{18} + \dfrac{1}{19} + \dfrac{1}{20}$

(e) $\dfrac{1}{0!} + \dfrac{1}{1!} + \dfrac{1}{2!} + \dfrac{1}{3!} + \dfrac{1}{4!} + \dfrac{1}{5!} + \dfrac{1}{6!} + \dfrac{1}{7!}$

(f) $\dfrac{1}{1\times 2} + \dfrac{1}{2\times 3} + \dfrac{1}{3\times 4} + \dfrac{1}{4\times 5} + \dfrac{1}{5\times 6} + \dfrac{1}{6\times 7} + \dfrac{1}{7\times 8}$

(g) $1 + 2\times 3 + 3\times 9 + 4\times 27 + 5\times 81 + 6\times 243 + 7\times 729$

(h) $\dbinom{5}{0} + \dbinom{5}{1} + \dbinom{5}{2} + \dbinom{5}{3} + \dbinom{5}{4} + \dbinom{5}{5}$

(i) $1 - \dfrac{1}{3} + \dfrac{1}{9} - \dfrac{1}{27} + \dfrac{1}{81} - \dfrac{1}{243} + \dfrac{1}{729} - \dfrac{1}{2187}$

(j) $t_1 - t_2 + t_3 - t_4 + t_5 - t_6 + t_7$

(k) $u_1 + 2u_2 + 3u_3 + 4u_4 + 5u_5 + 6u_6$

(l) $t_1^2 + t_2^2 + t_3^2 + t_4^2 + t_5^2 + t_6^2$

(m) $\dfrac{x}{x+1} + \dfrac{x+1}{x+2} + \dfrac{x+2}{x+3} + \dfrac{x+3}{x+4} + \dfrac{x+4}{x+5} + \dfrac{x+5}{x+6}$

7. Suppose $\displaystyle\sum_{i=1}^{100} t_i = 11$ and $\displaystyle\sum_{i=1}^{100} u_i = 43$.

Evaluate (use Properties I, II, III when appropriate) the following.

(a) $\displaystyle\sum_{i=1}^{100} (8t_i + 5u_i)$

(b) $\displaystyle\sum_{i=1}^{100} (-13t_i + 6u_i)$

(c) $\displaystyle\sum_{i=1}^{100} (t_i + 3)$

(d) $\displaystyle\sum_{i=1}^{100} (4.4 - u_i)$

8. Kristina starts work as a systems analyst for $24 500 per year. She has been assured that she will receive a $1000 raise every six months.

(a) What will her annual salary be at the beginning of her fourth year of employment with this company?

(b) How much will she earn in the first three years?

(c) What will her annual salary be at the beginning of her $(n+1)$st year of employment?

(d) How much will she earn in the first n years?

9. Carlos begins work at the same time as Kristina (see Question 8) at the annual salary of $20 500 because he is less qualified. He has been promised a 3% raise every six months.

(a) What will his annual salary be at the beginning of the fourth year?

(b) How much will he earn in the first three years?

(c) What will his annual salary be at the beginning of his $(n+1)$st year of employment?

(d) How much will Carlos earn in the first n years?

C **10.** Prove Property I by writing both sides out explicitly.

11. Prove Property II.

12. Prove Property III.

13. Prove Property IV.

14. Show that for $m < n$

$$\sum_{i=m}^{n} t_i = \sum_{j=1}^{n-m+1} t_{m-1+j}$$

15. Show that

$$\sum_{i=m}^{n} t_{2i} + \sum_{j=m}^{n} t_{2j-1} = \sum_{k=2m-1}^{2n} t_k$$

16. Let $S_n = \sum_{r=0}^{n} \binom{n}{r}$.

(a) Show that $S_1 = 2$.

(b) Show that $S_{n+1} = \binom{n+1}{0} + \sum_{r=1}^{n} \binom{n+1}{r} + \binom{n+1}{n+1}$.

(c) Apply Pascal's Theorem (Section 3.1) to expand $\binom{n+1}{r}$.

(d) Show that $\sum_{r=1}^{n} \binom{n}{r} = S_n - 1$.

(e) Show that $\sum_{r=1}^{n} \binom{n}{r-1} = S_n - 1$.

(f) Show that $S_{n+1} = 2S_n$.

(g) Finally, show that $S_n = 2^n$.

4.2 ARITHMETIC SERIES AND GEOMETRIC SERIES

Arithmetic Series

The series associated with an arithmetic sequence is called an **arithmetic series**.

Carl Friedrich Gauss, when he was eight years old, used the following method to find the sum of the first 1000 natural numbers. Letting

$$S_{1000} = \sum_{i=1}^{1000} i$$

we write out the series explicitly, and again in reverse, then we add:

$$S_{1000} = \quad 1 + \quad 2 + \ldots + \quad 999 + 1000$$
$$S_{1000} = 1000 + \quad 999 + \ldots + \quad 2 + \quad 1$$

So, $2S_{1000} = 1001 + 1001 + \ldots + 1001 + 1001$

$$\underbrace{}_{1000 \text{ terms}}$$

$$= 1000 \times 1001$$

$$\text{Thus,} \quad S_{1000} = \frac{1000 \times 1001}{2}$$

$$= 500\ 500$$

Example 1   Find the sum of 300 terms of the arithmetic series
$$1 + 5 + 9 + 13 + \dots .$$

Solution   To use Gauss' method, we first find t_{300} in the corresponding arithmetic sequence. We know that $t_n = a + (n-1)d$. Here

$$n = 300, a = 1, d = 4, \text{ so}$$
$$t_{300} = 1 + 299 \times 4$$
$$= 1197$$

So,
$$\begin{array}{rcrcrcrcr} S_{300} = & 1 & + & 5 & + \dots + & 1193 & + & 1197 \\ S_{300} = & 1197 & + & 1193 & + \dots + & 5 & + & 1 \\ \hline 2S_{300} = & 1198 & + & 1198 & + \dots + & 1198 & + & 1198 \end{array}$$

$$\underbrace{}_{\text{300 terms}}$$

$$= 300 \times 1198$$

$$\text{Thus,} \quad S_{300} = \frac{300 \times 1198}{2}$$

$$= 179\ 700$$

We now use Gauss' method to prove a formula for the nth partial sum of the general arithmetic series.

SUM OF AN ARITHMETIC SERIES

Let $t_1, t_2, \dots t_n \dots$ be an arithmetic sequence, with first term $a = t_1$ and common difference d. Then

$$S_n = \frac{n(t_1 + t_n)}{2}$$

Proof

$$\begin{array}{rcccccc} S_n = & t_1 & + (t_1 + d) & + \dots + & (t_n - d) & + & t_n \\ S_n = & t_n & + (t_n - d) & + \dots + & (t_1 + d) & + & t_1 \\ \hline 2S_n = & (t_1 + t_n) & + (t_1 + t_n) & + \dots + & (t_1 + t_n) & + & (t_1 + t_n) \end{array}$$

$$\underbrace{}_{n \text{ terms}}$$

$$= n(t_1 + t_n)$$

$$\text{Thus,} \quad S_n = \frac{n(t_1 + t_n)}{2}$$

In particular, we take $t_i = i$ and deduce that the sum of the first n natural numbers is $\dfrac{n(1+n)}{2}$, since $t_1 = 1$ and $t_n = n$.

$$\sum_{i=1}^{n} i = \frac{n(n+1)}{2}$$

Note that $\dfrac{n(n+1)}{2} = \dbinom{n+1}{2}$ and the result stated was obtained by another method in Section 3.1.

In an arithmetic sequence we have $t_1 = a$ and $t_n = a + (n-1)d$, so $t_1 + t_n = 2a + (n-1)d$. Therefore, the sum S_n of the first n terms of the arithmetic series $a + (a+d) + (a+2d) + \ldots$ is

$$S_n = \frac{n[2a + (n-1)d]}{2}$$

Example 2   Find the sum of the arithmetic series $1 + 4 + 7 + \ldots + 301$.

Solution   Here we see that $a = 1$, and $d = 3$. Before we can use either formula we must determine n, the number of terms.

$$t_n = a + (n-1)d$$
$$301 = 1 + (n-1)3$$
So, $n = 101$

Using the first formula, we find that

$$S_n = \frac{101(1 + 301)}{2} = 15\ 251$$

or, using the second formula,

$$S_n = \frac{101(2 + 100 \times 3)}{2} = 15\ 251$$

Geometric Series

The series associated with a geometric sequence is called a **geometric series**.

The method used for obtaining a formula for the sum of the first n terms is, like the method used for the arithmetic series, based on insight. For the geometric series

$$1 + 3 + 9 + 27 + 81 + 243 + 729$$

with $a = 1$, $r = 3$, we write out the series explicitly, multiply each term by the common ratio 3 and subtract:

$$S_7 = 1 + 3 + 9 + 27 + 81 + 243 + 729$$

$$3S_7 = \quad\ \ 3 + 9 + 27 + 81 + 243 + 729 + 2187$$

$$-2S_7 = 1 + 0 + 0 + \ \ 0 + \ \ 0 + \ \ 0 + \ \ 0 - 2187$$

$$= -2186$$

So, $\quad S_7 = 1093$

This method is used to develop a formula for the general geometric series.

SUM OF A GEOMETRIC SERIES

Let a, ar, ar^2, ... , ar^{n-1}, ... be a geometric sequence with first term a and common ratio $r \neq 1$. Then

$$S_n = \frac{a(1 - r^n)}{1 - r}$$

Proof

$$S_n = a + ar + ar^2 + \ldots + ar^{n-2} + ar^{n-1}$$

$$rS_n = \quad\ \ ar + ar^2 + \ldots + ar^{n-2} + ar^{n-1} + ar^n$$

$$S_n - rS_n = a \qquad\qquad\qquad\qquad\qquad - ar^n$$

$$(1 - r)S_n = a(1 - r^n)$$

Since $r \neq 1$ we may divide by $1 - r$ ($\neq 0$) and obtain $S_n = \dfrac{a(1 - r^n)}{1 - r}$.

Note that when $r = 1$ we have

$$S_n = \sum_{i=1}^{n} a(1^{i-1})$$

$$= \sum_{i=1}^{n} a$$

$$= na \qquad \text{(Property I)}$$

Hence,

$$a + ar + \ldots + ar^{n-1} = \begin{cases} \dfrac{a(1 - r^n)}{1 - r} & r \neq 1 \\ \\ na & r = 1 \end{cases}$$

Example 3   Find the sum of the geometric series $5 + 15 + \ldots + 10\ 935$ by using
(a)   the method above and
(b)   the formula.

Solution   Let $S = 5 + 15 + \ldots + 10\,935$; here 5, 15, ... is a geometric sequence with $a = 5$ and $r = 3$.

(a) $S = 5 + 15 + \ldots + 10\,935$

Subtract $3S = \qquad 15 + \ldots + 10\,935 + 32\,805$

$$-2S = 5 \qquad\qquad\qquad - 32\,805$$
$$2S = 32\,800$$
$$S = 16\,400$$

(b) To apply the formula, we need to know n, the number of terms. Now,

$$t_n = ar^{n-1}$$

So, $t_n = 5(3)^{n-1}$

$$10\,935 = 5(3)^{n-1}$$
$$2187 = 3^{n-1}$$
$$3^7 = 3^{n-1}$$

Thus, $n = 8$

The formula gives

$$S_8 = \frac{5(1 - 3^8)}{1 - 3}$$
$$= \frac{5(-6560)}{-2}$$
$$= 16\,400$$

EXERCISE 4.2

A **1.** Classify the following series as arithmetic or geometric.
(a) $1 + (-1) + 1 + (-1) + \ldots + (-1)^{n-1} + \ldots$
(b) $1 + (-2) + (-5) + (-8) + (-11) + \ldots$
(c) $1 + 1 + 1 + 1 \ldots$
(d) $1 + 0 + 0 + \ldots$

2. Find the sum of n terms for the arithmetic series given.
(a) $t_1 = 4, t_n = 9, n = 6$
(b) $t_1 = 5, t_n = 29, n = 9$
(c) $t_1 = -4, t_n = 17, n = 8$
(d) $t_1 = 0, t_n = 64, n = 16$

B **3.** Evaluate the following:

(a) $\displaystyle\sum_{i=1}^{15} (1 + 4i)$ (b) $\displaystyle\sum_{i=1}^{20} (5i + 15)$

(c) $\displaystyle\sum_{i=1}^{14} (6i - 20)$ (d) $\displaystyle\sum_{i=1}^{21} (16 - 8i)$

4. What is the sum of the first 12 terms of the arithmetic series $7 + 11 + 15 + \ldots$?

5. Find the sum of the arithmetic series $-2 + 3 + \ldots + 493$.

6. In the following, solve for n.

   (a) $\displaystyle\sum_{i=1}^{n} i = 78$ (b) $\displaystyle\sum_{i=1}^{n} (4i - 1) = 1830$

   (c) $\displaystyle\sum_{i=1}^{n} (9 - 4i) = -345$ (d) $\displaystyle\sum_{i=3}^{n} i = 88$

7. Suppose $t_1, t_2, \ldots$ is an arithmetic sequence and

   $$\sum_{i=1}^{8} t_i = 52 \qquad \sum_{i=1}^{16} t_i = -88$$

   Find the first term t_1, and the common difference d.

8. Find the sum for the following geometric series.

   (a) $S_8 = 10 + 20 + 40 + \ldots + t_8$
   (b) $S_6 = 3 + 15 + 75 + \ldots + t_6$
   (c) $S_8 = 2 - 6 + 18 - \ldots + t_8$
   (d) $S_7 = 972 + 324 + \ldots + t_7$

9. Evaluate the following.

   (a) $\displaystyle\sum_{i=1}^{12} 3^i$ (b) $\displaystyle\sum_{i=1}^{10} 2^{-i}$

   (c) $\displaystyle\sum_{i=1}^{8} 3(0.8)^{i-1}$ (d) $\displaystyle\sum_{i=10}^{20} 2^i$

10. An experimental theatre has 25 seats in the front row, 26 seats in the second row; and in general the $(n+1)$st row has one more seat than the nth row. How many seats are there if the theatre has 25 rows of seats?

11. Every person has two natural parents, four grandparents, and so on, into the ancestral past. What is the total number of direct ancestors in ten generations?

12. Find the sum of the even numbers between 193 and 4271.

13. Suppose $t_1, t_2, \ldots$ is a geometric sequence and

    $$\sum_{i=1}^{10} t_i = 244 \sum_{i=1}^{5} t_i$$

    Find the common ratio.

14. Find the sum of the divisors of 1024. (Hint: $1024 = 2^{10}$, so each divisor is of the form 2^i for $0 \leq i \leq 10$).

15. Find the sum of the divisors of 65 536.

16. Find a formula for the sum of the first n odd natural numbers.

C **17.** Boxes are stored in a warehouse. The stack is four boxes wide and 20 boxes long at the bottom. Each layer is one box shorter than the previous layer but the same width. How many boxes are there if the top layer is four boxes long?

18. Show that for each $n \in N$

$$\sum_{i=1}^{n} 2^{-i} < 1$$

19. If $a \neq 0$ show that
$$a^n + a^{n-1}b + \dots + b^n$$
is S_{n+1} for an appropriate geometric series. Sum this series using the standard formula, and so show that
$$a^{n+1} - b^{n+1} = (a-b)(a^n + a^{n-1}b + \dots + b^n)$$
[The case $n = 1$ of this result is familiar!]

4.3 ARITHMETICO-GEOMETRIC SERIES

An example of the type of series in this section is given by

$$1 + 2 \times 3 + 3 \times 3^2 + 4 \times 3^3 + 5 \times 3^4 + 6 \times 3^5 + \dots + n3^{n-1} \dots$$

where $1, 2, 3, \dots, n, \dots$ is an arithmetic sequence and $1, 3, 3^2, \dots, 3^{n-1}, \dots$ is a geometric sequence: it is a mixture of both.

In general, an **arithmetico-geometric** series is one of the form

$$a + (a+d)r + (a+2d)r^2 + \dots + [a+(n-1)d]r^{n-1} + \dots$$

These series can be summed using the method applied to geometric series.

Consider $S_6 = 1 + 2 \times 3 + 3 \times 3^2 + 4 \times 3^3 + 5 \times 3^4 + 6 \times 3^5$

Subtract $3S_6 = \qquad 1 \times 3 + 2 \times 3^2 + 3 \times 3^3 + 4 \times 3^4 + 5 \times 3^5 + 6 \times 3^6$

$$-2S_6 = 1 + 1 \times 3 + 1 \times 3^2 + 1 \times 3^3 + 1 \times 3^4 + 1 \times 3^5 - 6 \times 3^6$$

Geometric Series $a = 1, r = 3, n = 6$.

$$= \frac{1(1 - 3^6)}{1 - 3} - 6 \times 3^6$$
$$= 364 - 4374$$
$$= -4010$$

So, $S_6 = 2005$

In this way we prove the general result

SUM OF AN ARITHMETICO-GEOMETRIC SERIES

If $r \neq 1$ then $\displaystyle\sum_{i=1}^{n} ir^{i-1} = \frac{1 - r^n}{(1-r)^2} - \frac{nr^n}{1-r}$

Proof

Let $S_n = \sum_{i=1}^{n} ir^{i-1}$. Then,

$$S_n = 1 + 2r + 3r^2 + \ldots + (n-1)r^{n-2} + \quad nr^{n-1}$$
$$rS_n = \quad 1r + 2r^2 + \ldots + (n-2)r^{n-2} + (n-1)r^{n-1} + nr^n$$

$$S_n - rS_n = 1 + r + r^2 + \ldots + \quad r^{n-2} + \quad r^{n-1} - nr^n$$

$$\underbrace{\qquad\qquad\qquad\qquad\qquad\qquad\qquad}_{\text{Geometric Series, } n \text{ terms, } a=1,\, r\neq 1}$$

$$= 1\frac{(1-r^n)}{1-r} - nr^n$$

So,
$$(1-r)S_n = \frac{1-r^n}{1-r} - nr^n$$

Dividing by $1-r$ we obtain $S_n = \dfrac{1-r^n}{(1-r)^2} - \dfrac{nr^n}{1-r}$ ◇

Example 1   Using the formula and properties of sums, find the sum of the first 10 terms of the series $1 + 3\times 2 + 5\times 2^2 + \ldots$

Solution   In this arithmetico-geometric series, the arithmetic sequence is

$$1, 3, 5, 7, 9 \ldots$$

whose 10th term is $1 + (10-1)2 = 19$, and the geometric sequence is

$$1, 2, 2^2, \ldots$$

whose 10th term is $2^{10-1} = 2^9$

$$S_{10} = \sum_{i=1}^{10} (2i-1)2^{i-1}$$

$$= \sum_{i=1}^{10} 2i(2)^{i-1} - \sum_{i=1}^{10} 2^{i-1} \quad \text{(Property III)}$$

$$= 2\sum_{i=1}^{10} i2^{i-1} - \sum_{i=1}^{10} 2^{i-1} \quad \text{(Property II)}$$

$$= 2\left[\frac{1-2^{10}}{(1-2)^2} - \frac{10\times 2^{10}}{(1-2)}\right] - \frac{1(1-2^{10})}{1-2}$$

$$= 2[1 - 2^{10} + 10\times 2^{10}] + 1 - 2^{10}$$

$$= 2 + 18\times 2^{10} + 1 - 2^{10}$$

$$= 3 + 17\times 2^{10}$$

$$= 17\,411$$ ◇

PROBLEMS PLUS

Given the sequence $9^{\frac{1}{11}}$, $9^{\frac{2}{11}}$, $\ldots$, $9^{\frac{n}{11}}$, find the least value of n such that the product of the first n terms of this sequence exceeds $1\,000\,000$.

EXERCISE 4.3

B **1.** The general term t_n of the general arithmetico-geometric sequence
a, $(a+d)r$, $(a+2d)r^2$, ... is given by
$$t_n = [a+(n-1)d]r^{n-1}$$
In the following arithmetico-geometric sequences identify a, d, r.
(a) 1, 2×3, 3×3^2, ...   (b) 4, 5×2, 6×2^2, ...
(c) 1, 1, 1, ...   (d) 1, 4, 16, ...
(e) 2, $4\times\frac{1}{2}$, $6\times\frac{1}{4}$, ...   (f) 1, -2, 3, ...

2. Evaluate the following. Use the sum formula.
(a) $\frac{1}{2} + \frac{2}{4} + \frac{3}{8} + \frac{4}{16} + \frac{5}{32} + \frac{6}{64} + \frac{7}{128} + \frac{8}{256} + \frac{9}{512} + \frac{10}{1024}$
(b) $1 + 2(0.01) + 3(0.01)^2 + \ldots + 19(0.01)^{18}$
(c) $\sum_{i=1}^{10} i(0.13)^{i-1}$

(d) $\sum_{i=1}^{19} i(1.5)^{i-1}$

3. Evaluate the following:
(a) $\sum_{i=1}^{7} (2i-1)2^{-i}$ (b) $\sum_{i=1}^{6} (3i-2)(1.4)^i$
(c) $\sum_{i=1}^{10} (3i+4)3^{i-2}$ (d) $\sum_{i=1}^{9} (5-4i)3^{-i}$

C **4.** Show that for $m \leqslant n$, $r \neq 1$,
(a) $\sum_{i=m}^{n} r^{i-1} = \dfrac{r^{m-1} - r^n}{1-r}$
(b) $\sum_{i=m}^{n} ir^{i-1} = \dfrac{r^{m-1} - r^n}{(1-r)^2} - \dfrac{nr^n - (m-1)r^{m-1}}{1-r}$

5. Find a formula for the nth partial sum of the general arithmetico-geometric series
$$a + (a+d)r + (a+2d)r^2 + \ldots + (a+(n-1)d)r^{n-1}$$
(a) when $r = 1$
(b) when $r \neq 1$, $d = 0$
(c) when $r \neq 1$, $d \neq 0$
(d) Comment on the results obtained in parts (a) and (b).

4.4 INFINITE GEOMETRIC SERIES

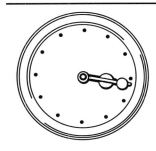

When, between three and four o'clock, will the hands of a clock be together? In this section we develop a method of solving this problem by using the idea of the sum of an **infinite geometric series**.

The formula for the sum of n terms of the geometric series

$$a + ar + ar^2 + \ldots$$

is

$$S_n = a\left(\frac{1-r^n}{1-r}\right) \quad r \neq 1$$

If $-1 < r < 1$ then r^n becomes very small (approaches 0) as n increases indefinitely. For example, with $r = \frac{1}{2}$,

$$r^{10} = \frac{1}{1024}, \quad r^{20} = \frac{1}{1\,048\,576} \quad \text{and} \quad r^{30} = \frac{1}{1\,073\,741\,824}$$

Thus, if $-1 < r < 1$, S_n approaches $a\left(\dfrac{1-0}{1-r}\right) = \dfrac{a}{1-r}$ as n increases indefinitely.

So, we define

$$\boxed{S_\infty = a + ar + ar^2 + \ldots = \frac{a}{1-r}, \quad -1 < r < 1}$$

and we use the infinity symbol, ∞, to remind us that S_∞ is the limit of S_n as n increases indefinitely. An alternate notation for this. (When $-1 < r < 1$) is

$$a + ar + ar^2 + \ldots = \sum_{i=1}^{\infty} ar^{i-1}$$

Example 1   Which rational number has the repeating decimal expansion $0.1111 \ldots$?

Solution   Let $q = 0.1111 \ldots$

Then, $q = 0.1 + 0.01 + 0.001 + 0.0001 + \ldots$

$$q = \frac{1}{10} + \frac{1}{10^2} + \frac{1}{10^3} + \frac{1}{10^4} + \ldots$$

This is an infinite geometric series with $a = \frac{1}{10}$, $r = \frac{1}{10}$.

$$q = \frac{a}{1-r}$$

$$= \frac{\dfrac{1}{10}}{1 - \dfrac{1}{10}}$$

$$= \frac{\dfrac{1}{10}}{\dfrac{10-1}{10}}$$

$$= \frac{1}{9}$$

◇

Example 2   Identify the rational number q whose decimal expansion is $0.13\overline{71}$.

Solution   Let $q = 0.13\overline{71}$
Then, $q = 0.1 + 0.03 + 0.0071 + 0.000071 + \dots$

$$= \frac{1}{10} + \frac{3}{10^2} + \frac{71}{10^4} + \frac{71}{10^6} + \dots$$

$$= \frac{13}{100} + \underbrace{\frac{71}{10^4} + \frac{71}{10^6} + \frac{71}{10^8} + \dots}$$

Infinite Geometric Series

$$a = \frac{71}{10^4} \quad r = \frac{1}{10^2}$$

$$= \frac{13}{100} + \frac{\dfrac{71}{10^4}}{1 - \dfrac{1}{10^2}}$$

$$= \frac{13}{100} + \frac{\dfrac{71}{10^4}}{\dfrac{10^2 - 1}{10^2}}$$

$$= \frac{13}{100} + \frac{71}{10^4} \times \frac{10^2}{10^2 - 1}$$

$$= \frac{13}{100} + \frac{71}{10^4 - 10^2}$$

$$= \frac{13}{100} + \frac{71}{9900}$$

$$= \frac{1358}{9900}$$

So $0.13\overline{71} = \dfrac{679}{4950}$

◇

Now we return to the clock problem with which we began this section.

Example 3   When, between three and four o'clock, will the hands of a clock be together?

Solution 1   At three o'clock the minute hand would have to travel 15 minute-spaces to reach the place occupied by the hour hand. Meanwhile, the hour hand has gone $\frac{1}{12}$ as far, that is $\frac{15}{12}$ minute-spaces. (The hour hand travels 5 minute-spaces in the hour in which the minute hand travels 60 minute-spaces.)

The minute hand then traverses the $\frac{15}{12}$ minute-spaces, but during this time the hour hand travels $\frac{1}{12}\left(\frac{15}{12}\right) = \frac{15}{12^2}$ minute-spaces.

The number m of minute-spaces passed over by the larger hand is thus the sum of the infinite geometric series

$$15 + \frac{15}{12} + \frac{15}{12^2} + \frac{15}{12^3} + \ldots$$

Since $a = 15, r = \dfrac{1}{12}$ we have

$$m = \frac{a}{1-r}$$

$$= \frac{15}{1 - \dfrac{1}{12}}$$

$$= \frac{15}{\dfrac{12-1}{12}}$$

$$= \frac{180}{11}$$

$$= 16\tfrac{4}{11}$$

Thus, at $16\frac{4}{11}$ minutes after three o'clock, the two hands of the clock will be together.

Solution 2   Let m denote the number of minute-spaces the large hand must traverse, starting at three o'clock, before it reaches the hour hand.

Since the hour hand travels $\dfrac{1}{12}$ as fast, the hour hand will traverse $\dfrac{m}{12}$ minute-spaces. So the hour hand will be at $15 + \dfrac{m}{12}$ minutes after the

hour. The equation is

$$m = 15 + \frac{m}{12}$$
$$12m = 180 + m$$
$$11m = 180$$
$$m = \frac{180}{11}$$
$$m = 16\tfrac{4}{11}$$

This is precisely the answer obtained by the first (infinite series) method!

EXERCISE 4.4

A **1.** Using the formula for the sum of an infinite geometric series, we deduce that $1 + 2 + 4 + 8 + 16 + \ldots = -1$. What is wrong?

2. We can "prove" that $1 - 1 + 1 - 1 + \ldots = \tfrac{1}{2}$. How? What is the error in this argument?

B **3.** Evaluate the following:

(a) $\displaystyle\sum_{i=1}^{\infty} 2(3)^{-i}$

(b) $\displaystyle\sum_{i=1}^{\infty} \left(-\frac{1}{2}\right)^{i-1}$

(c) $\displaystyle\sum_{i=1}^{\infty} 8(2)^{-i-1}$

(d) $5 + 4.5 + 4.05 + \ldots$

(e) $\tfrac{1}{3} + \tfrac{1}{4} + \tfrac{3}{16} + \ldots$

(f) $5 + 2.5 + 1.25 + 0.625 + \ldots$

4. Express the following repeating decimals as common fractions
(a) $0.\overline{63}$
(b) $0.6\overline{72}$
(c) $0.1\overline{853}$
(d) $0.485\,\overline{714\,2}$

5. Show that $1.\overline{0} = 0.\overline{9}$.

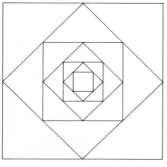

6. A square with 1 cm sides is drawn. A second square is drawn having as its vertices the midpoints of the sides of the front square; a third square is drawn having as its vertices the midpoints of the second square; and so on.
(a) Find the area of the 10th square.
(b) Show that the sum of the lengths of the sides of all the squares is $2 + \sqrt{2}$ cm.

7. Suppose $s > 0$. Evaluate $(1+s)^{-1} + (1+s)^{-2} + (1+s)^{-3} + \ldots$.

8. When, between five and six o'clock, are the hands of a clock together?
(Solve by *both* methods given in Example 3.)

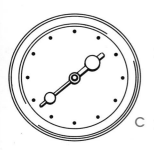

9. When, between one and two o'clock, are the hands of a clock directly opposite?

10. Two marathoners are running laps of a 400 m track in training for an upcoming race. If one runs at a steady rate of 20 km/h and the other at 15 km/h, and they begin at the start line at noon, at what time will the faster runner first lap the slower?

C 11. Two cyclists, cycling towards each other at a rate of 30 km/h, are 10 km apart on a straight road. A bumblebee, which flies at a steady rate of 45 km/h, leaves the nose of one cyclist and flies to the other cyclist's nose; it then turns around and flies back to the first cyclist. It repeats this till the cyclists meet.

(a) Using geometric series, find how far the bumblebee flew.

(b) Using a distance-time argument, confirm your results in part (a).

12. Show that the infinite product
$$2^{\frac{1}{4}} \times 2^{\frac{1}{16}} \times 2^{\frac{1}{64}} \times \ldots = 2^{\frac{1}{3}}$$

13. In the fifth century B.C., the Greek philosopher, Zeno of Elea, posed four problems, now known as Zeno's paradoxes. These problems were intended to challenge some of the then-current ideas about space and time.

Zeno's second paradox concerns a race between the Greek hero, Achilles, and a tortoise, who was given a head start. Zeno argued that Achilles could never pass the tortoise. His argument runs this way: Suppose that Achilles starts at position a_1 and the tortoise starts at position t_1. When Achilles reaches the point $a_2 = t_1$, the tortoise is further ahead, at position t_2. When Achilles reaches $a_3 = t_2$, the tortoise is at t_3. This process continues indefinitely, so it appears that the tortoise will always be ahead!

How can this paradox be resolved by using the ideas in this section?

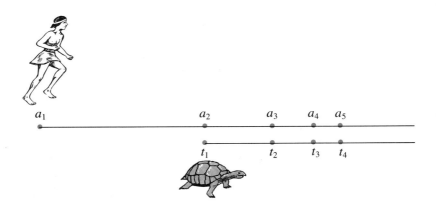

4.5 PROBLEM SOLVING WITH SERIES AND SEQUENCES

One of the main sources of problems involving sequences and series is banking and finance. See, for instance, the problems on present value in the Review and Preview, where geometric sequences are introduced.

In Example 1, we discover the *arithmetico-geometric series* in computing the present value of the cost of a loan repaid according to a certain schedule.

Example 1   A small company, Westend Roofing, decides to borrow $60 000. The repayment schedule is this:

(1) On each anniversary of the loan, $6000 must be applied to the outstanding principal, and

(2) All the interest for the preceding year must be paid at 12 percent per annum.

What is the present value of all these installment payments, assuming an interest rate of 7 percent, compounded annually?

Solution   We calculate the present value using the formula

$$P = \frac{A}{(1+i)^n}$$

**FIND
A
PATTERN**

where A is an annual installment. So we first find a pattern for the annual payments, using (1) and (2). Let A_k denote the dollar amount of the kth payment, for $k = 1, 2, \ldots 10$. Then

$$A_1 = 6000 + 0.12 \times 60\ 000$$

Since the principal of $60 000 is decreased by $6000 (see (1) above) for the second year of the loan, we have

$$A_2 = 6000 + 0.12 \times (60\ 000 - 1 \times 6000)$$

Since the principal of $60 000 is decreased by two payments of $6000 for the third year of the loan, we have

$$A_3 = 6000 + 0.12 \times (60\ 000 - 2 \times 6000)$$

and in general,

$$\begin{aligned}
A_k &= 6000 + 0.12 \times (60\ 000 - (k-1)6000) \\
&= 6000 + 0.12 \times (66\ 000 - 6000k) \\
&= 13\ 920 - 720k
\end{aligned}$$

Next, using the present value formula to obtain the present value P_k of the amount A_k, k years from now at $i = 7\%$ we have

$$P_k = \frac{A_k}{(1+0.07)^k}$$

So the present value P of all the installments is

$$
\begin{aligned}
P &= \sum_{k=1}^{10} P_k \\
&= \sum_{k=1}^{10} \frac{A_k}{(1.07)^k} \\
&= \sum_{k=1}^{10} \frac{13\ 920 - 720k}{(1.07)^k} \\
&= \sum_{k=1}^{10} \frac{13\ 920}{(1.07)^k} - \sum_{k=1}^{10} \frac{720k}{(1.07)^k}
\end{aligned}
$$

Now the first sum is the sum of a geometric series with

$$
a = \frac{13\ 920}{1.07} \quad \text{and } r = \frac{1}{1.07}
$$

So,
$$
\sum_{k=1}^{10} \frac{13\ 920}{(1.07)^k} = \frac{13\ 920}{1.07} \frac{1 - \left(\frac{1}{1.07}\right)^{10}}{1 - \frac{1}{1.07}}
$$

The second sum is an arithmetico-geometric series, and we evaluate it as follows.

$$
\sum_{k=1}^{10} \frac{720k}{(1.07)^k} = \frac{720}{1.07} \sum_{k=1}^{10} k \left(\frac{1}{1.07}\right)^{k-1}
$$
Arithmetico-Geometric Series, $r = \frac{1}{1.07}$, $n = 10$

$$
= \frac{720}{1.07} \left[\frac{1 - \left(\frac{1}{1.07}\right)^{10}}{\left(1 - \frac{1}{1.07}\right)^2} - \frac{10\left(\frac{1}{1.07}\right)^{10}}{\left(1 - \frac{1}{1.07}\right)} \right]
$$

Using the full accuracy of our calculators, we have

$$
\frac{1 - \left(\frac{1}{1.07}\right)^{10}}{1 - \frac{1}{1.07}} \doteq 7.515\ 232\ 249
$$

$$
\frac{1 - \left(\frac{1}{1.07}\right)^{10}}{\left(1 - \frac{1}{1.07}\right)^2} \doteq 114.875\ 692\ 9
$$

$$
\frac{10\left(\frac{1}{1.07}\right)^{10}}{1 - \frac{1}{1.07}} \doteq 77.704\ 820\ 37
$$

Thus

$$\sum_{k=1}^{10} \frac{13\ 920}{(1.07)^k} \doteq \frac{13\ 920}{1.07} \times 7.515\ 232\ 249$$

$$\doteq 97\ 768.26$$

and

$$\sum_{k=1}^{10} \frac{720k}{(1.07)^k} \doteq \frac{720}{1.07} \times (114.875\ 692\ 9 - 77.704\ 820\ 37)$$

$$\doteq 25\ 012.18$$

So, $$P \doteq 97\ 768.26 - 25\ 012.18$$

$$\doteq 72\ 756.08$$

This shows that the present value of the repayment schedule is about $72 756.

Growth and decay in the natural world are other sources of problems involving sequences and series. For instance, physicists investigate the decay of radioactive substances. Experiments have shown, for example, that a certain fraction r $(0 < r < 1)$ of a radioactive substance decays each hour. Carbon-14, which is contained in every living organism and which is radioactive, has $r \doteq 0.000\ 000\ 014\ 2$ and radium-224 has $r \doteq 0.008$.

Carbon Dating

If a grams of the radioactive substance are given at $t = 0$ then the amount that decays in the first hour between $t = 0$ and $t = 1$ is ar, and the amount remaining at $t = 1$ is $a - ar = a(1-r)$. We can make a table to show how this process continues.

Time Interval	Amount Decayed in this Interval	Amount Remaining at End of Interval
0 to 1	ar	$a - ar = a(1-r)$
1 to 2	$a(1-r)r$	$a(1-r) - a(1-r)r = a(1-r)^2$
$\vdots$	$\vdots$	$\vdots$
$(n-1)$ to n	$a(1-r)^{n-1}r$	$a(1-r)^n$
$\vdots$	$\vdots$	$\vdots$

We see that $a(1-r)^n$ remains at $t = n$.

Since $0 < 1-r < 1$, $(1-r)^n$ approaches 0, so the amount remaining, as time goes by, is decreasing and approaches 0.

Using an *infinite* geometric series we can also show that all the material decays. Refering to the table, we see that the amount that decays between $t = k-1$ and $t = k$ is $ar(1-r)^{k-1}$, for $k \in N$.

So, the total amount that decays is

$$\sum_{k=1}^{\infty} ar(1-r)^{k-1}$$

which is an infinite geometric series with first term ar and common ratio $1-r$. Hence the amount that decays is

$$\frac{ar}{1-(1-r)} = a$$

Example 2   Suppose 1 g of carbon-14 is present initially. How much will be present after fifty million hours? (Use $r = 0.000\ 000\ 014\ 2$).

Solution   From the table, the amount present at $t = n$ is $a(1-r)^n$.
Here $a = 1$, $1-r = 0.999\ 999\ 985\ 8$ and $n = 50\ 000\ 000$

so $(0.999\ 999\ 985\ 8)^{50\ 000\ 000} \doteq 0.491\ 644$ g
will be present after 50 000 000 h (roughly 5600 years!).

The **half-life** (in hours) of a radioactive substance is that number n of hours with the property that half the substance decays in n hours. We see that the half-life of carbon-14 is about 50 000 000 hours.

Example 3   Given that $r = 0.008$ find the half-life of radium-224.

Solution   If we begin with 1 g at $t = 0$ we will have $(1-r)^n$ grams at $t = n$.

So we must find n such that

$$(1-r)^n = \frac{1}{2}$$

$$(0.992)^n = \frac{1}{2}$$

We try $n = 10$, $n = 100$, and $n = 1000$ and make a table of values.

n	$(0.992)^n$
10	0.922 819
100	0.447 886
1000	0.000 325

We see that the half-life is between 10 and 100. Trial and error gives a half-life of about 86 years.

EXERCISE 4.5

B **1.**   City Plumbing decides to borrow $120 000. The repayment schedule is this: (1) On each anniversary of the loan, $10 000 must be applied to the outstanding principal. (2) All the interest for the preceding year must be paid at 12 percent per annum. What is the present value of all these installment payments, assuming an interest rate of 8 percent, compounded annually?

2. Suppose that in Question 1, City Plumbing negotiates a lower interest rate on the loan, say 11 percent. What is the present value of the cost of the loan now?

3. Suppose that in Question 1, City Plumbing has to pay the loan off in six years under the same rules, and so makes payments of $20 000 each, plus the interest on the balance. Find the present value of the cost of the loan.

4. Heather White arranges the financing of her new car for which she paid $18 000 as follows: each month for three years she repays $500 on the principal plus the interest at 1 percent per month on the outstanding balance. Find the present value of the cost of the loan assuming 8 percent per annum compound interest, compounded monthly.

5. One-tenth of a certain substance disintegrates each *day*. Assume that 12 mg of the substance is present initially.
   (a) Compute the amount of the substance that remains at times $t = 1, 2, \ldots , 8$ d.
   (b) Draw a graph to show the amount that remains at $t = 0$, 1, ... 8 by using the horizontal axis for time (in days) and the vertical axis for amount (in grams).
   (c) Estimate the half-life of the substance.

C **6.** Suppose an amount of A dollars is borrowed to be repaid in n years, and the interest rate of the loan is r percent per annum. Annual payments of $\dfrac{A}{n}$ dollars plus the interest on the previous years' balance are to be made.
   (a) For $k = 1, 2, \ldots , n$ find the amount A_k of the kth installment.
   (b) Assuming an interest rate of i percent, find the present value P_k of A_k.
   (c) Find the present value of the cost of the loan.

7. How many pairs of rabbits will be produced in a year if in every month each pair bears a new pair, which becomes productive in the second month?

Let a_n denote the number of pairs of adult rabbits in the nth month, b_n denote the number of pairs of baby rabbits, and t_n denote the total number of pairs of rabbits, that is, $t_n = a_n + b_n$. Show that

(a) $a_{n+1} = a_n + b_n$

(b) $b_{n+1} = a_n$

(c) $t_{n+2} = t_{n+1} + t_n$

(d) $t_1 = 1$, $t_2 = 1$.

Using (c), (d), compute t_{12}.

The sequence $t_1, t_2, \ldots$ is called the Fibonacci sequence. It is named after the 13th-century Italian mathematician Fibonacci who included this problem in his book *Liber Abaci* in 1202.

*4.6 FURTHER SERIES: TELESCOPING SUMS

In Section 4.2, we found formulas for the sums of arithmetic, geometric, and arithmetico-geometric series. In this section we explore a method called the **method of telescoping sums**, which enables us to evaluate the sums of certain other series quite simply.

Given the series

$$\frac{1}{2} + \frac{1}{6} + \frac{1}{12} + \frac{1}{20} + \frac{1}{30} + \frac{1}{42}$$

we note that it is not arithmetic, not geometric, and not arithmetico-geometric. Consider the following, admittedly non-obvious, way of writing it.

$$\frac{1}{2} + \frac{1}{6} + \frac{1}{12} + \frac{1}{20} + \frac{1}{30} + \frac{1}{42}$$

$$= \left(\frac{1}{1}-\frac{1}{2}\right) + \left(\frac{1}{2}-\frac{1}{3}\right) + \left(\frac{1}{3}-\frac{1}{4}\right) + \left(\frac{1}{4}-\frac{1}{5}\right) + \left(\frac{1}{5}-\frac{1}{6}\right) + \left(\frac{1}{6}-\frac{1}{7}\right)$$

$$= 1 - \frac{1}{2} + \frac{1}{2} - \frac{1}{3} + \frac{1}{3} - \frac{1}{4} + \frac{1}{4} - \frac{1}{5} + \frac{1}{5} - \frac{1}{6} + \frac{1}{6} - \frac{1}{7}$$

This part folds like a telescope to become 0.

$$= 1 - \frac{1}{7}$$

$$= \frac{6}{7}$$

Example 1 Using the above idea, evaluate

$$\sum_{i=1}^{n} \frac{1}{i(i+1)} = \frac{1}{1 \times 2} + \frac{1}{2 \times 3} + \ldots + \frac{1}{n(n+1)}$$

Solution The sum we evaluated before this example is the case $n = 6$ of this problem, so we mimic its solution.

$$\sum_{i=1}^{n} \frac{1}{i(i+1)} = \frac{1}{1\times2} + \frac{1}{2\times3} + \dots + \frac{1}{n(n+1)}$$

$$= \left(\frac{1}{1}-\frac{1}{2}\right) + \left(\frac{1}{2}-\frac{1}{3}\right) + \dots + \left(\frac{1}{n}-\frac{1}{n+1}\right)$$

$$\left[\text{Verify:}\quad \frac{1}{n} - \frac{1}{n+1} = \frac{n+1}{n(n+1)} - \frac{n}{n(n+1)} = \frac{n+1-n}{n(n+1)} = \frac{1}{n(n+1)}\right]$$

$$= 1 - \frac{1}{2} + \frac{1}{2} - \frac{1}{3} + \dots + \frac{1}{n} - \frac{1}{n+1}$$

This parts folds to 0.

$$= 1 \qquad\qquad\qquad\qquad\qquad - \frac{1}{n+1}$$

$$= \frac{n+1}{n+1} - \frac{1}{n+1}$$

$$= \frac{n}{n+1}$$

So $\quad\displaystyle\sum_{i=1}^{n} \frac{1}{i(i+1)} = \frac{n}{n+1}$

In general, to evaluate $\displaystyle\sum_{i=1}^{n} t_i$ by the method of telescoping sums you must find, invent, discover, or chance upon a sequence T_i such that

$$t_1 = T_1 - T_2,\ t_2 = T_2 - T_3,\ \dots,\ t_i = T_i - T_{i+1}$$

For if you can find such a sequence $T_1, T_2, \dots$ then

$$\sum_{i=1}^{n} t_i = \quad t_1 \quad + \quad t_2 \quad + \dots + \quad t_n$$

$$= (T_1 - T_2) + (T_2 - T_3) + \dots + (T_n - T_{n+1})$$

$$= T_1 - T_2 + T_2 - T_3 + \dots + T_n - T_{n+1}$$

This telescopes to 0.

$$= T_1 \qquad\qquad\qquad\qquad\qquad - T_{n+1}$$

> If $t_i = T_i - T_{i+1}$ for all $i \in N$ then
>
> $$\sum_{i=1}^{n} t_i = T_1 - T_{n+1}$$

Example 2

(a) Evaluate $\displaystyle\sum_{i=1}^{n} (3i^2 + 3i + 1)$.

(b) Evaluate $\displaystyle\sum_{i=1}^{n} i^2$ using part (a).

Solution   (a)   The sequence 3, 3, 1 reminds us of the 4th row of Pascal's triangle and hence of the formula for $(a+b)^3$.

FIND
A
PATTERN

Now $(i+1)^3 = i^3 + 3i^2 + 3i + 1$

so, $3i^2 + 3i + 1 = -i^3 + (i+1)^3$

$= -i^3 - (-(i+1)^3)$

$= T_i - T_{i+1}$

if we set $T_i = -i^3$ for $i = 1, 2, \dots, n+1$. By the result on telescoping sums we have

$$\sum_{i=1}^{n} (3i^2 + 3i + 1) = T_1 - T_{n+1}$$

$$= -1^3 - (-(n+1)^3)$$

$$= -1 + n^3 + 3n^2 + 3n + 1$$

$$= n^3 + 3n^2 + 3n$$

(b)   Let $S_n = \sum_{i=1}^{n} i^2$. Then from (a) we have

$$n^3 + 3n^2 + 3n = \sum_{i=1}^{n} (3i^2 + 3i + 1)$$

$$= 3\sum_{i=1}^{n} i^2 + 3\sum_{i=1}^{n} i + \sum_{i=1}^{n} 1$$

We know that

$$\sum_{i=1}^{n} i = \frac{n(n+1)}{2}$$

and $$\sum_{i=1}^{n} 1 = n$$

so, $n^3 + 3n^2 + 3n = 3S_n + \dfrac{n(n+1)}{2} + n$

Hence, $3S_n = n^3 + 3n^2 + 3n - \left(\dfrac{n^2}{2} + \dfrac{n}{2}\right) - n$

$= n^3 + \tfrac{3}{2}n^2 + \tfrac{1}{2}n$

$= \dfrac{2n^3 + 3n^2 + n}{2}$

$= \dfrac{n(n+1)(2n+1)}{2}$

and so, $S_n = \dfrac{n(n+1)(2n+1)}{6}$

EXERCISE 4.6

B **1.** Evaluate the following by the method of telescoping sums.

(a) $\displaystyle\sum_{i=1}^{n} (2i+1)$ (Hint: $(i+1)^2 - i^2$)

(b) $\displaystyle\sum_{i=1}^{n} (4i^3 + 6i^2 + 4i + 1)$ (Hint: $(i+1)^4 - i^4$)

(c) $\displaystyle\sum_{i=1}^{n} (5i^4 + 10i^3 + 10i^2 + 5i + 1)$

2. Look at Example 1 and use the method of telescoping sums to evaluate.

(a) $\displaystyle\sum_{i=1}^{n} \frac{1}{(2i-1)(2i+1)}$

(b) $\displaystyle\sum_{i=1}^{n} \frac{1}{(3i-2)(3i+1)}$

(c) $\displaystyle\sum_{i=1}^{n} \frac{1}{(4i-3)(4i+1)}$

3. Evaluate $\displaystyle\sum_{i=1}^{n} \frac{1}{i(i+1)(i+2)}$.

4. Evaluate $\displaystyle\sum_{i=1}^{n} i(i!)$.

5. Let $r \geqslant 0$ be given. Show that $\displaystyle\sum_{i=r}^{n} \binom{i}{r} = \binom{n+1}{r+1}$ by the method of telescoping sums and recalling Pascal's Theorem in the form
$$\binom{i+1}{r+1} - \binom{i}{r+1} = \binom{i}{r}$$

C **6.** Using the results obtained in Question 1 find formulas for

(a) $\displaystyle\sum_{i=1}^{n} i^3$ (b) $\displaystyle\sum_{i=1}^{n} i^4$

7. Let $r \in N$. For $x \in R$ define the notation $x^{(r)}$ by
$$x^{(r)} = x(x-1) \dots (x - (r-1))$$
So, $x^{(1)} = x,\ x^{(2)} = x(x-1),\ x^{(3)} = x(x-1)(x-2)$

Show that
$$\sum_{k=1}^{n} k^{(r)} = \frac{(n+1)^{(r+1)}}{r+1}$$

*4.7 PROOFS BY MATHEMATICAL INDUCTION

Propositions can be divided into general and particular. An example of a general proposition is:

All numbers ending with a 5 are divisible by 5.

The corresponding example of a particular proposition is:

The number 75 is divisible by 5.

The transition from general propositions to corresponding particular ones is called deduction. In the above we could write

(1) all numbers ending with a 5 are divisible by 5.

(2) 75 ends in a 5.

(3) 75 is divisible by 5.

The transition from particular propositions to general ones is called *induction*, and it is a cornerstone of the scientific method. However, induction can lead to incorrect as well as correct conclusions. Here is an example of an incorrect induction.

(1) 75 is divisible by 5.

(2) 75 is a two-digit number.

(3) all two-digit numbers are divisible by 5.

We see that (1) and (2) are true but (3) is false since we can find a two-digit number, for example, 11, which is not divisible by 5.

The principle of mathematical induction enables us to guarantee that the induction is correct.

A proposition is true for every natural number n if:

THE PRINCIPLE OF MATHEMATICAL INDUCTION

A proposition is true for every natural number n if:

(1) it is true for $n = 1$,

and

(2) it follows from the truth of the proposition for $n = k$ that the proposition is true for $n = k+1$.

FOOTIES AT THE INDUCTION STEP

Example 1 Prove that, for each natural number n

$$\sum_{i=1}^{n} \frac{1}{i(i+1)} = \frac{n}{n+1}$$

(This was proved in Section 4.6 by the method of telescoping sums.)

Solution Let $S_n = \sum_{i=1}^{n} \frac{1}{i(i+1)}$

Then we have to prove the general proposition that for every natural number n,

$$S_n = \frac{n}{n+1}$$

(1) This is true for $n = 1$ since

$$S_1 = \sum_{i=1}^{1} \frac{1}{i(i+1)} = \frac{1}{1(2)} = \frac{1}{2} = \frac{1}{1+1}$$

(2) Suppose that the proposition is true for $n = k$, that is,

$$S_k = \frac{k}{k+1}$$

Then we have to prove that

$$S_{k+1} = \frac{k+1}{k+1+1} = \frac{k+1}{k+2}$$

So, consider

$$
\begin{aligned}
S_{k+1} &= \sum_{i=1}^{k+1} \frac{1}{i(i+1)} \\
&= \sum_{i=1}^{k} \frac{1}{i(i+1)} + \sum_{i=k+1}^{k+1} \frac{1}{i(i+1)} \quad \text{(Property IV)} \\
&= S_k \qquad\qquad + \frac{1}{(k+1)(k+2)} \\
&= \frac{k}{k+1} \qquad\;\; + \frac{1}{(k+1)(k+2)} \quad \text{(Induction Hypothesis)} \\
&= \frac{k(k+2)}{(k+1)(k+2)} + \frac{1}{(k+1)(k+2)} \\
&= \frac{k^2 + 2k + 1}{(k+1)(k+2)} \\
&= \frac{(k+1)^2}{(k+1)(k+2)} \\
&= \frac{k+1}{k+2}
\end{aligned}
$$

Both parts of the principle of mathematical induction have been verified and so $S_n = \dfrac{n}{n+1}$ is true for all natural numbers n. ◇

Sometimes we do not know the formula (if there is one) for the sum of a series. So we gather data by computing the first few partial sums, guess a result and then try to prove it by mathematical induction.

Example 2   Let $S_n = \displaystyle\sum_{i=1}^{n} \dfrac{1}{4i^2 - 1}$

     (a)   Calculate S_1, S_2, S_3, S_4, and S_5.
     (b)   Guess a formula for S_n from (a).
     (c)   Prove that your guess is correct.

Solution   (a)

$$S_1 = \dfrac{1}{4(1)^2 - 1} \qquad\qquad\qquad = \dfrac{1}{3}$$

$$S_2 = S_1 + \dfrac{1}{4(2)^2 - 1} = \dfrac{1}{3} + \dfrac{1}{15} = \dfrac{2}{5}$$

$$S_3 = S_2 + \dfrac{1}{4(3)^2 - 1} = \dfrac{2}{5} + \dfrac{1}{35} = \dfrac{3}{7}$$

$$S_4 = S_3 + \dfrac{1}{4(4)^2 - 1} = \dfrac{3}{7} + \dfrac{1}{63} = \dfrac{4}{9}$$

$$S_5 = S_4 + \dfrac{1}{4(5)^2 - 1} = \dfrac{4}{9} + \dfrac{1}{99} = \dfrac{5}{11}$$

**FIND
A
PATTERN**

     (b)   When we look at the above common fractions, it seems that the numerator of S_n is n. What is the pattern for the denominator?

n	1	2	3	4	5
Denominator of S_n	3	5	7	9	11

The denominators 3, 5, 7, 9, 11 look like the first 5 terms of an arithmetic sequence with $a = 3$ and $d = 2$. So the nth term is $3 + (n-1)2 = 2n+1$. Our guess for the formula is:

$$S_n = \dfrac{n}{2n + 1}$$

     (c)   We now try to prove our guess by mathematical induction.

         (1)   This is true for $n = 1$, since $S_1 = \dfrac{1}{3} = \dfrac{1}{2(1)+1}$.

         (2)   Assume that the result is true for $n = k$; so we assume that

$$S_k = \dfrac{k}{2k + 1}$$

Then we have to prove that

$$S_{k+1} = \frac{(k+1)}{2(k+1)+1} = \frac{k+1}{2k+3}$$

Now, $S_{k+1} = \displaystyle\sum_{i=1}^{k+1} \frac{1}{4i^2-1}$

$$= \sum_{i=1}^{k} \frac{1}{4i^2-1} + \sum_{i=k+1}^{k+1} \frac{1}{4i^2-1}$$

$$= S_k \qquad\qquad + \frac{1}{4(k+1)^2-1}$$

$$= \frac{k}{2k+1} \qquad + \frac{1}{4k^2+8k+3}$$

$$= \frac{k}{2k+1} \qquad + \frac{1}{(2k+1)(2k+3)}$$

$$= \frac{k(2k+3)}{(2k+1)(2k+3)} + \frac{1}{(2k+1)(2k+3)}$$

$$= \frac{2k^2+3k+1}{(2k+1)(2k+3)}$$

$$= \frac{(2k+1)(k+1)}{(2k+1)(2k+3)}$$

$$= \frac{k+1}{2k+3}$$

Hence, the truth of the proposition for $n = k$ implies its truth for $n = k + 1$. So by mathematical induction it is true that, for every natural number n,

$$S_n = \frac{n}{2n+1}$$

so, $\displaystyle\sum_{i=1}^{n} \frac{1}{4i^2-1} = \frac{n}{2n+1}$

Here is an example of a general proposition, not involving series, that can be proved by mathematical induction.

Example 3   Prove that $n^3 + 2n$ is divisible by 3 for every natural number n.

Solution   Let P_n be the proposition: $n^3 + 2n$ is divisible by 3.
(1) P_1 is true, since $1^3 + 2(1) = 3$ is divisible by 3.
(2) Assume the proposition is true for $n = k$; hence P_k is true, that is $k^3 + 2k$ is divisible by 3. We have to prove that P_{k+1} is true: $(k+1)^3 + 2(k+1)$ is divisible by 3. In other words we have to prove that

$$k^3 + 3k^2 + 3k + 1 + 2k + 2$$
is divisible by 3.

But $k^3 + 3k^2 + 3k + 1 + 2k + 2 = k^3 + 2k + 3(k^2+k+1)$.
Since $k^3 + 2k$ is divisible by 3, by assumption (the case $n = k$), and $3(k^2+k+1)$ is divisible by 3, we have shown that
$$k^3 + 3k^2 + 3k + 1 + 2k + 2$$
is divisible by 3, and hence P_{k+1} is true.

By the principle of mathematical induction, P_n is true for every n, that is, $n^3 + 2n$ is divisible by 3.   ◇

EXERCISE 4.7

Prove each of the following propositions by mathematical induction.

B 1. $\displaystyle\sum_{i=1}^{n} \frac{1}{(3i-2)(3i+1)} = \frac{n}{3n+1}$

2. $\displaystyle\sum_{i=1}^{n} i^2 = \frac{n(n+1)(2n+1)}{6}$

3. $\displaystyle\sum_{i=1}^{n} (-1)^{i-1}i^2 = (-1)^{n+1}\frac{n^2+n}{2}$

4. For each $r \neq 1$, $\displaystyle\sum_{i=1}^{n} r^{i-1} = \frac{1-r^n}{1-r}$

5. $\displaystyle\sum_{i=1}^{n} i^3 = \left(\frac{n^2+n}{2}\right)^2$ [Hint: Work Backwards.]

6. $\displaystyle\sum_{i=1}^{n} i\binom{n}{i} = n2^{n-1}$

7. The sum of the first n natural numbers is $\dfrac{n(n+1)}{2}$.

8. The nth odd number is $2n - 1$.

9. The sum of the first n odd natural numbers is n^2.

10. $n^2 + n$ is divisible by 2.

11. $n^3 - n$ is divisible by 6. (Hint: Exercise 10 could be helpful.)

12. The sum of the cubes of three consecutive natural numbers is divisible by 9.

13. Use Example 2 as a guide to the following.

Let $S_n = \displaystyle\sum_{i=1}^{n} \frac{i}{(i+1)!}$

(a) Calculate S_1, S_2, S_3, and S_4.

(b) Guess a formula from (a) for S_n.

(c) Prove that your guess is correct.

C 14. In the following, find a formula and prove it (compare Question 13, and Example 2).

(a) $\displaystyle\sum_{i=1}^{n} i(i+1)$

(b) $\displaystyle\sum_{i=1}^{n} i(i+1)(i+2)$

(c) $\displaystyle\sum_{i=1}^{n} \frac{1}{(4i-3)(4i+1)}$ (d) $\displaystyle\sum_{i=1}^{n} \frac{1}{\left(\dfrac{i+1}{2}\right)}$

(e) $\displaystyle\sum_{i=1}^{n} i(i!)$

PROBLEMS PLUS

Twenty-seven used books are arranged from left to right in order of increasing prices. The price of each book differs by $1.50 from that of each adjacent book. For the price of the most costly book a customer can buy the middle book and an adjacent one.

a)   Is the adjacent book referred to at the left or the right of the middle book?

b)   What is the cost of the cheapest book?

c)   How much would it cost to buy all the books?

4.8   REVIEW EXERCISE

1.   Write $1 + x + x^2 + \dots + x^{16}$ by using sigma notation.

2.   Write the summation $\displaystyle\sum_{i=2}^{8} \frac{i}{i+1}$ in expanded form.

3.   Write $\frac{1}{14} + \frac{1}{15} + \frac{1}{16} + \frac{1}{17} + \dots + \frac{1}{42} + \frac{1}{43}$ by using sigma notation with the lower limit of summation equal to 1.

4.   Suppose $\displaystyle\sum_{i=1}^{60} t_i = -3.8$ and $\displaystyle\sum_{i=1}^{60} u_i = 14.2$.

   Evaluate $\displaystyle\sum_{i=1}^{60} (17.1t_i + 8.6u_i)$.

5.   Louis starts work as an investment counsellor for $38 000 a year. He will receive a $1000 raise every three months.
   (a)   How much will he be earning (per annum) at the beginning of his $(n+1)$st year of employment?
   (b)   How much does he earn in his first n years?

6.   Ten percent of the wine in a cask is drawn off and replaced by water; then another ten percent is drawn and replaced by water; and this process is carried out ten times. What percent of the final mixture is wine?

7.   There is a legend that the inventor of chess chose the following reward: One grain of wheat on the first square, two grains of wheat on the second square, four on the third, eight on the fourth, and so on, for all the 64 squares on the chessboard. Find an expression for the amount of wheat required to satisfy his request.

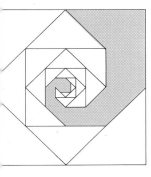

8. The midpoints of a square of length L are joined to form a new square and the process is repeated. A portion of each square is coloured as shown. Assume the pattern of coloured regions continues indefinitely. What is the total area of the coloured region?

9. Evaluate $\displaystyle\sum_{i=1}^{10} i3^{i-1}$.

10. Find the sum of the arithmetic series $t_1 + t_2 + \ldots + t_n$ with $t_1 = 4$, $t_n = 9$, and $n = 6$.

11. Find the sum of all the multiples of three between 181 and 2402.

12. Find the least value of n for which the sum of the first n terms of
$$4 + 9 + 14 + \ldots$$
exceeds 2000.

13. Evaluate $\displaystyle\sum_{i=1}^{\infty} 3^{1-i}$

14. What common fraction has the decimal expansion $0.8\overline{642}$?

15. When, between four and five o'clock, are the hands of a clock together?

16. Hajung arranges the financing of his new car, for which he paid $12 060, as follows: each month for 3 years he repays $335 plus the interest at 2 percent per month on the outstanding balance. Find the present value of the cost of the loan assuming 1 percent per month compound interest.

17. Evaluate $\displaystyle\sum_{i=1}^{n} \frac{2}{i(i+2)}$ by using telescoping sums.

18. Suppose that an arithmetic sequence has first term 1 and common difference 3. Prove, by mathematical induction, that the nth term is $3n-2$.

19. Guess and prove a formula for
$$\sum_{i=1}^{n} \frac{2i+1}{[i(i+1)]^2}$$

20. Let f_n denote the nth Fibonacci number; so $f_1 = 1, f_2 = 1$, and $f_{n+2} = f_{n+1} + f_n$. Let P_n be the proposition that $f_k < 2^k$ for $k = 1$, $2, \ldots , n$. Prove that P_n is true for every natural number n.

4.9 CHAPTER 4 TEST

1. Write the summation $\displaystyle\sum_{i=1}^{7} \frac{i^2}{i^3+1}$ in expanded form.

2. Write $\frac{1}{11} + \frac{1}{14} + \frac{1}{17} + \ldots + \frac{1}{29} + \frac{1}{32}$ using sigma notation with the lower limit of summation equal to 1.

3. Suppose $\sum\limits_{i=1}^{50} t_i = 41$ and $\sum\limits_{i=1}^{50} u_i = -3$.

   Evaluate $\sum\limits_{i=1}^{50} (t_i + 13u_i)$.

4. Evaluate $\sum\limits_{i=1}^{n} r^{i-1}$ if $r \neq 1$.

5. State the formula for the sum of the first n terms of the arithmetic sequence $t_1, t_2, \dots , t_n, \dots$

6. What common fraction has the decimal expansion $0.\overline{076\ 923}$?

7. If $x > 0$ evaluate $(1+x)^{-1} + (1+x)^{-2} + (1+x)^{-3} + \ \dots$.

8. (a) State the principle of mathematical induction.
   (b) Use it to prove that the nth odd number is $2n-1$.

PROBLEMS PLUS

Find the sum of the infinite series $\dfrac{1}{9} + \dfrac{2}{9^2} + \dfrac{3}{9^3} + \dfrac{4}{9^4} + \ \dots$

whose n^{th} term is $\dfrac{n}{9^n}$.

CUMULATIVE REVIEW FOR CHAPTERS 1 TO 4

1. Evaluate each of the following expressions.

   (a) $3!P(5,2)$

   (b) $6! + \dbinom{6}{4} - P(5,0)$

   (c) $(9 - 9)! + \dbinom{4}{4} + P(5,5)$

   (d) $\dbinom{9}{8} + P(7,6)$

   (e) $\dbinom{11}{7} - \dbinom{11}{4}$

   (f) $4!P(9,4)$

   (g) $\dbinom{7}{4}\dbinom{3}{2}$

   (h) $P(9,6) + 6!\dbinom{9}{6}$

   (i) $\dbinom{12}{5}\dbinom{7}{3}\dbinom{4}{4}$

2. (a) Explain why the number of 7-arrangements of nine objects is greater than the number of 7-subsets of a set containing nine elements.

   (b) Explain why $P(n,r) = r!\dbinom{n}{r}$.

3. Express each of the following using factorial notation.

   (a) The number of seven-digit numbers in which no digit appears more than once.

    (b) The number of ''words'' that can be formed using all the letters of PROBLEMS.

    (c) The number of ''words'' that can be formed using all the letters of TOMORROW.

    (d) The number of choices of three witch costumes from a wardrobe of eight such costumes.

    (e) The number of inspection teams of two mechanics and three supervisors chosen from seven mechanics and five supervisors.

4. Carmencita and her four sisters compete in a race at the family reunion picnic. In how many ways can the first and second prizes be awarded for the race?

5. There are eight runways at the regional airport. Three planes are coming in for a landing at approximately the same time. In how many ways can air-traffic control assign the planes to different runways?

6. Six candidates run for class representative to the student council. If two reps are to be chosen, how many possible results are there?

7. In how many ways can nine people be seated around a circular table?

8. How many even five-digit numbers can be formed using only the numbers 1 through 7?

9. There are seven seats in the family's new mini-van. If four of the seven family members can drive, how many possible seating arrangements are there for a family trip in the van?

10. A freight train is to consist of three flatcars, five tankers, six boxcars, an engine, and caboose. In how many ways can the train be made up?

11. The prime factorization of 2520 is $2 \times 2 \times 2 \times 3 \times 3 \times 5 \times 7$. Find the number of even divisors of 2520.

12. How many different routes can Timothy take to the neighbourhood convenience store which is four blocks west and three blocks south of his house if he is always travelling toward his destination?

13. Find the number of ways in which at least one piece of fruit could be chosen from a basket containing four apples, five bananas, two cantaloupes, and three pears.

14. How many five-digit numbers greater than 60 000 are divisible by 5?

15. The basketball team carries 14 players: three first-year players, five second-year players, and six experienced third-year players.

    (a) In how many ways can the coach choose a starting lineup (five players) with at least one first-year player?

    (b) In how many ways can he set up a starting lineup with two second-year and three third-year players, or the reverse (two third-year and three second-year)?

16. (a) If $n(A \cap B) = n(A)$, what relationship exists between the sets A and B?

(b) If $n(A \cup B) = n(A)$, what relationship exists between the sets A and B?

(c) If $n(A \cup B) = n(A) + n(B)$, what relationship exists between the sets A and B?

17. "We could form several groups," said Sophie. "We have got five who play the guitar and can also handle drums; two of us play piano and guitar; and three play drums as well as piano." Sam smiled. "And you do all three. Anyone else do that?" Sophie shook her head. "No, but everyone else plays at least one of the three. Eleven play drums, seven the piano, and nine the guitar." How many musicians were there?

18. To what other expressions in the form $\binom{n}{r}$ is each of the following equal?

(a) $\binom{16}{7}$

(b) $\binom{21}{9} + \binom{21}{10}$

(c) $\binom{n-3}{k+1} + \binom{n-3}{k+2}$

(d) $\binom{8}{3} + \binom{8}{4} + \binom{9}{5} + \binom{10}{6}$

19. Use the properties of Pascal's Triangle to evaluate the following.

(a) $\binom{7}{0} + \binom{7}{1} + \binom{7}{2} + \binom{7}{3} + \binom{7}{4} + \binom{7}{5} + \binom{7}{6} + \binom{7}{7}$

(b) $\binom{8}{0} - \binom{8}{1} + \binom{8}{2} - \binom{8}{3} + \binom{8}{4} - \binom{8}{5} + \binom{8}{6} - \binom{8}{7} + \binom{8}{8}$

(c) $\binom{5}{0}^2 + \binom{5}{1}^2 + \binom{5}{2}^2 + \binom{5}{3}^2 + \binom{5}{4}^2 + \binom{5}{5}^2$

20. An eight-square by eight-square checkerboard is given.

A checker, indicated by O, is positioned in the fourth square of the bottom row. The checker is allowed to move one square at a time, diagonally left or right, to the row above. After seven moves the checker will be in the top row. How many different paths will lead to the top row?

21. In the arrangement of the letters given, starting from the top, proceed to the row below by moving diagonally to the immediate right or left. How many different paths will spell ARITHMETICO?

```
                    A
                R       R
            I       I       I
        T       T       T       T
    H       H       H       H       H
M       M       M       M       M       M
    E       E       E       E       E
        T       T       T       T
            I       I       I
                C       C
                    O
```

22. In the game illustrated, a disc is dropped from the top and the player is rewarded by an amount determined by where it lands at the bottom.
    (a) How many different paths will lead to a reward of $100?
    (b) What is the total number of paths?

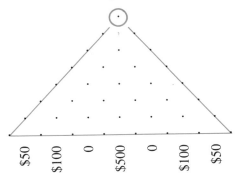

$$\$50 \quad \$100 \quad 0 \quad \$500 \quad 0 \quad \$100 \quad \$50$$

23. (a) If $\sum_{r=0}^{n} \binom{n}{r} = 1024$, find n.

    (b) If $\sum_{r=0}^{n} \binom{n}{r}^2 = 252$, find n.

24. If $\sum_{r=0}^{n} (-1)^r \binom{n}{r} = 0$, find all possibilities for n.

25. How many terms are there in the expansion of $(a + b)^{23}$?

26. If the numerical coefficients are disregarded, terms of the following form appear in the expansion of $(x + y)^{34}$. State the value of k in each case.
    (a) $x^{12}y^k$
    (b) $x^k y^{18}$
    (c) $x^{2k+1}y^k$

27. Expand and simplify each of the following.
    (a) $(a + b)^6$
    (b) $(2x - y)^5$
    (c) $\left(x^2 + \dfrac{1}{x}\right)^4$
    (d) $\left(2x - \dfrac{1}{2\sqrt{x}}\right)^3$

28. Find the first three terms in the expansion of each of the following.
    (a) $(a + b)^{13}$
    (b) $\left(x^2 - \dfrac{1}{x}\right)^8$
    (c) $\left(2a + \dfrac{2}{a^2}\right)^7$

29. Find the general term in the expansion of each of the following.
    (a) $(a + b)^9$
    (b) $\left(x + \dfrac{1}{x}\right)^6$
    (c) $\left(\dfrac{2}{x} - \dfrac{x}{2}\right)^5$

30. In the expansion of $\left(x + \dfrac{1}{x}\right)^{11}$, find the coefficient of x^5.

31. In the expansion of $\left(x - \dfrac{1}{x^2}\right)^8$, find the term containing x^{-1} and the coefficient of the term containing x^2.

32. In the expansion of $\left(2x - \dfrac{1}{2x}\right)^6$, find the constant term.

33. If $a + b = -2$, evaluate $\displaystyle\sum_{r=0}^{7} \binom{7}{r} a^{7-r} b^r$.

34. In the expansion of $(1 - ax)^n$, the first three terms are $1 - 12x + 63x^2$. Find a and n.

35. In the expansion of $(1 - x)^4 (1 + x^2)^5$ find the first three terms.

36. In the expansion of $(x^2 - 1)^5 \left(1 + \dfrac{1}{x}\right)^6$ find the coefficient of x^4.

37. (a) Use the Binomial Theorem to prove
    $$\binom{n}{0} - 5\binom{n}{1} + 25\binom{n}{2} - 125\binom{n}{3} + \ldots + (-5)^n \binom{n}{n} = (-4)^n$$
    (b) Write the equation in part (a) by using sigma notation.

38. Write the following summations in expanded form. Do not simplify.
    (a) $\displaystyle\sum_{i=1}^{6} (i^2 - i)$ (b) $\displaystyle\sum_{i=3}^{7} \binom{7}{i}$ (c) $\displaystyle\sum_{i=3}^{9} t_{2i-1}$

39. Write the following by using sigma notation with the lower limit equal to 1.

(a) $1 - \frac{1}{2} + \frac{1}{4} - \frac{1}{8} + \frac{1}{16} - \frac{1}{32} + \frac{1}{64} - \frac{1}{128}$

(b) $\dfrac{x}{x-1} + \dfrac{x-1}{x-2} + \dfrac{x-2}{x-3} + \dfrac{x-3}{x-4} + \dfrac{x-4}{x-5} + \dfrac{x-5}{x-6}$

(c) $1 + 5 + 9 + 13 + 17 + 21 + 25 + 29$

40. Suppose $\displaystyle\sum_{i=1}^{250} t_i = 12$ and $\displaystyle\sum_{i=1}^{250} u_i = 34$. Evaluate $\displaystyle\sum_{i=1}^{250} (8t_i - 5u_i)$.

41. Renato starts work as an air traffic controller for $25 000 a year. He has been assured that he will receive a $500 raise every six months.

(a) What will his annual salary be at the beginning of his sixth year of employment?

(b) How much will Renato earn in the first five years?

(c) What will his annual salary be at the beginning of his $(n + 1)$st year?

(d) How much will he make in the first n years?

42. Find the sum for the arithmetic series given.

(a) $t_1 = 3$ $t_n = 51$ $n = 13$

(b) $t_1 = -2$ $t_n = 61$ $n = 22$

43. Evaluate each of the following.

(a) $\displaystyle\sum_{i=1}^{18} (2 + 4i)$

(b) $\displaystyle\sum_{i=1}^{30} (7 - 3i)$

44. What is the sum of the first 15 terms of the arithmetic series $-7 - 3 + 1 + 5 + \ldots$?

45. In the following, solve for n.

(a) $\displaystyle\sum_{i=1}^{n} (5i - 7) = 910$

(b) $\displaystyle\sum_{i=1}^{n} (7 - 4i) = -2275$

46. Suppose $t_1, t_2, t_3, \ldots$ is an arithmetic sequence and $\displaystyle\sum_{i=1}^{9} t_i = 90$ and $\displaystyle\sum_{i=10}^{18} t_i = 333$. Find the first term, t_1, and the common difference, d.

47. Find the indicated sum for the following geometric series.

(a) $S_9 = 2 + 6 + 18 + \ldots$

(b) $S_7 = 10 - 5 + \frac{5}{2} - \ldots$

48. Evaluate each of the following.

(a) $\displaystyle\sum_{i=1}^{10} 3(2)^i$

(b) $\displaystyle\sum_{i=1}^{6} 2(3)^{-i}$

49. Every person has two natural parents, four natural grandparents, and so on. What is the total number of direct ancestors in eight generations?

50. Evaluate each of the following.

(a) $\displaystyle\sum_{i=1}^{6} i(3)^i$

(b) $\displaystyle\sum_{i=1}^{8} (4 - 3i)(2)^{-i}$

51. Find the sum of the divisors of 531 441.

52. Evaluate each of the following.

(a) $\displaystyle\sum_{i=1}^{\infty} 5\left(\frac{1}{2}\right)^i$

(b) $\displaystyle\sum_{i=1}^{\infty} \frac{1}{2}(3)^{-i}$

(c) $\frac{3}{4} + \frac{1}{2} + \frac{1}{3} + \ldots$

53. Express each of the following repeating decimals as common fractions.

(a) $0.8\overline{7}$ (b) $0.3\overline{74}$ (c) $0.123\,\overline{456}$

54. When, between one and two o'clock, will the hands of a clock be together?

55. A small company decides to borrow $100 000. The repayment schedule is this:
(1) On each anniversary of the loan a sum of $10 000 must be applied to the outstanding principal.
(2) All the interest for the preceding year must be paid at 10 percent per annum.
What is the present value of all these installment payments, assuming an interest rate of 7 percent compounded annually?

56. One-tenth of a certain radioactive substance disintegrates each day. Assume that 100 mg of the substance is present initially
(a) Compute the amount of the substance that remains at times $t = 1, 2, 3, 4, \ldots, 8$ d.
(b) Estimate the half-life of the substance.

57. Evaluate the following by the method of telescoping sums.

$$\sum_{i=1}^{n} (6i^2 + 12i + 8)$$

58. Evaluate each of the following by the method of telescoping sums.

(a) $\displaystyle\sum_{j=1}^{n} \frac{1}{(3j - 1)(3j + 2)}$

(b) $\displaystyle\sum_{j=1}^{n} \frac{1}{(5j - 4)(5j + 1)}$

59. Prove each of the following by mathematical induction.

(a) $\displaystyle\sum_{i=1}^{n} \frac{1}{i(i + 1)} = \frac{n}{n + 1}$

(b) $\displaystyle\sum_{i=1}^{n} \frac{1}{(2i - 1)(2i + 1)} = \frac{n}{2n + 1}$

(c) $1 + 4 + 7 + \ldots + (3n - 2) = \dfrac{n(3n - 1)}{2}$

60. Use mathematical induction to prove that $n^2(n + 1)^2$ is divisible by 4.

61. Use mathematical induction to prove that the sum of the first n even natural numbers is equal to $n(n + 1)$.

PROBLEMS PLUS

The lengths a_1, a_2, a_3, ... are obtained from the figures in the manner shown. Find the infinite sum $a_1 + a_2 + a_3 + \ldots$ ($a_1 = AB$, $a_2 = CD$, ...) given that $a_1 = 1$ and $BC = \frac{2}{3}$.

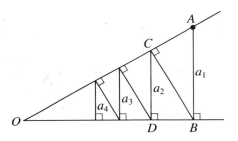

CHAPTER 5

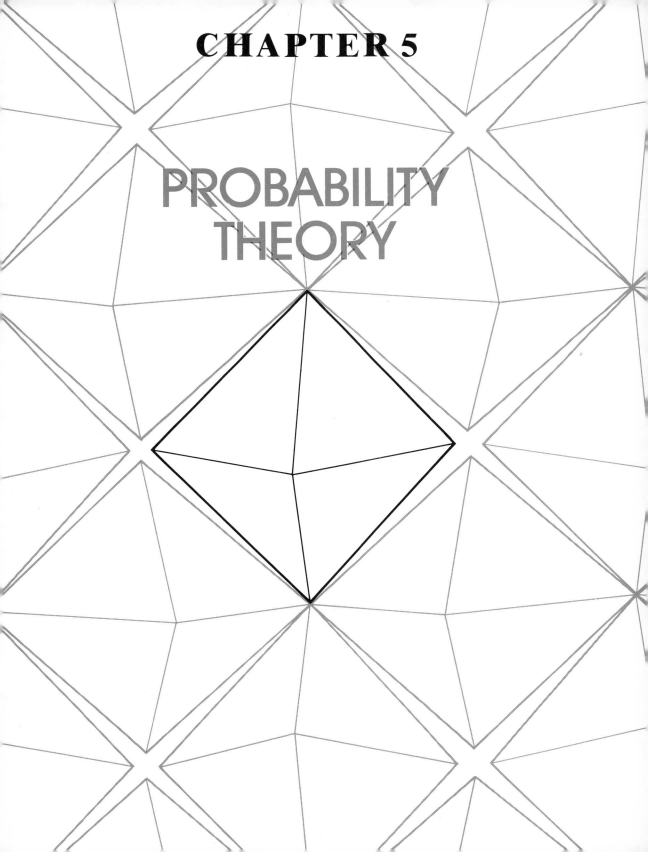

PROBABILITY THEORY

REVIEW AND PREVIEW TO CHAPTER 5

Tree Diagrams

Tree diagrams are used to organize and visualize a set.

EXERCISE 1

1. Barb owns three cars and two boats. She intends to go for an outing on the lake to which she must drive. Draw a tree diagram to illustrate her possible choices of transportation for her to get out on the water.

2. Dan has four hats and three overcoats. Draw a tree diagram to illustrate the number of hat and coat combinations he can wear.

3. Gino and Keith play a best-of-three (first player to win two games) tennis match. Draw a tree diagram to illustrate the possible combinations of wins before the match is completed.

4. Wen decides to paint her car two-tone, the roof one colour and the sides another. She is going to choose from the colours orange, black, and white. Draw a tree diagram to illustrate the possible colour combinations.

5. A vending machine requires 45 cents for a purchase. Use a tree diagram to determine the number of ways in which the 45-cent total may be made up in nickels, dimes, and quarters.

Permutations

A permutation is an arrangement of r *objects taken from a set of* n *objects in a definite order.* The number of permutations of *r* objects taken from *n* objects is given by

$$P(n, r) = \frac{n!}{(n-r)!}$$

EXERCISE 2

1. Evaluate.
   (a) $P(5,3)$ (b) $P(5,5)$
   (c) $P(k,3)$ (d) $P(k,c)$

2. How many permutations are there of the letters a, b, c?

3. How many permutations are there of six numbers chosen from 49 numbers?

4. Telephone area codes in North America are made up of three digits. What is the total number of area codes possible under this system if the first digit of the area code cannot be a zero or a one?

5. A cricket batting line-up consists of eleven players. How many possible batting line-ups can one choose from a team of 13 players?

Combinations

A combination is the selection of r *objects taken from* n *objects without regard to order.* The number of combinations is given by:

$$\binom{n}{r} = \frac{n!}{r!(n-r)!}$$

EXERCISE 3

1. Evaluate
   (a) $\binom{5}{3}$ (b) $\binom{10}{10}$
   (c) $\binom{k}{2}$ (d) $\binom{k}{c}$

2. How many ways can three fruits be taken from a basket of eight fruits?

3. A basketball team has 12 players on it. What is the total number of ways in which the starting five players may be chosen?

4. How many ways can a staff of 20 teachers be chosen from a teacher pool of 40 teachers?

5. In a family car there is seating for a driver and five passengers. In how many ways can we choose the three seats that will be occupied by the children?

INTRODUCTION

The concept of *likelihood* or *chance* is an intuitive one. Its use is commonplace in the news and other media. The following phrases all represent a general understanding of the concept of chance.

''The likelihood of a nuclear disaster is very slight.''

''The Leafs have a good chance of getting into the playoffs.''

''It's quite likely that I will get over 90 percent on my next Finite Math test.''

Once a *numerical value* has been assigned to these estimates of likelihood, then we have introduced the concept of probability.

In this chapter we develop the principles of probability theory and apply them to such situations as games of chance, self-confidence in test-writing and sports, genetic traits, and learning patterns.

5.1 PROPERTIES OF PROBABILITY

In our discussion and development of probability theory we use the term **experiment** to describe a well-defined process from which observations may be made. For example, as an experiment we could roll a die and observe which face is turned up, or we could select a batting line-up for a baseball team and observe the order of the players.

The term **outcomes** will be used to describe the possible results of an experiment. In the example of the rolling die, the outcomes would be the six possible faces that could be turned up. We are often interested in a subset of the set of all outcomes. We will refer to such a subset as an **event**.

The likelihood of an event's occurring will vary from completely impossible to absolutely certain.

```
Impossible                           Certain
└─────────────────────────────────────┘
```

For example, ''It will rain tomorrow.'' is a statement whose truth will certainly vary from highly improbable to highly probable, depending upon the geographic location and the season of the year. Most of us would choose an intermediate position based on our knowledge of local weather patterns and our personal biases.

Let us now take this range of likelihoods from impossible to certain and *impose a numerical scale* from 0 to 1 upon it.

```
Impossible                           Certain
    0                                   1
└─────────────────────────────────────┘
```

The **probability** assigned to an event is a number lying between 0 and 1, and is an attempt to quantify the concept of chance or likelihood.

The notation used is: $P(A)$, read "the probability of the event A."
Hence,

> for any event A, $0 \leqslant P(A) \leqslant 1$

How do we arrive at these probabilities? Many probabilities can be assigned, based on our expectations of the outcomes of situations.

Intuitively, most of us assume that the "chance" of tossing a head with a coin is one-in-two because we have no reason to suspect that one outcome of the toss is more likely than the other. Similarly, the "chance" of rolling a three with a die is one-in-six. This concept of chance relates directly to probability.

In fact, we arrive at a numerical value for a probability by defining:

> $$P(A) = \frac{n(A)}{n(S)}$$

where $n(S)$ is the number of all possible outcomes, and $n(A)$ is the number of outcomes that belong to the event A.

This method of determining a probability is based on the assumption that all outcomes are **equally likely**. That is, we are not playing with a loaded die or a weighted coin; no one outcome is more likely to occur than another.

Example 1   ***Given:***   Experiment: tossing a coin
                    Event: the coin turning up heads

            Find: the probability of tossing a head with the coin

Solution   The outcomes are assumed to be equally likely. Since the set of all possible outcomes is $S = \{H(\text{ead}), T(\text{ail})\}$

$$n(S) = 2$$

and the set of the event outcomes is $A = \{H\}$.

$$n(A) = 1$$
$$P(A) = \frac{n(A)}{n(S)}$$
$$= \frac{1}{2}$$

The probability of tossing a head with a coin is $\frac{1}{2}$.

Example 2   ***Given:***   Experiment: rolling a die
                    Event: the roll turns up a three

            Find: the probability of rolling a three with a die

Solution Assume the outcomes are equally likely.

The outcome set is $S = \{1, 2, 3, 4, 5, 6\}$, so
$$n(S) = 6$$
The event set is $A = \{3\}$, so
$$n(A) = 1$$
$$P(A) = \frac{n(A)}{n(S)}$$
$$= \frac{1}{6}$$

The probability of rolling a three with a die is $\frac{1}{6}$.

Example 3 *Given:* Experiment: drawing a card at random from a deck of cards.
Event: an ace is drawn

Find: the probability that an ace is drawn from a deck of cards.

Solution In a random selection each card is equally likely to be drawn.

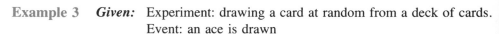

The outcome set is $S = \{2\clubsuit, 3\clubsuit, \ldots, K\clubsuit, A\clubsuit, \ldots, 2\spadesuit, 3\spadesuit, \ldots, K\spadesuit, A\spadesuit\}$. So,
$$n(S) = 52$$
The event set is $A = \{A\clubsuit, A\diamondsuit, A\heartsuit, A\spadesuit\}$. So, $n(A) = 4$
$$P(A) = \frac{n(A)}{n(S)}$$
$$= \frac{4}{52}$$
$$= \frac{1}{13}$$

The probability that an ace is drawn is $\frac{1}{13}$.

Example 4 Find the probability of rolling either a three or a five with a die.

Solution Assume the outcomes are equally likely.

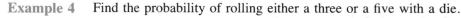

The outcome set is $S = \{1, 2, 3, 4, 5, 6\}$. So
$$n(S) = 6$$
The event set is $A = \{3, 5\}$. So,
$$n(A) = 2$$
$$P(A) = \frac{n(A)}{n(S)}$$
$$= \frac{2}{6}$$
$$= \frac{1}{3}$$

The probability of rolling a three or a five is $\frac{1}{3}$.

Example 5   Find the probability that a number picked at random between 1 and 10 is

2 4 6 8 10
4   9

(a)   even,

(b)   a perfect square.

Solution   Each number is equally likely to be selected in a random selection process.

The outcome set is $S = \{1, 2, 3, 4, 5, 6, 7, 8, 9, 10\}$. So,
$$n(S) = 10$$

(a)   The event set is $A = \{2, 4, 6, 8, 10\}$, so
$$n(A) = 5$$
$$P(A) = \frac{n(A)}{n(S)}$$
$$= \frac{5}{10}$$
$$= \frac{1}{2}$$

The probability that an even number is picked is $\frac{1}{2}$.

(b)   The event set is $A = \{1, 4, 9\}$. So
$$n(A) = 3$$
$$P(A) = \frac{n(A)}{n(S)}$$
$$= \frac{3}{10}$$

The probability that a perfect square is picked is $\frac{3}{10}$.

One immediate consequence of the definition of probabilities is the relationship between an event and its **complement**, that is, the set of outcomes in which the event does *not* occur. For example, if A is the event that a three occurs on the roll of a die, then the complement of A, denoted A', is the event that the three does not occur on the roll. In this example it is easy to see that $P(A) = \frac{1}{6}$, and $P(A') = \frac{5}{6}$.

In general,

$$P(A') = 1 - P(A)$$

Example 6   What is the probability of *not* selecting a prime number in a random selection of a number from 1 to 20?

Solution   Consider the probability of selecting a prime.

The outcome set is $S = \{1, 2, 3, \dots, 18, 19, 20\}$. So,
$$n(S) = 20$$

The event set of selecting a prime is
$$A = \{2, 3, 5, 7, 11, 13, 17, 19\}.$$
So, $n(A) = 8$

$$P(A) = \frac{n(A)}{n(S)}$$

$$= \frac{8}{20}$$

$$= \frac{2}{5}$$

Then the probability of the complement is
$$P(A') = 1 - P(A)$$

$$= 1 - \frac{2}{5}$$

$$= \frac{3}{5}$$

The probability of not selecting a prime is $\frac{3}{5}$.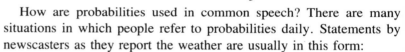

How are probabilities used in common speech? There are many situations in which people refer to probabilities daily. Statements by newscasters as they report the weather are usually in this form:
     "There is a 40% chance of rain tomorrow."
or "There is a 10% chance of flurries in the late afternoon."
Instead of using the probability scale from 0 to 1, a scale that is more familiar to the general public is used. That scale is *percentages*.

Percentage Scale (%)	Probability Scale
0	0
⋮	⋮
25	0.25
⋮	⋮
50	0.50
⋮	⋮
75	0.75
⋮	⋮
100	1.00

So really, the newscasters mean to say:
     "The probability of rain tomorrow is 0.4."
or "The probability of flurries in the late afternoon is 0.1."
By using a well-known and frequently-used scale such as percentages, the general public is confronted with a mathematical concept such as probability and has no problem with its use or interpretation.

     In fact, probabilities are constantly estimated by each one of us every day. When we cross the street we estimate the available time between cars and we do not attempt crossing until we have a high probability of making it to the other side. When we hear or read an opinion, we estimate the validity of the opinion—a probability estimate. Estimation of likelihood and chance is a natural process performed daily; we are merely formalizing it in this chapter.

EXERCISE 5.1

A **1.** For each of the following experiments, (i) suggest a set of possible outcomes, and (ii) decide whether the outcomes are equally likely.

(a) spinning a roulette wheel

(b) throwing a dart at a dart board

(c) choosing a job applicant for a position of employment from ten applicants whom you have interviewed

(d) selecting a dress from a rack of dresses

(e) spinning a racquet to determine ''rough'' or ''smooth'' in order to start a game

(f) selecting the winner of a lottery

(g) playing a game of bingo

2. Estimate the probabilities of the following events based on your intuition and general knowledge.

(a) The incumbent prime minister will be re-elected in the next election.

(b) Next summer there will be an earthquake in California.

(c) Next summer there will be an earthquake in Ontario.

(d) The Toronto Blue Jays will win the World Series.

(e) Taxes in Canada will be lowered.

(f) We will make contact with extra-terrestrial life before the turn of the century.

(g) You will win a million dollars in one of the lotteries.

For the following experiments assume that the outcomes are equally likely.

3. (a) *Given:* $S = \{1, 3, 5, 7, 9\}$
  $A = \{3, 9\}$

 Find: $P(A)$

(b) *Given:* $S = \{HH, HT, TT, TH\}$
  $A = \{HT, TH\}$

 Find: $P(A)$

(c) *Given:* $S = \{a, b, c, d, e, f, \ldots, w, x, y, z\}$
  $A = \{a, e, i, o, u\}$

 Find: $P(A), P(A')$

B **4.** (a) *Given:* Experiment: rolling a die
  Event: an odd number turns up

 Find: the probability of rolling an odd number with a die.

(b) *Given:* Experiment: choosing a number at random from 1 to 100 inclusive.

Event: the number is divisible by 3.

Find: the probability that a number chosen at random between 1 and 100 is *not* divisible by 3.

(c) *Given:* Experiment: cutting a deck of cards

Event: the card cut is a face card

Find: the probability of cutting a face card from a deck of cards

5. The game "Dungeons and Dragons" is played with a dodecahedral die, that is, a die with twelve faces. What is the probability of rolling a number greater than seven?

6. A record collection consists of eight rock albums, twelve blues albums, and four classical albums. If a record is chosen at random, find the probability that the one chosen is

(a) rock.

(b) classical.

(c) blues.

(d) not classical.

(e) neither blues nor classical.

7. An integer from 1 to 50 inclusive is chosen at random. What is the probability that the integer

(a) is odd?

(b) is even?

(c) is less than nine?

(d) is divisible by 11?

(e) ends in a 7?

(f) is a perfect cube?

(g) is not a perfect square?

(h) is not divisible by 7?

(i) is not a multiple of 5?

8. A drawer contains three pairs of red socks, two pairs of white socks, and four pairs of black socks and the socks are not matched or organized in any special way.

(a) If the lights are out, and one sock is drawn from the drawer, what is the probability that a red sock is drawn?

(b) Once a sock has been drawn and discovered to be red, what is the probability of drawing another red sock to make a pair?

9. Three downhill skiers, Lawrie, Gavin, and Alan are competing in a race. Their positions in the starting order are chosen by lot, that is, randomly. What is the probability that

(a) Gavin races before Lawrie?

(b) Alan is the last racer?

(c) Lawrie races first?

(d) Gavin follows immediately after Alan?

C **10.** Find the probability that a number chosen at random between 1 and 100 inclusive is:
(a) divisible by 3 or 5.   (b) not divisible by 3 or 5.

5.2   COUNTING THE OUTCOMES

In calculating probabilities, we usually
  (i) list the outcome set;
 (ii) list the event set; and
(iii) count the number of elements in each list, that is, $n(S)$ and $n(A)$.

There are useful techniques to aid us in accomplishing this – tree diagrams, permutations, and combinations.

Tree Diagrams

A tree diagram, as introduced in Section 1.1, *orders and organizes* a sequence of outcomes.

Example 1   Find the probability of tossing exactly two heads when a coin is tossed three times.

Solution   A tree diagram that illustrates the three tosses is as follows.

First Toss	Second Toss	Third Toss	Outcomes	Event A (2 Heads)
H	H	H	HHH	
		T	HHT	HHT
	T	H	HTH	HTH
		T	HTT	
T	H	H	THH	THH
		T	THT	
	T	H	TTH	
		T	TTT	

Assume the outcomes at each branch are equally likely. The outcome set is

$$S = \{HHH, HHT, HTH, HTT, THH, THT, TTH, TTT\}.$$

So, $n(S) = 8$

The event set is $A = \{HHT, HTH, THH\}$.

So, $n(A) = 3$

$$P(A) = \frac{n(A)}{n(S)}$$

$$= \frac{3}{8}$$

The probability of tossing exactly two heads is $\frac{3}{8}$. [Note that this tree diagram also lists the outcome set of an experiment in which three coins are tossed all at once.]

Example 2 Find the probability of rolling a sum of 7 or 11 when rolling a pair of dice.

Solution A tree diagram that illustrates the rolling of the dice is as follows.

First die	Second die	Outcomes	Event A (sum is 7 or 11)
1	1	1, 1	
	2	1, 2	
	3	1, 3	
	4	1, 4	
	5	1, 5	
	6	1, 6	1, 6
2	1	2, 1	
	2	2, 2	
	3	2, 3	
	4	2, 4	
	5	2, 5	2, 5
	6	2, 6	
3	1	3, 1	
	2	3, 2	
	3	3, 3	
	4	3, 4	3, 4
	5	3, 5	
	6	3, 6	
4	1	4, 1	
	2	4, 2	
	3	4, 3	4, 3
	4	4, 4	
	5	4, 5	
	6	4, 6	
5	1	5, 1	
	2	5, 2	5, 2
	3	5, 3	
	4	5, 4	
	5	5, 5	
	6	5, 6	5, 6
6	1	6, 1	6, 1
	2	6, 2	
	3	6, 3	
	4	6, 4	
	5	6, 5	6, 5
	6	6, 6	

From the tree diagram we see
$$n(S) = 36$$
and $n(A) = 8$

$$P(A) = \frac{n(A)}{n(S)}$$

$$= \frac{8}{36}$$

$$= \frac{2}{9}$$

The probability of rolling a sum of either 7 or 11 with a pair of dice is $\frac{2}{9}$.

Tree diagrams often become quite cumbersome and complicated. So we may bypass listing the outcome and event sets and just calculate the size of the sets directly, that is, $n(S)$ and $n(A)$, by using counting principles based on permutations and combinations as seen in Chapters 1 and 2.

Permutations

A permutation is an arrangement of r objects taken from a set of n objects in a *definite order*. Using the principles from Chapter 1, we will be able to determine terms like $n(A)$ for problems that are concerned with order.

Example 3   Three people form a queue at a grocery store. What is the probability that they line up in descending order of age?

Solution   We assume that the three people are of different ages and they line up randomly. The outcome set consists of the ways that the three people can line up, so,

$$n(S) = 3!$$
$$= 6$$

The event set contains the one outcome where the people are in descending order of age, so,

$$n(A) = 1$$
$$P(A) = \frac{1}{6}$$

The probability that the three people are in order is $\frac{1}{6}$.

Example 4   Nine horses are entered in a race. In an attempt to predict the finish of the race, three horses are selected by lot to finish first, second, and third. What is the probability that the choice is correct?

Solution   The outcome set consists of the ways that three horses chosen from nine can place first, second, and third.

Hence, $n(S) = \dfrac{9!}{(9-3)!}$

$= 9 \times 8 \times 7$

$= 504$

The event set contains exactly one element, the outcome where the order is correct.

Hence, $n(A) = 1$

$P(A) = \frac{1}{504}$

The probability that the choice of the finish is correct is $\frac{1}{504}$.

Combinations

A combination is the selection of r objects taken from n objects *without regard to order*. Using the principles from Chapter 1, we will be able to count the number of these combinations and hence find terms like $n(A)$, which are necessary to calculate probabilities.

Example 5   A committee of five people is to be selected from ten males and eight females. What is the probability that there are exactly three males on the committee?

Solution   Assume each outcome is equally likely.

The experiment is to select five people from a set of 18 people (ten male, eight female). So,

$$n(S) = \binom{18}{5} \quad \text{(selecting 5 from 18)}$$

$$= \frac{18!}{5!(18-5)!}$$

$$= \frac{18 \times 17 \times 16 \times 15 \times 14 \times 13!}{5 \times 4 \times 3 \times 2 \times 1 \times 13!}$$

$$= \frac{18 \times 17 \times 16 \times 15 \times 14}{5 \times 4 \times 3 \times 2 \times 1}$$

$$= 8568$$

The event A is to select three males from ten males, and two females from eight females.

The number of ways of selecting the three males is

$$\binom{10}{3} = \frac{10!}{3!7!}$$

$$= \frac{10 \times 9 \times 8}{3 \times 2 \times 1}$$

$$= 120$$

The number of ways of selecting the two females is

$$\binom{8}{2} = \frac{8!}{2!6!}$$
$$= \frac{8 \times 7}{2}$$
$$= 28$$

The total number of ways of selecting the committee is

$$n(A) = \binom{10}{3}\binom{8}{2} \qquad \text{(Fundamental Counting Principle)}$$
$$= 120 \times 28$$
$$= 3360$$

$$P(A) = \frac{n(A)}{n(S)}$$
$$= \frac{3360}{8568}$$
$$= \frac{20}{51}$$
$$\doteq 0.4$$

The probability of selecting a committee with exactly three males is approximately 0.4. We would expect that about four of ten committees chosen in this fashion would have exactly three males on them.

Example 6   The school yearbook is to be produced by a student staff of two boys and three girls, chosen by lot from five boys and six girls. One of the boys is the boyfriend of one of the girls. What is the probability that both will be chosen to be on the editorial staff of the yearbook?

Solution   The experiment is to select five people (two boys, three girls) from 11 people (five boys, six girls).

The number of ways of selecting the two boys is $\binom{5}{2}$

The number of ways of selecting the three girls is $\binom{6}{3}$

Hence, $n(S) = \binom{5}{2}\binom{6}{3}$ (Fundamental Counting Principle)
$$= \frac{5!}{2!3!} \times \frac{6!}{3!3!}$$
$$= 10 \times 20$$
$$= 200$$

The event is that the staff contains the boyfriend and girlfriend. If the boyfriend is on the staff, the remaining boy may be selected in $\binom{4}{1}$ ways.

If the girlfriend is on the staff, the remaining girls may be selected in $\binom{5}{2}$ ways.

The number of possible selections with the boyfriend and girlfriend both on the staff is

$$n(A) = \binom{4}{1}\binom{5}{2}$$
$$= \frac{4!}{1!3!} \times \frac{5!}{2!3!}$$
$$= 4 \times 10$$
$$= 40$$

Thus, $P(A) = \dfrac{n(A)}{n(S)}$
$$= \frac{40}{200}$$
$$= \frac{1}{5}$$

The probability of selecting an editorial staff including both the boyfriend and girlfriend is $\frac{1}{5}$.

EXERCISE 5.2

Unless otherwise indicated, leave answers in fractional form, reduced to lowest terms.

B **1.** Draw a tree diagram to list the outcome set for the experiment that tosses a coin four times. Find the probabilities of the following events.
(a) Four heads turn up.
(b) More tails than heads turn up.
(c) Exactly one tail turns up.
(d) No heads turn up.
(e) Two heads and two tails turn up.
(f) The last toss is a head.

2. Draw a tree diagram to represent the experiment in which first a coin is tossed, then a die is rolled. Find the probabilities of the following events.
(a) A head and an even number turn up.
(b) A tail and a roll greater than 4 turn up.
(c) A head and a one turn up.
(d) A three turns up.

3. (a) Assuming that the probability of giving birth to a boy or a girl is equally likely, draw a tree diagram to represent the sex of the children of a family with three children.
   (b) If a family is selected at random from families with three children, find the probability that
       (i) the children are all the same sex.
       (ii) the oldest is a girl.
       (iii) the family is all boys.
       (iv) there are more boys than girls in the family.
       (v) there is a girl in the family.
       (vi) the middle child is a boy.

4. The president of the Hippopotamus party is chosen by lot. Assuming that there is equal representation from each sex and each region, draw a tree diagram that would represent the possible combinations of sex and region for the candidates (use the ten provinces and the two territories to identify the regions). Find the probability that
   (a) the candidate is a female from the North (the two territories).
   (b) the candidate is from the West (west of Ontario).
   (c) the candidate is male and from the Maritimes.
   (d) the candidate is female.
   (e) the candidate is from Quebec.

5. An annual squash tournament has the format that competitors play exactly three games of squash. Marion and Michael are two competitors who are evenly matched in ability.
   (a) Draw a tree diagram that would represent the possible win/loss combinations for the three games.
   (b) What is the probability that
       (i) Marion wins all three games?
       (ii) Michael wins the first two games?
       (iii) Marion wins the first game?
       (iv) Michael wins only one game?

6. Construct a tree diagram that would represent the outcomes in the first four games of a World Series played between the Toronto Blue Jays and the Montreal Expos. If the two teams are considered to be evenly matched, find the probability that
   (a) the Expos win the series four straight.
   (b) the Blue Jays win three of the first four games.
   (c) the Expos win the opener of the series.
   (d) the two teams split the first four games.

7. A turn in the game of Yahtzee consists of rolling five dice. What is the probability of getting a "Yahtzee", that is, all five of the dice turning up the same?

8. In the game of backgammon, it can be very advantageous to roll doubles with the pair of dice. What is the probability of rolling doubles (both dice are the same)?

It is recommended that Questions 9, 10, 11 be solved using permutations.

9. In a lottery called "6-in-a-row", six different numbers are chosen at random from 1 through 49, inclusive. If a ticket has been purchased, find the probabilities of the following events.
   (a) The first number on the ticket matches the first number in the draw.
   (b) The first two numbers match.
   (c) The grand prize is won where all six numbers match.

10. In a track meet, five entrants of equal ability are competing. What is the probability that
    (a) the finish will be in the descending order of the entrants' ages?
    (b) Sandy will be first?
    (c) Shanaze is first and Sandy is second?

11. An infant typed three strokes on a keyboard. If all of the characters typed were letters of the alphabet, what is the probability that the characters that were struck were three consecutive letters in alphabetical order?

It is recommended that Questions 12 through 17 be solved using combinations.

12. The starting line-up for a basketball team is to consist of two forwards and three guards. Two brothers, Matthew and Tony, play on the team and Matthew is a forward and Tony a guard. There are four forwards and six guards from which to choose the line-up. If the starting players are chosen at random, what is the probability that the two brothers will end up in the starting line-up?

13. Hans has 12 good friends, five of them male and seven of them female. He decides to have a dinner party but can invite only seven because his dining room table will seat only eight people. He decides to invite his guests by lot. What is the probability that
    (a) there will be four males and four females at the party?
    (b) Rivka will be among those invited?
    (c) Hans will have only female guests?

14. A group of 12 people is going out on the town on Saturday night. The group will take three cars with four people in each car. If they distribute themselves among the cars at random, what is the probability that Rafael and Chantal will be in the same car?

15. Ten boys and 12 girls decide to rent a 16-passenger van and a six-passenger car to drive to a rock concert in a nearby city. If the group is distributed randomly between the vehicles, what is the probability that
    (a) there are no boys in the car?
    (b) there are no girls in the car?
    (c) Alan and Margaret are both in the van?
    (d) there are more girls than boys in the car?

16. A committee is to be struck to review the philosophy of education in today's technological age. The committee is to consist of seven people chosen randomly from 28 people comprised of the following interest groups: eight students, ten teachers, six business executives, and four members of the clergy. What is the probability that
   (a) there will be exactly one student on the committee?
   (b) there will be exactly two executives on the committee?
   (c) there will be no members of the clergy on the committee?
   (d) there will be no teachers on the committee?
   (e) there will be at least one teacher on the committee?
   (f) there will be exactly two students and two teachers on the committee?
   (g) the committee will be made up entirely of students?

17. In the 6/49 lottery six different numbers must be selected between 1 through 49 inclusive. To win the grand prize of the lottery your six numbers must match the six numbers that are drawn from the lottery drum (order is unimportant). What is the probability of winning the grand prize?

5.3   MUTUALLY EXCLUSIVE EVENTS

When an experiment takes place, we might be interested in a combination of events occurring. We have already seen this situation in Section 5.1 on the Properties of Probability. For example, we considered the probability of rolling either a 3 or a 5 with a die. Our definition of the event set was $A = \{3, 5\}$. However, we could have defined two event sets: $A = \{3\}$ and $B = \{5\}$. If we had done that, then the probability that we would be trying to determine would be the probability of the combination that either event A or event B occurred: $P(A \cup B)$.

In our example of the rolling of the die we note that

$$P(A) = \tfrac{1}{6}$$

$$P(B) = \tfrac{1}{6}$$

and $P(A \cup B) = \tfrac{2}{6}$

Notice that the sum of the component probabilities equals the probability of the combination of events. This is true only if the two event sets share no outcomes.

If two event sets have *no outcomes in common*, then they are said to be **mutually exclusive** events (in Chapter 2 the term *disjoint* was used to describe the sets). It is very important to be able to determine whether two events are mutually exclusive because this relation between the two events will dictate whether the following result will be used.

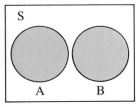

$$P(A \cup B) = P(A) + P(B) \quad \text{if } A, B \text{ are mutually exclusive}$$

Proof

Assume A and B are mutually exclusive.

Then, $\quad P(A \cup B) = \dfrac{n(A \cup B)}{n(S)}$

$\qquad\qquad\quad = \dfrac{n(A) + n(B)}{n(S)} \quad$ (because A and B have no common elements)

$\qquad\qquad\quad = \dfrac{n(A)}{n(S)} + \dfrac{n(B)}{n(S)}$

$\qquad\qquad\quad = P(A) + P(B)$

Example 1 **Given:** Experiment: rolling a die
  Events: A is that a 3 turns up.
    B is that a 5 turns up.

Find: the probability that a 3 or a 5 turns up when a die is rolled

Solution The outcome set is $S = \{1, 2, 3, 4, 5, 6\}$. So,
$$n(S) = 6$$
The event sets are $A = \{3\}$ and $B = \{5\}$. So,
$$n(A) = 1$$
$$n(B) = 1$$

Since A and B are mutually exclusive,

$$P(A \cup B) = P(A) + P(B)$$
$$= \frac{n(A)}{n(S)} + \frac{n(B)}{n(S)}$$
$$= \frac{1}{6} + \frac{1}{6}$$
$$= \frac{2}{6}$$
$$= \frac{1}{3}$$

The probability of rolling a 3 or a 5 with a die is $\frac{1}{3}$.

Example 2 If a committee of five is to be chosen randomly from six males and eight females, what is the probability that the committee is either all male or all female?

Solution The number of possible committees is $n(S) = \dbinom{14}{5} = 2002$.

Let A be the event that all the members of the committee are male.

The number of ways of selecting the five males is $n(A) = \binom{6}{5} = 6.$

Let B be the event that all the members of the committee are female. The number of ways of selecting the five females is $n(B) = \binom{8}{5} = 56.$

Since the events A and B are mutually exclusive,

$$
\begin{aligned}
P(A \cup B) &= P(A) + P(B) \\
&= \frac{n(A)}{n(S)} + \frac{n(B)}{n(S)} \\
&= \frac{6}{2002} + \frac{56}{2002} \\
&= \frac{62}{2002}
\end{aligned}
$$

The probability that the committee chosen is either all female or all male is $\frac{62}{2002}$ or approximately 0.03.

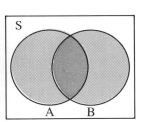

What happens when the events are *not* mutually exclusive? If two events are not mutually exclusive, then this means that they must share common outcomes. This is the *principle* of *inclusion/exclusion* as seen in Chapter 2 which stated that

$$n(A \cup B) = n(A) + n(B) - n(A \cap B)$$

Applying this theory to sets of outcomes in probability theory, we obtain the following result, which must be used if A and B are not mutually exclusive.

$$\boxed{P(A \cup B) = P(A) + P(B) - P(A \cap B)}$$

Proof

$$
\begin{aligned}
P(A \cup B) &= \frac{n(A \cup B)}{n(S)} \\
&= \frac{n(A) + n(B) - n(A \cap B)}{n(S)} \\
&= \frac{n(A)}{n(S)} + \frac{n(B)}{n(S)} - \frac{n(A \cap B)}{n(S)} \\
&= P(A) + P(B) - P(A \cap B)
\end{aligned}
$$

Example 3   Find the probability of turning up an even number or a number greater than 3 when rolling a die.

Solution   The outcome set is $S = \{1, 2, 3, 4, 5, 6\}$. So,

$$n(S) = 6$$

The event sets are $A = \{2, 4, 6\}$ and $B = \{4, 5, 6\}$. So,
$$n(A) = 3$$
$$n(B) = 3$$

The set of common elements is $(A \cap B) = \{4, 6\}$. So,

$$n(A \cap B) = 2$$
$$P(A \cup B) = P(A) + P(B) - P(A \cap B)$$
$$= \frac{n(A)}{n(S)} + \frac{n(B)}{n(S)} - \frac{n(A \cap B)}{n(S)}$$
$$= \frac{3}{6} + \frac{3}{6} - \frac{2}{6}$$
$$= \frac{4}{6}$$
$$= \frac{2}{3}$$

The probability of rolling an even number or a number greater than 3 is $\frac{2}{3}$.

Example 4 As a result of a recent survey conducted by the Substance Abuse League, it was estimated that 85 percent of a targeted population enjoys an alcoholic beverage at least once a week; 35 percent of the population smokes at least one cigarette a day; and 25 percent of the population indulges in both habits. What is the probability that an individual chosen at random from the targeted population either smokes or drinks alcohol?

Solution Let A be the event that the individual drinks.
Let B be the event that the individual smokes.

Given: $P(A) = 0.85$
$P(B) = 0.35$
$P(A \cap B) = 0.25$

The events A and B are *not* mutually exclusive.

Hence, $P(A \cup B) = P(A) + P(B) - P(A \cap B)$
$$= 0.85 + 0.35 - 0.25$$
$$= 0.95$$

The probability that an individual chosen at random either smokes or drinks is 0.95.

EXERCISE 5.3

A **1.** Classify the following two events, *A* and *B*, as either mutually exclusive or not mutually exclusive.

(a) *Experiment:* tossing two coins
A: At least one head occurs.
B: Two heads occur.

(b) *Experiment:* rolling a die
A: The roll is greater than 3
B: The roll is an even number.

(c) *Experiment:* cutting a deck of cards
A: The card is a face card.
B: The card is smaller than a seven.

(d) *Experiment:* choosing a student from your class
A: The student is female.
B: The student wears glasses.

(e) *Experiment:* selecting a chocolate bar.
A: The bar has nuts on it.
B: The bar contains caramel.

(f) *Experiment:* choosing an activity for a Saturday evening
A: The activity takes place in the home.
B: The activity is going to a dance.

(g) *Experiment:* answering a multiple choice question
A: The answer is correct.
B: The choice is part (i).

(h) *Experiment:* choosing a tie from a rack of ties
A: The tie is a solid colour.
B: The tie is blue and polka-dotted.

B **2.** (a) *Given:* The events *A* and *B* are mutually exclusive.
$P(A) = 0.5$
$P(B) = 0.3$
Find: $P(A \cup B)$

(b) *Given:* $P(A) = 0.6$
$P(B) = 0.2$
$P(A \cap B) = 0.1$
Find: $P(A \cup B)$

(c) *Given:* *A* is the event of tossing a head with a coin.
B is the event of tossing a tail with a coin.
Find: $P(A \cup B)$

(d) *Given:* *A* is the event of rolling a prime number with a die.
(Note: One is not considered a prime number.)
B is the event of rolling a perfect square with a die.
C is the event of rolling an even number with a die.

$Find:$ (i) $P(A \cup B)$
(ii) $P(A \cup C)$
(iii) $P(B \cup C)$

(e) *Given:* A is the event of cutting a face card from a deck.
B is the event of cutting a spade.
C is the event of cutting an ace.

$Find:$ (i) $P(A \cup B)$
(ii) $P(A \cup C)$
(iii) $P(B \cup C)$

3. The probability that an adolescent enjoys rock music is 0.7, and the probability that an adolescent enjoys country and western music is 0.2. If only one in ten adolescents enjoys rock as well as country and western, what is the probability that an adolescent chosen at random listens to either rock or country and western?

4. If a five-minute segment is chosen at random from a full-length movie, the probability that it contains a violent scene is 0.4. The probability that it contains a humorous scene is 0.3, and the probability that it contains both a humorous and a violent scene within the five minute segment is 0.1. Find the probability that a five-minute segment chosen at random from a movie contains either violence or humour.

5. The following table illustrates the distribution of elementary and secondary school enrolment in public and private institutions in Canada in 1977.

Province/Territory	Public	Private
Canada	5 285 274	185 035
Newfoundland	157 803	293
Prince Edward Island	27 919	—
Nova Scotia	201 759	1 410
New Brunswick	163 317	393
Quebec	1 319 511	86 110
Ontario	1 974 266	58 226
Manitoba	225 854	7 642
Saskatchewan	219 327	1 573
Alberta	441 255	6 070
British Columbia	536 481	23 318
Yukon	4 866	—
Northwest Territories	12 916	—

If a Canadian student was selected at random, what would be the probability that the student was:
(a) from Ontario?
(b) from either Ontario or Quebec?
(c) from the public system?
(d) from either Ontario or from the private system?
(e) from either Manitoba or the Yukon?

(f)   from either Alberta or the western provinces?

(g)   from the private system or Atlantic Canada?

5.4   CONDITIONAL PROBABILITY

Often when you are considering probabilities, additional information may become available that will affect the calculation of the probability of an outcome. For example, if you are interested in the probability that Miriam will pass her Mathematics test, then the probability of that outcome may depend on whether or not she attended the rock concert the night before! If this information becomes available, then a more accurate calculation of the probability can be made.

When additional information is known that will affect the probability of an outcome, we calculate what is called a **conditional probability**, denoted $P(A|B)$, using the definition

$$P(A|B) = \frac{P(A \cap B)}{P(B)}$$

where the notation $P(A|B)$ is read "the probability of the event A, given that the event B has occurred," or more succinctly, "the probability of A, given B."

Justification for this definition arises from the observation that once B is known then the event set for A is restricted to those outcomes in the set $(A \cap B)$. Furthermore, the outcome set has been reduced from the set S to the set B. Hence,

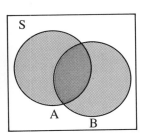

$$P(A|B) = \frac{n(A \cap B)}{n(B)}$$

This can be expressed in probabilities by multiplying the numerator and the denominator by $\frac{1}{n(S)}$, which will not alter the expression.

$$P(A|B) = \frac{n(A \cap B) \times \dfrac{1}{n(S)}}{n(B) \times \dfrac{1}{n(S)}}$$

$$= \frac{P(A \cap B)}{P(B)}$$

Example 1   What is the probability of rolling a sum greater than 7 with two dice if it is known that the first die rolled is a 3?

Solution   Let A be the event that a sum greater than 7 is rolled.

Let B be the event that the roll of the first die is a three.

The outcome set could be listed by a tree diagram identical to the one in Section 5.2, Example 2. However, another common method used to list the outcome set of two dice is with a table where each entry in the table is the sum of the dice. Along each margin of the table is the specific roll of each die.

First Die

		1	2	3	4	5	6
	1	2	3	4	5	6	7
	2	3	4	5	6	7	8
Second	3	4	5	6	7	8	9
Die	4	5	6	7	8	9	10
	5	6	7	8	9	10	11
	6	7	8	9	10	11	12

For example, this entry represents the sum of 7 when the first die is a 6 and the second is a 1.

Now, $P(A|B) = \dfrac{P(A \cap B)}{P(B)}$

and $P(A \cap B) = \dfrac{n(A \cap B)}{n(S)}$

From the table, $n(A \cap B) = 2$ (see coloured outcomes) and $n(S) = 36$, so

$$P(A \cap B) = \frac{2}{36}$$

$$= \frac{1}{18}$$

and $P(B) = \dfrac{1}{6}$

Hence $P(A|B) = \dfrac{P(A \cap B)}{P(B)}$

$$= \frac{\frac{1}{18}}{\frac{1}{6}}$$

$$= \frac{1}{18} \times \frac{6}{1}$$

$$= \frac{1}{3}$$

The probability of rolling a sum greater than 7, given that the first roll is 3, is equal to $\frac{1}{3}$.

Example 2   If a family is chosen at random from the set of all families with exactly two children, find the probability that

(a)   the family has two boys if it is known that one child is a boy.

(b)   the family has two boys if it is known that the first child is a boy.

Solution   Assume the probability of a child being a boy is $\frac{1}{2}$.

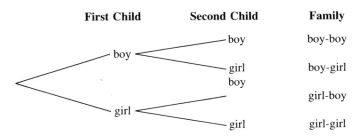

The outcome set is $S = \{$boy-boy, boy-girl, girl-boy, girl-girl$\}$, so,

$n(S) = 4$

(a)   Let A be the event that the family has two boys.
      Let B be the event that the family has at least one boy.

Then, $n(B) = 3$

and so, $P(B) = \dfrac{3}{4}$

The set $A \cap B = \{$boy-boy$\}$, so,

$$P(A \cap B) = \frac{1}{4}$$

Then, $P(A|B) = \dfrac{P(A \cap B)}{P(B)}$

$$= \frac{\frac{1}{4}}{\frac{3}{4}}$$

$$= \frac{1}{4} \times \frac{4}{3}$$

$$= \frac{1}{3}$$

The probability that there are two boys in the family, given that there is one boy, is $\frac{1}{3}$.

(Our intuition may have led us to think that the probability would have been one-half.)

(ii)   Let A be the event that the family has two boys.
      Let B be the event that the first child is a boy.

$$n(B) = 2$$
$$n(A \cap B) = 1$$

$$P(A|B) = \frac{P(A \cap B)}{P(B)}$$

$$= \frac{\frac{1}{4}}{\frac{1}{2}}$$

$$= \frac{1}{2}$$

The probability that a family has two boys, if it is know that the first child is a boy, is equal to $\frac{1}{2}$.   ◇

It is interesting to note how the subtle differences in information, as illustrated in parts (a) and (b), affect the conditional probabilities.

The equation for the conditional probability

$$P(A|B) = \frac{P(A \cap B)}{P(B)}$$

may be rearranged to the form

$$\boxed{P(A \cap B) = P(B) \times P(A|B)}$$

This form is useful when the conditional probability is known and it is necessary to determine the compound probability $P(A \cap B)$.

Example 3   The probability that Pat will go to Eastern University is $\frac{1}{5}$. The probability that she will go to another university is $\frac{1}{2}$. If Pat goes to Eastern, the probability that her boyfriend Gilles will follow her and go to Eastern is $\frac{3}{4}$. What is the probability that both Pat and Gilles attend Eastern University?

Solution   Let A be the event that Pat goes to Eastern.
Let B be the event that Gilles goes to Eastern.

We are given: $P(A) = \frac{1}{5}$

and $P(B|A) = \frac{3}{4}$

Then, $P(B \cap A) = P(A) \times P(B|A)$

$$= \frac{1}{5} \times \frac{3}{4}$$

$$= \frac{3}{20}$$

The probability that both Pat and Gilles attend Eastern is equal to $\frac{3}{20}$.   ◇

EXERCISE 5.4

A **1.** (a) **Given:** $P(A \cap B) = 0.5$
$P(B) = 0.7$
  Find: $P(A|B)$

(b) **Given:** $P(S) = 0.1$
$P(T|S) = 0.3$
  Find: $P(S \cap T)$

(c) **Given:** $P(A \cap B) = 0.2$
$P(A \cap C) = 0.3$
$P(B \cap C) = 0.4$
$P(A) = 0.4$
$P(B) = 0.6$
$P(C) = 0.7$
  Find: (i) $P(A|B)$ (ii) $P(B|C)$
      (iii) $P(C|A)$ (iv) $P(C|B)$

(d) **Given:** $P(A|B) = 0.3$
$P(B|A) = 0.4$
$P(A \cap B) = 0.2$
  Find: (i) $P(A)$ (ii) $P(B)$

2. (a) A die is rolled. What is the probability that it is a 5, given that it is greater than 3?

(b) A card is drawn from a deck of cards. What is the probability that it is a jack, given that it is a face card?

(c) In a family of four, Rob and Lesa are the parents and Michael and Jonathan are the children. Each family member has three Christmas presents under the tree. If one present is selected at random, what is the probability that the present is for
  (i) Jonathan, if it is known that the present is for a male?
  (ii) Lesa, if it is known that the present is for one of the parents?

3. A die is thrown twice. What is the probability that the sum of the rolls is less than 4 given that
(a) one of the rolls is a 1?
(b) the first roll is a 1?

4. When a hockey team, the Tigers, gets possession of the puck, the following probabilities have been estimated from team statistics: the probability that they carry the puck over the opposing team's blue line is 0.6; the probability that they get a shot on net is 0.3; the probability that they get a shot away and score is 0.01; and the probability that they cross the blue line and score is 0.005. Find the probability that they score given that
(a) they cross the blue line.
(b) they get a shot away.

5. After a recent Canadian census it was discovered that among all of the families in Canada, 40 percent have no children, 25 percent have one child, 18 percent have two children, 10 percent have three children, 5 percent have four children, and 2 percent have five or more children. If a Canadian family is selected at random,
   (a) what is the probability that the family has more than two children?
   (b) what is the probability that the family has more than two children, given that it has at least one child?

6. In an election for the president of the student council, it is estimated that Anne has a 40 percent chance of winning, Tanya has a 30 percent chance, Graham has a 20 percent chance, and Maria has a 10 percent chance. Just before the election, Graham withdraws. Now, what are the chances of winning for Anne, Tanya, and Maria? Hint: being withdrawn from the election is equivalent to knowing that he does not win the election.

7. Two brands of headache remedy are on the market: Acetylin and Salicin. One in 400 people taking Acetylin suffers side-effects and one in 1200 taking Salicin. At the present time it is estimated that equal numbers of people take each kind of drug. If Acetylin is taken off the market because of industrial sabotage during the processing of the drug, show that the probability of side-effects will be halved.

8. (a) Mary Catherine takes a five-question true-false quiz on Probability Theory. What is the probability that she will get all the answers correct if she is only guessing but knows that her teacher puts more true than false questions on the quiz?
   (b) What is her probability of passing the quiz?

5.5 INDEPENDENT EVENTS

When two events have *no effect upon one another* then they are said to be **independent**. For example, if event A is that a head is uppermost on a coin when a coin is tossed and event B is that the number six is uppermost on the roll of a die, it is reasonable to expect that neither event will have any effect on the other. These two events are said to be independent.

In conditional probability language the following statements describe the independence of two events.

$$P(A|B) = P(A)$$
or $$P(B|A) = P(B)$$

That is, given that one of the events has occurred does not alter our calculation of the probability of the other event occurring.

In the previous section, we saw that the conditional probability equation could be rearranged to the form

$$P(A \cap B) = P(A) \times P(B|A)$$

If the events are independent, then the result becomes

$$P(A \cap B) = P(A) \times P(B) \quad \text{if } A \text{ and } B \text{ are independent events}$$

Example 1   A game consists of rolling a die, then cutting a deck of cards. Find the probability that a six is rolled and a six is cut from the deck of cards.

Solution   The event A is to roll a six with a die.
The event B is to cut a six from the deck.
The two events are independent; the occurrence of one does not affect the occurrence of the other.

Now
$$n(A) = 1$$
and
$$n(S) = 6$$
then
$$P(A) = \frac{n(A)}{n(S)}$$
$$= \frac{1}{6}$$

The event set $B = \{6\clubsuit, 6\diamondsuit, 6\heartsuit, 6\spadesuit\}$. So,
$$n(B) = 4$$
and
$$n(S) = 52$$
then
$$P(B) = \frac{n(B)}{n(S)}$$
$$= \frac{4}{52}$$
$$= \frac{1}{13}$$
$$P(A \cap B) = P(A) \times P(B)$$
$$= \frac{1}{6} \times \frac{1}{13}$$
$$= \frac{1}{78}$$

The probability of rolling a six with the die and cutting a six from the deck of cards is $\frac{1}{78}$.   ◇

Example 2   Justin estimates that his probability of passing Mathematics is 0.8 and his probability of passing English is 0.9. Find the probability that Justin
(a)   will pass both Mathematics and English.
(b)   will pass Mathematics but will fail English.
(c)   will not pass either Mathematics or English.

Solution   Let A be the event that Justin passes Mathematics and A', the complement, that he fails.

Let B be the event that Justin passes English and B', the complement, that he fails.

Assume A and B are independent!

Given: $P(A) = 0.8$

   $P(B) = 0.9$

(a) *Find:* $P(A \cap B)$

$$
\begin{aligned}
P(A \cap B) &= P(A) \times P(B) \\
&= 0.8 \times 0.9 \\
&= 0.72
\end{aligned}
$$

The probability that Justin passes both Mathematics and English is equal to 0.72.

(b) *Find:* $P(A \cap B')$

$$
\begin{aligned}
P(A \cap B') &= P(A) \times P(B') \\
&= P(A) \times [1 - P(B)] \\
&= 0.8 \times [1 - 0.9] \\
&= 0.8 \times 0.1 \\
&= 0.08
\end{aligned}
$$

The probability that Justin passes Mathematics but fails English is equal to 0.08.

(c) *Find:* $P(A' \cap B')$

$$
\begin{aligned}
P(A' \cap B') &= P(A') \times P(B') \\
&= [1 - P(A)] \times [1 - P(B)] \\
&= [1 - 0.8] \times [1 - 0.9] \\
&= 0.2 \times 0.1 \\
&= 0.02
\end{aligned}
$$

The probability that Justin fails both courses is equal to 0.02.

Independent events not only simplify computations of a joint probability such as $P(A \cap B)$ but they also allow us to make assumptions that lead to situations of equally likely outcomes in which we can use our counting techniques developed in Section 5.2. The following examples will introduce this point. This example is sometimes referred to as the "birthday paradox" because it tends to contradict one's intuition. There are times when our intuition can be very misleading. The translation of a problem or situation into a mathematical model can reveal surprising results.

Example 3   There are 35 students in a Finite Mathematics class. What is the probability that at least two students have the same birthday?

(Intuition: Because there are 365 days among which the 35 birthdays may be distributed, you might guess that the chances may be 1 in 10 or less!)

Solution   The 35 birthdays may be assumed to be independent events. We will therefore assume each day of the year to be equally likely as a date of birth.

Let A be the event that at least two students have their birthdays on the same day. Consider the complementary event A', that is, that *no two* students have the same birthday.

The outcome set is the set of all possible combinations in which 35 people may have birthdays. Each person has 365 possibilities (ignore February 29).

Then, $n(S) = 365^{35}$

The event set is the set of 35 birthdays chosen from 365 days in which *no two* are the same. The number of ways in which you can select 35 days from 365 with *no two* alike is found by using permutations.

Then, $\quad n(A') = \dfrac{365!}{(365-35)!}$

$\qquad\qquad = 365 \times 364 \times 363 \times \ldots \times 332 \times 331$

So, $\qquad P(A') = \dfrac{n(A')}{n(S)}$

$\qquad\qquad = \dfrac{365 \times 364 \times 363 \times \ldots \times 332 \times 331}{365^{35}}$

$\qquad\qquad \doteq 0.186$

The probability of *no two* birthdays being alike is approximately 0.186.

Then the probability that there will be at least two students with the same birthday is

$\qquad P(A) = 1 - P(A')$

$\qquad\qquad \doteq 1 - 0.186$

$\qquad\qquad = 0.814$

Surprise! A probability of the magnitude of 0.814 suggests that the chances of two students having the same birthday are very good. Notice the contradiction to the chances that our intuition suggested to us.

EXERCISE 5.5

This question is for class discussion.

A 1. Which of the following pairs of events would you classify as independent?
   (a) A: A student has poor eyesight.
       B: A student has poor hearing.
   (b) A: A worker is well-trained.
       B: A worker meets the production quota.
   (c) A: The sky is cloudy.
       B: The season is winter.

   (d)   *A*: An ace of spades is cut from a deck of cards.
         B: A pair of sixes are rolled with the toss of two dice.
   (e)   *A*: A person is left-handed.
         B: A person has blonde hair.
   (f)   *A*: A person plays squash.
         B: A person plays tennis.

B **2.**   Suppose the probability that a person is over 178 cm tall is $\frac{1}{6}$ and the probability that a person completes a university degree is $\frac{1}{10}$.
   Assuming the two are independent, find the probability that someone chosen at random:
   (a)   is over 178 cm tall and has a university degree.
   (b)   is less than 178 cm in height and does not have a university degree.
   (c)   is over 178 cm tall or has a degree.

3.   Two single-digit random numbers (0 to 9 inclusive) are selected independently. Find the probability that their sum is 7.

4.   Find the probability of rolling "snake-eyes" (two ones) three times in a row with a pair of dice.

5.   In backgammon it is much to a player's advantage to roll pairs with the dice. Nicole seems to roll pairs back to back (twice in a row) all of the time. If after one game Nicole was counted rolling six sets of back-to-back pairs, and the game consisted of a total of 42 rolls, would you consider Nicole lucky?

6.   A car manufacturing plant has three shifts working on the assembly line. The morning shift produces 38% of the total production; the afternoon shift produces 34%; and the evening shift 28%. Of their output 3%, 2%, and 1%, respectively, do not pass quality control. If a vehicle is selected at random from the inventory and found defective, what is the probability that it was manufactured by
   (a)   the morning shift?
   (b)   the afternoon shift?
   (c)   the evening shift?

7.   What is the probability that there are at least two people with the same birthday in a class of 40 students?

8.   A small town has a network of 115 residential streets, all containing approximately the same number of residents. If a canvasser randomly selects 20 people from the phone book to promote a product, what is the probability that at least two of the people live on the same street?

9.   In a dinner party of six people, what is the probability that at least two of the people have a birthday in the same month?

10. Estimate the probability that at least two of the next ten Prime Ministers of Canada will be born in the same month.

11. A restaurant offers a choice of ten entrées on a menu. If a party of six arrives at the restaurant for dinner and chooses its entrées at random, what is the probability that at least two people will choose the same entrée?

12. Find an expression for the probability that at least two selections from a set of m distinct elements are the same in a random sample of size n.

5.6 ODDS

Canadian Series odds 21-1

TORONTO (CP)—The odds of an all-Canadian World Series, estimated in excess of 1000-1 prior to the 1987 season, now stand at 21-1 and are coming down with every Expo or Blue Jays win, a Las Vegas oddsmaker said Wednesday.

On Tuesday, a spokesman for the Riviera Sports and Race Book quoted 25-1 odds on Montreal taking on Toronto in the World Series. Wednesday afternoon, the odds were 21-1, said Riviera oddsmaker Jack Lysaght.

"Montreal's really the shocker," he said from Las Vegas. "Everyone knew Toronto was a good team."

Lysaght said the preseason odds on an all-Canadian World Series were "in excess of 1000-1" and the odds on the Expos winning their division a conservative 150-1.

"At the beginning, Montreal was generally considered to be one of the worst teams in baseball," he said.

The general interpretation of **odds** is *the degree of confidence* that someone has that an event will occur. The odds in favour of an event A are represented by a ratio. The higher the ratio, the greater is the degree of confidence that one has in the occurrence of the event. For example, odds of three to one suggest that there is greater confidence that the event will occur than if the odds were two to one. In the article above, the odds quoted are odds *against* an event's occurring. This concept will be developed later in this section.

Odds are often used in wagers. If a gambler states that he will give ten to seven odds that an event A will occur, he usually means that he is willing to bet ten dollars to win only seven. The reason he is willing to bet more than he will win is because he has confidence that there is a better than even chance that the event will occur.

The odds in favour of an event are the ratio of *the probability of the event occurring* to *the probability of the event not occurring*. If an event is four times more likely to occur than not to occur then the odds are four to one; if an event is 20 times more likely to occur than not, then the odds are 20 to 1; and so on.

In general,

$$(\text{odds in favour of } A) = P(A):P(A') = \frac{P(A)}{P(A')}$$

where A is the desired event and A' its complement.

Or, in another form:

$$(\text{odds in favour of } A) = \frac{n(A)}{n(S) - n(A)}$$

where $n(A)$ is the number of elements in the event set A and $n(S)$ is the number of elements in the outcome set S.

It is worth showing that the second form of determining odds follows directly from the first.

$$(\text{odds in favour of } A) = \frac{P(A)}{P(A')}$$

$$= \frac{P(A)}{1 - P(A)} \qquad \text{(Complementary Event)}$$

$$= \frac{\dfrac{n(A)}{n(S)}}{1 - \dfrac{n(A)}{n(S)}}$$

$$= \frac{\dfrac{n(A)}{n(S)}}{\dfrac{n(S) - n(A)}{n(S)}} \qquad \text{(Common Denominator)}$$

$$= \frac{n(A)}{n(S)} \times \frac{n(S)}{n(S) - n(A)} \quad \text{(Invert and Multiply)}$$

$$= \frac{n(A)}{n(S) - n(A)}$$

Example 1   *Given:*   odds in favour of A are 10:7

                Find: $P(A)$

Solution $(\text{Odds in favour of } A) = \dfrac{P(A)}{P(A')}$ (Definition)

Then, $\dfrac{10}{7} = \dfrac{P(A)}{1 - P(A)}$

Now we can solve for $P(A)$.

$$10(1 - P(A)) = 7P(A)$$
$$10 - 10P(A) = 7P(A)$$
$$10 = 17P(A)$$
$$\frac{10}{17} = P(A)$$

The probability of A, given the odds 10 to 7, is equal to $\frac{10}{17}$.

In general, we have the following.

If (odds in favour of A) $= \dfrac{h}{k}$, then $P(A) = \dfrac{h}{h+k}$

The proof is left as an exercise. (See Question 5.)

Example 2 **Given:** $P(A) = \frac{10}{13}$

Find: odds in favour of A

Solution (Odds in favour of A) $= \dfrac{P(A)}{P(A')}$ (Definition)

$$= \frac{P(A)}{1 - P(A)}$$

$$= \frac{\frac{10}{13}}{\frac{3}{13}}$$

$$= \frac{10}{13} \times \frac{13}{3}$$

$$= \frac{10}{3} \quad \text{or} \quad 10:3 \quad \text{or} \quad 10 \text{ to } 3$$

The odds in favour of event A are 10 to 3.

The use of odds is widespread in gambling and betting. Not only is it common to be exposed to odds at the race tracks, but odds are used to describe the likelihood of the outcomes of major political or sports events, which often turn into more wagering situations.

The relationship between *odds* and *wagers* is simply the ratio of the amount wagered to the amount that would be won, that is,

(odds in favour of A) $= \dfrac{\text{amount wagered (\$)}}{\text{amount won (\$)}}$

Example 3 The odds in favour of the Argonauts winning the Grey Cup are 10 to 7.
(a) What would be the winnings if a \$2.00 bet is placed and the Argos win?

(b) How much money must one wager in order to win $20.00 if the Argos win?

Solution (a) (odds in favour) = (amount wagered):(amount won)

Let w represent the winnings.
Then, $10 : 7 = 2 : w$

$$\frac{10}{7} = \frac{2}{w}$$

$$10w = 2 \times 7 \qquad \text{(Clear fractions)}$$

$$w = \frac{14}{10}$$

$$= 1.4$$

The winnings on a $2.00 bet would be $1.40.

(b) Let b represent that amount of money that must be bet. Then,

$$10 : 7 = b : 20$$

$$\frac{10}{7} = \frac{b}{20}$$

$$\frac{200}{7} = b$$

$$b = 28.57$$

It would be necessary to bet $28.57 to win $20.00.

It is natural to assume that if there are odds in favour of an event then there must be the obvious complement to this, which would be odds *against* an event. The relationship between the odds in favour to the odds against are quite simply that one is the *reciprocal* of the other.

$$\text{(odds against } A) = \frac{P(A')}{P(A)}$$

$$= \frac{1}{\text{(odds in favour of } A)}$$

Example 4 The odds against a university graduate being employed within one year after graduation are estimated to be 1 to 20.
(a) What are the odds in favour of a university graduate being employed within a year after graduation?
(b) What is an estimate of the probability that a university graduate will be employed within a year of graduation?

Solution (a) Let A be the event that a university graduate is employed within a year of graduation.

$$(\text{odds in favour of } A) = \frac{1}{(\text{odds against } A)}$$

$$= \frac{1}{\frac{1}{20}}$$

$$= \frac{20}{1}$$

or 20 : 1

The odds in favour of a university graduate being employed is 20 to 1.

(b) From part (a), the (odds in favour of A) $= h : k$ where $h = 20$ and $k = 1$. Then the relationship to probabilities is

$$P(A) = \frac{h}{h+k}$$

$$= \frac{20}{20+1}$$

$$\doteq 0.95$$

The probability that a university graduate is employed is about 0.95. ◁

EXERCISE 5.6

B **1.** (a) ***Given:*** $P(A) = \frac{7}{36}$

        Find: odds in favour of A

   (b) ***Given:*** $P(A') = \frac{2}{6}$

        Find: odds in favour of A

   (c) ***Given:*** (odds against A) $= 5:4$

        Find: $P(A)$

   (d) ***Given:*** (odds in favour of A) $= 10:8$

                (odds against B) $= 5:1$

                A and B mutually exclusive

        Find: (i) $P(A \cup B)$

                (ii) odds in favour of either A or B occurring.

   (e) ***Given:*** $P(A) = 0.5$

                $P(B) = 0.3$

                A and B are independent

        Find: odds in favour that both A and B occur.

 2. The odds in favour of the Lancers winning their division championship are 7:3. What would you win on a $10.00 wager if the Lancers win?

3. The winnings received from a $5.00 wager were $7.50. What were the odds in favour of the win?

4. It is estimated that the probability of winning in blackjack is 0.46. If you are given corresponding odds in favour of winning, what must you wager to win $15.00?

5. Show that if (odds in favour of A) $= \dfrac{h}{k}$ then $P(A) = \dfrac{h}{h+k}$.

6. What are the odds in favour of rolling a pair, followed by two even numbers in two successive rolls of a pair of dice?

7. Over time, Natalie has experienced that if she washes her car, it rains the next day 80 percent of the time. What are the odds in favour of rain tomorrow if Natalie is washing her car today?

8. Statistics show that in 75 percent of the fatal accidents involving two cars, at least one of the drivers is impaired. If you have the misfortune to witness such an accident, what are the odds in favour of one of the drivers being impaired?

9. Remo is convinced that he is a lucky card player. He boasts that he can cut a face card (jack, queen, king) 30 percent of the time.
   (a) What odds would you give him, based on the calculated probability of cutting a face card from a normal deck of cards?
   (b) What odds would Remo be willing to give based on his estimate of his luck?
   (c) If Remo puts down 25¢ based on his boastful odds, what do you stand to lose if he wins and does cut a face card?

10. Owen has bet $20.00 with his son, Murray, that in a blind-taste-test, his baked beans will be selected as the best in a baked bean cook-off. Owen has given Murray 5 to 3 odds against his winning. What will Murray pay Owen if he wins?

11. What odds would you be willing to give on the bet that at least two of the past prime ministers of Canada have died on the same day of the year? (Research whether or not you would win the bet!)

12. Mrs. Liu asks her Finite Mathematics class of 32 students to write down a random number from 1 and 100. She is willing to wager spares against extra classes that there will be at least two numbers the same. If Mrs. Liu offers odds of 5:3, should the class accept the bet?

13. A confident and boastful coach claims that on the next league game the odds of her team winning are 3:1; the odds against losing are 5:1; and the odds against tieing are 7:1. Can these odds be right?

14. The "birthday paradox" is a fascinating problem (See Example 3 in Section 5.5). Fill in the following table for the situations suggested and determine how much you would win on a $1.00 wager.

Number of People in the Room	Probability of at Least Two with the Same Birthday	Approximate Odds
10	0.117	117:883
20		
30		
40		
50		
60		

15. A race track betting board has the following odds against winning listed for the six horses in the race:

Horse	Odds
Ace	9:2
Deuce	6:1
Trez	11:3
Quatro	19:2
Cinqo	10:1
Sexto	13:2

(a) Which horse is the favourite to win?

(b) If you bet $20.00 on Quatro to win, and in fact he did, how much would you win?

(c) In betting on horses there is a bet called the "triactor", which is naming the exact order of the first three horses in the race. Based on the betting board, which horses would you bet on for the triactor?

(d) What is the probability that you would win the triactor? Hence, what odds should you get for your $10.00 bet?

5.7 STOCHASTIC PROCESSES

A **stochastic process** is a sequence of experiments that depend on some chance element. The situations presented earlier in this chapter have been simple stochastic processes. For example, rolling a die twice is a stochastic process because each outcome has a chance element to it. In this example, the outcomes (that is, $\{1, 2, 3, 4, 5, 6\}$) are independent and the probabilities are not affected by the previous outcome. In general, this does not have to be the case. Many stochastic processes will be dependent upon outcomes of previous experiments. This immediately suggests that conditional probability will play a large role in this theory.

Writing an exam might be construed as a stochastic process, although one would hope that not too much is left to chance. If you can answer the first question readily, then your confidence is increased. Your chance of success on the second question will be much better than if the first question stumps you and you panic and become unnerved for the remaining questions.

Example 1   Indira estimates that the probability of getting the next question right if the previous one was right on a Finite Mathematics test is $\frac{4}{5}$. But the probability of getting it right if the previous one was wrong is only $\frac{2}{5}$. If the probability of her getting the first question right is $\frac{3}{4}$, what is the probability of getting

  (i) the second question right?

 (ii) the third question right?

Solution   Let A, B, C be the events that Indira gets the first, second, and third questions right, respectively.

Let A', B', C' be the complements, that is, the questions are answered incorrectly.

(i) Construct a tree diagram and mark the probabilities on the branches of the diagram.

Note that probabilities placed on the second set of branches of the tree are conditional probabilities based on the outcome of the previous experiment.

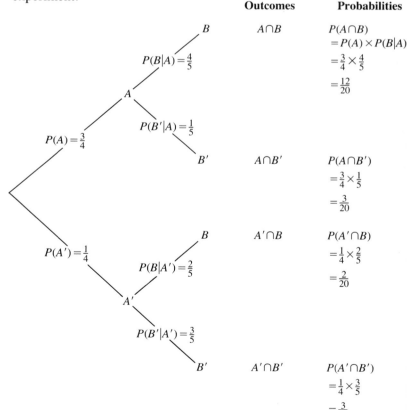

Outcomes	Probabilities

$A \cap B$ $P(A \cap B)$
$= P(A) \times P(B|A)$
$= \frac{3}{4} \times \frac{4}{5}$
$= \frac{12}{20}$

$A \cap B'$ $P(A \cap B')$
$= \frac{3}{4} \times \frac{1}{5}$
$= \frac{3}{20}$

$A' \cap B$ $P(A' \cap B)$
$= \frac{1}{4} \times \frac{2}{5}$
$= \frac{2}{20}$

$A' \cap B'$ $P(A' \cap B')$
$= \frac{1}{4} \times \frac{3}{5}$
$= \frac{3}{20}$

The outcomes from the tree diagram that have the second question right are $A \cap B$ and $A' \cap B$.

Then
$$P(B) = P(A \cap B) + P(A' \cap B)$$
$$= \frac{12}{20} + \frac{2}{20}$$
$$= \frac{14}{20}$$
$$= 0.7$$

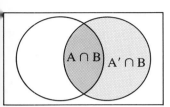

The probability of Indira getting the second question right is 0.7.

(ii) Extend the tree diagram to a third question.

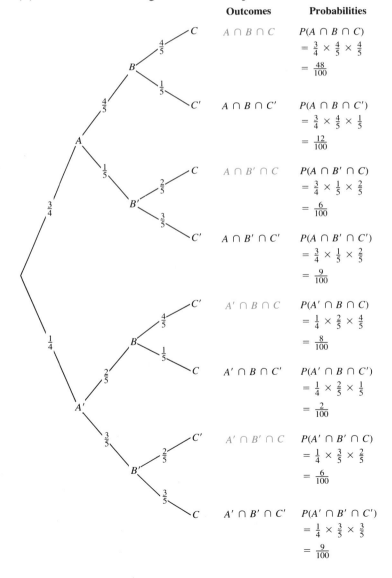

	Outcomes	Probabilities
C	$A \cap B \cap C$	$P(A \cap B \cap C)$ $= \frac{3}{4} \times \frac{4}{5} \times \frac{4}{5}$ $= \frac{48}{100}$
C'	$A \cap B \cap C'$	$P(A \cap B \cap C')$ $= \frac{3}{4} \times \frac{4}{5} \times \frac{1}{5}$ $= \frac{12}{100}$
C	$A \cap B' \cap C$	$P(A \cap B' \cap C)$ $= \frac{3}{4} \times \frac{1}{5} \times \frac{2}{5}$ $= \frac{6}{100}$
C'	$A \cap B' \cap C'$	$P(A \cap B' \cap C')$ $= \frac{3}{4} \times \frac{1}{5} \times \frac{2}{5}$ $= \frac{9}{100}$
C'	$A' \cap B \cap C$	$P(A' \cap B \cap C)$ $= \frac{1}{4} \times \frac{2}{5} \times \frac{4}{5}$ $= \frac{8}{100}$
C	$A' \cap B \cap C'$	$P(A' \cap B \cap C')$ $= \frac{1}{4} \times \frac{2}{5} \times \frac{1}{5}$ $= \frac{2}{100}$
C'	$A' \cap B' \cap C$	$P(A' \cap B' \cap C)$ $= \frac{1}{4} \times \frac{3}{5} \times \frac{2}{5}$ $= \frac{6}{100}$
C	$A' \cap B' \cap C'$	$P(A' \cap B' \cap C')$ $= \frac{1}{4} \times \frac{3}{5} \times \frac{3}{5}$ $= \frac{9}{100}$

The outcomes from the tree diagram that have the third question right are $A \cap B \cap C$, $A \cap B' \cap C$, $A' \cap B \cap C$, and $A' \cap B' \cap C$.

So $P(C) = P(A \cap B \cap C) + P(A \cap B' \cap C) + P(A' \cap B \cap C) + P(A' \cap B' \cap C)$

$$= \frac{48}{100} + \frac{6}{100} + \frac{8}{100} + \frac{6}{100}$$

$$= \frac{68}{100}$$

$$= 0.68$$

The probability of Indira getting the third question right is equal to 0.68.

When the number of events or the number of trials become numerous, a tree diagram may become unwieldy and a different organization of the analysis is required. This organization will be developed in Chapter 8 when we study Markov Chains.

Example 2 An interesting example of stochastic processes arises in the dice game craps. The rules of the game are:

(1) On the first roll of two dice, you win if the roll is 7 or 11; you lose if the roll is a 2, 3, or 12; and any other roll is called your *point*.

(2) If on the first roll you rolled a point, then you must continue to roll the dice as many times as necessary until you roll either a 7, in which case you lose, or your point, in which case you win.

What is the probability of winning at craps?

Solution Let us construct the table for the outcomes of the roll of two dice for easy reference and calculation of the outcome probabilities..

Sum of the dice:

		One Die					
		1	2	3	4	5	6
	1	2	3	4	5	6	7
	2	3	4	5	6	7	8
Other	3	4	5	6	7	8	9
Die	4	5	6	7	8	9	10
	5	6	7	8	9	10	11
	6	7	8	9	10	11	12

To illustrate the use of the table in this problem we can see that the number of outcomes that will lead to a 7 or an 11 is 8 (the numbers 7 and 11 were counted in the table). The total number of outcomes is 36, so

P(win on the first roll) is $\frac{8}{36}$.

All of the probability values that follow were determined in this way.

Now we construct the tree diagram for the game of craps and mark on the winning branches the probabilities for each outcome as determined with the aid of the table.

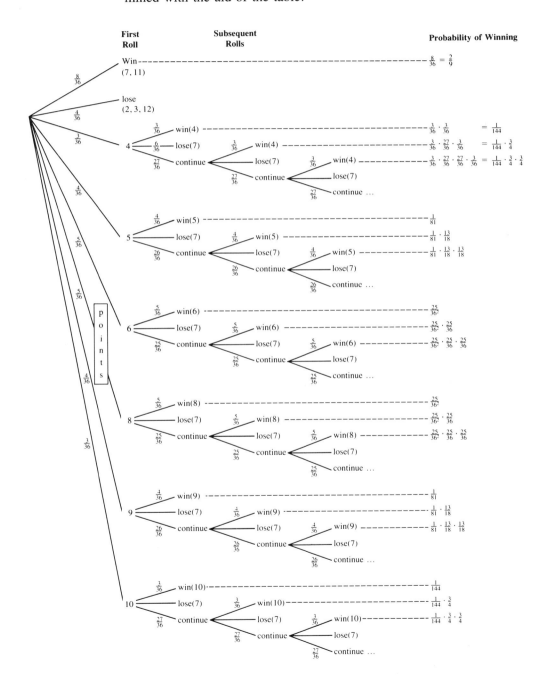

Analyzing each winning branch, we have:

$$P(\text{win}|\text{point}=4) = \tfrac{1}{144} + \tfrac{1}{144} \cdot \tfrac{3}{4} + \tfrac{1}{144} \cdot \tfrac{3}{4} \cdot \tfrac{3}{4} + \ldots$$

Notice that this is an *infinite geometric series* (Section 4.3) with common ratio $\tfrac{3}{4}$ and first term $\tfrac{1}{144}$.

Using our result from Chapter 4 for the sum of an infinite geometric series,

$$S_\infty = \frac{a}{1-r}$$

then,

$$P(\text{win}|\text{point}=4) = \frac{\dfrac{1}{144}}{1-\dfrac{3}{4}} \qquad\qquad P(\text{win}|\text{point}=5) = \frac{\dfrac{1}{81}}{1-\dfrac{13}{18}}$$

$$= \frac{1}{144} \cdot \frac{4}{1} \qquad\qquad\qquad\qquad = \frac{2}{45}$$

$$= \frac{1}{36}$$

$$P(\text{win}|\text{point}=6) = \frac{\dfrac{25}{36^2}}{1-\dfrac{25}{36}} \qquad\qquad P(\text{win}|\text{point}=8) = \frac{\dfrac{25}{36^2}}{1-\dfrac{25}{36}}$$

$$= \frac{25}{396} \qquad\qquad\qquad\qquad\qquad = \frac{25}{396}$$

$$P(\text{win}|\text{point}=9) = \frac{\dfrac{1}{81}}{1-\dfrac{13}{18}} \qquad\qquad P(\text{win}|\text{point}=10) = \frac{\dfrac{1}{144}}{1-\dfrac{3}{4}}$$

$$= \frac{2}{45} \qquad\qquad\qquad\qquad\qquad = \frac{1}{36}$$

$$
\begin{aligned}
P(\text{win}) ={}& P(\text{win on first roll}) + P(\text{win}|\text{point}=4) \\
&+ P(\text{win}|\text{point}=5) + P(\text{win}|\text{point}=6) \\
&+ P(\text{win}|\text{point}=8) + P(\text{win}|\text{point}=9) \\
&+ P(\text{win}|\text{point}=10) \\
={}& \frac{2}{9} + \frac{1}{36} + \frac{2}{45} + \frac{25}{396} + \frac{25}{396} + \frac{2}{45} + \frac{1}{36} \\
\doteq{}& 0.493
\end{aligned}
$$

The probability of winning at craps is equal to 0.493 (a remarkably "fair" game!).

The crap game example is of considerable interest because it illustrates a tree diagram that is *not symmetrical*, that is, some branches stop long before others. It also illustrates a situation that requires knowledge of *infinite geometric series*. Even though it is conceivable that this crap game never ends, it is still possible to determine its winning probability!

EXERCISE 5.7

B 1. Andrea and Ling are evenly matched tennis players. However, each time Ling loses a game his probability of winning the next game is decreased by $\frac{1}{5}$. But when he wins, his probability of winning the next game increases by $\frac{1}{10}$.
   (a) Make a tree diagram for a three-game sequence and label the diagram with the probabilities associated with each branch of the diagram.
   (b) Find the probability that Ling wins at least two games.
   (c) Find the probability that Andrea wins exactly two games.

2. Jere is a local old-timer who has created a reliable weather predicting scheme to compete with the modern computer analysis of meteorological patterns used to predict the weather. Jere predicts that whatever the weather is like today, there is a 75 percent chance that the conditions will be the same tomorrow, and a 25 percent chance that the conditions will reverse. If the weather is fair today,
   (a) What chances would Jere give that the weather is foul two days hence?
   (b) What chances would Jere give that the weather is fair for the weekend, which is three days away?

3. A simple betting game has the following rules. A coin is tossed. If the coin is heads then a die is rolled. If the coin is tails then the coin is tossed a second time. Construct a tree diagram to represent the game. What are the odds in getting
   (a) a one on the die?
   (b) two tails?
   (c) an even number on the roll of the die?

4. An unusual genetic trait occurs in 0.1 percent of the population. The reliability of a test to discover the trait is: if the person has the trait then the test is positive 95 percent of the time, but the test is also positive 2 percent of the time for those that do not have the trait. Construct a tree diagram to represent the population and the testing reliability for the genetic trait. If a person is selected at random, what are the following probabilities?

(a) The person will test positive

(b) The person will have the trait and test positive

(c) The person has the trait, given that he tested positive

5. A simple maze is used in scientific research on learning patterns in rats. Food is placed at the end of the maze as a reward for the rodent if it successfully passes through the maze. The maze is diagrammed below. The passages are very narrow so that the rat cannot backtrack if it makes the wrong turn. As the rat gets closer to the food, its aroma increases, so we estimate that if the rat makes the first turn correctly then the probability that the rat will make the next correct turn increases by 0.1 to a maximum of 0.9 (at which time the maze is considered to be "learned").

(a) A rat new to the maze is introduced to it. Find the probability that it successfully completes it, if the probability of making the first turn correctly is 0.5.

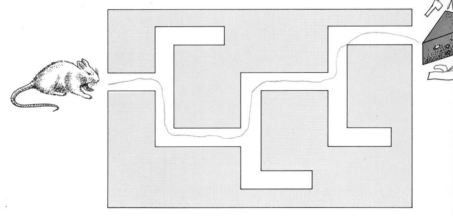

On subsequent trials with the same rat, we estimate that if it successfully completed the maze on the preceding trial, the probability of it making the first correct turn is increased by 0.2 to a maximum of 0.9.

(b) Find the probability that the rat completes the maze on its second attempt.

(c) Find the probability that the rat completes the maze correctly at least once in three trials.

6. If Rhys is late for his Finite Mathematics class, he makes a greater effort to arrive on time for the next class and the probability that he is on time is $\frac{3}{4}$. However if he is on time, he is liable to be less concerned about punctuality for the next class and his probability of being on time drops to $\frac{1}{2}$. Rhys is on time on Monday. Find the probability that

(a) Rhys is on time on Wednesday.

(b) Rhys is late on Thursday.

7. A squash match is won when one player wins three games. This situation is often referred to as winning the "best-three-out-of-five".

(a) Draw a tree diagram for a squash match between Barbara and Maria in which Barbara has the slight edge in winning each game with the odds in her favour at 5 to 4.

(b) What is the probability that Maria will win in three straight games?

(c) What is the probability of Barbara's winning the match?

5.8 REVIEW EXERCISE

A **1.** With the aid of an example, explain the difference between an outcome and an event as the terms are used in probability theory.

B **2.** (a) *Given:* Experiment: rolling a die (assume the outcomes are equally likely)
Event: a multiple of 3 turns up

Find: the probability of rolling a multiple of 3 with a die.

(b) *Given:* Experiment: cutting a shuffled deck of cards
Event: an ace or a face is cut

Find: the probability of cutting an ace or a face from a shuffled deck of cards

3. (a) *Given:* A is the event of rolling "box cars" (double sixes) with a pair of dice.
B is the event of rolling two odd numbers with a pair of dice.
C is the event of rolling "snake eyes" (double ones) with a pair of dice.

Find: (i) $P(A \cup B)$ (ii) $P(A \cup C)$
(iii) $P(B \cup C)$

(b) *Given:* $P(A \cap B) = 0.2$
$P(A \cap C) = 0.1$
$P(B|A) = 0.25$
$P(B) = 0.3$

Find: (i) $P(A|B)$ (ii) $P(A)$
(iii) $P(C|A)$ (iv) the odds in favour of B
(v) the odds against A

4. A bookshelf contains an equal number of books in the areas of fiction, biographies, philosophy, mathematics, and history. If a book is chosen at random from the shelf, what is the probability that it is

(a) a mathematics book?

(b) neither a novel nor a biography?

5. The track at a local school has four lanes. If the lanes are assigned randomly to four runners, what is the probability that
(a) the inside lane is assigned to Lulu?
(b) Renato is beside Lulu?

6. Two newlyweds are planning their family and have decided to have three children and one pet (either a dog or a cat).
(a) Draw a tree diagram that would illustrate the sex of the children and the choice of pet.
(b) If a family of this composition was selected at random, what is the probability that there are more girls in the family than boys?

7. A committee is to be struck to look into the problem of overloading students with too much homework. If the committee is to be five people chosen randomly from a group of four teachers and four students, what is the probability that
(a) there is only one teacher on the committee?
(b) the students outnumber the teachers on the committee?

8. If a monkey typed four strokes on a keyboard and each stroke was a different letter of the alphabet, what is the probability that the monkey typed the word "math"?

9. Two dice are rolled. What is the probability that the roll displays
(a) doubles or an even sum of the two dice?
(b) doubles or an odd sum?
(c) doubles or a three on one of the dice?

10. A market survey estimated that the probability of a household subscribing to *Maclean's* is 0.4 and to *National Geographic* 0.6; and the probability that a household subscribes to neither is 0.2. What is the probability that a household chosen at random subscribes to
(a) either magazine?
(b) both magazines?

11. The 13 spades in a deck of cards are removed and shuffled. If you draw one of the cards, what is the probability that
(a) it is an ace?
(b) it is an ace, given that it is not a face card?

12. Four political parties are preparing for an election. The polls indicate that their support from the electorate is 10 percent, 30 percent, 35 percent, and 25 percent. If the party with the 10 percent share of the voter support drops out of the election race, what are the probabilities of winning for the remaining three parties?

13. If six people choose a letter from the alphabet, what is the probability that at least two choose the same letter?

14. A game consists of tossing a coin, cutting a deck of cards, and rolling a die.
(a) What is the probability that on your turn you get a head, an ace, and an even number on the die?

(b) You get bonus points if on your turn you repeat exactly the outcomes of your previous turn. What is the probability of getting bonus points?

15. The odds against the Huskies winning the hockey tournament are 7 to 1. If you make a $10.00 wager that they will win, what will you win if they do?

16. What odds would you give someone to cut a face card in a game of cribbage if three face cards and nine numbered cards are already in the two players' hands?

17. If the odds in favour of Boris beating Vladimir in a chess game are 5 to 4, what is the probability that Vladimir will win an upset victory in a best-of-five chess tournament?

18. The following table represents the probabilistic effects of a previous game on the next game.

Previous Game	Probabilities for Next Game		
	Win	Draw	Lose
Won	0.6	0.2	0.2
Drawn	0.5	0.3	0.2
Lost	0.4	0.1	0.5

If at some point during the season a game is won, what is the probability of winning the third game hence?

PROBLEMS PLUS

Playoffs
Two evenly matched teams, the Eagles and the Hawks, are playing a final series to determine the season's champion. Because of the season record the Eagles only have to win two games and the Hawks must win three. What are the odds favouring the Eagles to win the championship?

PROBLEMS PLUS

Bull's-eye
The finalists in a shooting contest prepare for the last event. The event is that all of them fire simultaneously at a target on the signal of the referee. The chances of hitting the bull's-eye for each of the three finalists are $\frac{1}{7}$, $\frac{1}{6}$, and $\frac{2}{13}$. Determine the probability that one, and only one, bullet will hit the bull's-eye.

5.9 CHAPTER 5 TEST

1. (a) *Given:* Experiment: rolling two dice
   Event: doubles are rolled

   Find: (i) the probability that doubles are rolled with a pair of dice
   (ii) the odds in favour of rolling doubles with a pair of dice

   (b) *Given:* Experiment: rolling three dice
   Event: triples are rolled

   Find: the probability of rolling triples with the roll of three dice.

2. (a) Draw a tree diagram that would represent the combination of heads and tails that could result when a coin is tossed three times.

   (b) Draw a tree diagram that would represent the combination of nickels and dimes it could take to total twenty-five cents.

3. A young couple is planning to have five children. What is the probability that at least two of the children will have a birthday in the same month?

4. Four cherry pies and two apple pies are to be divided between two families, the Whittys and the Rasmussens. If the pies are distributed randomly and each family gets the same number of pies, what is the probability that the Rasmussens will get three cherry pies?

5. A card is cut from a shuffled deck and removed; then a second card is cut from the deck. What is the probability of cutting two face cards, given that the first card is a face card?

6. The probability that an incumbent politician will be re-elected into office declines by 0.25 after each term of office. If he is voted out for a term, the probability of his being elected again in the next election is 0.3. If an incumbent politician presently has a 60 percent chance of being elected in the next election, what is the probability that this politician will serve at least two of the next three terms of office?

PROBLEMS PLUS

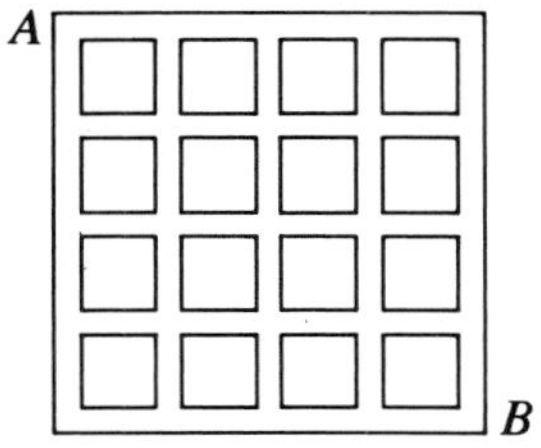

Chance meeting
A network of city streets forms square blocks as shown in the diagram. Two individuals cross the network, Alexandra from A to B and Boris from B to A. No preference is given to a particular route by either Alexandra or Boris except that they are always advancing toward their destinations. What is the probability that they meet if they both leave at the same time and they both walk at the same rate?

CHAPTER 6

PROBABILITY MODELS

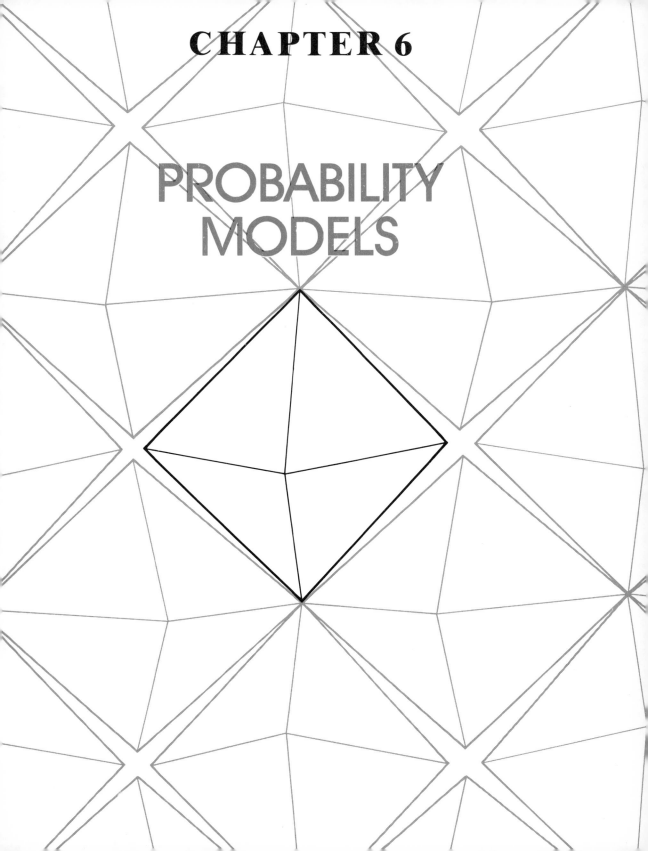

REVIEW AND PREVIEW TO
CHAPTER 6

Sigma Notation

Sigma notation may be used to sum a series of subscripted variables. For example,

$$x_1 + x_2 + x_3 + x_4 + x_5 + x_6 + x_7 + x_8 = \sum_{i=1}^{8} x_i$$

EXERCISE 1

1. Write the following in sigma notation.
   (a) $a_1 + a_2 + a_3 + a_4 + a_5 + a_6$
   (b) $\dfrac{x_1 + x_2 + x_3 + x_4 + x_5 + x_6 + x_7 + x_8 + x_9}{9}$
   (c) $x_1 f_1 + x_2 f_2 + x_3 f_3 + x_4 f_4 + x_5 f_5$
   (d) $\sqrt{\dfrac{(x_1 - k)^2 + (x_2 - k)^2 + (x_3 - k)^2 + (x_4 - k)^2 + \ldots + (x_n - k)^2}{n}}$

2. Expand the following series.
   (a) $\displaystyle\sum_{i=1}^{4} x_i$
   (b) $\displaystyle\sum_{i=1}^{n} x_i f_i$
   (c) $\dfrac{1}{n} \displaystyle\sum_{i=1}^{n} x_i$
   (d) $\displaystyle\sum_{i=1}^{n} (x_i - k)^2 f_i$
   (e) $\displaystyle\sum_{x=0}^{n} \binom{n}{x} p^x q^{n-x}$

Binomial Theorem

The binomial theorem describes the expansion of binomials to a given power. It is stated as

$$(a+b)^n = \binom{n}{0}a^n + \binom{n}{1}a^{n-1}b + \binom{n}{2}a^{n-2}b^2 + \ldots + \binom{n}{n}b^n$$

EXERCISE 2

1. Use the binomial theorem to expand.
   (a) $(x + 2)^4$
   (b) $\left(\frac{1}{3} + \frac{2}{3}\right)^3$
   (c) $(0.9 + 0.1)^4$
   (d) $\left(\frac{2}{5} + \frac{3}{5}\right)^5$
   (e) $(p + q)^n$
   Note that the expansions of questions (b), (c), and (d) all add up to one.

INTRODUCTION

The major emphasis in all applied mathematics is the attempt to create mathematical models by which observed data may be further analyzed. The mathematics courses throughout secondary schools incorporate this applied nature of mathematics on a regular basis. Every time students face a "word problem," they are attempting to translate a described situation into a mathematical model. Through this model they can provide a solution to the problem as well as determine further required information.

In this chapter we see four mathematical models, in fact, probability models, that accurately describe the probabilities that arise out of experiments with certain characteristics.

6.1 PROBABILITY DISTRIBUTIONS

To define a probability distribution, the probability of each outcome must be determined. The distribution of these probabilities may then be presented in either a tabular form or a graphic form.

Example 1 Determine the probability distribution for the sum of the roll of two dice.

Solution The outcomes are conveniently organized in the table below.

		One Die					
		1	2	3	4	5	6
	1	1, 1	1, 2	1, 3	1, 4	1, 5	1, 6
	2	2, 1	2, 2	2, 3	2, 4	2, 5	2, 6
Other	3	3, 1	3, 2	3, 3	3, 4	3, 5	3, 6
Die	4	4, 1	4, 2	4, 3	4, 4	4, 5	4, 6
	5	5, 1	5, 2	5, 3	5, 4	5, 5	5, 6
	6	6, 1	6, 2	6, 3	6, 4	6, 5	6, 6

We are interested in only the sum of the two dice so we modify the table to contain the sums of the rolls. For example, the entry corresponding to the roll 5, 4 would now become 9. The table follows.

		One Die					
		1	2	3	4	5	6
	1	2	3	4	5	6	7
	2	3	4	5	6	7	8
Other	3	4	5	6	7	8	9
Die	4	5	6	7	8	9	10
	5	6	7	8	9	10	11
	6	7	8	9	10	11	12

The probabilities are readily obtained from the table (as seen in Section 5.5, Example 1).

We tabulate the probability distribution as follows:

Sum	Probability
2	$\frac{1}{36}$
3	$\frac{2}{36}$
4	$\frac{3}{36}$
5	$\frac{4}{36}$
6	$\frac{5}{36}$
7	$\frac{6}{36}$
8	$\frac{5}{36}$
9	$\frac{4}{36}$
10	$\frac{3}{36}$
11	$\frac{2}{36}$
12	$\frac{1}{36}$

We graph the probability distribution as follows.

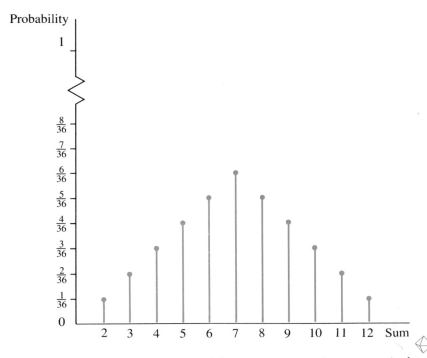

To construct a probability model it is necessary *to assign a numerical value to each outcome*. This *assignment* of a numerical value to a real-life occurrence is called the **random variable** and is usually denoted by X.

In Example 1 the random variable X was the sum of the two dice. The definition of a random variable will depend on the experiment and on the information that you want to determine.

Example 2   Define appropriate random variables for the following experiments and indicate the values that the random variables may take.
(a) A machine produces bolts, and the manufacturer is interested in the following:
   (i)   the number of bolts produced whose shafts are longer than 60 cm;
   (ii) the variability of the width of the thread of the bolt.
(b) A task force committee is to be selected and it is important that there is fair representation of males on the committee.
(c) Three dice are rolled and the sum of the three dice is used to move a piece in a game.

Solution   (a) (i) Let the random variable X be the number of bolts that have shafts longer than 60 cm.
There can be the situations that none of the shafts are longer than 60 cm, one is longer, two are longer, and so on, so X may take the values 0, 1, 2, 3, ...
(ii) Let the random variable X be the width of the thread of the bolt. Then X may take any real value within an appropriate domain. For example, if the widths are usually between 1 mm and 2 mm then X may take the values 1.00, 1.01, 1.02, ... , 1.98, 1.99, 2.00 if two-decimal accuracy is sufficient.
(b) Let the random variable X be the number of men on the committee. On the committee there can be no men, one man, two men, and so on, so X may take the values 0, 1, 2, 3, ...
(c) Let the random variable X be the sum of the three dice. The minimum sum that can be rolled is 3 (three ones) and the maximum roll is 18 (three sixes), so X may take the values 3, 4, 5, ... , 18.

All random variables that we see in this chapter deal with outcomes that can be assigned integral values (that is, 0, 1, 2, ...). Random variables of this nature are called **discrete** random variables. Associated with each value of the random variable will be a probability of the value occurring. This is denoted by $P(X=x)$, which is often abbreviated to just $p(x)$. This function, $p(x)$, of the random variable X is called the **probability distribution**.

Example 3   Determine the probability distribution for the tossing of a coin.

Solution   Let the random variable X take the value 0 if a head is tossed and 1 if a tail is tossed.

Assuming the outcomes are equally likely we have

$$P(X=0) = p(0) = \tfrac{1}{2}$$
$$P(X=1) = p(1) = \tfrac{1}{2}$$

The table and the graph of the distribution follow.

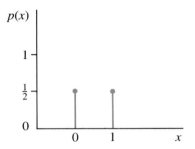

Toss (x)	Probability $p(x)$
0	$\tfrac{1}{2}$
1	$\tfrac{1}{2}$

Once a probability distribution has been explicitly defined, then this mathematical model of the experiment can be used to further analyze the experiment. One very useful piece of information that may be obtained is the expected value.

The **expected value** is that quantity that you can expect to obtain when the experiment is performed. To calculate the expected value we use the definition

$$E(X) = \sum_{x} xp(x)$$

The abbreviated sigma notation $\displaystyle\sum_{x}$ means the summation over all of the possible values that the random variable X may take. It is necessary to use this abbreviation because the random variable may be defined such that it does not take consecutive integer values.

This definition of the expected value makes intuitive sense because the value of each outcome is multiplied by the probability of its occurrence and then these values are added to obtain the expected value of the experiment. The quantity $E(X)$ is also referred to as the **expectation**.

Example 4   A game is defined by the rules that two dice are rolled and the player wins varying amounts depending on the sum of the two dice according to the following table.

Sum	Winnings
2	$10
3	9
4	8
5	7
6	6
7	5
8	6
9	7
10	8
11	9
12	10

The cost to play the game is $7.50.

(a) What can a player expect to win by playing this game?

(b) What would be a fair value to pay to play this game?

Solution   (a) Let the random variable X be the winnings associated with each roll.

From the table above you can see that the winnings range from $5.00 to $10.00, inclusive, so X may take the values 5, 6, 7, 8, 9, or 10. You can obtain the probabilities with the aid of the tabulated rolls of two dice in Example 1.

	1	2	3	4	5	6
1	2	3	4	5	6	7
2	3	4	5	6	7	8
3	4	5	6	7	8	9
4	5	6	7	8	9	10
5	6	7	8	9	10	11
6	7	8	9	10	11	12

Winnings (x)	Sum	Probabilities $p(x)$	$xp(x)$
5	7	$\frac{6}{36}$	$\frac{30}{36}$
6	6, 8	$\frac{10}{36}$	$\frac{60}{36}$
7	5, 9	$\frac{8}{36}$	$\frac{56}{36}$
8	4, 10	$\frac{6}{36}$	$\frac{48}{36}$
9	3, 11	$\frac{4}{36}$	$\frac{36}{36}$
10	2, 12	$\frac{2}{36}$	$\frac{20}{36}$

$$\sum_x p(x) = \frac{36}{36} \qquad \sum_x xp(x) = \frac{250}{36}$$
$$= 1 \qquad\qquad = 6.94$$

Therefore, the expected value of the defined game is

$$E(X) = \sum_x xp(x)$$

$$= \$6.94$$

(b) If you pay $7.50 per game, then you would expect to lose $7.50 − $6.94 = $0.56 per game in the long run. This would be a fair game only if the cost to play was $6.94.

The expected value need not always refer to money. The value of an outcome may be defined according to the situation.

Example 5   A committee of four people is to be chosen randomly from four males and six females. What is the expected number of females on the committee?

Solution   To find the expectation we must first determine the probability distribution. Let the random variable X be the number of females on the committee. There can be exactly 0, 1, 2, 3, 4 females on the committee, so X may take the values 0, 1, 2, 3, 4.

TAKE CASES

The total number of committees is $\binom{10}{4} = 210$.

The number of committees with no females is 1 (all 4 males are chosen). So, $p(0) = \frac{1}{210}$.

The number of committees with 1 female:

The number of ways of selecting 3 males is $\binom{4}{3} = 4$.

The number of ways of choosing the 1 female is $\binom{6}{1} = 6$.

The total number of ways of selecting a committee with only 1 female is $\binom{4}{3}\binom{6}{1} = 4 \times 6 = 24$(Fundamental Counting Principle)

So, $p(1) = \frac{24}{210}$

Similarly, the number of committees with 2 females is

$$\binom{4}{2}\binom{6}{2} = 6 \times 15 = 90$$

So, $p(2) = \frac{90}{210}$

The number of committees with 3 females is

$$\binom{4}{1}\binom{6}{3} = 4 \times 20 = 80$$

So, $p(3) = \frac{80}{210}$

The number of committees with 4 females is

$$\binom{4}{0}\binom{6}{4} = 1 \times 15 = 15$$

So, $p(4) = \frac{15}{210}$

The tabulated probability distribution is

Number of Females (x)	Probability $p(x)$	$xp(x)$
0	$\frac{1}{210}$	0
1	$\frac{24}{210}$	$\frac{24}{210}$
2	$\frac{90}{210}$	$\frac{180}{210}$
3	$\frac{80}{210}$	$\frac{240}{210}$
4	$\frac{15}{210}$	$\frac{60}{210}$

$$\sum_x p(x) = \frac{210}{210} \qquad \sum_x xp(x) = \frac{504}{210}$$
$$= 1 \qquad\qquad = 2.4$$

[handwritten margin notes: $\sum p(x)$ sum of prob. $Ex = \sum xp(x)$ - expected value.]

Then the expected value, $E(X) = \sum_x xp(x)$

$$= 2.4$$

Therefore, we would expect to find on average, about 2.4 females on a committee of four people chosen randomly from four males and six females.

All probability distributions must obey the following condition:

$$\boxed{\sum_x p(x) = 1}$$

This says that the sum of the probabilities of all of the outcomes must equal one.

EXERCISE 6.1

A 1. Define appropriate random variables for the following experiments and indicate the values that the random variables may take.
   (a) A group of people is asked to estimate the size of a crowd.
   (b) An athlete is practising her aim at darts.
   (c) A keyboard operator is checking for typographical errors in a wordprocessor document file.
   (d) An advertising agency is conducting a survey to assess the success of a promotional campaign.

B 2. ✓ (a) Represent the following probability distributions in both tabular form and graphical form.

   (i) $p(x) = \frac{1}{6}$ where $x \in \{1, 2, 3, 4, 5, 6\}$

   (ii) $p(x) = \frac{1}{n}$ where $x \in \{1, 2, 3, \dots, n\}$

(b) Verify that each of the distributions defined above satisfies the condition that

$$\sum_x p(x) = 1$$

3. (a) Use a tree diagram to help you construct the table form of the probability distribution for the number of heads turning up in the tossing of a coin two times.

(b) Find the expected value of the number of heads.

4. Given the following tabulated probability distributions, determine the expected values.

(a)

x	$p(x)$
2	0.25
5	0.40
7	0.35

(b)

x	$p(x)$
60	$\frac{2}{7}$
70	$\frac{4}{7}$
80	$\frac{1}{7}$

5. Marion reaches into her purse and randomly draws two coins from those that have accidentally accumulated at the bottom of her purse. The coins were five pennies, two nickels, three dimes, and one quarter.

(a) Draw a tree diagram to illustrate the possible outcomes of her draws.

(b) Determine the probability for each outcome.

(c) Determine the coin value for each outcome.

(d) What is the expected amount that Marion withdraws?

6. Orazio and his tennis partner, Marieka, win a mixed doubles tennis tournament. Their win allows them the first selection from the prize table. However, the prizes are indistinguishable from each other because all of the prizes are identically wrapped. There are three prizes worth $50.00, two worth $25.00, and five worth $10.00. What is the expected value of the prize that Orazio and Marieka receive?

7. A game is played by rolling two dice. If the sum of the dice is either 2 or 12 then you win $2.00. If the sum is 7, you win $1.00. The cost to play the game is 50 cents.

(a) Is this a fair game?

(b) If you played the game 100 times, how much would you expect to win/lose?

8. A game consists of tossing two coins. If the result is two heads, you win $1.00; if the result is a head and a tail, then you win 50 cents; and if the result is two tails, you lose $2.00.

(a) What is the expected value of this game?

(b) For the game to be fair, what should you lose on the toss of two tails if you win $3.00 for two heads and $2.00 for a head and a tail?

9. A game consists of cutting a shuffled deck of cards. If you cut a face card (jack, queen, king of any suit) you win 10 cents. If you cut an ace you win 25 cents. If you cut anything else you lose a nickel. What is the expectation for this game?

10. An international committee to discuss trade between Canada and the United States is to be created. The committee is to contain four people chosen randomly from a select group of three Canadians and four Americans. What is the expected number of Canadians on the committee?

11. Jean-Marc is enthusiastic about fly fishing. In a rush to get to the stream at the break of dawn, he reaches into his rucksack and randomly selects five flies. If the sack contains four wet flies and nine dry flies what is the expected number of wet flies that he takes with him?

12. The Finite Insurance Company has analyzed its claims per policy in the following table.

Claim Amount ($)	Probability
No Claims	0.7
1 000	0.2
5 000	0.05
10 000	0.04
25 000	0.01

(a) Determine the expected amount of money to be paid out per policy.
(b) What premiums should the Finite Insurance Company officials charge each policy holder if they add a 33 percent margin to the expectation?

13. A tetrahedral die (four faces) is weighted so that the probability of it landing on one of its faces is directly proportional to the number on that face.
(a) Determine the probability distribution for the die.
(b) Find the expectation for each roll of the die.

14. Banking transactions are estimated to take the following amounts of time.

Transaction	Frequency (%)	Time (Minutes)
Opening an account	5	10
Making a withdrawal	30	3
Cashing a cheque	25	2
Making a deposit	38	4
Miscellaneous	2	1

What is the expected waiting time if you are next in line in a queue?

C 15. Given a probability distribution $P(X=x)$ with expectation E, show that if k is added to each of the possible payoffs, then the expectation becomes $E + k$.

6.2 UNIFORM DISTRIBUTIONS

The simplest probability distribution is the one in which each outcome is equally likely. An example of this situation is the rolling of a single die. Each outcome has probability $\frac{1}{6}$, so the algebraic form of the probability distribution is

$$P(X=x) = \tfrac{1}{6}, \text{ where } x \in \{1, 2, \ldots , 6\}$$

Graphically, the distribution looks like this.

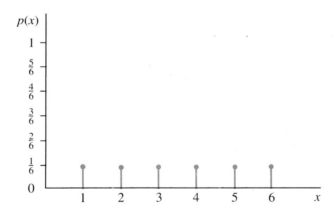

Distributions that have the characteristic that each outcome is equally likely are called uniform distributions.

In general, **uniform distributions** are defined as follows.

The Uniform Distribution

$$P(X=x) = \frac{1}{n} \text{ where } n \text{ is the number of outcomes in the experiment}$$

Example 1   A woman has 16 units of framing to enclose a rectangle. The width of the rectangle is chosen randomly and only integer widths are to be chosen.

(a) What is the expected width of the rectangle?
(b) What is the expected area of the rectangle?

Solution   (a) The widths are all equally likely.
The possible choices for the widths are $\{1, 2, \ldots , 7\}$.

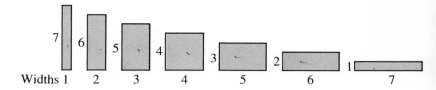

Widths 1   2   3   4   5   6   7

Let the random variable X be the widths of the rectangles.
The probability distribution is uniform and is given by $p(x) = \frac{1}{7}$.

Widths	Probability $p(x)$	$xp(x)$
1	$\frac{1}{7}$	$\frac{1}{7}$
2	$\frac{1}{7}$	$\frac{2}{7}$
3	$\frac{1}{7}$	$\frac{3}{7}$
4	$\frac{1}{7}$	$\frac{4}{7}$
5	$\frac{1}{7}$	$\frac{5}{7}$
6	$\frac{1}{7}$	$\frac{6}{7}$
7	$\frac{1}{7}$	$\frac{7}{7}$

$$\sum_x p(x) = 1 \qquad \sum_x xp(x) = \frac{28}{7}$$
$$= 4$$

Therefore, the expected width of the rectangle is 4 units.

(b) Let the random variable X be the areas of the rectangles. The possible areas for the rectangles are $7 \times 1 = 7$, $6 \times 2 = 12$, $5 \times 3 = 15$, $4 \times 4 = 16$, $3 \times 5 = 15$, $2 \times 6 = 12$, $1 \times 7 = 7$, so the random variable can take the values 7, 12, 15, or 16.

Areas (x)	Width of Rectangles	Probability $p(x)$	$xp(x)$
7	1 or 7	$\frac{2}{7}$	$\frac{14}{7}$
12	2 or 6	$\frac{2}{7}$	$\frac{24}{7}$
15	3 or 5	$\frac{2}{7}$	$\frac{30}{7}$
16	4	$\frac{1}{7}$	$\frac{16}{7}$

$$\sum_x p(x) = 1 \qquad \sum_x xp(x) = \frac{84}{7}$$
$$= 12$$

Therefore the expected area of the rectangles is 12 square units.
Note: The probability distribution of the areas of the rectangles is *not* uniform because the possible areas are not equally likely!

EXERCISE 6.2

A **1.** (a) Which of the following experiments would you conclude to have uniform probability distributions?
  (i) cutting a card from a shuffled deck of cards
  (ii) a computer-generated random number from 1 to 100
  (iii) the colour of automobiles on a major throughway
  (iv) drawing a name from a hat
  (v) winning a lottery
  (b) For each of the situations in part (a) that you concluded were uniform distributions, find or state how you would find the defining statement for the distribution.

B **2.** (a) Determine the probability distribution for a number chosen randomly between the integer values 10 and 15, inclusive.
  (b) Determine the probability distribution for a number chosen randomly between the integer values i and j, where $i < j$.

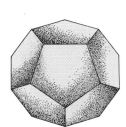

3. A game consists of rolling a dodecahedral (12 faced) die and receiving the dollar amount equivalent to the roll. If the cost to play the game is $6.00, is this a fair game? How much would you expect to win/lose if you play ten times?

4. Liz, a clever mathematics student, made up a dice game. The rules state that if the roll, n, is a prime number then Liz is willing to pay the player 2^n, whereas if the roll is not a prime the player pays Liz n^2. What is the expectation of this game?

5. (a) The dimensions of a square are to be determined by the roll of a die. The roll will indicate the length of the sides of the square. (A roll of 3 would mean a 3 × 3 square.)
  (i) What are the expected dimensions of the square?
  (ii) What is the expected perimeter of the square?
  (iii) Make a table showing the probability distribution of the area of the square and hence find the expected area of the square.
  (b) The dimensions of a cube are to be determined by the roll of a die.
  (i) What is the expected volume of the cube?
  (ii) What is the expected surface area of the cube?

6. A kennel is to be enclosed with 20 m of fencing. The length of the kennel is to be an integer length and is to be chosen randomly. What is the expected area of the kennel?

7. Mr. Mawhinney asks his class how many of the ten Finite Mathematics problems they would like to do for homework. He secretly decides to take "ten minus the square root of their response, rounded up to the next integer" and to assign that number for homework. If the student response is a random choice (!), what is the expected number of homework questions Mr. Mawhinney will assign?

8. A provincial lottery has 5 000 000 tickets in the draw and each ticket costs $1.00. The prizes and the number of tickets that will receive each prize are listed in the table below.

Prize ($)	Number of Tickets
100 000	2
50 000	2
10 000	50
1 000	200
500	500
100	2 000
25	20 000

What is the expected value of each ticket?

C 9. What is the expected value of a uniform distribution whose random variable can take the values 1, 2, 3, ... , n?

6.3 BINOMIAL DISTRIBUTIONS

In Section 5.7, a stochastic process was described as a sequence of experiments that depend on some chance element. We now consider a special type of stochastic process.

A stochastic process is referred to as **repeated trials** if
(1) the experiments are identical, and
(2) the experiments are independent.

So, in repeated trials, each experiment is exactly the same and the results of any one experiment do not affect the results of any other experiment.

Examples

(1) Tossing a coin one hundred times is an example of repeated trials. Each toss (experiment) is identical to the previous one, and the tosses are independent (one toss does not affect another).

(2) Rolling a pair of dice 20 times would be considered to be a repeated trial stochastic process. The rolls are identical and do not influence one another.

(3) Assembly line manufacturing of any product may be assumed to be repeated trials since the assembly of each product is identical and not affected by the assembly of a previous product. In fact, manufacturing is a very important field in which applied probability theory plays a major role.

Each experiment in repeated trials has the same probability distribution because each experiment is identical. Often in repeated trials we are interested only in the frequency of occurrence of a single event, for example, the number of heads in the repeated tossing of a coin; the number of double sixes in the repeated rolling of a pair of dice; or the number of defective products in a manufacturing process. If the event occurs in one of the experiments, then this trial (experiment) is a "**success**" and if the event does not occur, then the trial is a "**failure**." Whenever we reduce the outcomes of the experiment in repeated trials to success/failure outcomes the trials are called **Bernoulli trials** (named after James Bernoulli, 1654–1705).

Bernoulli trials are repeated trials in which on each trial there are only two possible outcomes, *success and failure*.

Each Bernoulli trial has a probability, p, of success. For example, in the tossing of a coin the success may be defined to be tossing a head with probability $p = \frac{1}{2}$; in the rolling of a pair of dice the success may be defined as double sixes with $p = \frac{1}{36}$; in a manufacturing situation the "success" may be defined as producing a defective product with probability estimated to be 0.001 (perhaps based on past inventory analysis). Furthermore, each Bernoulli trial has associated with it the complementary event—failure—whose probability is denoted by q (where $q = 1 - p$).

The probability distribution of the *number of successes in a sequence of Bernoulli trials* is called the **binomial distribution**. If the random variable X is the number of successes in n Bernoulli trials with each trial having probability p of success and probability q of failure, then the algebraic form of the binomial distribution is given by the following.

The Binomial Distribution

$$p(x) = \binom{n}{x} p^x q^{n-x}$$

This definition makes intuitive sense because to have x successes we would also have $n - x$ failures in n trials. Therefore, the probability of obtaining a particular sequence of x successes and $n - x$ failures is $p^x q^{n-x}$.

In a sequence of n trials these x successes may occur in $\binom{n}{x}$ ways.

This gives the result above.

Example 1   Tabulate and graph the probability distribution for the number of heads in the tossing of a coin five times.

Solution   Let a success be that a head is tossed.

We have $n = 5$ Bernoulli trials with $p = \frac{1}{2}$ and $q = 1 - p = \frac{1}{2}$.

Let the random variable X be the number of heads. The probability distribution is the binomial distribution.

Number of Heads (x)	Probability $p(x)$
	$p(x) = \binom{n}{x} p^x q^{n-x}$
0	$p(0) = \binom{5}{0}\left(\frac{1}{2}\right)^0\left(\frac{1}{2}\right)^{5-0} = 1 \times 1 \times \frac{1}{32} = \frac{1}{32}$
1	$p(1) = \binom{5}{1}\left(\frac{1}{2}\right)^1\left(\frac{1}{2}\right)^{5-1} = 5 \times \frac{1}{2} \times \frac{1}{16} = \frac{5}{32}$
2	$p(2) = \binom{5}{2}\left(\frac{1}{2}\right)^2\left(\frac{1}{2}\right)^{5-2} = 10 \times \frac{1}{4} \times \frac{1}{8} = \frac{10}{32}$
3	$p(3) = \binom{5}{3}\left(\frac{1}{2}\right)^3\left(\frac{1}{2}\right)^{5-3} = 10 \times \frac{1}{8} \times \frac{1}{4} = \frac{10}{32}$
4	$p(4) = \binom{5}{4}\left(\frac{1}{2}\right)^4\left(\frac{1}{2}\right)^{5-4} = 5 \times \frac{1}{16} \times \frac{1}{2} = \frac{5}{32}$
5	$p(5) = \binom{5}{5}\left(\frac{1}{2}\right)^5\left(\frac{1}{2}\right)^{5-5} = 1 \times \frac{1}{32} \times 1 = \frac{1}{32}$
	$\displaystyle\sum_x p(x) = \frac{32}{32}$
	$= 1$

The graph of the distribution follows.

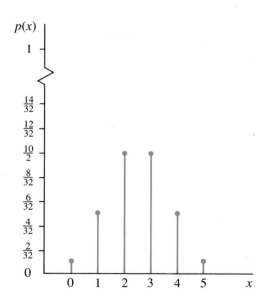

Example 2   A pair of dice are rolled 20 times. What is the probability that:
(a) double sixes are rolled exactly twice?
(b) at least two double sixes are rolled?

Solution   Let a success be the roll of double sixes.

We have $n = 20$ Bernoulli trials with $p = \frac{1}{36}$ and $q = 1 - p = \frac{35}{36}$.

Let the random variable X be the number of double sixes. The probability distribution is the binomial distribution.

(a) The probability of two double sixes is given by

$$p(2) = \binom{20}{2}\left(\frac{1}{36}\right)^2\left(\frac{35}{36}\right)^{20-2}$$

$$= \frac{20!}{2!18!} \times \left(\frac{1}{36}\right)^2 \times \left(\frac{35}{36}\right)^{18}$$

$$\doteq 0.088$$

The probability of rolling exactly two double sixes in 20 rolls of a pair of dice is approximately 0.088.

(b) The probability of at least two double sixes is given by

$$P(X \geqslant 2) = p(2) + p(3) + \ldots + p(20)$$

However, since $\sum_x p(x) = 1$,

$$P(X \geqslant 2) = 1 - p(0) - p(1)$$

which is much simpler to calculate.

$$p(0) = \binom{20}{0}\left(\frac{1}{36}\right)^0\left(\frac{35}{36}\right)^{20-0}$$

$$\doteq (1)(1)(0.569)$$

$$= 0.569$$

$$p(1) = \binom{20}{1}\left(\frac{1}{36}\right)^1\left(\frac{35}{36}\right)^{20-1}$$

$$\doteq 0.325$$

So, $$P(X \geqslant 2) \doteq 1 - 0.569 - 0.325$$

$$= 0.106$$

The probability of at least two double sixes in 20 Bernoulli trials is approximately 0.106.   ◇

Example 3   In a manufacturing process it is estimated that 0.1% of the products are defective. If a client places an order for 25 of the products what is the probability that at least one of them is defective?

Solution   Let a success be a defective product.

Note the paradoxical definition of success.

We have $n = 25$ Bernoulli trials in which $p = 0.001$ and $q = 0.999$.
Let the random variable X be the number of defective products (successes) whose probability distribution is the binomial distribution.

The probability of at least one defective product is given by

$$P(X \geqslant 1) = p(1) + p(2) + \ldots + p(25)$$
$$= 1 - p(0)$$
$$= 1 - \binom{25}{0}(0.001)^0(0.999)^{25}$$
$$\doteq 1 - 0.975$$
$$= 0.025$$

The probability of at least one defective product in the order of 25 is approximately 0.025.

The *binomial distribution* is so named because of the algebraic form of its distribution $\binom{n}{x}p^x q^{n-x}$.

We have seen this mathematical expression before. The Binomial Theorem states that

$$(a+b)^n = \sum_{i=0}^{n} \binom{n}{i} a^{n-i} b^i$$

or, in equivalent form,

$$(a+b)^n = \sum_{i=0}^{n} \binom{n}{i} a^i b^{n-i}$$

Hence, we can recognize that the terms of the expansion of

$$(p+q)^n = \sum_{x=0}^{n} \binom{n}{x} p^x q^{n-x}$$
$$= \binom{n}{0} p^0 q^{n-0} + \binom{n}{1} p^1 q^{n-1} + \ldots + \binom{n}{n} p^n q^{n-n}$$

are the probabilities of the binomial distribution, that is,

$$(p+q)^n = p(0) + p(1) + \ldots + p(n)$$

Because of this close association that the probabilities have with the binomial expansion, it is indeed appropriate to call this probability distribution the binomial distribution.

What is the *expected value* of the binomial distribution?

> The *expectation* of the number of successes in a binomial distribution of n Bernoulli trials with probability p of success on each trial is np.

Proof

By definition, the expectation is $E(X) = \sum_{x} xp(x)$.

So, in the general binomial distribution,

$$E(X) = \sum_{x=0}^{n} x\binom{n}{x}p^x q^{n-x}$$

$$= 0\binom{n}{0}p^0 q^{n-0} + \binom{n}{1}p^1 q^{n-1} + \dots + n\binom{n}{n}p^n q^{n-n}$$

$$= 0 \qquad + \sum_{x=1}^{n} x\binom{n}{x}p^x q^{n-x}$$

$$= \sum_{x=1}^{n} x\,\frac{n!}{x!(n-x)!}p^x q^{n-x}$$

Factoring out np and recognizing that $\dfrac{x}{x!} = \dfrac{1}{(x-1)!}$, we obtain

$$E(X) = np \sum_{x=1}^{n} \frac{(n-1)!}{(x-1)!(n-x)!}p^{x-1}q^{n-x}$$

$$= np \sum_{x=1}^{n} \binom{n-1}{x-1}p^{x-1}q^{(n-1)-(x-1)}$$

$$= np \sum_{x=0}^{n-1} \binom{n-1}{x}p^x q^{(n-1)-x} \qquad \text{(change of index)}$$

$$= np(p+q)^{n-1}$$

$$= np(1)^{n-1}$$

$$= np$$

Example 4 A game consists of rolling a pair of dice ten times. For each sum that equals either six, seven, or eight on the two dice, you win one dollar. If it costs five dollars to play the game, is this a fair game?

Solution Let a success be that a sum of a six, seven, or eight is rolled. We have $n = 10$ Bernoulli trials. The probability of success, p, on each trial is readily obtained from the tabulated sums of the outcomes of the roll of two dice.

		One Die 1	2	3	4	5	6
	1	2	3	4	5	6	7
	2	3	4	5	6	7	8
Other	3	4	5	6	7	8	9
Die	4	5	6	7	8	9	10
	5	6	7	8	9	10	11
	6	7	8	9	10	11	12

The number of outcomes that lead to a success is 16 (as indicated in the table). Therefore $p = \frac{16}{36}$.

The expectation of this binomial distribution with $n = 10$ and $p = \frac{16}{36}$ is

$$np = 10 \times \tfrac{16}{36} \doteq 4.44$$

The expected winnings would be $1 \times 4.44 = \$4.44$. It costs $5.00 to play, so the game is not fair.

It is important to be able to recognize situations in which the binomial distribution is an appropriate model. Look for the following three criteria in a stochastic process:

(1) The outcome of each trial may be described as either a success or a failure.

(2) The trials are identical.

(3) The trials are independent.

If the description of a stochastic process satisfies the above three conditions then you can conclude that the number of successes in the repeated trials (Bernoulli trials) will have a binomial distribution.

EXERCISE 6.3

B **1.** Tabulate and graph the binomial distributions for the following cases.

    (a) $p = 0.1$, $n = 5$ (b) $p = 0.9$, $n = 5$

    (c) $p = 0.3$, $n = 4$ (d) $p = 0.3$, $n = 8$

    (e) $p = \frac{1}{6}$, $n = 6$

2. Use the results of Question 1 and the Binomial Theorem to expand.

    (a) $(0.1 + 0.9)^5$ (b) $(0.9 + 0.1)^5$

    (c) $(0.3 + 0.7)^4$ (d) $(0.3 + 0.7)^8$

    (e) $\left(\frac{1}{6} + \frac{5}{6}\right)^6$

3. Show that the binomial distribution satisfies the fundamental probability distribution criterion that

$$\sum_x p(x) = 1$$

Hint: Relate the sum of the probabilities to the binomial expansion.

4. A coin is tossed ten times. Find the probability that

    (a) exactly four heads are tossed.

    (b) at least two heads are tossed.

    (c) no more than two tails are tossed.

5. In a multiple choice test that contains ten questions with each question having five possible answers, what is the probability that

    (a) Colin will pass the test if he merely guesses at each question?

    (b) Diane will pass the test if she has studied and feels that her probability of answering each question correctly is 0.75?

6. Assuming that the chance of giving birth to a girl or a boy is even, what are the chances that

    (a) a couple planning to have three children will have all girls?

    (b) a couple planning to have five children will have at least one girl?

7. Assume that every time Murray, a hockey player, gets a breakaway on the opposition's net, he has a probability of 0.6 of scoring. If he averages two breakaways a game, what is the expected number of goals that he will score on breakaways in a season with 75 games.

8. If a chain link is stressed over its recommended maximum limit, the probability that it will break is 0.7. What is the probability that
    (a) a chain five links long will break if it is overloaded?
    (b) a chain ten links long will break if it is overloaded?
    (Hint: Regard this as a situation where repeated trials are occurring simultaneously.)

9. The number of immigrants living in a certain country with a large population makes up 20 percent of the population. In a random sample poll of 100 people what is
    (a) the expected number of immigrants to be polled?
    (b) the probability that no immigrants will be polled?

10. In a manufacturing process, it is estimated that only 2 percent of the bolts that are machined are declared defective, that is, they are either too large or too small. In a package of 50 bolts, what is the probability that there is at least one defective bolt?

11. If the probability is 0.15 that Luciana will hit a bull's eye on a dart board, what is the probability that she will get at least one bull's eye in ten attempts?

12. It seems that every carton of eggs at the supermarket contains at least one broken egg. If, in fact, it has been determined that 3 percent of the eggs supplied to a supermarket are cracked, what is the probability that if you buy two dozen eggs none of your eggs will be cracked?

13. Find the probability that at least three students in a class of 30 students were born on a Saturday.

14. At the height of the Beatles' popularity, it was estimated that their music was played on every popular music radio station 40 percent of the time. What is the probability that if you tuned through ten such stations at any given moment at least one of the stations would be playing a Beatles song?

C **15.** In the game of Backgammon, there is a stage that is often reached where one tries to return a piece to the playing board after it has been removed. To do this, the player must roll two dice and hope that the roll of one of the dice is equal to an open position on the board. For example, if positions 2 and 5 are open then the player must roll either a 2 or a 5 with the dice to return a piece to the playing board.

Determine the probabilities that Ashley can return a piece to the playing board if Carlos has left her the following situations.

(a)   only one position is open
(b)   two positions are open
(c)   three positions are open
(d)   four positions are open
(e)   five positions are open
(f)   six positions are open

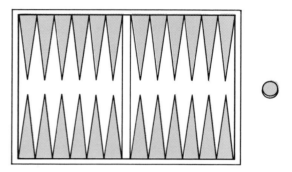

6.4   WAITING TIMES

In this section we see a probability model that allows us to determine how long it will take until a success occurs in a stochastic process consisting of Bernoulli trials. We will be able to answer questions such as the following:

(1)   What is the probability that you can roll a sum of seven on a pair of dice in fewer than three rolls?

(2)   If traffic flows at a given rate, what is the expected length of time that a pedestrian must wait before crossing the street?

The probability model that enables us to answer these questions is the **geometric distribution**. Given a stochastic process consisting of Bernoulli trials (identical, independent and success/failure outcomes), the number of trials *prior* to the first success is called *the waiting period* before success. Let X be the random variable equal to the number of trials required before a success. The probability distribution of X is given by

> ## The Geometric Distribution
> $$P(X=x) = q^x p$$
> where p is the probability of success on each trial
> $q = 1-p$ is the probability of failure on each trial
> and $x = 0, 1, 2, \ldots$.

This definition results from the observation that the trials must result in x failures, each having probability q of occurring and then one success. No arrangements need be considered, hence the result.

It can be proved that the *expectation* of a random variable that is geometrically distributed is given by

$$E(X) = \frac{q}{p}$$

The proof will be left to the reader in Exercise 6.4, Question 13.

Example 1 In repeated rolling of a pair of dice,
(a) what is the probability that the first roll of doubles occurs on the third roll?
(b) what is the expected waiting time (number of rolls) before you roll doubles?

Solution Let a success in these Bernoulli trials be a roll of doubles with $p = \frac{6}{36} = \frac{1}{6}$, and $q = 1-p = \frac{5}{6}$.

Let the random variable X be the number of rolls prior to the first double being rolled.

(a) If the first double is to occur on the third roll then $x = 2$.

So, $P(X=2) = \left(\frac{5}{6}\right)^2 \left(\frac{1}{6}\right)$

$= \frac{25}{216}$

The probability of the first doubles occurring on the third roll is equal to $\frac{25}{216}$.

(b) The expected waiting time is $E(X) = \frac{q}{p}$

$= \frac{\frac{5}{6}}{\frac{1}{6}}$

$= 5$

On average we would expect five rolls of non-doubles before doubles would appear.

Example 2   In a gambling game a player tosses a coin until a head is uppermost. He then receives $2n$, where n is the number of tosses.

(a)   What is the probability that the player receives $8.00 in one play of the game?

(b)   If the player must pay $5.00 to play, what is the win/loss per game?

Solution   We have Bernoulli trials with $p = \frac{1}{2}$.

Let the random variable X be the number of tosses before a head.

(a)   To win $8.00 the first head must occur on the fourth toss. Therefore $x = 3$.
So,

$$P(X = 3) = \left(\tfrac{1}{2}\right)^3 \left(\tfrac{1}{2}\right)$$
$$= \tfrac{1}{16}$$

The probability of winning $8.00 is equal to $\frac{1}{16}$.

(b)   The expected waiting time before a head is

$$E(X) = \frac{q}{p}$$
$$= \frac{\frac{1}{2}}{\frac{1}{2}}$$
$$= 1$$

We can then conclude that we can expect to toss a head on the second toss, which would win $4.00. The expected gain per game is $4 - $5 = -$1 (a loss per game of $1.00).

Now we consider the questions posed earlier in the introduction to this section.

Example 3   What is the probability of rolling a sum of seven in fewer than three rolls of a pair of dice?

Solution   Let the random variable X be the number of trials before a success. We must roll the seven on the first or the second roll, so the number of trials before a success must be either 0 or 1.
We have Bernoulli trials with $p = \frac{1}{6}$.

So, $$P(X < 2) = p(0) + p(1)$$
$$= q^0 p + q^1 p$$
$$= \left(\tfrac{5}{6}\right)^0 \left(\tfrac{1}{6}\right) + \left(\tfrac{5}{6}\right)^1 \left(\tfrac{1}{6}\right)$$
$$= \tfrac{1}{6} + \tfrac{5}{36}$$
$$= \tfrac{11}{36}$$

The probability of a seven being rolled before the third roll is equal to $\frac{11}{36}$.

Example 4   At a certain corner you need ten seconds on average to cross the street. If during 70 percent of the ten-second intervals there is traffic on the street, how long will you expect to wait to cross?

Solution   Let a success be that there is no traffic in the interval.
We can assume we have Bernoulli trials with $p=0.3$ and each trial is a ten-second interval.
Let the random variable X be the number of intervals before a success. Then the expected waiting time is

$$E(X) = \frac{q}{p}$$
$$= \frac{0.7}{0.3}$$
$$\doteq 2.3$$

The expected number of ten-second intervals that one would have to wait before attempting the crossing is about 2.3. So, the waiting time would be 23 seconds.

EXERCISE 6.4

We assume that samples are taken from populations in which the relevant characteristics are randomly distributed.

A **1.** Identify the probability distribution in which the following random variables are distributed.
   (a) Let the random variable X be the number uppermost on the roll of a die.
   (b) Let the random variable X be the roll of a one in the repeated rolling of a die.
   (c) Let the random variable X be the number of rolls before rolling a one in the repeated rolling of a die.

B **2.** Tabulate and graph the geometric distributions for $x=0, 1, 2, 3$ in the following situations.
   (a) $p=0.5$ (b) $p=0.2$ (c) $p=0.7$

3. In the repeated rolling of a single die, what is the probability that you will roll a five or a six for the first time on the fourth roll?

4. If you repeatedly cut a deck of cards, what is the probability that you will cut an ace in fewer than five cuts?

5. What are the odds against your rolling doubles in fewer than four rolls of two dice?

6. What is the expected number of people you would have to sample to find someone with the same birthday as yours?

7. If a recent poll indicated that the Hippopotamus party had 9% popular support, what would be the expected number of people that a television interviewer must survey to obtain the opinion of a Hippo supporter?

8. If 2 percent of the transactions at a bank are applications for loans what is the probability that the first loan request on a given day occurs with the tenth customer?

9. It is estimated that on a daily basis 15 percent of the customers at local supermarket use the express checkout. What is the probabili that one of the first five customers on a given day uses the expres checkout?

10. If the probability of Michiko getting an A on her mathematics tes is 0.6, what is the probability that
   (a) she will get her first A on the second test?
   (b) she will get an A on one or more of her first three tests?

11. A production process produces components of which 3 percent are defective.
   (a) What is the expected number of components produced before defective one is made?
   (b) What is the probability that the first defective component will occur within the first five components off the line?

C 12. Another form of the geometric distribution is given by
$$P(X=x) = q^{x-1}p$$
where $x = 1, 2, 3, \ldots$ and X is defined as the number of trials to a first success with expectation $E(X) = \dfrac{1}{p}$.
Explain why this form is equivalent to the one introduced in this section.

13. Use the sum of the arithmetico-geometric series (Section 4.3) to show that the expectation of a geometrically-distributed random variable is $\dfrac{q}{p}$.

6.5 HYPERGEOMETRIC DISTRIBUTIONS

The **hypergeometric distribution** arises from the probability model that describes a stochastic process whose repeated experiments are *not* independent. Repeated sampling *without replacement* exhibits this type of process. Card deals and draws are examples of processes in which the probability of the outcomes for each trial changes.

Let us first consider experiments that can be classified as success/ failure outcomes. Note that we cannot call these trials Bernoulli trials or repeated trials because these terms are reserved for *identical and independent* trials.

Suppose we have a outcomes that would be classified as successful outcomes and b outcomes that would be failure outcomes. If a stochastic process of n trials involving sampling without replacement took place, then the probability of x successes in the n trials is given by

---

The Hypergeometric Distribution

$$P(X=x) \; = \; \frac{\binom{a}{x}\binom{b}{n-x}}{\binom{a+b}{n}}$$

This form derives directly from the fundamental definition of probability.

$$P(A) \; = \; \frac{n(A)}{n(S)}$$

The number of selections of n items chosen from $a+b$ is

$$\binom{a+b}{n}$$

Hence, $n(S) \; = \; \binom{a+b}{n}$

The number of selections of x successes chosen from a is

$$\binom{a}{x}$$

The number of selections of $n-x$ failures chosen from b is

$$\binom{b}{n-x}$$

So, by the Fundamental Counting Principle, $n(A) \; = \; \binom{a}{x}\binom{b}{n-x}$

Then the probability of the outcome becomes $\dfrac{\binom{a}{x}\binom{b}{n-x}}{\binom{a+b}{n}}$ which is the

form of the hypergeometric distribution.

Example 1   Tabulate and graph the probability for the number of spades dealt from a well-shuffled deck of cards if three cards are dealt.

Solution   Let a success be that a spade is dealt.
Let the random variable X be the number of successes (spades). We have two groups of outcomes, spades and non-spades (success/failure), and we are sampling without replacement, so the random variable is distributed hypergeometrically where

$a \; = \;$ the number of spades in the deck
$\quad = \; 13$
$b \; = \;$ the number of cards in the other suits
$\quad = \; 39$
$n \; = \;$ the number of cards dealt
$\quad = \; 3$

Spades (x)	Probability $p(x)$		
	$$p(x) = \frac{\binom{a}{x}\binom{b}{n-x}}{\binom{a+b}{n}}$$		
0	$$p(0) = \frac{\binom{13}{0}\binom{39}{3}}{\binom{52}{3}}$$	$= \dfrac{(1)(9139)}{22100}$	$\doteq 0.414$
1	$$p(1) = \frac{\binom{13}{1}\binom{39}{2}}{\binom{52}{3}}$$	$= \dfrac{(13)(741)}{22100}$	$\doteq 0.436$
2	$$p(2) = \frac{\binom{13}{2}\binom{39}{1}}{\binom{52}{3}}$$	$= \dfrac{(78)(39)}{22100}$	$\doteq 0.138$
3	$$p(3) = \frac{\binom{13}{3}\binom{39}{0}}{\binom{52}{3}}$$	$= \dfrac{(286)(1)}{22100}$	$\doteq 0.013$
		$\sum_x p(x) = 1$	

The fact the probabilities do not appear to add to exactly 1 is a result of rounding error.

The graph of the distribution follows.

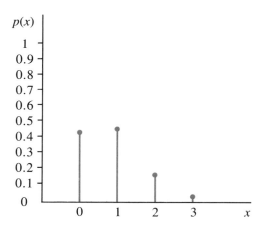

Example 2 A hat contains 20 names, 12 of which are female. If five names are drawn from the hat, what is the probability that there are at least two female names drawn?

Solution Let a success be that a female name is drawn.
Let the random variable X be the number of successes (female names drawn). We are drawing without replacement and we have success/failure outcomes, so the probability distribution is hypergeometric where

a = the number of female names in the hat

= 12

b = the number of male names

= 20 − 12

= 8

n = the number of trials

= 5

The probability of at least two female names drawn is

$$P(X \geqslant 2) = 1 - p(0) - p(1)$$

where

$$p(0) = \frac{\dbinom{a}{x}\dbinom{b}{n-x}}{\dbinom{a+b}{n}}$$

$$= \frac{\dbinom{12}{0}\dbinom{8}{5}}{\dbinom{20}{5}}$$

$$= \frac{(1)(56)}{15504}$$

$$\doteq 0.0036$$

and

$$p(1) = \frac{\dbinom{12}{1}\dbinom{8}{4}}{\dbinom{20}{5}}$$

$$= \frac{(12)(70)}{15504}$$

$$\doteq 0.0542$$

Therefore,

$$P(X \geqslant 2) \doteq 1 - 0.0036 - 0.0542$$

$$= 0.9422$$

The probability of at least two female names being drawn is approximately 0.9422.

The hypergeometric distribution does not necessarily restrict itself to trials that have only two outcomes (success/failure). It is easily generalized to the case where there may be several classes of outcomes for each trial. For example, let a trial contain three classes of size a, b, and c, respectively. If a sample of size n is taken, then the probability that it contains x_1 elements of the first, x_2 elements of the second, and x_3 elements of the third class is

$$P(X_1 = x_1, X_2 = x_2, X_3 = x_3) = \frac{\binom{a}{x_1}\binom{b}{x_2}\binom{c}{x_3}}{\binom{a+b+c}{n}}$$

$$\text{with } x_1 + x_2 + x_3 = n$$

Example 3   What is the probability that a bridge hand of 13 cards contains six spades, four hearts, two diamonds, and one club?

Solution   Let the random variables X_1, X_2, X_3, X_4 be the number of spades, hearts, diamonds, and clubs, respectively, in the hand.
The X_i's are hypergeometrically distributed with

a = the number of spades in a deck of cards
  = 13
b = the number of hearts
  = 13
c = the number of diamonds
  = 13
d = the number of clubs
  = 13
n = the number of cards in a bridge hand
  = 13

and $a + b + c + d = 52$

Then,

$$P(X_1 = 6, X_2 = 4, X_3 = 2, X_4 = 1) = \frac{\binom{13}{6}\binom{13}{4}\binom{13}{2}\binom{13}{1}}{\binom{52}{13}}$$

$$\doteq \frac{(1716)(715)(78)(13)}{6.35013 \times 10^{11}}$$

$$\doteq 0.002$$

The probability that a bridge hand will have a configuration of six spades, four hearts, two diamonds, and one heart is approximately 0.002.

The *expectation* of the hypergeometric distribution may be determined directly from the definition of the expected value which is

$$E(X) = \sum_x xp(x)$$

We state the following result without proof.

> The *expectation of the hypergeometric distribution* is given by
>
> $$E(X) = \frac{na}{a+b}$$
>
> where x is the number of successes
> n is the number of trials
> a is the number of items in the population that would be classified
>   as successful
> b is the number of items in the population classified as failures

Example 4 A box of thumbtacks contains 15 red and 20 blue tacks. If 10 tacks are withdrawn at random from the box, what is the expected number of red tacks drawn?

Solution Let a success be that a red thumbtack is drawn.
Let the random variable X be the number of successes.
The probability distribution is hypergeometric (sampling without replacement) where

$$a = \text{the number of red tacks}$$
$$= 15$$
$$b = \text{the number of blue tacks}$$
$$= 20$$
$$n = \text{the number of trials}$$
$$= 10$$

The expected value is

$$E(X) = \frac{na}{a+b}$$
$$= \frac{10 \times 15}{15 + 20}$$
$$= \frac{150}{35}$$
$$\doteq 4$$

One would expect to draw four red tacks on average.

A very interesting zoological application uses the *expectation* of a hypergeometric distribution to estimate the size of an animal population by using a marking system. The following example illustrates this application.

Example 5 A thousand fish in one of the lakes of Ontario were caught and tagged by the Department of Fisheries. After a while a new catch of 500 fish was caught and it was found that 60 among them had tags. What conclusions could be made concerning the number of fish in the lake?

Solution Let the random variable X be the number of tagged fish caught. The probability distribution is hypergeometric where

a = the number of tagged fish in the lake
   = 1000
b = the number of untagged fish
n = the number of fish caught
   = 500

The 60 fish that were caught provide an estimate of $E(X)$.

To estimate the number of fish in the lake we solve for the unknown variable b in the equation for the expectation

$$E(X) = \frac{na}{a+b}$$

Substituting the known information we have,

$$60 = \frac{500 \times 1000}{1000 + b}$$

Solving for b, we obtain

$$60(1000) + 60b = 500\ 000$$
$$60b = 500\ 000 - 60\ 000$$
$$60b = 440\ 000$$
$$b \doteq 7\ 000$$

An estimate of the total number of fish in the lake is

$$a + b \doteq 1000 + 7000$$
$$= 8000$$

EXERCISE 6.5

A **1.** Identify the probability distribution in which the following random variables are distributed.
   (a) Let the random variable X be the number of red cards drawn in the drawing of cards from a deck.
   (b) Let the random variable X be the number of times a coin is tossed before a head is tossed.
   (c) Let the random variable X be the number of red Smarties randomly drawn from a handful of Smarties.
   (d) Let the random variable X be the number of people that are born on a Monday in a class of 40 students.

2. A fish bowl contains ten guppies and eight goldfish. Four of the fish are removed randomly. Identify the values of the variables a, b, n, and x, if you were to find the probability that two of the fish removed were guppies.

B **3.** (a) Tabulate and graph the hypergeometric distributions for the following cases.
   (i) $a = 5$, $b = 5$, $n = 4$
   (ii) $a = 5$, $b = 10$, $n = 4$
   (iii) $a = 10$, $b = 5$, $n = 4$
   (b) For each of the distributions of part (a), verify that $\sum_x p(x) = 1$

   and also find the expectation for each case. Mark the expectation on your graph of the distribution.

4. A marble bag contains ten "steelies" and 15 "cat's eyes." If Lawrie reaches into the bag and withdraws five marbles, what is the probability that she will get:
   (a) exactly one steelie?
   (b) at least two steelies?
   (c) no cat's eyes?

5. In a club with 20 members, five have positions of authority. If a random poll of ten of the club members is taken, what is the probability that at least two of those polled have positions of authority?

6. A poker hand of five cards is dealt.
   (a) What is the probability that the hand does not contain any face cards?
   (b) Answer the same question for a bridge hand of 13 cards.

7. Nick organized a school fund-raising draw to raise money for the purchase of a rowing shell. There were 500 tickets sold at $5.00 each. Two hundred of the tickets were sold internally to members of the student body and the remainder were sold in the community at large. If three prizes were drawn, what is the probability that
   (a) none of the prizes were won by students?
   (b) all of the prizes were won by students?

8. At an office party names were drawn out of a hat to pick teams for charades. There were ten females and six males at the party. What is the probability that the first team drawn (four members to a team) was all female?

9. In a special education class of 12 students, four have advanced aptitudes in Mathematics. If a ministry official randomly tests three students, what is the probability that all three of the students tested are gifted in Mathematics?

10. A box contains 80 good and ten defective screws. If ten screws are used, what is the probability that none are defective?

11. What is the probability of having a four-three-three-three distribution of cards (spades-hearts-diamonds-clubs, respectively) in a bridge hand?

12. What is the probability of being dealt a straight (not necessarily all of the same suit) from a ten to the ace in a poker hand?

13. A bag of jelly beans contains ten red, 12 yellow and six green. What is the probability that a selection of five jelly beans
    (a) contains all red jelly beans?
    (b) contains two red, two yellow and one green?
    (c) has no red beans.

14. Estimate the size of the seal population in a certain region of the Arctic if in a hunt of 50 seals 20 were tagged, and it is known that 1000 seals had been tagged before the hunt.

15. Estimate the population size of a bird species if in 100 sightings along a migration path, 25 were ringed, and it is known that 500 of the birds had been ringed before the sightings?

16. An endangered species is on the verge of extinction. Conservationist groups are closely monitoring its population each month. Last month, of 50 animals that were sighted, 20 were seen to be marked, and this month 25 of 40 animals sighted were seen to be marked. If the conservationists know that 100 of the animals in the population had been marked before the sightings, what is the estimated percentage decline in the animal population over the two months?

PROBLEMS PLUS

Consumers challenge

A school lottery is held in order to raise funds for a local charity. The rules of the lottery are as follows: 300 tickets are sold per week at $1.00 each. Each week a winner is drawn and receives $50.00. All the tickets for each draw are entered into the next week's draw. For example, the second week's draw contains 600 tickets, the third week, 900 tickets, and so on.

The lottery is advertised with the statement, "You get ten chances to win a one-in-three hundred draw: an overall winning chance of one in thirty!"

What is the actual probability of winning at least one $50.00 prize if you enter the lottery on every draw?

What is the expected return on your tickets?

6.6 REVIEW EXERCISE

1. Identify possible random variables for the following experiments and the possible values that the random variable may take.
   (a) tossing a coin
   (b) throwing a dart
   (c) rolling a die
   (d) cutting a deck of cards
   (e) drawing names from a hat

(f)   dealing five cards from a shuffled deck of cards

(g)   scrutinizing a box of bolts in a manufacturing process

(h)   guessing at the results of an election

(i)   checking baskets of fruit for overripe fruit

(j)   waiting for the first correct answer to a question

(k)   looking for the first roll of a seven with a pair of dice

2.   For each of the random variables defined in Question 1, identify their probability distributions.

3.   Graph the probability distributions, given their defining statement.

(a) $P(X=x) = \dfrac{1}{n}$ where $x \in \{1, 2, 3, \ldots , n\}$

(b) $P(X=x) = \dbinom{n}{x} p^x q^{n-x}$ where $n=4$, $p=\frac{1}{3}$

(c) $P(X=x) = \dfrac{\dbinom{a}{x}\dbinom{b}{n-x}}{\dbinom{a+b}{n}}$ where $a=4$, $b=5$, $n=2$

(d) $P(X=x) = q^x p$ where $p=\frac{1}{4}$ and $x=0, 1, 2, 3, \ldots$.

4.   Determine the expected value of the following tabulated probability distributions:

(a)

x	$P(X=x)$
0	$\frac{1}{2}$
1	$\frac{1}{4}$
2	$\frac{1}{4}$

(b)

x	$P(X=x)$
10	0.32
12	0.15
14	0.26
16	0.27

5.   A game consists of cutting a shuffled deck of cards and receiving the dollar value of the face value of the card. Jacks are considered to be worth 11, queens 12, kings 13, and aces 1. What is the expectation of this game?

6.   A scratch-and-win box on the reverse of a label is used as a promotional gimmick. The consumer removes the label and scratches the box to reveal a prize. The following table lists the prizes and the number of labels containing each prize during a promotion by Nutty Peanut Butter.

Prize ($)	Number of Labels
10 000	3
5 000	10
1 000	25
100	50
10	1 000

Nutty produces 200 000 jars of peanut butter for the promotion. To cover the costs of the promotion, Nutty increases the price on a jar by an amount equal to the expected prize money per jar. What is the price of the peanut butter during the promotion if it normally sells for $2.79 per jar?

7. From Canadian statistics based on the 1976 census, 18.8 percent of the population over the age of 15 has a secondary school graduation certificate. If a random survey is taken of 20 employed individuals, what is the probability that:
   .203 (a) exactly three have a secondary school graduation certificate?
   .912 (b) at least two have a graduation certificate?

8. A quality control inspector uses the rule that if in a random sample of ten products from a large batch, two or more are defective, then the batch is rejected. If the probability of a defective product in the production process is 0.03, what is the probability that a batch gets rejected?

9. A child removes the name cards on ten wrapped Christmas gifts of which six are for the Changs and four are for the Andersens. If the presents are distributed to the two families without reopening the packages,
   (a) what is the probability that the Changs get five of the presents originally intended for them?
   (b) what is the expected number of correct presents distributed to the Changs?

10. A fast-food outlet has 12 young employees, five of whom are female. If four of the employees are selected at random to work the counter rather than the hot kitchen, what is the probability that at least two of the girls are chosen?

11. The DJ of a local radio show conducts a contest in which the listeners phone in the answer to the contest question. If the DJ estimates that the probability of a caller giving the correct answer is 0.24,
   (a) what is the probability that the third caller is the winner?
   (b) what is the expected number of calls before a correct answer is received?

12. A lottery has 1 000 000 tickets and draws 100 tickets to award prizes. How many tickets would you expect to have to purchase before you would win a prize?

13. Lesley claims she can roll triples with three dice in fewer than 20 rolls?
   (a) What is the expected number of rolls that it would take to roll the first set of triples?
   (b) What is the probability that she will roll the triples in fewer than five rolls?

CHAPTER 6 TEST

1. Graph the given binomial probability distribution whose defining statement is

$$P(X=x) = \binom{n}{x}p^x q^{n-x} \quad \text{where } n=3, p=\tfrac{1}{4}$$

2. Show that the expectation of a uniform distribution of an experiment with n outcomes is given by

$$E(X) = \frac{1}{n}\left(\sum_x x\right)$$

3. A quiz is given to a Finite Mathematics class and each question requires one of these responses: true, false, or cannot tell from the given information. If the quiz has ten questions in it,
   (a) what is the probability that Mustafa will get exactly six questions correct if he merely guesses?
   (b) what is the probability that the first question he gets correct (by guessing) is the third question?
   (c) what is the expected number of correct questions that Mustafa will guess?

4. In a political science class, seven of the 18 students have strong socialist views. If a random selection of four of them is chosen to represent the class in a debate, what is the probability that
   (a) half of the debaters will be socialists?
   (b) none of the debaters will be socialists?
   (c) there will be a majority of socialists on the debating team?

5. One year the Department of Fisheries tagged 300 bass in a lake. The bass were released and given time to mix with the fish population of the lake. Then 200 bass were caught, of which 20 were found to be tagged. What is estimate of the size of the bass population in this lake?

6. Prove that the expectation of the binomial distribution is np.

PROBLEMS PLUS

In the seventeenth century, probability theory received a boost when a French nobleman, the Chevalier de Méré, asked Blaise Pascal to analyze some gambling problems. One problem involved obtaining repetitions in throws of dice. The chevalier believed it was equally likely to get at least one "one" with the roll of four dice as to get at least one "double ones" with 24 rolls of two dice.

(a) Find the true probabilities of each event.

(b) Why might he have thought the events to be equally likely?

TWENTIETH CENTURY MATHEMATICIANS

Herbert Robbins is best known for his joint book with Richard Courant *What Is Mathematics?* Although it is almost 50 years old now, it still has much to say to the interested reader.

Professor Robbins is the Higgins Professor of Mathematical Statistics at Columbia University in New York City. He became a statistician partly by accident. While in the US Navy in the Second World War, he overheard some officers discussing a military problem involving statistics. He solved their problem while they talked and then approached them to show them the solution but they couldn't respond since he didn't have security clearance to discuss the problem! In 1946, his solution appeared in a statistics journal just after the paper containing the "official" solution written by Neyman and J. Bronowski (*The Ascent of Man*). Professor Robbins's solution really is much better!

Here is how he describes his work. "I've merely been the vehicle by which something has done them [the problems]—my fingers are writing but there's a lot of "noise" and it's hard for me to get the message. Most of the time I am just sitting there.... Over and over again I keep working at it, trying to understand something which after months and even years turns out to be so simple that I should have seen it in the first ten minutes."

He stresses that the field of statistics is still evolving. "Let's just take one field, called biostatistics, that deals with the application of statistical methods to human health and disease. If I were given ten million dollars to spend for advancing science I could spend it trying to produce good biostatisticians. The methodology for handling important problems in biostatistics does not exist. It is just beginning now; its Newton or Einstein has yet to appear."

PROBLEMS PLUS

Spread of rumours

Assume that when a rumour is spread, only 90 percent of the truth in the story is retained at each telling. If the originator of the rumour hears it after it has been passed through ten people, how much truth from the original story remains?

If a rumour is spread through a social group of thirty students and at each step the recipient of the rumour is chosen at random, find the probability that the rumour returns to the originator with more than 50 percent truth left in the story.

CHAPTER 7

STATISTICS

REVIEW AND PREVIEW TO
CHAPTER 7

Absolute Value

The **absolute value** of a number is the distance that the number is from 0 on the number line. For example, the number 3 is three units from 0 so the absolute value of 3 is 3. The number -5 is five units from 0 so its absolute value is 5. The notation used to indicate absolute value is $|a|$ which is read "the absolute value of a."

EXERCISE 1

1. Determine the indicated absolute values.
   (a) $|4.2|$
   (b) $|-3.6|$
   (c) $|2-3|$
   (d) $|3 \times 4|$
   (e) $|17.3-18.5|$

2. If $x_1 = 12$, $x_2 = 16$, $x_3 = 17$, $X = 15$, and $n = 3$ determine the following.
   (a) $|x_1 - X|$

   (b) $\sum_{i=1}^{3} |x_i - X|$

   (c) $\dfrac{\sum_{i=1}^{n} |x_i - X|}{n}$

EXERCISE 2   Interpreting Graphs

1. Graphs are a form of representing information. In most mathematics courses they are widely used to represent information about equations.

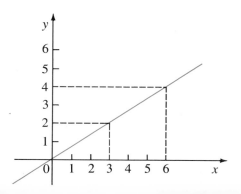

Given the graph, complete the following statements.
   (i)   If $x = 3$ then $y = $ ... .
  (ii)   If $y = 4$ then $x = $ ... .
 (iii)   The slope of the graph is ... .

2. The following graphs were taken from newspaper articles and magazines.
   (a)   The "War on the Deficit," adapted from *Maclean's*, March 2, 1987

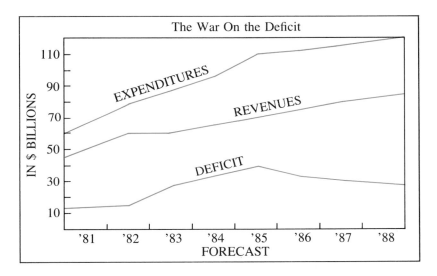

Given the graph, complete the following statements.
    (i)   In '81 the expenditures in $ billions were ... .
   (ii)   In '81 the revenues in $ billions were ... .
  (iii)   The deficit graph is obtained from the expenditures and revenues graphs by ... .
   (iv)   In '81 the deficit in $ billions was ... . [Confirm this result by referring to the answers to parts (i) and (ii).]
    (v)   The deficit was largest in the year ... .
   (vi)   To reduce the deficit, the slope of the expenditures graph must be ... the slope of the revenues graph.
  (vii)   The number of years that the deficit has been greater than $30 billion is ... .
 (viii)   In what way has the graphic artist who drew this graph tried to exaggerate the tendency for the curves to rise?

(b) "The Killing Curve," adapted from *Maclean's*, March 16, 1987

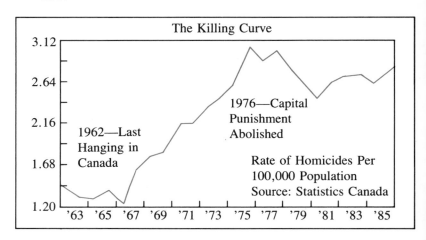

Given the graph, complete the following statements.
  (i) The rate of homicides in '73 was ... .
 (ii) The rate of homicides per 100 000 population was 2.64 in the years ... .
(iii) The rate of homicides declined in the time periods ... .
 (iv) Since capital punishment has been abolished, the lowest rate of homicides was in the year ... .
  (v) A steep positive slope on the graph suggests a ... in the homicide rate.
 (vi) Notice that the vertical scale on the graph does not start at zero. How does this omission tend to influence the reader regarding the fluctuation of the homicide rate?

(c) Toronto Stock Exchange Composite Index, *Globe and Mail*, July 21, 1987

Given the graph, complete the following statements.
  (i) In the month of March the highest the TSE 300 attained was ... .
 (ii) The TSE index was below 3650 in the months ... .
(iii) The highest TSE total volume in millions of shares in the month of June was ... .
 (iv) The number of times in May that the TSE total volume was above 32 million shares was ... .
  (v) The months in which the TSE 300 composite index reached over 3850 were ... .
 (vi) It appears that the TSE 300 index has fluctuated wildly over the six-month period. What feature of the vertical scale misleads us to this conclusion?

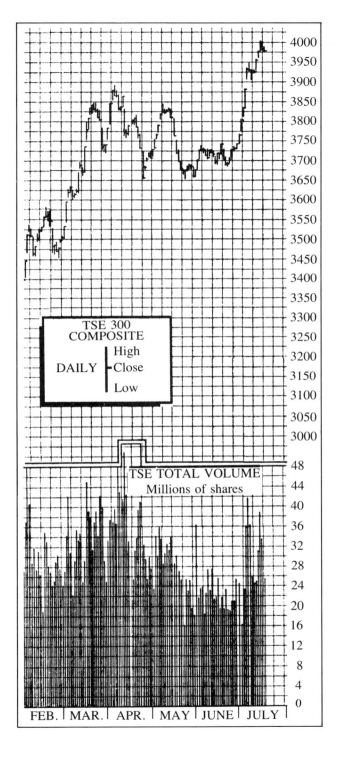

INTRODUCTION

The focus of many research studies is to build a convincing argument in support of a position. Believing strongly that something is true is generally not enough. One must present the argument in a clear and convincing manner. Saying "Smoking is hazardous to your health," has little impact in comparison to this statement, "Sixty percent of all men who are heavy smokers will die of cancer-related diseases before they are 70 years old, while for non-smokers the rate is 30 percent." Notice what makes the latter statement more powerful. The comments are defined (that is, they focus on the specific hazard that may result from smoking) and, furthermore, quantitative assessment (numerical data) has been introduced.

Statistics is a branch of mathematics that deals with the collection, analysis, interpretation, and presentation of data. It enables one to prepare convincing and factual statements similar to the one above.

7.1 GRAPHICAL PRESENTATIONS OF DATA

Large sets of data are generally not very revealing in a table form. For example, the following measurements of blood samples were taken during the study of anemia in pregnant women. The measurements taken were:

MCHC: mean corpuscular hemoglobin count
PCV: packed cell volume
HB: hemoglobin
SF: serum folate
WF: whole folate
TIBC: total iron binding capacity

Anyone, including a doctor, would face difficulty when confronted with the data on table 1 because most of the important information is lost in the columns of numbers. For data in a table to become meaningful, important representative details must be selected and graphed.

This section introduces a variety of techniques for displaying data in graphs to help us visualize the characteristics of the data.

TABLE 1

Patient	MCHC	PCV	HB	SF	WF	TIBC
1	31.9	42	12	4	190	620
2	32.4	39	12	5	192	351
3	31.5	38	13	13	511	282
4	31.3	42	11	1	170	167
5	31.3	39	11	5	339	274
6	31.8	35	13	4	139	401
7	31.9	37	11	6	263	284
8	32.3	43	12	3	215	332
9	31.9	38	12	14	177	118
10	31.0	34	11	4	252	259
11	31.5	39	11	5	198	378
12	31.9	39	13	4	239	499
13	31.7	43	12	7	188	372
14	32.0	38	10	4	72	392
15	32.1	40	12	2	96	349
16	31.4	42	11	5	150	382
17	31.4	38	12	7	229	373
18	31.1	35	12	4	126	494
19	31.3	40	12	3	165	292
20	31.5	35	12	12	115	480
21	30.5	38	11	34	395	226
22	31.0	41	12	3	282	241
23	31.5	38	11	25	327	287
24	31.6	40	12	2	179	363
25	31.6	36	11	9	447	244
26	31.6	41	12	8	302	362
27	32.0	35	14	4	228	428
28	31.7	34	13	3	249	415
29	31.4	39	12	6	286	423
30	31.8	40	13	34	210	525
31	31.5	41	13	7	252	339
32	31.6	41	14	4	314	312
33	32.0	38	12	4	206	179
34	32.0	40	10	3	284	455
35	31.2	39	11	4	172	287
36	31.4	37	13	25	305	361
37	31.2	39	10	3	210	157
38	31.9	40	13	8	447	539
39	31.6	34	12	6	420	181
40	31.4	36	11	8	290	197

In 1973, when Herman Chernoff was studying fossil samples at Stanford University, he developed an ingenious technique for relating sets of measurements to facial characteristics. Unusual as this may seem, the graphical form that results from Chernoff's method is a caricature of each patient's measurements. For example, if MCHC represents the size of the eyes, PCV the length of the nose, HB the eccentricity of the upper head, SF the eccentricity of the lower head,

WF the smile of the mouth, and TIBC the angle of the eyebrows, then a pair of patients' measurements above might appear like this. (The faces were plotted by computer.)

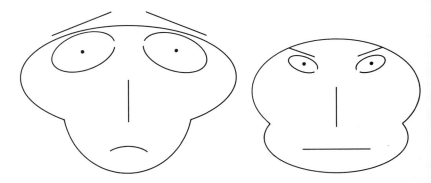

A doctor presented with these two sets of measurements in this graphical form would immediately identify contrasting details such as patient Number one's high MCHC count (large eyes) in comparison to patient Number two's; the high TIBC count (steep angle) for patient Number one, the low WF (frown) of patient Number two, etc.

Though we are not using Chernoff's technique, it illustrates the range of graphing methods. When you acquire a general understanding of the data from some form of a graphical presentation such as the faces, you can enter into more rigorous and quantitative analysis.

This section introduces a variety of presentations of data. The graphical forms introduced are **frequency diagrams** and **cumulative frequency diagrams**.

Frequency Diagrams

The first step in graphing is to organize the data in a manner that will be easily transferable to a graph. For this we use a **frequency table** that tallies the number of times a datum is recorded. Let us consider the sample data of the 40 patients, and in particular, the measurements on the PCV. After a quick scan of the column of numbers it is evident that the smallest reading is 34 and the largest is 43. We can construct a table counting the frequency of occurrence of each of the readings.

Original Data

Patient	PCV
1	42
2	39
3	38
4	42
5	39
6	35

Original Data	
Patient	**PCV**
7	37
8	43
9	38
10	34
11	39
12	39
13	43
14	38
15	40
16	42
17	38
18	35
19	40
20	35
21	38
22	41
23	38
24	40
25	36
26	41
27	35
28	34
29	39
30	40
31	41
32	41
33	38
34	40
35	39
36	37
37	39
38	40
39	34
40	36

The Frequency Table

PCV	Tally	Frequency
34					3
35						4
36				2
37				2
38	ﾊﾙ ||	7
39	ﾊﾙ ||	7
40	ﾊﾙ		6
41						4
42					3
43				2

The frequency table may now be plotted on a set of axes with the PCV reading on the horizontal axis and the frequency on the vertical axis.

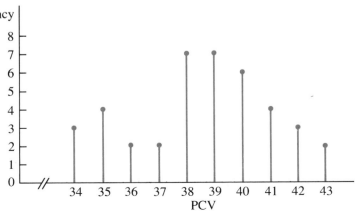

The frequency table and diagram can be modified in several ways. A **relative frequency table** may be constructed to calculate the proportion of the total number of observations that occurred at each reading. To obtain this table, divide the frequency for each reading by the total number of observations; in this case, divide by 40. Furthermore, this relative frequency value is often converted into a percentage (or a probability) for convenient interpretation. Hence, our frequency table becomes the following.

PCV	Frequency	Relative Frequency	Percentage %
34	3	$\frac{3}{40} = 0.075$	7.5
35	4	$\frac{4}{40} = 0.1$	10.0
36	2	$\frac{2}{40} = 0.05$	5.0
37	2	$\frac{2}{40} = 0.05$	5.0
38	7	$\frac{7}{40} = 0.175$	17.5
39	7	$\frac{7}{40} = 0.175$	17.5
40	6	$\frac{6}{40} = 0.15$	15.0
41	4	$\frac{4}{40} = 0.1$	10.0
42	3	$\frac{3}{40} = 0.075$	7.5
43	2	$\frac{2}{40} = 0.05$	5.0

The relative frequency diagram follows.

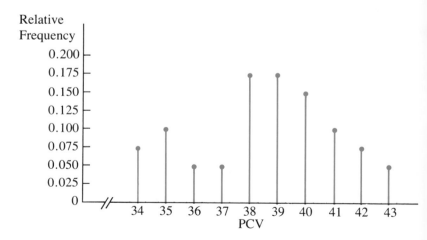

Notice that the "shape" of the frequency diagram and the relative frequency diagram are identical. Only the vertical scale has changed.

The other useful modification of the frequency table is the **cumulative frequency table** and **diagram**. With this table we can view the data in groups and answer questions such as, "How many patients had a PCV reading under 40?" This table is constructed by totaling the frequencies of the readings that are less than, or equal to, an actual reading. Cumulative percentages may be readily added to the table as well. Our table now becomes the following.

PCV	Frequency	Cumulative Frequency	Cumulative Percentage %
34	3	3	7.5
35	4	7	17.5
36	2	9	22.5
37	2	11	27.5
38	7	18	45.0
39	7	25	62.5
40	6	31	77.5
41	4	35	87.5
42	3	38	95.0
43	2	40	100.0

The cumulative frequency diagram follows.

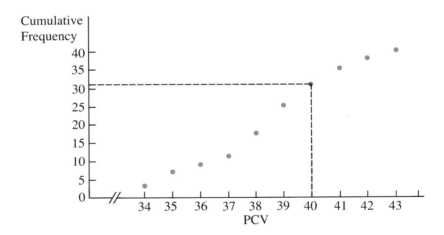

The question, "How many patients had PCV readings less than or equal to 40?" is easily answered from the diagram. As indicated by the dotted lines, the answer is 31 patients.

When we have a situation where few of the data occur more than once, as is the case with, say, the WF (whole folate) measurements of the blood samples above, it would not be very revealing to draw a frequency diagram with each measurement having a separate frequency column. In these situations we *group the data into intervals*. For example, with the whole folate data we might group the data into intervals of 10 units: 70–80, 80–90, 90–100, etc.; or intervals of 15 units: 70–85, 85–100, 100–115, etc. How do we decide which grouping to choose? There are generally a few rules-of-thumb.

> **Grouping Data**
> 1. The number of intervals should usually be between 5 and 20 to cover all of the measurements.
> 2. Make all of the intervals the same length.
> 3. Choose the intervals so that there are no gaps between them and so none of the data lies on an interval boundary.

Example 1   Construct a frequency table and draw the frequency diagram and cumulative diagram of the whole folate (WF) data in Table 1.

Solution   An initial scan of the data reveals that the smallest reading is 72 and the largest is 511, a range of $511 - 72 = 439$ numbers.

Based on Rule 1, the interval lengths should be between $\frac{439}{20} \doteq 22$ and $\frac{439}{5} \doteq 88$. We choose an interval length of 25 units. It is convenient to select the midpoints of our intervals to be integers. We choose 75, 100, 125, 150, and so on. To avoid any measurements occurring at a boundary (as suggested by Rule 3), we can let the interval boundaries be set to one decimal place more than in the data: 62.5–87.5, 87.5–112.5, 112.5–137.5, 137.5–162.5, and so on.

Our frequency table now becomes the following.

Original Data (WF)

190	192	511	170	339	139	263	215	177	252	198	239	188	72
96	150	229	126	165	115	395	282	327	179	447	302	228	249
286	210	252	314	206	284	172	305	210	447	420	290		

The Frequency Table

WF	Midpoint	Tally	Frequency	Cumulative Frequency
62.5– 87.5	75	|	1	1
87.5–112.5	100	|	1	2
112.5–137.5	125	||	2	4
137.5–162.5	150	||	2	6
162.5–187.5	175	|||||	5	11
187.5–212.5	200	|||||||	7	18
212.5–237.5	225	|||	3	21
237.5–262.5	250	||||	4	25
262.5–287.5	275	||||	4	29
287.5–312.5	300	|||	3	32
312.5–337.5	325	||	2	34
337.5–362.5	350	|	1	35
362.5–387.5	375		0	35
387.5–412.5	400	|	1	36
412.5–437.5	425	|	1	37
437.5–462.5	450	||	2	39
462.5–487.5	475		0	39
487.5–512.5	500	|	1	40

The frequency diagram

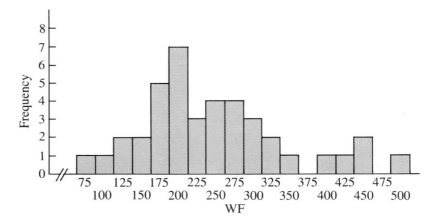

The cumulative frequency diagram

In the situation of grouped data the point that will be plotted will be the ordered pair: (upper interval boundary, cumulative frequency) because this point would represent the number of data less than or equal to the endpoint of the interval. For example, the first interval is 62.5–87.5 and the cumulative frequency is 1 at this interval, so we plot the point (87.5, 1). The second interval is 87.5–112.5 and the cumulative frequency to this interval is 2, so we plot (112.5, 2), and so on.

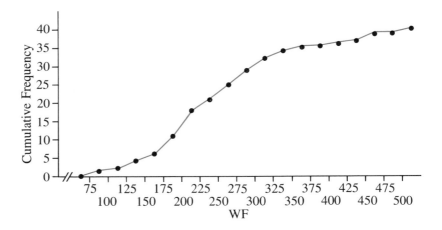

We often find tables of data that are being presented to us in newspapers or other publications. They may not follow our guidelines for grouping and they will need to be adapted to fit our rules. The following example illustrates this point.

Example 2   The following table was prepared by Statistics Canada (a governmental agency) based on census data.

Population by Age Groups, 1977.
(Source: *Canada Handbook*)

Age Group	Population in Thousands (1977)
0–4	1 745
5–9	1 856
10–14	2 209
15–19	2 369
20–24	2 198
25–34	3 749
35–44	2 639
45–54	2 476
55–64	1 979
65 +	2 069

Construct the frequency table and draw the frequency diagram.

Solution   In the grouping not all of the intervals are the same length and there are gaps between intervals (contrary to Rules 2 and 3).

The gaps can be accounted for by adding another decimal place to the interval boundaries. For example, the interval 5–9 becomes 4.5–9.5, and 10–14 becomes 9.5–14.5, and so on.

The unequal interval lengths will have to be converted to a common length 5 (the smallest interval length). We assume that over the intervals of length 10 the data were evenly distributed (this is probably why they were grouped into one interval in the first place), so when we construct the two new intervals the frequency will be divided in half. The interval 65 + can be treated as four intervals (assuming the population over 85 is comparatively small) so the frequency for each new interval will be one-fourth the frequency for the interval 65 +. Our frequency table follows.

Age	Midpoint	Frequency in Thousands
0–4.5	2	1 745
4.5–9.5	7	1 856
9.5–14.5	12	2 209
14.5–19.5	17	2 369
19.5–24.5	22	2 198
24.5–29.5	27	1 875
29.5–34.5	32	1 874
34.5–39.5	37	1 320
39.5–44.5	42	1 319
44.5–48.5	47	1 238
49.5–54.5	52	1 238
54.5–59.5	57	990
59.5–64.5	62	989
64.5–69.5	67	518
69.5–74.5	72	517
74.5–79.5	77	517
79.5–84.5	82	517

The frequency diagram follows.

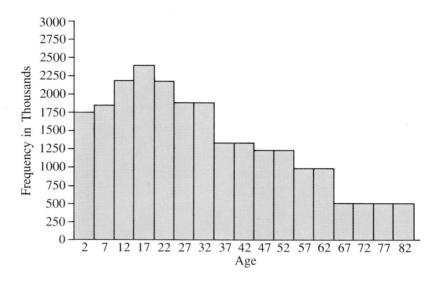

EXERCISE 7.1

 1. Suggest at least two sets of appropriate intervals based on Rules 1, 2, and 3, in which to group the following sets of data.

(a) ✔ 34 35 42 67 54 21 35 24 68 79 46 44 32 46 78 71
     31 24 23 27 89 53 61 54 67 24 65 37 39 43 55 51

(b) 1.79 2.10 1.15 2.13 1.82 1.73 1.84 2.01 2.11 1.68
     1.66 2.01 1.37 1.59 1.39 1.63 1.97 1.94 1.53 2.04

(c) −15 23 −14 20 11 15 16 −9 −12 −2 13 2 3
     10 11 −13 6 7 21 −1 21 11 19 −7 6 −8

 2. (a) Draw frequency diagrams from the following frequency tables.
       (b) Modify the frequency tables to include a relative frequency column and convert these values into percentages. Draw the relative frequency diagram.
       (c) Modify the frequency table to include a cumulative frequency column. Draw the cumulative frequency diagram.
          (i) The age distribution of students at a certain secondary school

Age	Frequency
12	15
13	25
14	123
15	136
16	101
17	87
18	71
19	12

(ii) The final-round golf scores in a major tournament

Score	Frequency
66	2
67	0
68	3
69	9
70	16
71	13
72	24
73	17
74	6
75	5
76	2

(iii)✓Collected in a telephone survey of 425 homes, the average weekly grocery bill to the nearest dollar for a family of four

Bill ($)	Frequency
29.50–39.50	7
39.50–49.50	11
49.50–59.50	18
59.50–69.50	47
69.50–79.50	33
79.50–89.50	67
89.50–99.50	82
99.50–109.50	51
109.50–119.50	40
119.50–129.50	32
129.50–139.50	16
139.50–149.50	7
149.50–159.50	9
159.50–169.50	4
169.50–179.50	1

3✓ Given the following frequency diagrams, reconstruct the frequency table and modify it to draw (i) the relative frequency diagram using percentages as the vertical scale and (ii) the cumulative frequency diagrams.

(a)

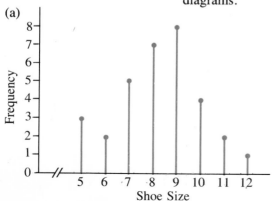

(b)✓

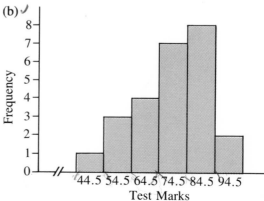

4. A promotion company suspects that the introduction of rock videos has negatively affected the attendance at live concerts. It is known from a previous survey that at least 50 percent of students attended concerts at least twice a year. A recent sample resulted in these data.

2 1 2 1 3 1 4 1 0 1 0 2 4 1 0 5 2 3 4 1
2 1 1 1 3 1 0 5 4 2 3 1 1 0 2 2 0 0 1 3

Each number is the number of concerts attended in the last year. Construct the appropriate diagram from these data to help you form an impression concerning the suspicion of the promoter.

5. The marks (%) on a recent Finite Math test were:

76 78 87 65 67 84 81 56 49 67 69 81 85 72 73 64
54 63 69 57 83 74 79 77 61 92 88 72 67

Use appropriate intervals and construct a frequency table to draw a relative frequency diagram and a cumulative frequency diagram.

6. Draw a relative frequency diagram of the TIBC data recorded on the forty patients in Table 1.

7. Draw a cumulative frequency diagram of the HB data from Table 1.

8. *Investigation:* Collect a set of numerical data (at least 40 measurements) that pertains to a topic of interest to you. Represent your data in all of the possible ways presented to you in this section. Retain your data and the diagrams for further analysis in the next section.

Suggested topics: time spent daily doing homework, heart rates after various time intervals of exercise, average daily calorie intake, academic achievements based on the number of students annually receiving A's, B's, C's and so on.

C *You often need to compare two or more frequency diagrams. It would be convenient to draw them on the same axes, but to superimpose two frequency diagrams would be very awkward. In this situation we use a **frequency polygon**, which is simply formed by joining the midpoints (for grouped data) of the tops of the frequency columns. A frequency polygon will look something like this.*

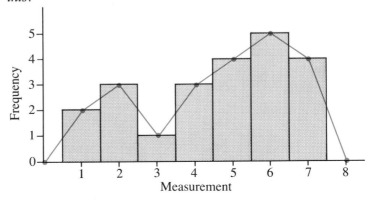

It is now quite easy to superimpose two frequency polygons on one another and you can make the necessary comparison.

9. (a) Draw frequency polygons on the same axes for the population of Canada organized by age for the years 1966 and 1977.

Population by Age Groups, 1966, 1977.
(source: *Canada Handbook*)

Age Group	Population in Thousands 1966	1977
0–4	2 197	1 745
5–9	2 301	1 856
10–14	2 093	2 209
15–19	1 838	2 369
20–24	1 461	2 198
25–34	2 483	3 749
35–39	1 272	1 320
40–44	1 271	1 319
45–49	1 050	1 238
50–54	1 028	1 238
55–59	1 220	1 000
60–64	1 260	979
65 +	1 540	2 069

(b) By comparing the frequency polygons, and by considering the effect of birth rates and life expectancy on population patterns, make a case for the argument that the population in Canada is becoming older. What implications does this pattern have on the planning required by the government to satisfy the needs of Canadians?

10. It is generally agreed that longer sentences are more difficult to read and comprehend. The following frequency table is an analysis of the first 100 sentences of *Moby Dick* by Herman Melville and *A Farewell to Arms* by Ernest Hemingway. Draw frequency polygons to compare the number of words per sentence in the two books. From your diagram discuss the construction of the sentences in the two books and decide which of the two novels would be more difficult to read. Read the novels.

Number of Words Per Sentence	Number of Sentences Moby Dick	A Farewell to Arms
0–4	8	6
5–9	19	45
10–14	10	11
15–19	12	10
20–24	12	7
25–29	12	5
30–34	10	4

| | Number of Sentences | |
Number of Words Per Sentence	Moby Dick	A Farewell to Arms
35–39	6	3
40–44	2	1
45–49	3	1
50–54	–	1
55–59	–	2
60–64	3	1
65–69	–	1
70–74	1	–
75–79	–	–
80–84	–	1
85–89	1	–
90–94	–	–
95–99	–	1
100–104	–	–
105–109	–	–
110–114	–	–
115–119	1	–
120–124	–	–
125–129	–	–
130–134	–	–
135–139	–	–
140–144	–	–
145–149	–	–
150–155	–	–
155–159	–	1

11. Further to the medical data that were collected in Table 1, a second group of 40 patients were measured and their serum folate (SF) readings were:

4 4 2 3 3 3 3 6 3 3 2 5 3 7 3 6 3 6 5 2
3 3 3 2 7 5 5 3 4 4 3 7 3 2 4 5 3 6 2 6

Compare the two groups of patients by using frequency polygons. If higher readings of SF indicate healthier patients, which group of patients do you feel is healthier?

7.2 MEASURES OF CENTRAL TENDENCY

The first stage in analyzing most numerical data is to represent them graphically as in Section 7.1. The next step is usually to find representative characteristics of the data. One of these characteristics is the centre of the data, that is, the value around which most of the data are located. Three measures of central tendency are the *mean*, the *median*, and the *mode*. Each of these measures of central tendency has unique strengths and weaknesses, which we will see in the discussion that follows.

Mean

This measure of the central tendency of the data is the sum of all of the data divided by the number of data. It is generally referred to as the **arithmetic mean** or just the **mean** and is denoted by $\bar{x}$.

$$\bar{x} = \frac{\sum\limits_{x} x}{n} \quad \text{where } \sum\limits_{x} x \text{ is the sum of all the data}$$
$$\text{and } n \text{ is the number of data}$$

Median

This is the middlemost datum. Once all of the data are put in numerical order, the middle datum is the **median**. If there is an odd number of data then the median is the $\frac{n+1}{2}$ datum; if there is an even number of data then the median is the average of the two middle data.

$$\text{median} = \begin{cases} \text{middle datum} & \text{if } n \text{ is odd} \\ \text{average of the two middle data} & \text{if } n \text{ is even} \end{cases}$$

Mode

If there is a datum that occurs *more frequently* than all of the other data, then this datum is called the **mode**. If there are two data that occur more frequently than the others, then there are two modes and the distribution of the data is described as being bimodal.

The mode is the datum that occurs most frequently.

Example 1   Five people earned annual salaries of $16 000, $21 000, $16 000, $20 000, and $150 000. Determine the mean, median, and mode of the salaries.

Solution   The mean is $\bar{x} = \dfrac{\sum\limits_{x} x}{n}$

$$= \frac{(16\ 000 + 21\ 000 + 16\ 000 + 20\ 000 + 150\ 000)}{5}$$

150 000
21 000
20 000
16 000
16 000

$$= 44\ 600$$

The median = 20 000   (the middle datum, which is the third lowest)
The mode = 16 000   (the datum that occurs the most frequently)

The mean salary is $44 600 and the median salary is $20 000 and the modal salary is $16 000.

As illustrated by the example, some measures of the centre are more appropriate than others. The mode, for instance, estimated the centre of the data as the lowest value in the data, which seems somewhat paradoxical. Let us discuss the possible situations in which each measure is appropriate or inappropriate.

1. If the data have *extreme values* that do not appear to be representative of the general nature of the information, the mean may not be the most appropriate estimate of the centre. The mean uses every datum in its calculation and the extreme values may mislead you as to the central tendency of the data. In our example, the very high salary of $150 000 inflated the mean.

2. If the nature of *the* situation suggests that *the frequency of the data is important*, the mode should be used to indicate the centre. For example, the owner of a shoe store would be very interested in the mode of the shoe sizes of a population in building stock according to the expected demand for the sizes.

3. If *further mathematical analysis* of the data is required, the mean lends itself best to this situation.

In light of these three points, it would appear that the median was the best estimator of the centre of the data in Example 1.

Example 2 The following grades were obtained on a Mathematics test marked out of 25. Determine the mean, median, and mode of the data and comment on which measure may be the most appropriate.

21 23 16 19 20 21 23· 22 17 16 18 14 17 15 16
20 21 22 17 18 23 15 14 16 15 19 21 21 17 21

Solution The mean:
$$\bar{x} = \frac{\sum\limits_{x} x}{n}$$
$$= \frac{558}{30}$$
$$= 18.6$$

The median: We order the data in a frequency table.

Grade	Tally	Frequency	Cumulative Frequency
14	||	2	2
15	|||	3	5
16	||||	4	9
17	||||	4	13
18	||	2	15
19	||	2	17
20	||	2	19
21	⧸⧸⧸⧸ |	6	25
22	||	2	27
23	|||	3	$n = 30$

The number of data is even and equal to 30. The two middlemost data would be the 15th and the 16th data. From the cumulative frequency column of the frequency table we see that the 15th datum is the grade 18 and the 16th datum is the grade 19.

So,   median $= \dfrac{18+19}{2}$

$= 18.5$

The mode: The most frequent grade from the frequency table is 21. The mode is 21.

To help us decide which measure is the most appropriate, the data can be illustrated in a frequency diagram with the measures of the central tendency marked on the horizontal axis.

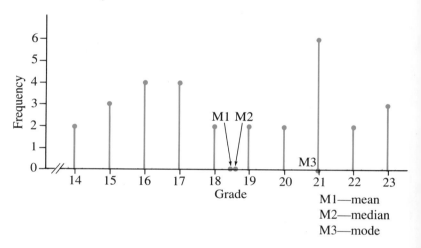

M1—mean
M2—median
M3—mode

The mode appears to have overestimated the centre of the data compared to the mean and the median. There are not any extreme values to be worried about so the mean can be considered to be a reliable measure of the centre. The median is also a good estimator of the centre.

Example 3   The averages (means) of five Finite Mathematics classes are 69, 72, 66, 75, and 78. If the class sizes were 26, 33, 25, 35, and 37 respectively, determine the overall average (mean) for the entire grade.

Solution   We require the sum of all the marks.

We know: mean $= \dfrac{\text{sum}}{n}$. Therefore, sum $= n \times (\text{mean})$

We can now determine the sum of the marks for each class and then total these to find the total grade sum.

Class	Mean	Class Size	Sum of Marks
1	69	26	$26 \times 69 = 1794$
2	72	33	$33 \times 72 = 2376$
3	66	25	$25 \times 66 = 1650$
4	75	35	$35 \times 75 = 2625$
5	78	37	$37 \times 78 = 2886$
		$n = 156$	11 331

$$\text{The overall mean} = \frac{26 \times 69 + 33 \times 72 + 25 \times 66 + 35 \times 75 + 37 \times 78}{156}$$

$$= \frac{11\ 331}{156}$$

$$\doteq 72.6$$

The average (mean) for the entire grade is 72.6%.

This last example can be generalized into what is called the *weighted mean*.

In general, the **weighted mean** is given by

$$\bar{x} = \frac{\sum wx}{\sum w}$$

where $\sum wx$ is the sum of the data times their
weightings
and $\sum w$ is the sum of the weightings.

The weightings may be determined in a variety of ways. If we have a set of data in which some data are more significant than others, then the calculation of the mean is adjusted by introducing weighting coefficients for each datum. In the example of the overall mean above, the weighting coefficients were the class sizes. The next example illustrates the subjective assignment of weightings when determining a student's report mark.

Example 4 In determining a final report mark, a teacher follows the department policy of weighting each term's work at 100 and the first and final exam at 150 each. If Orest gets the following marks for his year's work, what is his final report average?

Term 1	72	100
First exam	82	150
Term 2	68	100
Term 3	75	100
Final exam	79	150

Solution Organize the data in a table form.

Data(x)	Weighting(w)	wx
72	100	7 200
82	150	12 300
68	100	6 800
75	100	7 500
79	150	11 850
	$\sum w = 600$	$\sum wx = 45\ 650$

$$\text{the weighted average} = \frac{\sum wx}{\sum w}$$
$$= \frac{45\ 650}{600}$$
$$\doteq 76.1$$

The final report mark for Orest is 76 percent.

Our final consideration in this section is to decide what to do with data that have been *grouped* into intervals. With the convenience of computers and calculators, the *mean* should always be calculated using the original data before they are grouped into intervals. However, if you are presented with the data already summarized in a frequency table, and the original data are not available, only approximations of the centres of the data can be made. The approximation of the mean can be made using this formula.

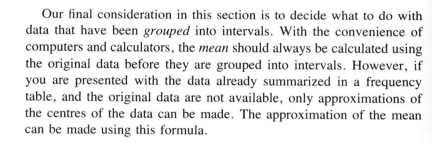

Mean for Grouped Data
$$\bar{x} = \frac{\sum fx}{\sum f} \text{ or } \frac{\sum fx}{n}$$

where $\sum fx$ is the sum of the interval midpoints times the number of data in the interval
and $\sum f$ is the sum of all of the frequencies.

This formula follows from the definition of the mean and the construction of the frequency table. The numerator in the calculation of the mean is the sum of all of the data, which can be closely approximated by multiplying the number of data that occur within an interval by the midpoint of the interval and then totalling all of these approximations to get the sum of the data. The denominator in the calculation of the mean is the number of the data, which is the total of the frequencies.

The *mode* now becomes the *modal interval*, which is readily determined from the frequency table or the frequency diagram by noting the highest number in the frequency table or the tallest column in the frequency diagram.

The *median* will now occur within an interval and can be approximated by the midpoint of the interval in which the middlemost datum occurs. (Note: An improved approximation of the median may be made by *linear interpolation* within the interval, as in Question 10 of the exercises.) This interval is readily found from the cumulative frequency column.

Example 6   The following table represents the number of hours per day of watching TV in a sample of 500 people.

Number of Hours	0–1	2–3	4–5	6–7	8–9	10–11	12–13
Frequency	64	92	141	86	71	35	11

(a)   What is the mean number of TV viewing hours in this group?
(b)   What length of time is most often spent in front of a TV by this group?
(c)   What is the median number of TV viewing hours?

Solution   (a)   Construct a frequency table with an added column for *fx*.

Interval	Midpoint (x)	Frequency (f)	Cumulative Frequency	fx
0– 1.5	0.5	64	64	64 × 0.5 = 32.0
1.5– 3.5	2.5	92	156	92 × 2.5 = 230.0
3.5– 5.5	4.5	141	297	141 × 4.5 = 634.5
5.5– 7.5	6.5	86	383	86 × 6.5 = 559.0
7.5– 9.5	8.5	71	454	71 × 8.5 = 603.5
9.5–11.5	10.5	35	489	35 × 10.5= 367.5
11.5–13.5	12.5	11	$n = 500$	11 × 12.5= 137.5
		$n = \sum f = 500$		$\sum fx = 2564.0$

So, the mean is $\bar{x} = \dfrac{\sum fx}{\sum f}$

$$= \frac{2564}{500}$$

$$\doteq 5.1$$

The mean number of viewing hours for this group was approximately five hours.

(b)   We must determine the mode to answer this question. From the table, the modal interval is identified by the largest frequency value, 141. The modal interval is 3.5–5.5. The most frequent period of time spent in front of a TV by this group is between four and five hours per day.

(c) The median is the middlemost datum. The number of data is even, so the median will be the average of the 250th datum and the 251st datum from an ordered list of the data. By referring to the cumulative frequency column we notice that the 250th and 251st data occur in the interval 3.5–5.5. We would then estimate the median to be 4.5 h of viewing time.

EXERCISE 7.2

A **1.** Determine the median from the following cumulative frequency diagrams.

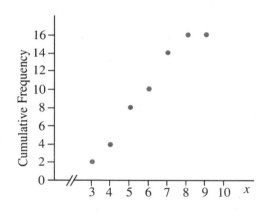 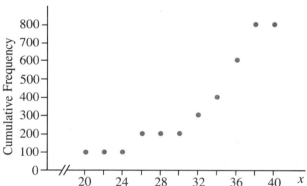

2. Discuss the appropriateness of each measure of the central tendency in the following situations.
(a) The data are a class set of Finite Mathematics test marks.
(b) The data are the ages of individuals involved in motor vehicle accidents.
(c) The data are the salaries of the players on a professional football team.
(d) The data are the model years of vehicles on the road.
(e) The data are the number of wage earners in a home.
(f) The data are the scores in a national Mathematics contest.

B **3.** The following data represent the ages of the teachers at a local secondary school.
25 27 54 34 36 31 29 32 47 48 59 24 33 45 48
32 37 39 41 51 26 24 33 49 58 57 25 27 55 51

(a) Determine the mean age of the teachers.

(b) What is the median age of the teachers?

(c) Group the data into eight intervals and determine the modal interval of their ages.

(d) Draw a frequency diagram of the grouped data. Which measure of central tendency do you think best describes the distribution of the ages?

4. The following table of data represents the distribution of salaries in a small company.

Fea

Salary in Thousands of Dollars	Number of Employees
9.5–19.5	26
19.5–29.5	10
29.5–39.5	6
39.5–49.5	3
49.5–59.5	0
59.5–69.5	0
69.5–79.5	0
79.5–89.5	2
89.5–99.5	3

(a) What is the mean salary in the company? *28 300*

(b) What is the median salary of the company? *14 500*

(c) It is a situation such as this that leads to the misuse of statistics. If contract negotiations were about to begin what measure would you expect labour to quote and which measure would you expect management to quote?

5. Facing accusations of discriminatory pay scales between male and female employees, an employer states that the women are paid better on the average than the men. Given the following data collected from the company, on what measure of central tendency is the employer basing his statement?

Salaries in $1000's	Number of Male Employees	Number of Female Employees
4.5– 9.5	3	5
9.5–14.5	8	7
14.5–19.5	7	10
19.5–24.5	5	3
24.5–29.5	4	2
29.5–34.5	6	1
34.5–39.5	4	0
39.5–44.5	3	0

6. In a certain school the valedictorian is chosen by popular vote of the entire student body. However, the votes are given weightings equal to the number of years that the voter has been in secondary school.

The voting is summarized in the table that follows.

Candidate	1-year Students	2-year Students	3-year Students	4-year Students	5-year Students
Tobias	23	12	13	11	7
Louise	34	21	16	23	19
Lulu	14	23	15	17	17
Orlon	19	17	19	24	14

(a) What is the weighted average for each candidate?

(b) Draw frequency polygons and compare the popularity of the candidates with the junior and senior students.

(c) Who is the valedictorian?

7. A teacher decides to weight her students' assignments using the following scheme.

(1) Tests are worth five times as much as homework assignments.

(2) Exams are worth three times as much as tests.

The results for one of her students for the term are the following.

Assignment	Grade (%)
Homework 1	75
Test 1	64
Homework 2	85
Homework 3	79
Test 2	72
Homework 4	90
Homework 5	85
Test 3	66
Exam	63

Determine the student's mark for the term.

8. (a) Further to our analysis of the novel *Moby Dick* by Herman Melville (Exercise 7.1, Question 10), we have counted the number of long words, that is, a word with three or more syllables, in the first 100 sentences.

Moby Dick

Number of Long Words Per Sentence	0	1	2	3	4	5	6	7	8	9	10	11	12	13	14	15
Number of Sentences	35	23	19	7	7	3	2	2	–	–	–	–	1	–	1	–

(i) Determine the *fog index*, which is an index number that indicates how difficult a passage of prose is to read. The **fog index**, FI, is given by the formula

$$FI = (L + W) \times 0.4$$

where L is the mean number of long words per sentence, and W is the mean number of words per sentence.

(The data on the number of words per sentence can be found in Question 10 of Exercise 7.1.)

(ii)   Now categorize the novel according to the following chart.

FI	Readability
0–9.5	A child can read it.
9.5–13.5	Suitable to the average reader.
13.5–17.5	You need a university degree.
>17.5	Good luck!

(b)   Determine the fog index of the following passage taken from a legal document, and categorize the prose as to its readability.

"In consideration of the premium charged and subject to the provisions hereof, it is understood and agreed that the insurer shall indemnify each eligible claimant for the amount that such eligible claimant is legally entitled to recover from an inadequately insured motorist as compensatory damages in respect of bodily injury or death sustained by an insured person by accident arising out of the use or operation of an automobile.

The insurer's maximum liability under this endorsement, regardless of the number of eligible claimants, or number of insured persons injured or killed, or number of automobiles insured under the policy shall be the amount by which the Limit of Family Protection Coverage exceeds the total of all limits of motor vehicle liability insurance, or bonds, or cash deposits, or other financial guarantees as required by law in lieu of such insurance, of the inadequately insured motorist and of any person jointly liable therewith."

C **9.**   (a)   Show that if a constant k is added to each datum the mean of the new data is $\bar{x} + k$.

(b)   Show that if every datum is multiplied by a factor c the mean is $c \times \bar{x}$.

10.   When you are dealing with grouped data, a better approximation of the median may be made by *linear interpolation*. This procedure first identifies the interval in which the median is found. Instead of selecting the midpoint of this interval, we approximate the median by choosing the point within the interval that is a distance proportional to the number of data required to reach the median.

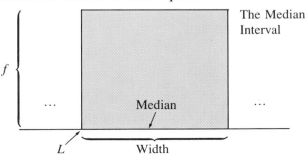

The median is given by

$$
\text{median} = L + \left(\frac{d}{f}\right) \times \text{width}
$$

where L is the lower boundary of the median interval,
 width is the width of the interval, that is, the upper boundary minus the lower boundary,
 d is the distance into the median interval to reach the middlemost datum,
 f is the frequency of the median interval,
Determine the median of the following data by linear interpolation.

Length in cm	Frequency
0.5–100.5	256
100.5–200.5	312
200.5–300.5	167
300.5–400.5	257
400.5–500.5	378
500.5–600.5	234
600.5–700.5	196

7.3 MEASURE OF SPREAD

We have graphed data and have determined measures of central tendency. The next most interesting and revealing characteristic to determine is the spread of the data. This characteristic describes how widely the data fluctuates about its central location. The following example illustrates two sets of data that have measures of central location that are very close but considerably different measures of spread.

Example 1   At a certain point during a 40-minute class, Finite Mathematics students were asked to estimate the number of minutes that they thought had elapsed in the period. They were asked to estimate it in two ways: (i) without the aid of a timepiece; (ii) with the aid of a timepiece. The estimates were collected and are summarized in the tables below and on the next page.

(a) Without a timepiece

Time Elapsed	10	11	12	13	14	15	16	17	18	19	20	21	22
Number of Students	1	2	1	3	5	6	8	5	2	1	0	1	2

(b) With a timepiece

Time Elapsed	14	15	16	17	18
Number of Students	1	2	22	11	1

Determine the mean of both sets of data and draw their frequency diagrams.

Solution Construct the frequency tables.

(a) Without a timepiece

Time (x)	Frequency (f)	fx
10	1	10
11	2	22
12	1	12
13	3	39
14	5	70
15	6	90
16	8	128
17	5	85
18	2	36
19	1	19
20	0	0
21	1	21
22	2	44
	$n = \sum f = 37$	$\sum fx = 576$

The mean is $\bar{x} = \frac{576}{37}$

$\doteq 15.6$

The mean estimate without a timepiece of the time that elapsed is approximately 16 minutes.

(b) With a timepiece

Time (x)	Frequency (f)	fx
14	1	14
15	2	30
16	22	352
17	11	187
18	1	18
	$n = \sum f = 37$	$\sum fx = 601$

The mean is $\bar{x} = \frac{601}{37}$

$= 16.2$

·The mean estimate with a timepiece of the time that elapsed is also approximately 16 minutes.

The frequency diagrams

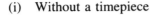

(i) Without a timepiece

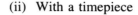

(ii) With a timepiece

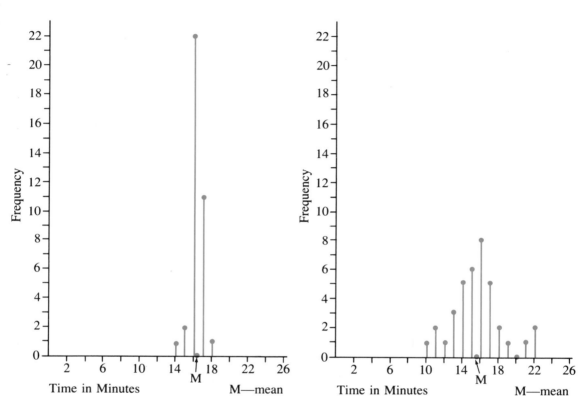

Notice that both sets of data centre around the value 16, but the fluctuation of the data about this central location is significantly different in each case.

In this section we see two measurements that are used to describe this spread of the data. They are called *the interquartile range* and *the mean deviation*.

Interquartile Range

The *range* of the data is, as the term suggests, the difference between the largest value and the smallest value. However, this measure of the spread of the data is of limited value because it relies on only two data to describe the variability of an entire set of data. To improve on this measure of spread we can determine the size of the interval in which the central half of the data lies.

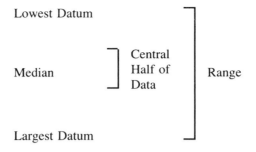

The lower point of this interval, chosen so that one quarter of the data are less than or equal to it, is called the **first quartile Q1**. The upper point of this interval, with three quarters of the data less than it, is the **third quartile Q3**. The difference between the two is called the **interquartile range**. Half of this interquartile range is called the **semi-interquartile range**.

Lowest Datum

First Quartile Q1 ⎤

Median ⎥ Interquartile range ⎤ Semi-interquartile
                    (central half of the data) ⎦ Range

Third Quartile Q3 ⎦   ⎤ Semi-interquartile
                                                 ⎦ Range

Largest Datum

These are often revealing values to mark on a frequency diagram.

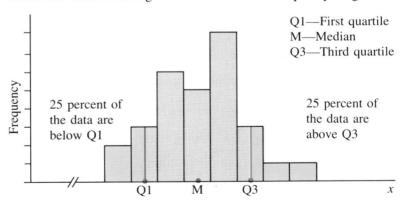

It is quite evident that we could use another name for the *median*, which would be the **second quartile** representing the datum for which two quarters of the data are less than or equal to it. This is precisely the definition of the median.

We sometimes speak of being "in" a quartile, which appears to contradict the definition of a quartile. How can one be inside a point?

What is implied by this common usage of the term is that we are in the interval up to that quartile. For example, if a datum is in the first quartile then at least 75 percent of the data are greater than this datum.

The quartiles are readily obtained from an *ordered list* of the data or from the *cumulative frequency* table or diagram in a way that is similar to determining the median.

Example 2   The following data represent 20 people's estimates of the size of a crowd at a public gathering.

650 400 500 600 700 500 600 700 450 750
1000 550 625 575 750 900 650 700 575 800

Determine the median and the interquartile range.

Solution   The number of data is even so the median will be the means of adjacent data. In fact, because the number of data is a multiple of four, the quartiles will be the means of adjacent data.

Order the data from smallest to largest.

Order	Data	
1	400	
2	450	
3	500	
4	500	
5	550	
6	575	] Q1
7	575	
8	600	
9	600	
10	625	
11	650	] Median
12	650	
13	700	
14	700	
15	700	
16	750	] Q3
17	750	
18	800	
19	900	
20	1000	

$$\text{Median} = \text{(average of 10th and 11th data)} \qquad \left[\tfrac{2}{4} \times 20 = 10\right]$$
$$= \frac{625 + 650}{2}$$
$$= 637.5$$

First quartile, Q1 = (average of 5th and 6th data) $\left[\frac{1}{4} \times 20 = 5\right]$

$$= \frac{550 + 572}{2}$$

$$= 567.5$$

Third quartile, Q3 = (average of 15th and 16th data) $\left[\frac{3}{4} \times 20 = 15\right]$

$$= \frac{700 + 750}{2}$$

$$= 725$$

Interquartile range = Q3 − Q1

$$= 725 - 567.5$$

$$= 157.5$$

Semi-interquartile range = $(157.5) \times \frac{1}{2}$

$$= 78.25 \text{ or } 78.2$$

The median of the estimates of the crowd is 637.5 with half of the estimates within 78.2 of this.

Mean Deviation

The second measurement used to describe the spread of data about its central location is called the mean deviation and is given by the following.

mean deviation $= \dfrac{\displaystyle\sum_{x} |x - \bar{x}|}{n}$ for ungrouped data

$= \dfrac{\displaystyle\sum_{x} |f(x - \bar{x})|}{n}$ for grouped data

$|x - \bar{x}|$ is the absolute value of the difference between the datum x and the mean $\bar{x}$;

$|f(x - \bar{x})|$ is the absolute value of the difference between the midpoint of an interval and the mean, times the number of data within that interval;

n is the number of data.

This measure of spread looks at each datum, calculates its deviation from the mean, totals all of these deviations and then divides by the number of data to find the mean of the deviations. The absolute value is used to ensure that negative deviations do not cancel out positive ones.

Example 3   Wen recently moved to a major city and was eager to know the average commuting time required to get to work. She recorded the following data, which represents the number of minutes from door to office over ten working days.

$$55 \quad 68 \quad 83 \quad 59 \quad 68 \quad 75 \quad 62 \quad 78 \quad 97 \quad 83$$

Determine the mean and mean deviation of her commuting time.

Solution   (a)   The mean is $\bar{x} = \dfrac{55 + 68 + \ldots + 97 + 83}{10}$

$$= 72.8$$

To determine the mean deviation, organize the data in a table.

Commuting Time (x)	Absolute Deviation $\lvert x - \bar{x} \rvert$
55	$\lvert 55 - 72.8 \rvert = 17.8$
68	$\lvert 68 - 72.8 \rvert = 4.8$
83	$\lvert 83 - 72.8 \rvert = 10.2$
59	$\lvert 59 - 72.8 \rvert = 13.8$
68	$\lvert 68 - 72.8 \rvert = 4.8$
75	$\lvert 75 - 72.8 \rvert = 2.2$
62	$\lvert 62 - 72.8 \rvert = 10.8$
78	$\lvert 78 - 72.8 \rvert = 5.2$
97	$\lvert 97 - 72.8 \rvert = 24.2$
83	$\lvert 83 - 72.8 \rvert = 10.2$
	$\sum\limits_{x} \lvert x - x \rvert = 104.0$

The mean deviation $= \dfrac{\sum\limits_{x} \lvert x - \bar{x} \rvert}{n}$

$$= \dfrac{104.0}{10}$$

$$= 10.4$$

Wen's mean commuting time to her office is approximately 73 min with a mean deviation of approximately 10 min.

To be relatively sure of being on time, perhaps Wen should allow the mean time plus one mean deviation or $73 + 10 = 83$ min.

EXERCISE 7.3

B **1.**   Given the following sets of data, determine the two measures of spread: the interquartile range and the mean deviation.

(a)   Lengths of machined bolts (mm)

$$33.2 \quad 34.0 \quad 33.5 \quad 33.6 \quad 33.7 \quad 34.1 \quad 34.0 \quad 33.9 \quad 33.2 \quad 33.7$$
$$33.2 \quad 33.1 \quad 33.5 \quad 33.6 \quad 34.0 \quad 33.9 \quad 33.8 \quad 33.4 \quad 33.6 \quad 33.5$$

(b) Distance from the bull's-eye (cm) in the throwing of darts

10.2 3.5 21.0 15.4 11.4 0.0 17.4 18.3 7.4
16.7 8.9 16.7 13.9 3.7 2.5 10.4 14.6 19.2

(c) Mass of individual students (kg)

Mass	45–49	50–54	55–59	60–64	65–69	70–74	75–79	80–84
Frequency	12	15	23	18	10	7	4	2

(d) Average daily interest ($) accumulated in savings accounts

Interest	0.50–10.50	10.50–20.50	20.50–30.50	30.50–40.50
Frequency	32	11	5	2

2. The following set of data represents the gas consumption (litres per 100 km) of a car under test conditions.

12.3 11.7 11.9 12.1 13.2 12.9 11.5 12.3 12.2
11.9 13.7 12.4 11.6 11.8 12.5 13.0 12.5 11.3

(a) Determine the mean and mean deviation.
(b) What percentage of the data are within one mean deviation of the mean?
(c) What percentage of the data are within two mean deviations of the mean?

3. *Investigation:* From a ball of string, cut 20 lengths of string approximately 10 cm long, first with your eyes open and a second time with your eyes closed (do not use a ruler or previous cuts to measure subsequent cuts). Measure your cuts and compare the variability of the two sets of data.

*Quartiles divide a set of data into quarters. We need not restrict ourselves to dividing the data into only fourths. If we divide the data into 100 parts then the term **percentile** is used. For example, the 99th percentile would represent the datum that exceeds 99 percent of the data. The 47th percentile is the datum that exceeds 47 percent of the data.*

4. (a) On a recent aptitude test, Carrie was rated in the 93rd percentile. If 1068 people wrote the test, how many people had a lower score on the test than Carrie did?
   (b) In a popular mathematics competition, only the contestants in the top 5 percentiles win Diplomas of Distinction. If there were 478 contestants, how many Diplomas of Distinction would be awarded?

5. The following set of data represents the decibel level of music that a sample of students prefers.

110 79 89 92 84 78 92 36 79 104 110
95 100 105 88 83 91 73 115 84 98 90

For reference, here are some common sounds in decibels:

Sound	Decibels
Jet takeoff at 50 m	120
Jet takeoff at 500 m	100
Highway traffic at 15 m	70
Noisy office	50
Soft whisper at 15 m	30

(a)   Determine the interquartile range that contains the middle 50 percent of the data.

(b)   Determine the decibel interval that contains the middle 20 percent of the data.

(c)   Determine the decibel interval that contains the upper 5 percent of the data.

C **6.**   Another measure of central tendency of data is called the **interquartile mean**. It is a weighted mean of the first, second (median), and third quartiles. It is given by,

$$\text{Interquartile mean} = \frac{Q1 + 4Q2 + Q3}{6}$$

(a)   What advantages do you see in this measure over both the arithmetic mean and the median?

(b)   Determine the interquartile mean of the following data that represent annual consumption (kg) of meat by wrestlers.

350   275   240   310   295   315   500   200   350   270   415   435
345   295   300   265   260   415   485   430   510   485   455   320
260   205   305   265   285   315   395   425   460   375   315   275

7.4   THE STANDARD DEVIATION

The previous section introduced the interquartile range and the mean deviation, which are used to describe the spread of data about their centre. We now look at the most commonly used measurement of spread: *the standard deviation*. The standard deviation is widely used because of its ease in computing and also because of its mathematical form that has facilitated the development of further statistical theories.

$$\textbf{Standard Deviation, } s = \sqrt{\frac{\sum\limits_{x} (x - \bar{x})^2}{n}}$$

Notice the similarity of its form to the mean deviation. The mean deviation used absolute values to ensure that there were no negative values in the summation, and the standard deviation uses the technique of squaring the deviations. The square root is taken after the summation to compensate for this squaring.

The computation of the standard deviation would appear to be very similar to the way in which we computed the mean deviations. However, we can express the standard deviation in another form that will be to our advantage.

$$s = \sqrt{\frac{\sum\limits_{x} (x - \bar{x})^2}{n}}$$

$$= \sqrt{\frac{\sum\limits_{x} (x^2 - 2x\bar{x} + \bar{x}^2)}{n}}$$

$$= \sqrt{\frac{\sum\limits_{x} x^2 - \sum\limits_{x} 2x\bar{x} + \sum\limits_{x} \bar{x}^2}{n}}$$

$$= \sqrt{\frac{\sum\limits_{x} x^2 - 2\bar{x} \sum\limits_{x} x + n\bar{x}^2}{n}}$$

$$= \sqrt{\frac{\sum\limits_{x} x^2}{n} - 2\bar{x} \frac{\sum\limits_{x} x}{n} + \bar{x}^2}$$

$$= \sqrt{\frac{\sum\limits_{x} x^2}{n} - 2\bar{x}(\bar{x}) + \bar{x}^2}$$

$$= \sqrt{\frac{\sum\limits_{x} x^2}{n} - \bar{x}^2}$$

$$= \sqrt{\frac{\left(\sum\limits_{x} x^2\right) - n\bar{x}^2}{n}}$$

This form implies that we need only sum the squares of all of the data $\left(\sum\limits_{x} x^2\right)$, determine the mean and substitute this information into this form. We omit the step of determining each deviation and squaring it.

The computational form of the standard deviation:

$$s = \sqrt{\frac{\left(\sum\limits_{x} x^2\right) - n\bar{x}^2}{n}}$$

Example 1 Calculate the standard deviation of Wen's commuting time in minutes (as seen in Example 3 of Section 7.3) from the following data:

$$55 \quad 68 \quad 83 \quad 59 \quad 68 \quad 75 \quad 62 \; 78 \quad 97 \quad 83$$

Solution The mean has already been calculated in Example 3 and is 72.8. Organize the computations in a table.

Commuting time (x)	x^2
55	3 025
68	4 624
83	6 889
59	3 481
68	4 624
75	5 625
62	3 844
78	6 084
97	9 409
83	6 889

$$\sum_x x^2 = 54\ 494$$

The standard deviation,

$$s = \sqrt{\frac{\left(\sum_x x^2\right) - n\bar{x}^2}{n}}$$

$$= \sqrt{\frac{54\ 494 - (10)(72.8^2)}{10}}$$

$$= \sqrt{149.56}$$

$$\doteq 12.23$$

Wen's average commuting time is 72.8 minutes with a standard deviation of 12.23 minutes.

The interpretation of the standard deviation is less intuitive than both the interquartile range and the mean deviation. It is another measure of the average deviations of data from the mean. But a theorem has been developed as well to describe what percentage of the data occur within so many standard deviations of the mean.

Peter Chebyshev was a Russian mathematician who lived from 1821 to 1894.

Chebyshev's Theorem

Given a set of data with mean $\bar{x}$ and standard deviation s, then at least $\left(1 - \dfrac{1}{k^2}\right)$, $k > 1$, of the data lies within k standard deviations of the mean.

Let us tabulate some of the results for this theorem for different values of k.

Value of k	Minimum Proportion of Data Within k Standard Deviations of the Mean	
2	$1 - \frac{1}{4} = \frac{3}{4}$	(or at least 75 percent)
3	$1 - \frac{1}{9} = \frac{8}{9}$	(or at least 89 percent)
4	$1 - \frac{1}{16} = \frac{15}{16}$	(or at least 94 percent)

These percentages are very conservative estimates because the theorem must account for every distribution, no matter how unusual. In fact, once the distribution of the data is known, these percentages become significantly larger. For example, with a certain distribution called the normal distribution (which we will encounter in Section 7.5) we find 95 percent of the data within two standard deviations of the mean rather than 75 percent as suggested by Chebyshev's theorem.

Example 2   An individual's commuting time (min) to work has mean 73 min and standard deviation 12 min. How early should the person leave home to be sure of arriving at work on time at least 80 percent of the time?

Solution   We need to determine the number of standard deviations, k, that encloses at least 80 percent or $\frac{4}{5}$ of the data.

$$\text{Using Chebyshev's Theorem, we solve } 1 - \frac{1}{k^2} = \frac{4}{5}$$
$$\frac{1}{k^2} = \frac{1}{5}$$
$$k = \sqrt{5}$$

The person should leave $73 + (\sqrt{5})(12) \doteq 100$ min before the start of work to be punctual at least 80 percent of the time.

The number of standard deviations that data are from the mean is a very important concept in statistics. The term used to describe a datum's fluctuation from the mean is its *z-score*.

> The **z-score** is the number of standard deviations a datum is from the mean, and is given by
>
> $$z = \frac{x - \bar{x}}{s}$$

Example 3 Show that the mean and standard deviation of the z-scores of the following set of data are 0 and 1, respectively.

$$10 \quad 11 \quad 14 \quad 16 \quad 19 \quad 20$$

Solution We tabulate the data to compute the mean and standard deviation.

x	x^2
10	100
11	121
14	196
16	256
19	361
20	400
$\sum\limits_{x} x = 90$	$\sum\limits_{x} x^2 = 1434$

The mean is $\bar{x} = \frac{90}{6} = 15$.

The standard deviation is $s = \sqrt{\dfrac{1434 - (6)(15^2)}{6}}$

$$= \sqrt{14}$$

$$= 3.74$$

The z-scores and their distribution can now be determined.

x	$z = \dfrac{(x - \bar{x})}{s}$	z^2
10	$\dfrac{(10-15)}{3.74} = -1.34$	1.79
11	-1.07	1.14
14	-0.27	0.07
16	0.27	0.07
19	1.07	1.14
20	1.34	1.79
	$\sum\limits_{z} z = 0$	$\sum\limits_{z} z^2 = 6.0$

The mean of the z-scores is $\dfrac{\left(\sum\limits_{z} z\right)}{n} = \dfrac{0}{6} = 0$.

The standard deviation of the z-scores is

$$\sqrt{\dfrac{\sum\limits_{z} z^2 - n\bar{z}^2}{6}} = \sqrt{\dfrac{6.0 - (6)(0)}{6}} = 1$$

The results seen in Example 3 are true in general.

> The distribution of the z-scores of a set of data has mean 0 and standard deviation 1.

You will be asked to prove this result in Question 7 of the exercises.

The standard deviation formula for grouped data follows.

> **Grouped Data**
>
> standard deviation, $s = \sqrt{\dfrac{\sum\limits_{x} f(x - \bar{x})^2}{n}}$
>
> and in computational form, $s = \sqrt{\dfrac{\sum\limits_{x} fx^2 - n\bar{x}^2}{n}}$

EXERCISE 7.4

B **1.** Given the following sets of data, determine the means and the standard deviations.
   (a) Lengths of machined bolts (mm)
      33.2 34.0 33.5 33.6 33.7 34.1 34.0 33.9 33.2 33.7
      33.2 33.1 33.5 33.6 34.0 33.9 33.8 33.4 33.6 33.5
   (b) Distance from the bull's-eye (cm) in the throwing of darts
      10.2 3.5 21.0 15.4 11.4 0.0 17.4 18.3 7.4
      16.7 8.9 16.7 13.9 3.7 2.5 10.4 14.6 19.2
   (c) Masses of students (kg)

Mass	45–49	50–54	55–59	60–64	65–69	70–74	75–79	80–84
Frequency	12	15	23	18	10	7	4	2

   (d) Average daily interest ($) accumulated in savings accounts

Interest	0.50–10.50	10.50–20.50	20.50–30.50	30.50–40.50
Frequency	32	11	5	2

2. A set of Finite Mathematics test marks has mean 70 and standard deviation 10.
   (a) What is the least estimate of the percentage of the marks one would find within one-and-a-half standard deviations of the mean?

(b) If the number of students in the class was 42, at most, how many of the marks would be outside one-and-a-half standard deviations of the mean?

(c) Within how many standard deviations would we find at least 50 percent of the marks?

(d) What is the minimum number of marks that we would find in the interval between 45 and 95?

3. The following set of data represents the fuel consumption (litres per 100 km) of a car under test conditions.

12.3 11.7 11.9 12.1 13.2 12.9 11.5 12.3 12.2
11.9 13.7 12.4 11.6 11.8 12.5 13.0 12.5 11.3

(a) Determine the mean and standard deviation.

(b) How many of the data should we find within two standard deviations of the mean according to Chebyshev's Theorem? Confirm that this is true by counting the number of data that actually lie within the two standard deviations.

4. A set of data has mean 65 and standard deviation 7. Determine the number of standard deviations

(a) the datum 72 is from the mean.

(b) the datum c is from the mean.

5. Academic prizes at secondary schools are often based on the means of the grades obtained in the various courses. David and Maureen, the top two students in the school, have grades as follows.

David:

Course	Canadian History	American History	English I	English II	World Issues	Geography
Grade	84	86	85	89	91	92

Maureen:

Course	Math I	Math II	Math III	Physics	Chemistry	Biology
Grade	95	94	97	94	89	95

(a) Based on the means, which of the two students would win the academic prize?

(b) Given the following table of the courses' means and standard deviations, find the z-scores for Maureen's and David's grades.

Course	Mean	Standard Deviation
Can. History	70	5
Am. History	68	7
English I	72	4
English II	71	8
World Issues	74	6
Geography	69	10
Math I	66	11

Course	Mean	Standard Deviation
Math II	68	9
Math III	69	12
Physics	70	8
Chemistry	69	11
Biology	73	8

(c) If the academic prize was awarded to the student with the highest mean of the z-scores of the courses, which student, David or Maureen, would receive the prize?

(d) Discuss the merits of awarding prizes based on z-scores rather than the actual course grades.

C **6.** Derive the computational form of the standard deviation for grouped data from the following definition

$$s = \sqrt{\frac{\sum f(x - \bar{x})^2}{n}}$$

7. Show that the distribution of the z-scores for any set of data has mean 0 and standard deviation 1.

8. What is the effect on the standard deviation of adding a constant k to every datum?

7.5 NORMAL DISTRIBUTION

Data are collected in many situations in industry to determine how accurately equipment is operating. For example, data are often collected in a production process to ensure that the product produced is within acceptable limits of its intended design.

The distribution of data of this type has been studied extensively and is often referred to as the "distribution of errors."

In these situations the following common characteristics arise in the data.

1. The data can be considered to be continuous, that is, the data can take any real values and not just integer values as was the case with discrete data.

2. The data are symmetrically distributed about the mean, that is, data are just as likely to be below the mean as they are to be above it.
3. The probability of getting a result in a certain interval will decrease as the distance the interval is from the mean increases.
4. The frequency diagram has the following shape.

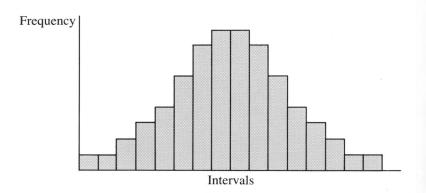

If the intervals were allowed to become very small, the relative frequency polygon of the distribution would be a smooth curve looking like the following.

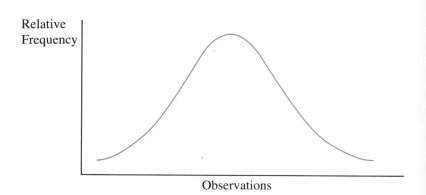

Such a curve that takes this characteristic bell shape is called a **normal curve**. It is also referred to as the *error curve* or the *Gaussian curve* because it was studied by Gauss in his research in the distribution of errors.

A normal curve has the following properties.

(i)   It is symmetric about the mean, denoted by the Greek letter mu, μ.
(ii) The standard deviation, sigma, σ, is the distance from the mean to the points of inflection of the curve (a point of inflection is a point on the curve where a 'hill' begins to turn into a 'valley')
(iii) the area under the curve equals one (the sum of the relative frequencies is one).

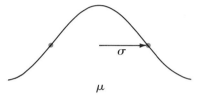

We use the Greek letters μ and σ for the mean and the standard deviation to indicate that we are describing an entire population of data while $\bar{x}$ and s describe a sample from a population of data.

The normal curve is completely determined by its mean and standard deviation so the notation used to describe a normal curve is $N(\mu, \sigma^2)$ where σ^2 is the standard deviation squared, called the **variance**. For example, the three normal distributions $N(0, 1)$, $N(5, 2^2)$, $N(15, 4^2)$ would look like the following.

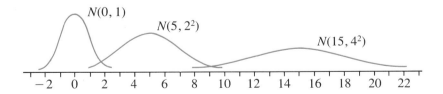

Recall that Chebyshev's Theorem from the previous section described the percentage of the data that occurred within so many standard deviations of the mean. Now that we know the distribution of the data we can make much more refined estimates of these percentages. In fact, the following diagrams summarize these estimates for data that are distributed normally.

Within one standard deviation of the mean approximately 68 percent of the data will be found.

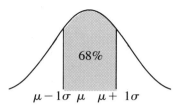

Within two standard deviations of the mean approximately 95 percent of the data will be found.

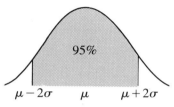

Verification of these approximations will be required in Question 14 of the exercises.

The area under every normal curve equals one and hence allows us to determine probabilities. The probability that an observation will be in a given interval will be equal to the area under the normal curve bounded by that interval. The following diagrams illustrate this point.

$X \sim N(75, 5^2)$
This area would represent $P(75 < X < 80)$

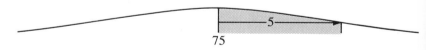

$X \sim N(20, 3^2)$
This area would represent $P(X > 23)$

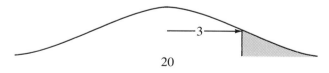

The notation $X \sim N(75, 5^2)$ is read "X is distributed normally with mean 75 and variance 5^2." In order to determine probabilities it is necessary to calculate the areas under the curves. The areas under the normal curve $N(0, 1)$ for various values of X have been tabulated and can be found in Table 1, Appendix A. The following example demonstrates the use of this table.

Example 1   If $X \sim N(0, 1)$, find the following probabilities using Table 1 in Appendix A.

(a) $P(X < 1)$

(b) $P(X > 1.5)$

(c) $P(-1 < X < 1.5)$

Solution   (a) The area under the normal curve $N(0, 1)$ to determine $P(X < 1)$ is pictured below.

$N(0, 1)$

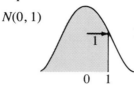

From the table, $P(X < 1) = 0.8413$

(b) The area under the normal curve $N(0, 1)$ to determine $P(X > 1.5)$ is pictured below.

$N(0, 1)$

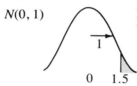

From the tables, $P(X<1.5) = 0.9332$
The total area under the curve is 1, so
$$P(X>1.5) = 1 - P(X < 1.5)$$
$$= 1 - 0.9332$$
$$= 0.0668$$

(c) The area under the normal curve $N(0, 1)$ to determine $P(-1 < X < 1.5)$ is pictured below.

$N(0, 1)$

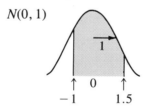

To determine this area we subtract areas that can be found from the table.

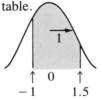 $=$ 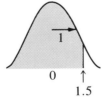 $-$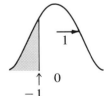

So, $P(-1 < X < 1.5) = P(X < 1.5) - P(X < -1)$
$$= 0.9332 - 0.1587 \quad \text{(from table)}$$
$$= 0.7745$$

For normal distributions other than $N(0, 1)$, we can perform a transformation on the variables to reduce the curve to the $N(0, 1)$ distribution.

Once we have done this we can use Table 1 to determine the required probability. The transformation is given by the following.

$$\text{If } X \sim N(\mu, \sigma^2), \text{ then } Z = \frac{X - \mu}{\sigma} \sim N(0, 1)$$

The reduction of a distribution to the $N(0, 1)$ distribution is called **standardizing** and the random variable Z is called the **standard variate**.

Example 2

Find the following probabilities.
(a) $P(X < 63)$ if $X \sim N(65, 4^2)$
(b) $P(70 < X < 80)$ if $X \sim N(72, 5^2)$

Solution

(a) The area under the normal curve $N(65, 4^2)$ to determine $P(X < 63)$ is pictured below.

$N(65, 4^2)$

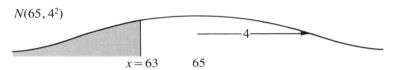

$x = 63$ 65

This can be standardized to $N(0, 1)$:

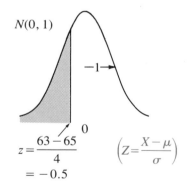

$N(0, 1)$

$z = \dfrac{63 - 65}{4}$ $\left(Z = \dfrac{X - \mu}{\sigma}\right)$

$= -0.5$

The probability that we now need to determine is

$$P(X < 63) = P\left(Z < \frac{63 - 65}{4}\right)$$

which is $P(Z < -0.5) = 0.3085$ (from table)

(b) The area under the normal curve $N(72, 5^2)$ to determine $P(70 < X < 80)$ is pictured below.

$N(72, 5^2)$

$x = 70$ 72 $x = 80$

This can be standardized to $N(0, 1)$:

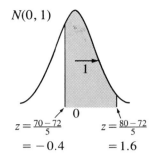

$N(0, 1)$

$z = \frac{70-72}{5}$

$= -0.4$

$z = \frac{80-72}{5}$

$= 1.6$

The probability that we now need to determine is

$$P(70<X<80) = P\left(\frac{70-72}{5} < Z < \frac{80-72}{5}\right)$$
$$= P(-0.4 < Z < 1.6)$$

We must relate this area to areas that can be determined from the table.

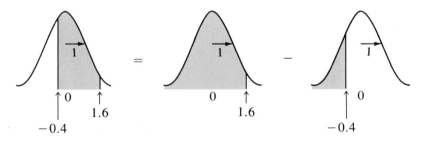

So, $P(-0.4 < Z < 1.6) =$ $P(Z < 1.6)$ $-$ $P(Z < -0.4)$
$= 0.9452 - 0.3446$ (from table)
$= 0.6006$

Example 3 A machine produces an engine part to a mean length of 51.15 mm and a standard deviation of 0.70 mm. Assuming the distribution of the part lengths to be normal, determine the following.
(a) What percentage would be rejected as less than 50 mm long?
(b) Verify that 95 percent of the parts are produced within two standard deviations of the mean length.

Solution (a) Let the random variable X be the length of the engine parts.

Then $X \sim N(51.15, 0.70^2)$

We are asked to find the percentage of parts that are less than 50 mm, which is equivalent to finding $P(X < 50)$.

The area required is

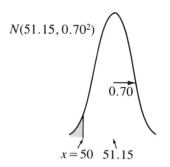

$$N(51.15, 0.70^2)$$

$$\overrightarrow{0.70}$$

$$x = 50 \quad 51.15$$

This can be standardized to $N(0, 1)$:

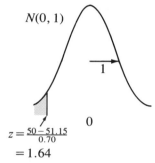

$$N(0, 1)$$

$$1$$

$$0$$

$$z = \frac{50 - 51.15}{0.70}$$

$$= 1.64$$

The probability we now need is $P(X < 50) = P(Z < -1.64)$
$$= 0.0495 \quad \text{(from table)}$$

Expressed as a percentage this probability is 4.95 percent. Therefore, approximately 5 percent of the engine parts would be rejected as under 50 mm in length.

(b) Two standard deviations from the mean would be $51.15 \pm 2(0.70) = 51.15 \pm 1.40$ which gives an interval from 49.75 to 52.55. To find the percentage of parts that are within this interval is equivalent to finding the probability $P(49.75 < X < 52.55)$.
The area required is

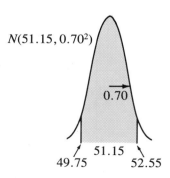

$$N(51.15, 0.70^2)$$

$$\overrightarrow{0.70}$$

$$51.15$$

$$49.75 \qquad 52.55$$

This can be standardized to $N(0, 1)$:

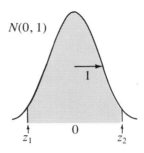

$N(0, 1)$

where $z_1 = \dfrac{49.75 - 51.15}{0.70}$ and $z_2 = \dfrac{52.55 - 51.15}{0.70}$

$\qquad\qquad = -2.0 \qquad\qquad\qquad\qquad = 2.0$

The probability we need is

$$P(49.75 < X < 52.55) = P(-2.0 < Z < 2.0)$$

The areas required to determine this probability are:

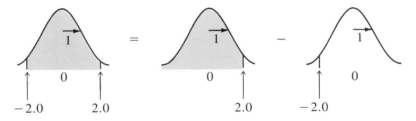

So, $P(-2.0 < Z < 2.0) = P(Z < 2.0) - P(Z < -2.0)$

$\qquad\qquad\qquad\qquad\quad\ = 0.9773 - 0.0227 \qquad$ (from table)

$\qquad\qquad\qquad\qquad\quad\ = 0.9546$

Expressed as a percentage this probability is 95.46 percent, which is the percentage of parts produced within two standard deviations of the mean.

Example 4   On a certain cherry farm in the Niagara region, 5 percent of the cherries weigh more than 8.5 g and 7 percent weigh less than 5.1 g. If the masses of cherries are assumed to be normally distributed, determine the following.

(a)   What is the mean mass and standard deviation of the cherries?

(b)   What percentage of the cherries are over 7.0 g?

Solution   (a)   Let the random variable X be the mass of the cherries. The information given can be translated into the probabilities

$$P(X > 8.5) = 0.05$$

and $P(X < 5.1) = 0.07$

If we refer to the $N(0, 1)$ distribution we can find from the table the points, z_1 and z_2, on this curve such that

$$P(Z > z_1) = 0.05$$
and $$P(Z < z_2) = 0.07$$

Pictorially, the situation is

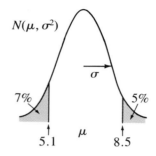

and this can be related to $N(0, 1)$.

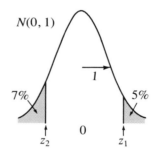

To find z_1 we need to look in the table for the value that would have 95 percent of the data to the left of it.

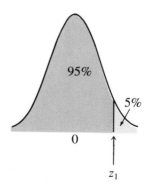

From the table we find that value to be 1.65.

We have $\quad P(Z < 1.65) = 0.95$.
So, $\qquad P(Z > 1.65) = 0.05$.
Hence, $\qquad\qquad z_1 = 1.65$.

Similarly, to find z_2 we look in the table for the value that would have 7 percent of the data to the left of it.

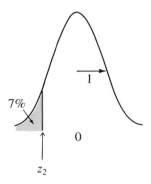

From the table the value is -1.48.

We have $P(Z < -1.48) = 0.07$

So, $z_2 = -1.48$

These points relate directly to the $N(\mu, \sigma^2)$ distribution by the relationship

$$Z = \frac{X - \mu}{\sigma}$$

Therefore, we have the relationship between 1.65 on $N(0, 1)$ and 8.5 on $N(\mu, \sigma^2)$ as

$$1.65 = \frac{8.5 - \mu}{\sigma} \tag{1}$$

and similarly,

$$-1.48 = \frac{5.1 - \mu}{\sigma.} \tag{2}$$

Clearing fractions and rearranging, we have

$$\mu + 1.65\sigma = 8.5 \tag{1}$$
$$\mu - 1.48\sigma = 5.1. \tag{2}$$

subtracting (2) from (1) we obtain

$$3.13\sigma = 3.4$$
$$\sigma \doteq 1.09.$$

Substituting into (1) we get

$$\mu + (1.65)(1.09) = 8.5$$
$$\mu \doteq 6.70.$$

The mean mass of the cherries is 6.70 g with a standard deviation of 1.09 g.

(b) We now have that the cherries are distributed $N(6.70, 1.09^2)$. To find the percentage over 7.0 g we determine $P(X > 7.0)$

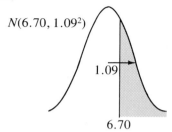

$$N(6.70, 1.09^2)$$

1.09

6.70

This can be related to $N(0, 1)$:

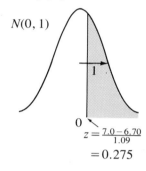

$$N(0, 1)$$

1

0

$$z = \frac{7.0 - 6.70}{1.09}$$

$$= 0.275$$

Then,

$$P(X > 7.0) = P\left(Z > \frac{7.0 - 6.70}{1.09}\right)$$

$$\doteq P(Z > 0.275)$$
$$= 1 - P(Z < 0.275)$$
$$\doteq 1 - 0.6064 \qquad \text{(from table)}$$
$$= 0.3936$$

Expressed as a percentage, 39 percent of the cherries are over 7.0 g.

EXERCISE 7.5

B **1.** If Z has the distribution $N(0, 1)$, determine the following probabilities.

(a) $P(Z < 0)$

(b) $P(Z < 1.0)$

(c) $P(Z > 1.0)$

(d) $P(-1.0 < Z < 1.0)$

(e) $P(|Z| < 2.0)$

(f) $P(1.1 < Z < 2.1)$

(g) $P(-0.25 < Z < 1.35)$

2. Given the distributions of the random variables as indicated, determine the following probabilities.

(a) $P(X > 75)$ where $X \sim N(70, 8^2)$

(b) $P(X < 4.5)$ where $X \sim N(6, 2^2)$

(c) $P(35 < X < 39)$ where $X \sim N(36, 16)$

(d) $P(X < -4.5)$ where $X \sim N(-3, 9)$

(e) $P(X > 2k)$ where $X \sim N(0, k^2)$

(f) $P(X < m + k)$ where $X \sim N(m, k^2)$

(g) $P(m - k < X < m + k)$ where $X \sim N(m, k^2)$

3. (a) It was estimated that batting averages in major league baseball in the 1940s were distributed $N(0.260, 0.07^2)$. What percentage of the batters would bat over 400, that is, their average would be greater than 0.400?

   (b) Recent estimates have the batting averages distributed with the same mean but less variability because of the general improvement in play. The distribution is now $N(0.260, 0.05^2)$. What percentage of the players would bat over 400 today?

4. Nylon strands are manufactured to a mean tensile strength of 1.5 N with a standard deviation of 0.04 N. What percentage of the strands would be rejected with a tensile strength of less than 1.4 N?

5. It is found that a certain brand of lightbulbs has a lifetime of 215 h with a standard deviation of 12 h. If the lifetime of the bulbs is assumed to be normally distributed, what percentage of the bulbs would you expect:

   (a) to fail in less than 200 h?

   (b) to have a lifetime of more than 250 h?

6. The accuracy of an automatic pitching machine is based on the off-line distance that a pitch is from a target line from 30 m. The off-line distance is distributed normally with a mean of 0.3 m and a standard deviation of 0.05 m. A machine will not meet safety standards if its off-line distance is greater than 0.4 m. What percentage of the machines will not meet the safety standards?

7. In a certain process, ball bearings manufactured on earth have a mean diameter of 2 mm and standard deviation of 0.01 mm. Using the same process, but manufacturing them in space in the absence of a gravitational field, the bearings have a mean diameter of 2 mm and a standard deviation of 0.001 mm. Bearings are rejected if they are less than 1.98 mm or greater than 2.02 mm in diameter. Assuming that the diameters are normally distributed, what are the rejection percentages under each environment?

8. (a) *Given:* $X \sim N(10, \sigma^2)$

       $P(X > 11) = 0.35$

   Find: the standard deviation σ

(b) *Given* $X \sim N(-15, \sigma^2)$
$$P(X < -20) = 0.15$$
Find: the standard deviation σ

(c) *Given:* $X \sim N(\mu, 4)$
$$P(X > 10) = 0.40$$
Find: the mean μ

(d) *Given:* $X \sim N(\mu, 25)$
$$P(X < 68) = 0.63$$
Find: the mean μ

(e) *Given:* $X \sim N(\mu, \sigma^2)$
$$P(X > 80) = 0.1$$
$$P(X < 72) = 0.2$$
Find: the mean μ and standard deviation σ

(f) *Given:* $X \sim N(\mu, \sigma^2)$
$$P(X > 11) = 0.65$$
$$P(X < 12) = 0.45$$
Find: the mean μ and standard deviation σ

(g) *Given:* $X \sim N(\mu, \sigma^2)$
$$P(X > 23) = 0.15$$
$$P(X > 25) = 0.05$$
Find: $P(X < 20)$

(h) *Given:* $X \sim N(\mu, \sigma^2)$
$$P(X < 4.1) = 0.75$$
$$P(X < 5.2) = 0.95$$
Find: $P(2.5 < X < 3)$

9. Equipment maintenance at a major factory operates on the principle of preventative maintenance to avoid a complete shutdown of the assembly line if a component fails. If one of the components of the line has a lifetime of 321 h with a standard deviation of 23 h, determine how frequently the component should be replaced so that the probability of its failing during operation is less than 0.001.

10. On a certain section of highway, 90 percent of the motorists drive at speeds greater than 100 km/h, and only 5 percent of the motorists drive at speeds less than 95 km/h. If the speeds are assumed to be normally distributed,
    (a) determine the motorists' mean driving speed and standard deviation.
    (b) determine the percentage of motorists that drive at speeds faster than 120 km/h.

11. A machine produces components whose length is dictated by the setting on a dial. At a setting of 43.5 on the dial the machine produces to a mean length of 43.5 mm, and 93 percent of the components are

longer than 40.0 mm. Determine the setting required so that 99 percent of the components are longer than 40.0 mm.

12. If test marks are assumed to be normally distributed and 70 percent of the students scored greater than a mark of 60 (out of 100), and 10 percent scored over 90, determine the mean and standard deviation of the test marks.

13. (a) Give a formula for converting marks in an examination distributed as $N(55, 169)$ to one with $N(70, 100)$. This is often referred to as "belling the marks."
    (b) What would happen to a mark of 94 under the belling process?

C 14. (a) If a random variable is normally distributed, verify that the percentage of data that would be:
    (i) within one standard deviation of the mean is 68 percent.
    (ii) within two standard deviations of the mean is 95 percent.
    (b) If the distribution of the random variable is unknown, what is the best estimate that we can give for the percentage of data within two standard deviations of the mean?

7.6 NORMAL APPROXIMATION OF THE BINOMIAL DISTRIBUTION

Recall from Section 6.3 that the binomial distribution arises in situations of independent repeated trials in which the outcome of each trial is either a success or a failure (Bernoulli trials). The graphical representation of a binomial distribution with $n = 15$ and $p = 0.4$ would be

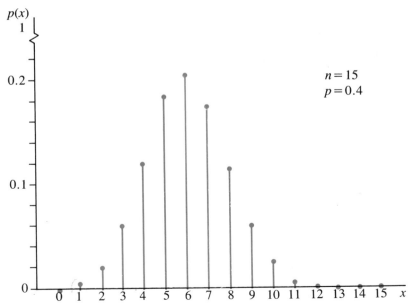

Notice the bell shape of the distribution. This suggests that we can approximate a binomial distribution by a normal distribution. The

advantage of making this approximation is that we do not have the arduous task of calculating binomial probabilities. For example, to determine the probability of one hundred or fewer successes in a binomial experiment of $n = 600$ trials with the probability of success on each trial being 0.3, we would need to compute the following.

$$P(X \leqslant 100) = p(0) + p(1) + \ldots + p(100)$$
$$= \sum_{x=0}^{100} \binom{600}{x} (0.3)^x (0.7)^{600 - x}$$

which is a formidable task indeed.

To make the approximation to the normal we must estimate the mean and standard deviation of a normal distribution that would be similar in shape to the binomial distribution in question. These estimates are given by:

$$\mu = np \qquad \text{and} \qquad \sigma^2 = npq$$

These approximations are considered to be reasonable if p is close to $\frac{1}{2}$ and n is fairly large. The further p is from $\frac{1}{2}$ the larger n should be to compensate and still maintain a good approximation. The general rule of thumb is that a normal approximation to the binomial distribution is acceptable if *both* np *and* nq *are at least five*. The following diagrams illustrate the appropriateness of this rule.

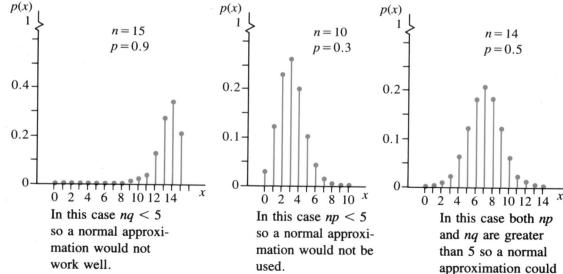

In this case $nq < 5$ so a normal approximation would not work well.

In this case $np < 5$ so a normal approximation would not be used.

In this case both *np* and *nq* are greater than 5 so a normal approximation could be used.

One final consideration is the need to account for approximating a discrete outcome experiment with a continuous distribution. This is done by treating each outcome as a unit interval. For example, 5 successes would be considered to be 4.5 to 5.5 successes in a normal distribution. So probabilities such as (i) $P(X \leq 5)$ would be approximated by $P(X \leq 5.5)$ in the normal distribution; and (ii) $P(X = 7)$ would be approximated by $P(6.5 \leq X \leq 7.5)$ in the normal distribution.

Example 1 The probability of tossing a head with a weighted coin is 0.3. If the coin is tossed 60 times, what is the probability that
(a) ten or fewer heads are tossed.
(b) exactly 20 heads are tossed.

Solution Let a success be the tossing of a head.
We have $n = 60$ Bernoulli trials with $p = 0.3$.
Let the random variable X be the number of heads whose probability distribution is the binomial distribution.

Check to see if a normal approximation is reasonable.

$$np = (60)(0.3) \qquad \text{and } nq = (60)(0.7)$$
$$= 18 \qquad\qquad\qquad = 42$$

Both are greater than five so we will continue with the normal approximation.
Estimate the mean and standard deviation.

$$\mu = np \qquad \text{and} \qquad \sigma^2 = npq$$
$$= 18 \qquad\qquad\qquad\quad = (60)(0.3)(0.7)$$
$$= 12.6$$
$$\sigma = \sqrt{12.6}$$
$$= 3.55$$

(a) We must determine

$P(X \leq 10)$ in the binomial distribution,
which can be approximated to

$P(X \leq 10.5)$ in the normal distribution.

$N(18, 12.16)$

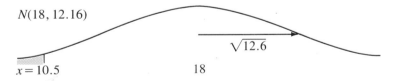

$x = 10.5$ 18

This can be standardized to $N(0, 1)$:

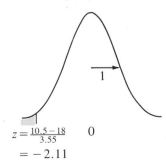

$$z = \frac{10.5 - 18}{3.55} \qquad 0$$
$$= -2.11$$

Then $P(X \leqslant 10.5) = P(Z \leqslant -2.11)$
$$= 0.0174 \qquad \text{(from table)}$$

The probability that ten or fewer heads are tossed is approximately 0.0174.

(b) We need to determine

$P(X = 20)$ in the binomial distribution,

which can be approximated to

$P(19.5 \leqslant X \leqslant 20.5)$ in the normal distribution.

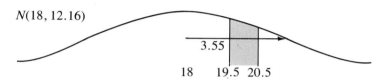

$N(18, 12.16)$

This can be standardized to $N(0, 1)$:

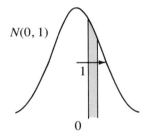

$N(0, 1)$

$$z_1 = \frac{19.5 - 18}{3.55} \qquad z_2 = \frac{20.5 - 18}{3.55}$$
$$= 0.423 \qquad\qquad = 0.704$$

Then, $P(19.5 \leqslant X \leqslant 20.5) = P(0.423 \leqslant Z \leqslant 0.704)$
$$= P(Z \leqslant 0.704) - P(Z \leqslant 0.423)$$
$$= 0.7580 - 0.6628 \qquad \text{(from table)}$$
$$= 0.0952$$

The probability of tossing exactly 20 heads is approximately 0.0952.

Example 2 It is estimated that 15 percent of the Canadian population is undecided as to which political party to vote for in the next election. If a poll is conducted and 1007 citizens respond to the questionnaire, what is the probability that more than 100 of them are undecided?

Solution Let a success be that a citizen is undecided.
We have $n = 1007$ Bernoulli trials with $p = 0.15$.
Let the random variable X be the number of undecided citizens, which is binomially distributed.
We need to determine $P(X > 100)$ or $P(X \geqslant 101)$.

Check to see if a normal approximation is reasonable.

$$np = (1007)(0.15) \quad \text{and} \quad nq = (1007)(0.85)$$
$$= 151.05 \qquad\qquad\qquad = 855.95$$

Both are greater than five so continue with the normal approximation. Estimate the mean and standard deviation.

$$\mu = np \quad \text{and} \quad \sigma^2 = npq$$
$$= 151.05 \qquad\qquad = (1007)(0.15)(0.85)$$
$$\doteq 128.39$$
$$\sigma \doteq 11.33$$

Then $P(X \geqslant 101)$ in the binomial distribution can be approximated to $P(X \geqslant 100.5)$ in the normal distribution $N(151.05, 128.39)$.

$N(151.05, 128.39)$

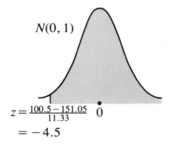

$x = 100.5$ 151.05

This can be standardized to $N(0, 1)$.

$$N(0, 1)$$

$$z = \frac{100.5 - 151.05}{11.33} \quad 0$$
$$= -4.5$$

Then, $P(X \geqslant 100.5) = P(Z \geqslant -4.5)$
$$= 1 - P(Z < -4.5)$$
$$= 1 - 0.0001 \qquad\qquad \text{(from table)}$$
$$= 0.9999$$

It is near certainty, a probability of 0.9999, that more than 100 citizens surveyed will be undecided.

EXERCISE 7.6

B   **1.**   Decide whether the following binomial situations would be reasonably approximated by a normal distribution.
(a) $n = 10, \ p = 0.4$
(b) $n = 15, \ p = 0.4$
(c) $n = 1000, \ p = 0.001$
(d) $n = 21, \ p = 0.21$

   2.   If the following probabilities refer to random variables that are binomially distributed, determine the intervals that you would use in relating to a normal distribution.
(a) $P(X = 3)$

(b) $P(X \geqslant 5)$

(c) $P(X \leqslant 5)$

(d) $P(X < 115)$

(e) $P(12 \leqslant X \leqslant 15)$

(f) $P(50 < X < 75)$

3. A multiple choice exam contains 50 questions and each question has four answers from which to choose. If a student merely guesses at the answers, what is the probability that

    (a) the student will get ten questions correct?

    (b) the student will pass?

4. It is estimated that an average of 10 percent of the vehicles crossing an international border between two countries are smuggling undeclared goods. If the customs officers search 400 vehicles at random, what is the probability that more than 100 of the motorists are smuggling?

5. A die is thrown 20 times and a success is defined as a one or a six is uppermost on the die.

    (a) Use the binomial distribution to determine the probability of getting exactly five successes in the 20 trials.

    (b) Use the normal approximation to the binomial to answer the same question, that is, that there are five successes in the 20 trials.

6. A machine produces articles and an average of 2 percent of these articles are defective. In a batch of 400 articles, what is the probability that there are fewer than five that are defective?

7. The choice of whether to receive or kickoff at the start of a football game is decided by the toss of a coin. In a season of 20 games what is the probability that the Ironmen will have their choice at least 12 times during the season?

8. It was determined in Section 5.7 that the theoretical probability of winning at the dice game, craps, is 0.493. If you play 50 games in Las Vegas, what is the probability that you will win more than you lose?

PROBLEMS PLUS

52 pick-up

A deck of cards is tossed into the air. Now they must be picked up! It takes one second to turn over a card and seven seconds to collect and stack the cards once they are all face down. What is the probability that the cards can be picked up in less than 25 seconds?

**7.7 HYPOTHESIS TESTING

The essence of statistics and its application to research is the ability to confidently accept or reject assertions (referred to as hypotheses). The testing of the effectiveness of newly-developed drugs is an excellent example of how statistics is used to evaluate scientists' claims. For example, a pharmacologist asserts that his newly-developed drug offers a significant improvement in the recovery rate of patients afflicted with a certain disease. He bases his assertion on the fact that 15 patients of 40 recovered with the aid of his drug when it was previously known that the recovery rate was about 33 percent. How do we confront this assertion? Is this recovery rate significantly better than the expected recovery rate or is it just because of chance fluctuation in the test group?

The principle behind a statistical test is to test the probability of arriving at a set of results under an assumed distribution. If the probability calculated is high, we conclude that the assumption is correct, that is, the distribution is plausible. If the probability is low, the assumption is considered to be poor and, hence, rejected. One could relate this to the approach made by juries in the trial of a legal case. The defendant is assumed innocent until that assumption is no longer believable.

To test an hypothesis statistically we follow the following steps.

1. State the hypothesis that is being challenged. In this example, we are challenging the recovery rate of 33 percent. We state this hypothesis with the following notation.

    H_0: $p = 0.33$

    where H_0 is called the **null hypothesis** (nothing has changed!) and p is the proportion attributed to the recovery rate.

2. State the **alternative hypothesis**, which in this case would be

    H_1: $p > 0.33$

    That is, the claim is that the recovery rate is now better than $p = 0.33$.

3. Establish a decision rule. This is the probability with which you will make your decision to reject the null hypothesis. For example, if you want to be 99 percent sure of your decision, then you are willing to accept a 1 percent chance of making an error. This probability is called *the significance level* and is denoted $\alpha = 0.01$.

4. Conduct an experiment to test the hypothesis.

5. Assume H_0 is true and calculate the probability of obtaining the results of the experiment under this assumption.

6. Accept or reject the null hypothesis based on the significance level and whether the experiment's results support the null hypothesis.

Let us restate the previous drug example and solve it.

Example 1   It is known that the recovery rate from a certain disease is 33 percent. A newly-developed drug is claimed to improve the recovery rate based on 15 people recovering in a sample of 40 patients. Test the claim at a significance level of 0.01.

Solution   We have H_0: $p = 0.33$
H_1: $p > 0.33$

From the sample, we determine the probability of obtaining 15 or more recovered patients from a group of 40.

Let the random variable X be the number of recovered patients. X is distributed binomially with $n = 40$ and the assumed $p = 0.33$ (null hypothesis).

Then, $P(X \geqslant 15)$ may be approximated with the normal distribution $N(np, npq)$ which equals $N(13.2, 8.84)$.

So, our probability becomes

$$P(X \geqslant 14.5) = P\left(Z \geqslant \frac{14.5 - 13.2}{\sqrt{8.84}}\right) \qquad \left(Z = \frac{X - \mu}{\sigma}\right)$$

$$\doteq P(Z \geqslant 0.437)$$
$$= 1 - P(Z \leqslant 0.437)$$
$$\doteq 1 - 0.6554 \qquad \text{(from table)}$$
$$= 0.3446$$

Our decision rule was to reject our assumption of $p = 0.33$ (null hypothesis) if the probability of our sample results was less than 0.01 ($\alpha = 0.01$). It is not, so we accept the null hypothesis and conclude that there is not a significant improvement in the recovery rate caused by the new drug.   ◇

This technique is generally streamlined by determining a rejection region based on our significance level α. This region is determined by finding the value of the standard variate z_α from the tables that satisfies the probability $P(Z > z_\alpha) = \alpha$.

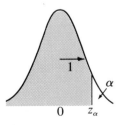

In our previous example we would have determined $P(Z \geqslant z_\alpha) = 0.01$ and from the tables $z_\alpha = 2.33$.

We then calculate the standardized z-value (z-score) from the sample data. In the example the value was 0.437. If this value is greater than

z_α then we reject H_0, if not we accept H_0 as is the case in this example. This standardized z-value is referred to as the **test statistic** for obvious reasons.

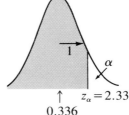

$z_\alpha = 2.33$

0.336

To summarize, the steps in testing an hypothesis are:
(1) State the null hypothesis, H_0, and the alternative hypothesis, H_1.
(2) Decide upon a significance level α and find the corresponding standard variate value z_α.
(3) Calculate the test statistic, z_t, from the sample data.
(4) Accept H_0 if $z_t < z_\alpha$, otherwise reject H_0.

Example 2   A major car manufacturer is interested in determining whether the company has made a significant improvement in its market share after a year-long advertising campaign. The company has had a 24 percent share of the market historically. In a random sample of 500 vehicle registrations, there are 152 of its product. Test whether there is a statistically significant increase in its market share at a significance level of 5 percent ($\alpha = 0.05$).

Solution   The hypothesis: H_0: $p = 0.24$
H_1: $p > 0.24$

At $\alpha = 0.05$, $z_\alpha = 1.64$.

The test statistic: Use a normal approximation to the binomial.
We have $n = 500$ and we assume $p = 0.24$.
The distribution is $N(np, npq) = N(120, 91.2)$.

Then $z_t = \dfrac{151.5 - 120}{\sqrt{91.2}}$ $\left(z = \dfrac{X - \mu}{\sigma} \right)$

$\doteq 3.30$

Compare: $z_t > z_\alpha$, therefore reject H_0.
There is evidence to support that there has been a significant improvement in the market share.

We have merely scratched the surface in this topic of hypothesis testing. There is much that is unsaid regarding experimental design, sampling techniques, various test statistics, and the situations in which they are used; one-sided versus two-sided tests, and so on. These topics would be well-developed in a course devoted to statistics. Our intention here was to introduce you to the decision-making tool that statistics can offer you.

EXERCISE 7.7

B **1.** Determine the values of the standard variates, z_α, for the following significance levels.
   (a) $\alpha = 0.025$ (b) $\alpha = 0.10$
   (c) $\alpha = 0.05$ (d) $\alpha = 0.001$

2. Test the significance of the following hypothesis, given the experimental data shown.
   (a) H_0: $p = 0.5$
       H_1: $p > 0.5$ at $\alpha = 0.05$
       Sample: $n = 100$, (number of successes) $= 58$
   (b) H_0: $p = 0.3$
       H_1: $p > 0.3$ at $\alpha = 0.01$
       Sample: $n = 50$, (number of successes) $= 25$
   (c) H_0: $p = 0.1$
       H_1: $p > 0.1$ at $\alpha = 0.05$
       Sample: $n = 400$, (number of successes) $= 45$
   (d) H_0: $p = 0.7$
       H_1: $p > 0.7$ at $\alpha = 0.025$
       Sample: $n = 30$, (number of successes) $= 25$
   (e) H_0: $p = 0.493$
       H_1: $p > 0.493$ at $\alpha = 0.05$
       Sample: $n = 250$, (number of successes) $= 175$

3. Test the assertion (at $\alpha = 0.05$) that it rains more often on weekends than it does on weekdays if in a sample of 31 rainy days, 10 were either Saturday or Sunday.

4. In a taste test, 15 of 25 people chose beverage X over beverage Y. Is this significant evidence to conclude that people prefer beverage X to beverage Y?

5. In a recent political poll of 1200 people, 123 indicated that they would support the Hippopotamus party in the next election. If on the previous election the Hippopotamus party received 9 percent of the popular vote, would you claim that they have made significant gains in their support?

6. To meet safety standards, drugs must not cause adverse side effects in more than 0.01 percent of the population before they will be allowed to be sold over the counter. In a sample of 100 000 people taking a certain drug 12 people suffered adverse side effects. Does this drug meet the safety standards at a significance level of 0.05?

7. In a manufacturing process it has been found that 99.5 percent of the products are defect-free. A new process is introduced to improve the quality of the product. If in a batch of 3000, 2993 are defect-free, has the new process significantly improved the quality of the product?

8. (a) You are often required to test an alternative hypothesis that suggests that the proportion is less than a given value. For example,

$$H_0: p = \tfrac{1}{2}$$

$$H_1: p < \tfrac{1}{2}$$

What change in the hypothesis testing procedure would you need to make?

   (b) Thirty percent of a certain school population smoked cigarettes. After an extensive health education program introduced by the school board, it was found that in a sample of 220 students, 45 smoked. Has there been a significant decline in the proportion of the students smoking?

9. Investigation: (a) Estimate (guess) the proportion of people in your school that wear glasses. Formulate an hypothesis, giving a value of p to one decimal place, and determine your rejection region for a sample of 25 people. Conduct a random sample in the school to test your hypothesis.

   (b) Make an assertion on an issue of interest to you. Test your hypothesis with an appropriate random sample and test statistic.

7.8 REVIEW EXERCISE

1. The following data are given.
   (a) Shoe sizes

9	9	8	6	7	6	7	8	9	8	7	6	10	11	9	8	7
10	12	7	6	7	7	8	9	10	9	9	11		7	9	6	8	9

   (b) Marks on an examination

Mark interval:	0–19	20–39	40–59	60–79	80–99
Number of students:	1	2	7	23	11

   Construct the following for each set of data.
   (i)   the frequency table
   (ii) the frequency diagram
   (iii) the relative frequency diagram
   (iv) the three measures of central tendency
   (v)   the three measures of spread of the data

2. Using the MCHC data from Table 1 in Section 7.1, select appropriate intervals to group the data and construct the frequency table and diagram for this data.

3. Given four numbers w, x, y, z such that $w, < x < y < z$ give formulas for:
   (a) the mean and median for the numbers.
   (b) the mean deviation and the standard deviation of the numbers.

4. How much of the data can we expect to find within two and a half standard deviations of the mean according to Chebyshev's theorem?

5. Three tests had means of 68 percent, 72 percent, 63 percent and standard deviations of 6 percent, 8 percent, and 7 percent, respectively. If Maureen achieved 75 percent, 80 percent, and 72 percent on the three tests, respectively,
   (i) which test would you consider was her best performance?
   (ii) determine the mean and standard deviation of her z-scores.

6. A grade-point system of evaluating students is often used in colleges and universities. The letter grades A, B, C, D are assigned the values 4, 3, 2, 1, respectively. The grade-point average is calculated by using the hours per week in the course as the weighting factors in a weighted mean. Determine the grade-point average of the following student.

Course	Letter Grade	Hours Per Week
Calculus	A	3
Economics	B	3
French	A	4
English	C	2
Sociology	D	2
Physics	B	3

7. Given that $X \sim N(50, 25)$ find:
   (a) $P(X > 60)$
   (b) $P(49 < X < 53)$
   (c) $P(X < 50)$
   (d) $P(X < 60) - P(X < 55)$

8. For the following situations, assume that the random variable X is distributed normally.
   (a) *Given:* $P(X > 24) = 0.1$ and the mean, $\mu = 20$
       Find: the standard deviation, σ
   (b) *Given:* $P(X < 15) = 0.6$ and the standard deviation, $\sigma = 2$
       Find: the mean, μ
   (c) *Given:* $P(X > 79) = 0.2$ and $P(X < 75) = 0.25$
       Find: the mean, μ, and the standard deviation, σ.
   (d) *Given:* $P(X > 8) = 0.4$ and $P(X > 9) = 0.1$
       Find: the mean, μ, and the standard deviation, σ.

9. A machine that fills peanut butter jars at a food processing plant has a standard deviation of 15 g. The mean fill of the machine is set by a dial. If we assume the distribution of the weight of the peanut butter in the jars to be normally distributed, what is the probability that a 1 kg jar will contain more than 1010 g of peanut butter?

10. An angler estimates that 10 percent of the smallmouth bass that she catches weigh less than 0.5 kg and 25 percent more than 1.0 kg. If the masses of the bass are assumed to be normally distributed, determine the mean mass of the bass that she catches.

11. Determine the mean and the standard deviation of the normal approximation to the following binomially distributed random variables, if an approximation can reasonably be made.

    (a) $n = 12$, $p = \frac{1}{2}$

    (b) $n = 500$, $p = 0.23$

12. It is estimated that 10 percent of the vehicles on the road require work on their brakes. In the interest of road safety, the police conduct a random vehicle inspection. What is the probability that more than ten of fifty vehicles inspected require a brake job?

13. The captain of an ocean-going freighter estimates that 40 percent of the passengers get seasick in rough weather. If on a trip with 13 passengers the ship sails into rough weather, determine the probability that all of the passengers get seasick,

    (a) by using a normal approximation to the binomial distribution.

    (b) by using the binomial distribution directly.

**14. Test the hypothesis that more than half the population dislikes Brussels sprouts if in a random survey of 30 people, 17 admitted that they were not fond of the vegetable. Use a significance level of $\alpha = 0.05$.

**15. It was estimated that 10 percent of a population could be classified as fit. After a government-sponsored program called Participactivity to encourage fitness, a random sample showed that of 500 people 78 were classified as fit. Test the hypothesis at $\alpha = 0.01$ that Participactivity is working.

PROBLEMS PLUS

Taking advantage of a statistical hypothesis

A resident on a busy street noted that the last eight tickets that he received for overnight parking were given either on a Wednesday or a Friday. The resident decided to rent a garage for only Wednesday and Friday nights. What factors should be considered in deciding if this action is statistically justified?

$\frac{m}{8}$ $\frac{w}{6}$ $\left(\frac{3}{2}\right)\left(\frac{6}{7}+\frac{8}{5}\frac{6}{3}\right)$

7.9 CHAPTER 7 TEST

1. The following data are measurements in centimetres of the circumference of body builders' biceps.

50 55 53 62 60 52 48 68 53 50 49 50 60
48 51 58 53 47 50 46 53 51 57 55 49 61

(a) (i) Determine the mean, median, and mode of the data.
(ii) Determine the semi-interquartile range.
(iii) Draw a cumulative frequency diagram of the data.

(b) (i) Determine the standard deviation.
(ii) What percentage of the data are within one standard deviation of the mean?

2. (a) Find $P(Z \geqslant -1.5)$ if $Z \sim N(0, 1)$.
(b) Find $P(X \leqslant 11)$ if $X \sim N(13, 3^2)$.
(c) Find $P(50 \leqslant X \leqslant 60)$ if $X \sim N(57, 25)$.
(d) Find μ if $X \sim N(\mu, 4)$ and $P(X \geqslant 20) = 0.05$.
(e) Find μ and σ if $X \sim N(\mu, \sigma^2)$ and
$P(X \geqslant 79) = 0.1$ and $P(X \geqslant 81) = 0.05$.

3. The length of the bolts in a manufacturing process are distributed normally with mean of 60 mm and standard deviation 2 mm.

(a) What is the probability that a bolt selected at random is longer than 63 mm?

(b) The manufacturer wants to improve the standard of the production of these bolts so that no more than 3 percent of the bolts produced are longer than 63 mm. To what must the standard deviation be reduced to satisfy this requirement?

4. It has been estimated that with a sophisticated mathematical strategy, a player can increase the odds in favour of winning at blackjack to 10 to 9. If you play with this strategy, what is the probability that you will win at least half of 20 games of blackjack?

**5. A sample survey was conducted to test the hypothesis that more males are born than females, at the significance level $\alpha = 0.05$. The survey revealed that of a sample of 835 babies born, 423 were male. Is the hypothesis statistically justified?

PROBLEMS PLUS

Belling marks

A challenging test was given to a class of good students. The marks were distributed $N(40, 100)$. It is desired to scale the marks such that a pass mark is 50 and 95 percent of the class pass, and a mark of distinction is 90 and 10 percent of the students get distinction. Calculate the new mark of a student who had an original mark of 50.

CUMULATIVE REVIEW FOR CHAPTERS 5 TO 7

1. Draw a tree diagram to illustrate the possible outcomes of getting dressed if one has three shirts (orange, black, and blue) from which to choose and two pairs of pants (orange and black). If your mother chooses them randomly for you to wear, what is the probability that the colour combination she chooses is orange and black?

2. A committee is to be formed to study the Canadian immigration policy. The committee is to be chosen randomly from five recent immigrants and five second-generation citizens. If the committee is to consist of seven members, what is the probability that
   (a) there are exactly three recent immigrants on the committee?
   (b) there are more recent immigrants than second-generation citizens on the committee?

3. The game of bingo has 15 numbers associated with each letter of the word bingo. For example, the letter B has the numbers 1 through 15; I the numbers 16 through 30, and so on. If your bingo card has five different numbers under the B, what is the probability that:
   (a) on the first draw one of your numbers under the B is drawn?
   (b) on the second draw one of your numbers under the B is drawn, given that on the first draw one of your numbers under the B was successfully drawn?

4. What is the probability that at least two of the 12 councillors elected in the next municipal election will have birthdays on the same day?

5. The odds against winning in craps are 507 to 493. What is your expected return on a $20.00 wager?

6. In the best-of-five hockey series, the probability of winning the next game increases for each team by 0.1 if the previous game was won. If the teams, the Ironmen and the Mustangs, are in such a series and at the start of the series are evenly matched, what is the probability that
   (a) the Ironmen win in three straight?
   (b) the Mustangs win the series?

7. Recent estimates indicate that the foreign car manufacturer Hoyda has 15 percent of the car market. If a random sample of 20 automobiles is conducted, what is the probability that
   (a) exactly one of the cars was made by Hoyda?
   (b) at least two of the cars were made by Hoyda?

8. A basketball game in a municipal league between the Sharks and the Jets was scheduled for Thursday night. Only four players from the Sharks showed up and so the Jets, who had six players, won by default. So the evening would not be spoiled, the players that arrived for the game decided to have a pick-up scrimmage, and picked the two teams by drawing names from a hat. What is the probability that the four Sharks end up on the same team?

9. The Canadian government is concerned about the impact of arctic development on the wildlife there. To study the effects of development, it is necessary to estimate the population sizes of the various species of animals. One year 100 polar bears were tagged. The following year 15 of 65 polar bears that were sighted were noted to have tags. What estimate could be made of the bear population?

10. At the outset of a billiard game, it is estimated that the probability of a professional billiard player sinking a ball in a pocket is 0.85, and it remains the same on each subsequent shot until the end of his turn.
    (a) What is the probability that he will miss on his third shot?
    (b) What is the expected number of shots that he will have in his turn?

11. Given the following frequency diagram,
    (a) construct the frequency table and draw the cumulative frequency diagram.
    (b) determine the mean, median, and mode.
    (c) determine the interquartile range.

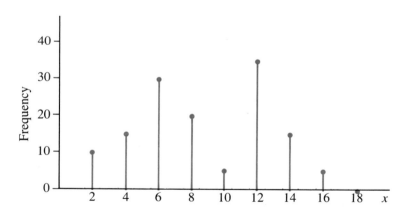

12. A DJ for a radio station is designing her morning program for the radio station CHCM FM. She is interested in the playing time for songs. The following data are the lengths of songs in seconds.
    185 200 210 170 165 234 240 160 180 170 180 210 205 230 190 170 230 205 195 220 215 170 185 190 185 200 150 260
    (a) Determine the mean and standard deviation of the lengths of the songs.
    (b) Verify that these data satisfy Chebyshev's theorem for $k = 2$.

13. A pension scheme is based on the last five years of employment. The annual pension received is a weighted average of the five annual salaries before retirement, according to the following weightings.

Years Before Retirement	Weighting
five	5
four	4
three	3
two	2
one	1

(a) If an employee is about to retire and his salaries for the past five years have been: $32 000, $33 500, $35 000, $36 000, $39 000, respectively, what will be the employee's pension?

(b) If the union negotiated that the weightings be reversed, that is, a weighting of one for the fifth year previous to retirement, a weighting of two for the fourth year previous, and so on, what would this employee's pension be?

14. In a certain manufacturing process the lengths of sides of silicon computer chips are distributed normally with mean 1.325 mm and standard deviation 0.005 mm. Find the expected proportion of the chips that will be outside the range 1.317 mm to 1.333 mm.

15. In a certain region of Canada it is estimated that it rains on 70 percent of the days in a year. In a month of 30 days what is the probability of rain on more than 20 days in the month?

**16. It is suspected that a booth at a local carnival is playing with a loaded die that favours the number six. The police investigate and discover that in 100 rolls of the die, the number six was uppermost 20 times. Is there enough evidence statistically to warrant further investigation into the matter?

**17. A consumer advocate group complains that more than 20 percent of the record albums that are sold are of poor quality. The recording industry challenges this assertion, and randomly samples 50 albums, and finds that 12 of them could be classified as having poor quality. Is the claim of the consumer advocate group refuted statistically by this sample?

TWENTIETH CENTURY MATHEMATICIANS

D r. Persi Diaconis is currently a professor of statistics at Stanford University in California. Most of his family are musicians and he attended a prestigious music school (studying the violin) until he was fourteen. At that time, he left home to become a magician. He was a magician (apprentice and master) for ten years. Magic is still his major passion, and if there were professorships of magic he would qualify for such a post.

With this background, he approaches mathematics and statistics with an undeniable flair. He says, "Statistics is the physics of numbers. Numbers seem to arise in the world in an orderly fashion. When we examine the world, the same regularities seem to appear again and again."

He is motivated by problems and applications yet retains a deep interest in number theory which is reputed to be the least applicable part of mathematics. When asked about this interest he replied, "At the heart of my thesis was a very concrete problem, namely the crazy first digit phenomenon. If you look at the first page of the New York Times and observe all the numbers which appear, how many of them do you think will begin with one? Some people think about a ninth. It turns out empirically that more numbers begin with one, and in fact it is a very exact proportion that begins with one: it is 0.301 ($\log_{10}2$). Now that's an empirical fact and it's sort of surprising. It comes up in all sorts of real data. If you open a book of tables, and look at all the numbers on the page, about 30% of them begin with a one. Why should that be?" He manages to give a mathematical explanation of this phenomenon using advanced number theory.

He says in general about the way he works, "There are some questions and some sets of tools, and often the question has been asked several times, and eventually the question drives you on to understand the set of tools, and then for me the game isn't finished until the set of tools yields the answer. This can take years. There are questions I have worked on for thirty years. Until I get the right answer I don't stop."

PROBLEMS PLUS

Productivity

The Mighty Muffler garage has determined that the average time required to replace a muffler system is 33.5 minutes with a standard deviation of 11.2 minutes. The average time required to do a minor brake job is 42.3 minutes with a standard deviation of 17.6 minutes. Assuming normal distributions, in what percentage of the cases will a muffler job take longer than an average brake job?

CHAPTER 8

MATRICES

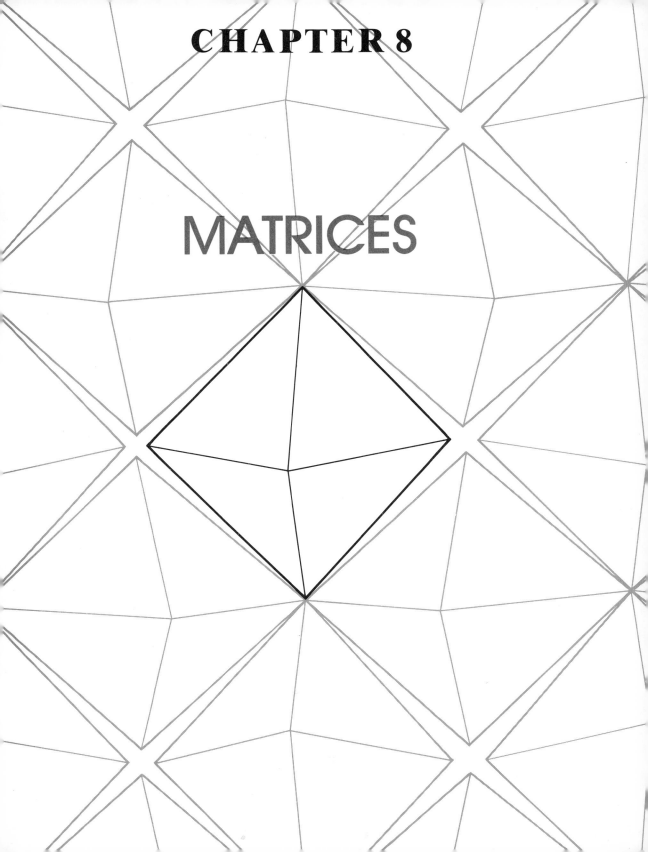

REVIEW AND PREVIEW TO
CHAPTER 8

Stochastic Processes

Recall: a stochastic process is a sequence of experiments that depends on some chance element. If each experiment is identical to the one before it and each experiment is *independent* (the results of any one experiment in no way affect the results in any other experiment), the stochastic process is referred to as *repeated trials*.

EXERCISE 1

1. A coin is tossed six times. Find the probability that
   (a) six heads are tossed.
   (b) exactly four heads are tossed.
   (c) at least three heads are tossed.

2. Assuming that the chances of giving birth to a girl or a boy are equal, what are the chances that
   (a) a couple planning to have two children will have one boy and one girl?
   (b) a couple planning to have three children will have three boys?
   (c) a couple planning to have four children will have at least two girls?

3. Carol and Rivka play one-on-one basketball every Saturday morning. Carol is better at basketball than Rivka and the probability of her winning is 0.6.
   (a) In three matches, what is the probability Carol will win all of them?
   (b) In five matches, what is the probability Rivka will win at least two of them?

4. In the dice game craps, a person wins on the first roll if the total on the two dice is either seven or eleven. Find the probability of rolling either seven or eleven four times in a row.

The experiments in a stochastic process are not always independent, as was seen in Section 5.7. The results of one experiment may affect the results of experiments that follow.

EXERCISE 2

1. Heather and Steve play cribbage every Tuesday evening. Every time Heather wins there is a probability of 0.6 she will win the next Tuesday. Every time Steve wins there is a probability of 0.7 he will win the next Tuesday. The initial probability of either player winning the first game is 0.5.
   (a) Make a tree diagram for a two-game sequence and label on the diagram the probabilities associated with each branch.
   (b) Find the probability that Heather wins both games.
   (c) Extend your tree diagram to include a third game.
   (d) Find the probability that Steve wins all three games.
   (e) Find the probability that Heather wins at least two games.

2. The weather reporter at a local television station uses the following procedure to determine future weather patterns. On any given day, if it is raining she predicts there will be a 50 percent chance of rain the next day. If it is not raining, she predicts there will be an 80 percent chance it will not rain the next day.
   (a) If it is raining on Monday, what would the reporter predict the chances of rain to be on Wednesday?
   (b) If it is not raining on Wednesday, what would the reporter predict the chances of rain for Saturday to be?

3. Gerry tries not to be late for school too often. Whenever he is late, there is a 95 percent chance he will be on time the next day. Whenever he is on time there is only an 80 percent chance he will be on time the next day.
   (a) If Gerry is late on Monday, what is the probability he will be on time on Wednesday?
   (b) If Gerry is on time on Monday, what is the probability he will be late on Thursday?

4. Kim and Angela made the finals of a regional tennis tournament. The match will consist of the best-three-out-of-five games. Angela is the hometown favourite, and the probability of her winning each game is 0.6.
   (a) What is the probability that Angela will win the match in three straight games?
   (b) What is the probability that Kim will win the match?

INTRODUCTION

Not too many years ago the study of matrices was left primarily to mathematicians. Today with the advent of computers capable of performing laborious calculations in seconds, matrix theory has become one of the most widely applied branches of mathematics. Matrices are being used to solve systems of equations in business and government, to investigate stochastic processes in the social and biological sciences, and to help predict transportation needs.

8.1 MATRICES

It is difficult to read through a newspaper and not find examples of matrices. In the following, a matrix is used to convey statistics in the Canadian Football League.

	G	W	L	T	F	A	P
Hamilton	8	5	2	1	128	87	11
Toronto	7	4	3	0	112	103	8
Ottawa	8	3	4	1	96	118	7
Winnipeg	7	2	5	0	77	143	4

Your Finite Mathematics teacher probably keeps a record of your marks in the form of a matrix with the rows labelled with the students' names and the columns labelled with the test numbers.

	T1	T2	T3	T4
TOTAL MARKS	50	50	50	50
Ascroft P.	34	28	39	22
Anderson S.	47	41	39	45
Battallia M.	21	20	15	9
.	.	.	.	.
.	.	.	.	.
Zikic Z.	33	37	39	30

From the preceding examples, it is easy to see that the concept of a matrix is not particularly difficult.

> A **matrix** (plural: **matrices**) is a rectangular array of numbers arranged in *rows* (horizontal) and *columns* (vertical).

Each number appearing in the array is said to be an **element** or **entry** of the matrix.

> An $m \times n$ (read m by n) **matrix** is a matrix with m rows and n columns. The numbers m and n are the **dimensions of the matrix**.

In mathematics, it is conventional to use capital letters to denote matrices, using either square brackets or parentheses around its elements.

$$A = \begin{bmatrix} 5 & 9 & -1 & 0 \\ 4 & -7 & 0 & 1 \\ 9 & -5 & 1 & 8 \end{bmatrix} \quad \text{or} \quad B = \begin{pmatrix} 5 & 2 \\ 6 & -1 \\ 0 & 4 \end{pmatrix}$$

In this text we use square brackets. Corresponding lower case letters, with two indices, are used to represent the elements of a matrix.

$$A = \begin{bmatrix} a_{11} & a_{12} & a_{13} \\ a_{21} & a_{22} & a_{23} \\ a_{31} & a_{32} & a_{33} \\ a_{41} & a_{42} & a_{43} \end{bmatrix} \quad \text{or} \quad B = \begin{bmatrix} b_{11} & b_{12} & b_{13} \\ b_{21} & b_{22} & b_{23} \end{bmatrix}$$

The first index refers to the row in which the element appears; the second index refers to the column in which the element appears. For example: a_{42} appears in the fourth row and the second column of matrix A, and b_{12} appears in the first row and the second column of matrix B. In general, a_{ij} appears in the ith row and the jth column of matrix A.

If A is an $m \times n$ matrix, sometimes we write

$$A = [a_{ij}]_{m \times n}$$

which is an abbreviation for

$$A = \begin{bmatrix} a_{11} & a_{12} & a_{13} & \cdots & a_{1n} \\ a_{21} & a_{22} & a_{23} & \cdots & a_{2n} \\ a_{31} & a_{32} & a_{33} & \cdots & a_{3n} \\ \vdots & \vdots & \vdots & & \vdots \\ a_{m1} & a_{m2} & a_{m3} & \cdots & a_{mn} \end{bmatrix}$$

Example 1 The following matrix represents the number of automobiles shipped from manufacturers of A, B and C to six Ontario cities.

	A	B	C
Ottawa	120	240	480
Kitchener	195	360	120
Toronto	144	720	60
Hamilton	128	412	96
Windsor	215	175	161
Guelph	84	113	87

(a) State the dimensions of the matrix.
(b) State the values of the following entries: a_{32}, a_{23}, a_{61}, and a_{16}.
(c) Write each of the following entries in the form a_{ij}.
    (i) 128   (ii) 113   (iii) 96   (iv) 120

Solution (a) The matrix has six rows (horizontal) and three columns (vertical). Therefore it has dimensions 6 × 3.

(b) a_{32} is the element in the third row and second column. This is 720.
a_{23} is the element in the second row and third column. This is 120.
a_{61} is the element in the sixth row and first column. This is 84.
a_{16} is the element in the first row and sixth column. There is no such element.

(c) (i) 128 is entry a_{41}.
(ii) 113 is entry a_{62}.
(iii) 96 is entry a_{43}.
(iv) There are two entries that have a value of 120. These are a_{11} and a_{23}.

Example 2 A medical clinic has three doctors, each with a specialty. Patients who attend the clinic may see more than one doctor, depending on their illnesses. The accounts are drawn up and submitted to OHIP on a monthly basis. The accounts for January, February, and March are shown in the following matrices. [We will use only five patients. In an actual clinic there would be hundreds and the information would be stored on a computer disc in matrix form.] The entries are the doctors' fees in dollars.

JANUARY

		Doctor I	II	III
	Anthony P.	25	15	0
	Anthony H.	20	0	65
Patient	Anthony X.	30	15	20
	Aston J.	0	35	40
	Aston E.	40	0	15

FEBRUARY

		Doctor I	II	III
	Anthony P.	40	20	55
	Anthony H.	10	0	25
Patient	Anthony X.	0	0	20
	Aston J.	0	0	0
	Aston E.	30	10	10

MARCH

		Doctor I	II	III
	Anthony P.	20	30	35
	Anthony H.	20	0	40
Patient	Anthony X.	0	0	0
	Aston J.	0	0	0
	Aston E.	20	0	40

(a) Find the accounts payable to each doctor for each patient during the first quarter of this year.

(b) Find the average monthly account payable to each doctor for each patient during the first quarter of this year.

Solution   (a)   We add the corresponding entries in the three matrices.

JANUARY				FEBRUARY				MARCH		
25	15	0		40	20	55		20	30	35
20	0	65		10	0	25		20	0	40
30	15	20	+	0	0	20	+	0	0	0
0	35	40		0	0	0		0	0	0
40	0	15		30	10	10		20	0	40

$$= \begin{bmatrix} 25+40+20 & 15+20+30 & 0+55+35 \\ 20+10+20 & 0+0+0 & 65+25+40 \\ 30+0+0 & 15+0+0 & 20+20+0 \\ 0+0+0 & 35+0+0 & 40+0+0 \\ 40+30+20 & 0+10+0 & 15+10+40 \end{bmatrix}$$

$$= \begin{bmatrix} 85 & 65 & 90 \\ 50 & 0 & 130 \\ 30 & 15 & 40 \\ 0 & 35 & 40 \\ 90 & 10 & 65 \end{bmatrix}$$

Therefore the accounts payable to each doctor for each patient during the first quarter are given by the entries (in dollars) in the following matrix.

		Doctor		
		I	II	III
	Anthony P.	85	65	90
	Anthony H.	50	0	130
Patient	Anthony X.	30	15	40
	Aston J.	0	35	40
	Aston E.	90	10	65

(b)   As these accounts were taken over three months, the average would be obtained by dividing each entry in the matrix of totals by 3 or, in other words, multiplying each entry by $\frac{1}{3}$.

$$\frac{1}{3}\begin{bmatrix} 85 & 65 & 90 \\ 50 & 0 & 130 \\ 30 & 15 & 40 \\ 0 & 35 & 40 \\ 90 & 10 & 65 \end{bmatrix} = \begin{bmatrix} \frac{1}{3}(85) & \frac{1}{3}(65) & \frac{1}{3}(90) \\ \frac{1}{3}(50) & \frac{1}{3}(0) & \frac{1}{3}(130) \\ \frac{1}{3}(30) & \frac{1}{3}(15) & \frac{1}{3}(40) \\ \frac{1}{3}(0) & \frac{1}{3}(35) & \frac{1}{3}(40) \\ \frac{1}{3}(90) & \frac{1}{3}(10) & \frac{1}{3}(65) \end{bmatrix}$$

$$= \begin{bmatrix} 28.33 & 21.67 & 30.00 \\ 16.67 & 0.00 & 43.33 \\ 10.00 & 5.00 & 13.33 \\ 0.00 & 11.67 & 13.33 \\ 30.00 & 3.33 & 21.67 \end{bmatrix}$$

Note: These entries have been rounded to the nearest cent.

Therefore, the average monthly account payable to each doctor for each patient is given by the entries (in dollars) in the following matrix.

		Doctor		
		I	**II**	**III**
	Anthony P.	28.33	21.67	30.00
	Anthony H.	16.67	0.00	43.33
Patient	Anthony X.	10.00	5.00	13.33
	Aston J.	0.00	11.67	13.33
	Aston E.	30.00	3.33	21.67

This example leads us to the following definitions.

$$A + B = [a_{ij} + b_{ij}]$$

> If A and B are two matrices with the same dimensions, then we define their **sum, $A + B$**, to be the matrix obtained by adding the corresponding elements.

$$cA = [ca_{ij}]$$

> **Scalar multiplication** is the operation of multiplying a matrix by a scalar (real number). The result is obtained by multiplying each element of the matrix by the scalar.

Example 3   Perform the indicated operations, where possible.

(a) $\begin{bmatrix} 12 & 3 & -7 \\ -8 & 4 & 9 \end{bmatrix} + \begin{bmatrix} 34 & -15 & 7 \\ 1 & -1 & 23 \end{bmatrix}$ (b) $\begin{bmatrix} 4 & -6 \end{bmatrix} + \begin{bmatrix} -8 \\ 5 \end{bmatrix}$

(c) $-4 \begin{bmatrix} 3 & -5 & 1 \\ -15 & 4 & 7 \\ -7 & 10 & 0 \end{bmatrix}$ (d) $3 \begin{bmatrix} 5 & -3 \\ 6 & 8 \\ -7 & 12 \end{bmatrix} - 4 \begin{bmatrix} 5 & -9 \\ -2 & 0 \\ 1 & -1 \end{bmatrix}$

Solution   (a)

$$\begin{bmatrix} 12 & 3 & -7 \\ -8 & 4 & 9 \end{bmatrix} + \begin{bmatrix} 34 & -15 & 7 \\ 1 & -1 & 23 \end{bmatrix} = \begin{bmatrix} 12 + 34 & 3 + (-15) & (-7) + 7 \\ (-8) + 1 & 4 + (-1) & 9 + 23 \end{bmatrix}$$

$$= \begin{bmatrix} 46 & -12 & 0 \\ -7 & 3 & 32 \end{bmatrix}$$

(b) The first matrix has dimensions 1×2 and the second matrix has dimensions 2×1. Since these are different, the matrices cannot be added.

(c) $-4 \begin{bmatrix} 3 & -5 & 1 \\ -15 & 4 & 7 \\ -7 & 10 & 0 \end{bmatrix} = \begin{bmatrix} -4(3) & -4(-5) & -4(1) \\ -4(-15) & -4(4) & -4(7) \\ -4(-7) & -4(10) & -4(0) \end{bmatrix}$

$$= \begin{bmatrix} -12 & 20 & -4 \\ 60 & -16 & -28 \\ 28 & -40 & 0 \end{bmatrix}$$

(d)

$$3 \begin{bmatrix} 5 & -3 \\ 6 & 8 \\ -7 & 12 \end{bmatrix} - 4 \begin{bmatrix} 5 & -9 \\ -2 & 0 \\ 1 & -1 \end{bmatrix} = \begin{bmatrix} 15 & -9 \\ 18 & 24 \\ -21 & 36 \end{bmatrix} + \begin{bmatrix} -20 & 36 \\ 8 & 0 \\ -4 & 4 \end{bmatrix}$$

$$= \begin{bmatrix} -5 & 27 \\ 26 & 24 \\ -25 & 40 \end{bmatrix}$$

EXERCISE 8.1

A **1.** For each matrix, state, where possible, the value of
(i) a_{23} (ii) a_{31} (iii) a_{14}.

(a)
$$A = \begin{bmatrix} 4 & 1 \\ -8 & 3 \\ 4 & -5 \\ 0 & 2 \end{bmatrix}$$

(b)
$$A = \begin{bmatrix} 1 & 12 & 0 \\ 8 & -4 & -14 \\ 6 & -7 & 15 \end{bmatrix}$$

(c) $A = [100 \quad 350 \quad 560 \quad 250]$

2. State the dimensions of each matrix in Question 1.

3. For the matrix given, state each of the following entries in the form a_{ij}.

(a) -37 (b) 15 (c) -7 (d) 0

$$A = \begin{bmatrix} 17 & -7 & 10 & 32 \\ 6 & -8 & 15 & 1 \\ 0 & -37 & 4 & 23 \end{bmatrix}$$

B **4.** Matrices are used in sociological studies to show the relationships among individuals in a group. In particular, the following matrix shows the power structure in a group with four individuals. In the matrix, we let

$$a_{ij} = \begin{cases} 1 & \text{if individual } i \text{ dominates individual } j \\ 0 & \text{otherwise} \end{cases}$$

Individual

	1	2	3	4
1	0	0	0	1
2	1	0	1	1
3	1	0	0	1
4	0	0	0	0

Individual (rows 1, 2, 3, 4)

In this group, (a) who is the most dominant individual?
(b) who is the least dominant individual?

5. Consider the relationship of "liking" in a group consisting of five individuals whom we refer to as Mario, Beatrice, Chantal, Derek, and Toru. In the following 5×5 matrix we let

$$a_{ij} = \begin{cases} 1 & \text{if individual } i \text{ likes individual } j \\ 0 & \text{if individual } i \text{ does not like individual } j \end{cases}$$

	Mario	Beatrice	Chantal	Derek	Toru
Mario	1	0	0	0	0
Beatrice	0	1	1	1	0
Chantal	1	1	1	0	1
Derek	0	1	1	1	0
Toru	1	1	0	0	0

(a) Who is the most liked person in the group?

(b) Who is the least liked person in the group?

(c) What significant piece of information might be suggested by a_{55}?

6. Planning committees use matrices to describe the traffic movement within their city. The city is divided into zones and an estimate of the daily traffic between zones is made. The following matrix could represent the traffic flow in a small city. To interpret the matrix, the entry in the ith row and jth column indicates the number of vehicles travelling from Zone i to Zone j.

Destination Zone

		I	II	III	IV
Origin Zone	I	1000	850	100	500
	II	750	600	270	150
	III	370	220	80	430
	IV	640	480	300	200

(a) How many vehicles travel from Zone III to Zone II?

(b) How many vehicles travel from Zone IV to Zone I?

(c) Of the vehicles starting from Zone II, how many remain in Zone II?

(d) In total, how many vehicles travel to Zone III from a different zone?

(e) How many vehicles actually leave Zone I?

7. The following Origin-Destination matrix indicates the traffic flow between zones in a small Canadian city during the morning rush hour.

Destination Zone

		I	II	III	IV
Origin Zone	I	257	312	56	387
	II	120	295	38	410
	III	217	315	97	560
	IV	35	27	16	355

Assuming people go directly home after leaving work, what matrix would represent the afternoon rush hour traffic flow? This matrix is called the **transpose** of the given matrix.

8. Networks of paths can be described using matrices. Here is an example and its associated matrix. The element in the ith row and jth column gives the number of direct paths from i to j.

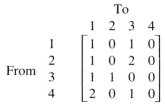

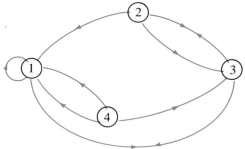

Construct the corresponding matrix for each of the following networks.

(a)   (b)

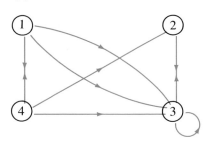   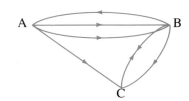

9. Draw a network with matrix $\begin{bmatrix} 1 & 2 & 0 \\ 1 & 0 & 1 \\ 3 & 1 & 0 \end{bmatrix}$

10. A matrix with only one row is called a **row matrix** or a **row vector**. A matrix with only one column is called a **column matrix** or a **column vector**. Give two examples of a row vector and two examples of a column vector.

11. A matrix with the same number of rows and columns is called a **square matrix**. Give two examples of square matrices.

12. Perform the indicated operations.

(a) $6\begin{bmatrix} 15 \\ -8 \\ 7 \end{bmatrix} - 9\begin{bmatrix} -14 \\ 12 \\ -8 \end{bmatrix}$

(b) $-3\begin{bmatrix} 8 & 10 \\ -9 & 15 \end{bmatrix} + 7\begin{bmatrix} -19 & 21 \\ -8 & -14 \end{bmatrix}$

(c) $\frac{1}{3} \begin{bmatrix} -6 & 18 & 5 \\ 12 & -7 & 1 \end{bmatrix} + \frac{1}{2} \begin{bmatrix} 6 & -8 & 3 \\ 18 & -7 & -14 \end{bmatrix}$

(d) $0.6 \begin{bmatrix} 7 & 12 \\ -6 & 9 \\ -15 & 4 \\ 8 & -7 \end{bmatrix} - 0.3 \begin{bmatrix} 1.5 & 7 \\ -14 & -.6 \\ 2.3 & 5 \\ -.7 & 0 \end{bmatrix}$

13. If
$$A = \begin{bmatrix} 2.5 & 3.7 & -0.3 \\ -4.5 & 2.9 & -0.7 \end{bmatrix}$$

$$B = \begin{bmatrix} 4.6 & -0.9 & 3.4 \\ -1.6 & 4.4 & -0.8 \end{bmatrix} \quad C = \begin{bmatrix} 0.5 & 1.7 \\ 2.8 & 4.4 \end{bmatrix}$$

find, where possible, each of the following.
(a) $A + B$ (b) $2A - 3B$ (c) $C + 2A$
(d) $0.2A + 1.3B$ (e) $5.1B - 3.2C$

Use matrices in answering the following questions.

14. Parkway TV records the monthly sales of its staff in matrix form. In January, Henri sold 10 Zenith, 8 Sony, 7 Electrohome, and 14 RCA televisions. Tran sold 7 Zenith, 9 Sony, 11 Electrohome, and 6 RCA televisions. Anya sold 15 Zenith, 12 Sony, 13 Electrohome, and 10 RCA televisions. In February, Henri sold 8 Zenith, 14 Sony, 10 Electrohome, and 9 RCA. Tran sold 13 Zenith, 17 Sony, 9 Electrohome, and 13 RCA. Anya was on holidays.
    (a) Represent each month's sales record with a matrix.
    (b) Represent the total sales for the two months with a matrix.
    (c) Represent the average sales per month with a matrix.

15. Domtec Industries has bought out a number of smaller competitors. There are many obvious advantages to this takeover, but one major disadvantage is that smaller competitors often tend to be more liberal in extending credit and Domtec has inherited a number of overdue accounts. The charts below give a summary of the number of overdue accounts classified according to amount and length of time overdue.

Past Year

Amount (in dollars)	30 Days	60 Days	90 Days
0 to 10 000	847	763	559
10 000 to 20 000	476	349	327
over 20 000	248	176	193

Current Year

Amount (in dollars)	30 Days	60 Days	90 Days
0 to 10 000	955	528	317
10 000 to 20 000	612	241	244
over 20 000	432	236	84

(a)   Construct a matrix showing the increase or decrease in the number of overdue accounts in each of the nine categories.

(b)   Next year Domtec would like to see a 15 percent decrease in each of the nine categories. Prepare a matrix showing their targets.

(c)   Some strategists suggest that there should be a concentrated effort to reduce the number of overdue accounts over $20 000. They recommend reducing these accounts by 25 percent and the remainder by 10 percent. Construct a matrix showing their targets in each of the nine categories.

16.   (a)   HAL Computer Ltd. has three outlets in the southern Ontario region. At the beginning of February the inventory at the Toronto outlet was 35 hard disc drives, 28 printers, 37 monitors, and 26 keyboards. The inventory at the St. Catharines outlet was 23 hard disc drives, 22 printers, 29 monitors, and 24 keyboards. The inventory at the Hamilton outlet was 32 hard disc drives, 38 printers, 25 monitors, and 29 keyboards. Represent this information in a matrix.

(b)   The February sales figures for each of the three outlets are given in the following chart.

	Hard Drives	**Printers**	**Monitors**	**Keyboards**
Toronto	22	20	18	21
St. Catharines	12	18	23	16
Hamilton	19	19	23	22

Represent the inventory at the end of February as a matrix.

(c)   The main office of HAL Computer Ltd. expects an increase in sales over the next month because of a strong advertising campaign. The company is going to make a shipment equal to 140 percent of the February sales for each outlet to add to the existing stock in anticipation of this demand increase. Construct a matrix showing the inventory at the beginning of March for each outlet.

C 17.   Construct a matrix $A = [a_{ij}]_{4 \times 4}$ whose entries show the distances between the four vertices of a square with sides of length one unit.

18. Construct a matrix $A = [a_{ij}]_{8 \times 8}$ whose entries show the distances between the eight vertices of a unit cube.

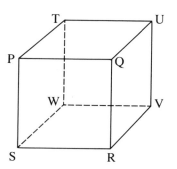

8.2 MULTIPLICATION OF MATRICES

Having introduced addition and scalar multiplication of matrices, we now introduce the multiplication of two matrices. The most natural way may seem to be to multiply the corresponding elements, but it has been found that this is not the most useful way of multiplying matrices. Matrix multiplication has been defined in a different and more applicable way. The reason behind the rule will be seen in the sections that follow. It is the purpose of this section to introduce the method, and the student is asked to accept it for the moment.

Matrix multiplication is based on *row-by-column* multiplication.

To multiply a row by a column, multiply the first element in the row by the first element in the column; then multiply the second element in the row by the second element in the column; then the third, and so on. Finally, add the products.

Example 1 (a)

$$[-3 \quad 0] \begin{bmatrix} 2 \\ 8 \end{bmatrix} = [(-3)(2) + (0)(8)] = [-6]$$

(b)

$$[9 \quad -2 \quad 4] \begin{bmatrix} 2 \\ 3 \\ 5 \end{bmatrix} = [(9)(2) + (-2)(3) + (4)(5)] = [32]$$

Notice that the row and the column *must have the same number of elements* in order to be multiplied.

$$[1 \quad 2] \quad \text{and} \quad \begin{bmatrix} 3 \\ 4 \\ 5 \end{bmatrix} \quad \text{cannot be multiplied}$$

Larger matrices can be multiplied, but you must be able to multiply the rows of the left matrix by the columns of the right matrix.

$$\begin{bmatrix} 3 & 4 & 6 \\ 2 & 9 & 1 \end{bmatrix} \begin{bmatrix} 13 & 0 & 4 \\ 8 & 0 & -2 \\ 1 & 1 & 4 \end{bmatrix} \quad \text{(can be multiplied)}$$

$$\begin{bmatrix} 3 & 4 & 6 \\ 2 & 9 & 1 \end{bmatrix} \begin{bmatrix} 13 & 0 & 4 \\ 8 & 0 & -2 \end{bmatrix} \quad \text{(cannot be multiplied)}$$

In general, the matrix product AB exists only when the number of elements in each row of A equals the number of elements in each column of B. The number of elements in each row of A is determined by the number of columns in A, and the number of elements in each column of B is determined by the number of rows in B.

If $C = AB$, then
$c_{ij} = a_{i1}b_{1j} + a_{i2}b_{2j} + \ldots$

> AB exists only when the number of columns of A equals the number of rows of B. In this case, the elements of AB are obtained by multiplying each row of A by each column of B.

It is helpful to know the size (or dimensions) of the product matrix when it exists.

> In general, when the product exists, AB has the same number of rows as A and the same number of columns as B.

We can write these results in the following way.

$$A_{m \times n} \times B_{n \times p} = (AB)_{m \times p} \qquad A_{m \times n} \times B_{n \times p} = (AB)_{m \times p}$$

These must be equal.   These give the dimensions of AB.

Example 2   Evaluate

$$\begin{array}{cc} A & B \end{array}$$
$$\begin{bmatrix} 2 & -3 & 1 \\ -4 & -2 & 0 \end{bmatrix} \begin{bmatrix} -1 & 6 \\ 4 & 3 \\ 5 & 7 \end{bmatrix}$$

Solution A has dimensions 2×3 and B has dimensions 3×2. Since the number of columns of A equals the number of rows of B, the product exists. AB will have the same number of rows as A and the same number of columns as B. Therefore AB will have dimensions 2×2.

$$
\begin{array}{ccc}
A & B & AB \\
\begin{bmatrix} 2 & -3 & 1 \\ -4 & -2 & 0 \end{bmatrix} & \begin{bmatrix} -1 & 6 \\ 4 & 3 \\ 5 & 7 \end{bmatrix} = & \begin{bmatrix} & \\ & \end{bmatrix} \\
2 \times 3 & 3 \times 2 & 2 \times 2
\end{array}
$$

The elements of AB are obtained by multiplying the rows of A with the columns of B. In particular, the element in the first row and first column of AB is obtained by multiplying the first row of A with the first column of B.

$$
\begin{bmatrix} 2 & -3 & 1 \\ -4 & -2 & 0 \end{bmatrix} \begin{bmatrix} -1 & 6 \\ 4 & 3 \\ 5 & 7 \end{bmatrix} = \begin{bmatrix} (2)(-1) + (-3)(4) + (1)(5) & \\ & \end{bmatrix}
$$

$$
= \begin{bmatrix} -9 & \\ & \end{bmatrix}
$$

The element in the first row and second column is obtained by multiplying the first row of A with the second column of B.

$$
\begin{bmatrix} 2 & -3 & 1 \\ -4 & -2 & 0 \end{bmatrix} \begin{bmatrix} -1 & 6 \\ 4 & 3 \\ 5 & 7 \end{bmatrix} = \begin{bmatrix} -9 & (2)(6) + (-3)(3) + (1)(7) \\ & \end{bmatrix}
$$

$$
= \begin{bmatrix} -9 & 10 \\ & \end{bmatrix}
$$

The element in the second row and first column is obtained by multiplying the second row of A with the first column of B.

$$
\begin{bmatrix} 2 & -3 & 1 \\ -4 & -2 & 0 \end{bmatrix} \begin{bmatrix} -1 & 6 \\ 4 & 3 \\ 5 & 7 \end{bmatrix} = \begin{bmatrix} -9 & 10 \\ (-4)(-1) + (-2)(4) + (0)(5) & \end{bmatrix}
$$

$$
= \begin{bmatrix} -9 & 10 \\ -4 & \end{bmatrix}
$$

The element in the second row and second column is obtained by multiplying the second row of A with the second column of B.

$$
\begin{bmatrix} 2 & -3 & 1 \\ -4 & -2 & 0 \end{bmatrix} \begin{bmatrix} -1 & 6 \\ 4 & 3 \\ 5 & 7 \end{bmatrix} = \begin{bmatrix} -9 & 10 \\ -4 & (-4)(6) + (-2)(3) + (0)(7) \end{bmatrix}
$$

$$
= \begin{bmatrix} -9 & 10 \\ -4 & -30 \end{bmatrix}
$$

Example 3   Evaluate each of the following.

(a) $\begin{bmatrix} -4 & 8 \\ -5 & 0 \\ -2 & 13 \end{bmatrix} \begin{bmatrix} 15 & 6 \\ -7 & 1 \end{bmatrix}$

(b) $\begin{bmatrix} -7 & 8 \\ 0 & 2 \\ -9 & 5 \\ 7 & -1 \end{bmatrix} \begin{bmatrix} 5 & -8 & 3 \\ 0 & -8 & 1 \\ -1 & 0 & -5 \end{bmatrix}$

(c) $\begin{bmatrix} 2 & -3 \\ -4 & 5 \end{bmatrix} \begin{bmatrix} x \\ y \end{bmatrix}$

Solution   (a)   *A* has dimensions 3 × 2 and *B* has dimensions 2 × 2. Since the number of columns of *A* equals the number of rows of *B*, the product exists. *AB* will have the same number of rows as *A* and the same number of columns as *B*. Therefore *AB* will have dimensions 3 × 2.

$$\begin{array}{ccc} A & B & AB \end{array}$$

$$\begin{bmatrix} -4 & 8 \\ -5 & 0 \\ -2 & 13 \end{bmatrix} \begin{bmatrix} 15 & 6 \\ -7 & 1 \end{bmatrix} = \begin{bmatrix} & \\ & \\ & \end{bmatrix}$$

$$\begin{array}{ccc} 3 \times 2 & 2 \times 2 & 3 \times 2 \end{array}$$

The elements of *AB* are obtained by multiplying the rows of *A* by the columns of *B*.

$$\begin{bmatrix} -4 & 8 \\ -5 & 0 \\ -2 & 13 \end{bmatrix} \begin{bmatrix} 15 & 6 \\ -7 & 1 \end{bmatrix} = \begin{bmatrix} (-4)(15) + (8)(-7) & (-4)(6) + (8)(1) \\ (-5)(15) + (0)(-7) & (-5)(6) + (0)(1) \\ (-2)(15) + (13)(-7) & (-2)(6) + (13)(1) \end{bmatrix}$$

$$= \begin{bmatrix} -116 & -16 \\ -75 & -30 \\ -121 & 1 \end{bmatrix}$$

(b)   *A* has dimensions 4 × 2 and *B* has dimensions 3 × 3. Since the number of columns of *A* does not equal the number of rows of *B*, we cannot multiply the two matrices.

(c)   *A* has dimensions 2 × 2 and *B* has dimensions 2 × 1. Since the number of columns of *A* equals the number of rows of *B*, the product exists. *AB* will have the same number of rows as *A* and the same number of columns as *B*. Therefore *AB* will have dimensions 2 × 1.

$$\begin{matrix} A & B & AB \end{matrix}$$

$$\begin{bmatrix} 2 & -3 \\ -4 & 5 \end{bmatrix} \begin{bmatrix} x \\ y \end{bmatrix} = \begin{bmatrix} \end{bmatrix}$$

$$\begin{matrix} 2 \times 2 & 2 \times 1 & 2 \times 1 \end{matrix}$$

The elements of AB are obtained by multiplying the rows of A by the columns of B.

$$\begin{bmatrix} 2 & -3 \\ -4 & 5 \end{bmatrix} \begin{bmatrix} x \\ y \end{bmatrix} = \begin{bmatrix} 2x - 3y \\ -4x + 5y \end{bmatrix}$$

Example 4 If

$$A = \begin{bmatrix} 2 & 1 \\ -3 & 5 \end{bmatrix} \quad \text{and} \quad B = \begin{bmatrix} -1 & 4 \\ 2 & -3 \end{bmatrix}$$

find

(a) AB (b) BA (c) $AB - BA$ (d) A^2

Solution (a)

$$AB = \begin{bmatrix} 2 & 1 \\ -3 & 5 \end{bmatrix} \begin{bmatrix} -1 & 4 \\ 2 & -3 \end{bmatrix}$$

$$= \begin{bmatrix} (2)(-1) + (1)(2) & (2)(4) + (1)(-3) \\ (-3)(-1) + (5)(2) & (-3)(4) + (5)(-3) \end{bmatrix}$$

$$= \begin{bmatrix} 0 & 5 \\ 13 & -27 \end{bmatrix}$$

(b)

$$BA = \begin{bmatrix} -1 & 4 \\ 2 & -3 \end{bmatrix} \begin{bmatrix} 2 & 1 \\ -3 & 5 \end{bmatrix}$$

$$= \begin{bmatrix} (-1)(2) + (4)(-3) & (-1)(1) + (4)(5) \\ (2)(2) + (-3)(-3) & (2)(1) + (-3)(5) \end{bmatrix}$$

$$= \begin{bmatrix} -14 & 19 \\ 13 & -13 \end{bmatrix}$$

(c)

$$AB - BA = \begin{bmatrix} 0 & 5 \\ 13 & -27 \end{bmatrix} - \begin{bmatrix} -14 & 19 \\ 13 & -13 \end{bmatrix}$$

$$= \begin{bmatrix} 14 & -14 \\ 0 & -14 \end{bmatrix}$$

(d) $A^2 = AA$

$$= \begin{bmatrix} 2 & 1 \\ -3 & 5 \end{bmatrix} \begin{bmatrix} 2 & 1 \\ -3 & 5 \end{bmatrix}$$

$$= \begin{bmatrix} (2)(2) + (1)(-3) & (2)(1) + (1)(5) \\ (-3)(2) + (5)(-3) & (-3)(1) + (5)(5) \end{bmatrix}$$

$$= \begin{bmatrix} 1 & 7 \\ -21 & 22 \end{bmatrix}$$

It is important to note that AB is not the same as BA so that the order in which we write the matrix multiplication matters. We say matrix multiplication is **not commutative**.

EXERCISE 8.2

A **1.** Which of the following multiplications can be performed?

(a) $\begin{bmatrix} 3 & 5 \\ -4 & 1 \end{bmatrix} \begin{bmatrix} 6 & -8 \\ 4 & -7 \end{bmatrix}$

(b) $\begin{bmatrix} 4 & -6 \end{bmatrix} \begin{bmatrix} 3 & -4 \\ -5 & 2 \end{bmatrix}$

(c) $\begin{bmatrix} 1 & -4 & 0 \\ 15 & 1 & -7 \\ 8 & 0 & 1 \end{bmatrix} \begin{bmatrix} -7 & 0 & -11 \end{bmatrix}$

(d) $\begin{bmatrix} 1 & 0 & 0 \\ 0 & 1 & 0 \\ 0 & 0 & 1 \end{bmatrix} \begin{bmatrix} -7 \\ 13 \\ 32 \end{bmatrix}$

(e) $\begin{bmatrix} -2 & 5 \\ 4 & 1 \\ 6 & -7 \end{bmatrix} \begin{bmatrix} 3 & -6 & 0 \\ 2 & -4 & -1 \end{bmatrix}$

(f) $\begin{bmatrix} 4 & -6 & 5 \\ -7 & 3 & 10 \end{bmatrix} \begin{bmatrix} -15 \\ 5 \end{bmatrix}$

(g) $\begin{bmatrix} 1 & -5 & -9 \\ 14 & 6 & -10 \\ 4 & 4 & -4 \end{bmatrix} \begin{bmatrix} 2 & -41 \\ 8 & 0 \\ 1 & 52 \end{bmatrix}$

(h) $\begin{bmatrix} 2 & -3 & 0 & 1 \\ 4 & 1 & 5 & 0 \\ 0 & 3 & 6 & 8 \\ 0 & 15 & -1 & 7 \end{bmatrix} \begin{bmatrix} 4 \\ -18 \\ 0 \\ 13 \end{bmatrix}$

2. State the dimensions of the product matrix, where it is defined.

(a) $\begin{bmatrix} 2 & -4 & 7 \end{bmatrix} \begin{bmatrix} 5 & 4 & -6 \\ 1 & 2 & 8 \\ 4 & 2 & 9 \end{bmatrix}$

(b) $\begin{bmatrix} -4 & 8 \\ -5 & 7 \end{bmatrix} \begin{bmatrix} -8 & 3 \\ 1 & 1 \end{bmatrix}$

(c) $\begin{bmatrix} -3 & 4 \\ 0 & -1 \end{bmatrix} \begin{bmatrix} 3 \\ 7 \end{bmatrix}$

(d) $\begin{bmatrix} 22 & -15 \\ 5 & -2 \end{bmatrix} \begin{bmatrix} 5 & -3 & 2 \\ -8 & 1 & 7 \end{bmatrix}$

(e) $\begin{bmatrix} 2 & -5 \\ 17 & 54 \end{bmatrix} \begin{bmatrix} 5 & 1 \\ -3 & 2 \\ 1 & 8 \end{bmatrix}$

(f) $\begin{bmatrix} 0 & 4 & 2 & -8 \\ 10 & 14 & 5 & 6 \\ -5 & -6 & 1 & 7 \\ -3 & 0 & 5 & -1 \end{bmatrix} \begin{bmatrix} 2 \\ 0 \\ -4 \\ -1 \end{bmatrix}$

3. The dimensions of matrix A and matrix B are given. In each part, determine
   (i) whether the product matrix, AB, exists.
   (ii) the dimensions of the product matrix (where it exists).
      (a) $A_{3 \times 2}$ and $B_{2 \times 4}$
      (b) $A_{1 \times 3}$ and $B_{3 \times 3}$
      (c) $A_{3 \times 3}$ and $B_{3 \times 2}$
      (d) $A_{1 \times 4}$ and $B_{4 \times 1}$
      (e) $A_{3 \times 1}$ and $B_{1 \times 3}$
      (f) $A_{3 \times 2}$ and $B_{3 \times 3}$
      (g) $A_{2 \times 2}$ and $B_{2 \times 2}$

4. For each part in Question 3, determine
   (i) whether the product matrix, BA, exists.
   (ii)) the dimensions of the product matrix (where it exists).

B 5. Multiply, where possible, each of the following.
   (a) $[-4 \quad 6] \begin{bmatrix} -5 \\ -9 \end{bmatrix}$

   (b) $[13 \quad -8 \quad -17] \begin{bmatrix} -6 \\ 15 \\ 12 \end{bmatrix}$

   (c) $[22 \quad -12] \begin{bmatrix} 8 \\ -19 \\ 23 \end{bmatrix}$

   (d) $[25 \quad -32 \quad -40 \quad 25] \begin{bmatrix} -8 \\ 7 \\ 15 \\ -10 \end{bmatrix}$

   (e) $\begin{bmatrix} 12 \\ -16 \end{bmatrix} [-11 \quad 8]$

   (f) $[2 \quad -3 \quad 5] \begin{bmatrix} x \\ y \\ z \end{bmatrix}$

6. Multiply, where possible, the following matrices.
   (a) $[3 \quad -5] \begin{bmatrix} -1 & 5 \\ 4 & 2 \end{bmatrix}$

   (b) $\begin{bmatrix} -6 & 3 \\ 7 & 8 \end{bmatrix} \begin{bmatrix} 4 & 1 \\ -2 & 3 \end{bmatrix}$

   (c) $\begin{bmatrix} 5 & -1 \\ 2 & -1 \\ 0 & 3 \end{bmatrix} \begin{bmatrix} -1 & 2 & 8 \\ 4 & 0 & -2 \end{bmatrix}$

   (d) $\begin{bmatrix} 2 & 1 & 4 \\ -3 & 4 & 3 \end{bmatrix} \begin{bmatrix} 1 & -2 \\ -3 & 4 \\ 1 & -5 \end{bmatrix}$

   (e) $\begin{bmatrix} 3 & -5 & 1 \\ 0 & -2 & -5 \\ 1 & 4 & -8 \end{bmatrix} \begin{bmatrix} -6 \\ 5 \\ -13 \end{bmatrix}$

   (f) $\begin{bmatrix} -8 & 4 & -6 \\ 12 & -11 & 0 \\ 1 & -4 & -5 \end{bmatrix} \begin{bmatrix} 0 & -3 & 7 \\ 9 & 10 & -16 \\ 1 & -6 & 14 \end{bmatrix}$

   (g) $\begin{bmatrix} 5 & -8 \\ 2 & 0 \end{bmatrix} \begin{bmatrix} 12 & -9 \\ 6 & 15 \\ -6 & 14 \end{bmatrix}$

   (h) $\begin{bmatrix} \frac{1}{2} & \frac{3}{4} \\ \frac{1}{2} & \frac{1}{4} \end{bmatrix} \begin{bmatrix} 3 \\ -1 \end{bmatrix}$

   (i) $\begin{bmatrix} 5 & -8 \\ 2 & 11 \end{bmatrix} \begin{bmatrix} x \\ y \end{bmatrix}$

   (j) $\begin{bmatrix} 3 & -1 & -4 \\ 6 & 2 & -5 \end{bmatrix} \begin{bmatrix} x \\ y \\ z \end{bmatrix}$

7. If

$$A = \begin{bmatrix} 2 & -1 & 6 \\ -5 & 8 & -10 \end{bmatrix} \quad \text{and} \quad B = \begin{bmatrix} 1 & -2 & 3 \\ 6 & 10 & -3 \\ -9 & 2 & 1 \end{bmatrix}$$

find, where possible,
(a) AB (b) BA (c) A^2 (d) B^2

8. If

$$A = \begin{bmatrix} -5 & -1 & 8 \\ -6 & 6 & 2 \end{bmatrix} \quad B = \begin{bmatrix} 7 & 1 \\ 0 & -2 \\ 5 & -3 \end{bmatrix} \quad C = \begin{bmatrix} -11 & 9 \\ 3 & -4 \end{bmatrix}$$

find
(a) AB (b) $(AB)C$ (c) BC (d) $A(BC)$

In general for matrices A, B, and C, (AB)C is the same as A(BC) whenever the products exists. We say matrix multiplication is **associative** *and will make use of this property in Section 8.4.*

9. If

$$I = \begin{bmatrix} 1 & 0 \\ 0 & 1 \end{bmatrix} \quad \text{and} \quad A = \begin{bmatrix} 3 & -8 \\ 7 & 9 \end{bmatrix}$$

find
(a) IA (b) AI

10. If

$$I = \begin{bmatrix} 1 & 0 & 0 \\ 0 & 1 & 0 \\ 0 & 0 & 1 \end{bmatrix} \quad \text{and} \quad A = \begin{bmatrix} 2 & -3 & 1 \\ 0 & -2 & 4 \\ 3 & 5 & 2 \end{bmatrix}$$

find
(a) IA (b) AI

The matrices, I, in Questions 9 and 10 are called **identity matrices***. A matrix A remains unchanged when multiplied by an identity matrix.*

$$AI = IA = A$$

11. In Exercise 8.1 you were introduced to networks and their corresponding matrices.
(a) Write the matrix A corresponding to the following network. Remember, each entry, a_{ij}, represents the number of *direct* paths from i to j.

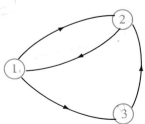 

(b) Find A^2.
(c) The entries of A^2 also represent the number of paths between the given points; however, they are not direct paths. They are

paths that involve two steps. Locate all the two-step paths in the given network.

(d) Find A^3.

(e) What do the entries in A^3 represent? Locate these paths in the network.

12. Repeat Question 11, parts (a) and (b), for the given network.

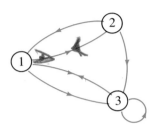

[Observe how the counting principles discussed in Chapter 1 apply here.]

13. The following network indicates the direct flights Alpha Airlines offers between Vancouver, Winnipeg, Toronto, and Halifax.

(a) Construct the matrix A corresponding to the given network.

(b) Find A^2 and A^3.

(c) How many ways can a person travel from Halifax to Vancouver making, at most, one stop?

(d) How many ways can a person travel from Winnipeg to Halifax making, at most, two stops?

14. If $A = \begin{bmatrix} 0.6 & 0.4 \\ 0.3 & 0.7 \end{bmatrix}$, find A^2, A^3, and A^4.

15. If $A = \begin{bmatrix} 0.2 & 0.5 & 0.3 \\ 0 & 0.9 & 0.1 \\ 0.7 & 0.1 & 0.2 \end{bmatrix}$, find A^2 and A^3.

16. Evaluate each of the following.

(a) $\begin{bmatrix} 2 & -5 \\ 6 & -7 \end{bmatrix} \left(\begin{bmatrix} 5 & 1 \\ -2 & 3 \end{bmatrix} + \begin{bmatrix} -4 & 2 \\ 1 & -2 \end{bmatrix} \right)$

(b) $\begin{bmatrix} 2 & 3 \end{bmatrix} \begin{bmatrix} 1 & 0 & 8 \\ -2 & 3 & -7 \end{bmatrix} + \begin{bmatrix} 2 & -9 & 1 \end{bmatrix} \begin{bmatrix} 4 & -2 & 6 \\ 10 & -1 & 3 \\ 5 & -4 & 0 \end{bmatrix}$

(c)
$$\left(2 \begin{bmatrix} 1 & -2 & 0 \\ 4 & -1 & 3 \\ -5 & 0 & 6 \end{bmatrix} - 3 \begin{bmatrix} 1 & 2 & -2 \\ 4 & -1 & 7 \\ 0 & -1 & 3 \end{bmatrix} \right) \begin{bmatrix} -2 \\ 1 \\ 3 \end{bmatrix}$$

17. Find x and y such that
$$\begin{bmatrix} 2 & -3 \\ 1 & 4 \end{bmatrix} \begin{bmatrix} x \\ y \end{bmatrix} = \begin{bmatrix} 7 \\ 5 \end{bmatrix}$$

18. Find x, y, and z such that
$$\begin{bmatrix} x & 0 & 1 \\ 2 & -3 & 5 \\ 7 & y & 0 \end{bmatrix} \begin{bmatrix} 2 & 0 \\ 1 & 0 \\ -3 & 1 \end{bmatrix} + \begin{bmatrix} -1 & 2 \\ 3 & -2 \\ 1 & 4 \end{bmatrix} = \begin{bmatrix} y & z \\ -11 & 3 \\ x & 4 \end{bmatrix}$$

19. It is possible to use matrices for coding messages. First, we let each letter of the alphabet be represented by a natural number.

A B C D E F G H I J K L M N O P Q R S T U V W X Y Z
1 2 3 4 5 6 7 8 9 10 11 12 13 14 15 16 17 18 19 20 21 22 23 24 25 26

Then the message NO HOMEWORK TONIGHT could be translated to read

14, 15   8, 15, 13, 5, 23, 15, 18, 11   20, 15, 14, 9, 7, 8, 20

Next, we write these numbers as entries in 2×2 matrices as follows.

$$\begin{bmatrix} 14 & 15 \\ 8 & 15 \end{bmatrix}, \begin{bmatrix} 13 & 5 \\ 23 & 15 \end{bmatrix}, \begin{bmatrix} 18 & 11 \\ 20 & 15 \end{bmatrix}, \begin{bmatrix} 14 & 9 \\ 7 & 8 \end{bmatrix}, \begin{bmatrix} 20 & 24 \\ 24 & 24 \end{bmatrix}$$

Note: We insert X's (24) to complete the last matrix when necessary. To make the code more challenging we introduce a *coding matrix* $\begin{bmatrix} 4 & 1 \\ 7 & 2 \end{bmatrix}$ by which the matrices are multiplied.

$$\begin{bmatrix} 4 & 1 \\ 7 & 2 \end{bmatrix} \begin{bmatrix} 14 & 15 \\ 8 & 15 \end{bmatrix} = \begin{bmatrix} 64 & 75 \\ 114 & 135 \end{bmatrix}$$

$$\begin{bmatrix} 4 & 1 \\ 7 & 2 \end{bmatrix} \begin{bmatrix} 13 & 5 \\ 23 & 15 \end{bmatrix} = \begin{bmatrix} 75 & 35 \\ 137 & 65 \end{bmatrix}$$

$$\begin{bmatrix} 4 & 1 \\ 7 & 2 \end{bmatrix} \begin{bmatrix} 18 & 11 \\ 20 & 15 \end{bmatrix} = \begin{bmatrix} 92 & 59 \\ 166 & 107 \end{bmatrix}$$

$$\begin{bmatrix} 4 & 1 \\ 7 & 2 \end{bmatrix} \begin{bmatrix} 14 & 9 \\ 7 & 8 \end{bmatrix} = \begin{bmatrix} 63 & 44 \\ 112 & 79 \end{bmatrix}$$

$$\begin{bmatrix} 4 & 1 \\ 7 & 2 \end{bmatrix} \begin{bmatrix} 20 & 24 \\ 24 & 24 \end{bmatrix} = \begin{bmatrix} 104 & 120 \\ 188 & 216 \end{bmatrix}$$

So, NO HOMEWORK TONIGHT becomes

$$\begin{bmatrix} 64 & 75 \\ 114 & 135 \end{bmatrix}, \begin{bmatrix} 75 & 35 \\ 137 & 65 \end{bmatrix}, \begin{bmatrix} 92 & 59 \\ 166 & 107 \end{bmatrix}, \begin{bmatrix} 63 & 44 \\ 112 & 79 \end{bmatrix}, \begin{bmatrix} 104 & 120 \\ 188 & 216 \end{bmatrix}$$

To understand such a message we need a *decoding matrix*, in this case

$$\begin{bmatrix} 2 & -1 \\ -7 & 4 \end{bmatrix}$$

$$\begin{bmatrix} 2 & -1 \\ -7 & 4 \end{bmatrix} \begin{bmatrix} 64 & 75 \\ 114 & 135 \end{bmatrix} = \begin{bmatrix} 14 & 15 \\ 8 & 15 \end{bmatrix} \qquad \text{NOHO}$$

$$\begin{bmatrix} 2 & -1 \\ -7 & 4 \end{bmatrix} \begin{bmatrix} 75 & 35 \\ 137 & 65 \end{bmatrix} = \begin{bmatrix} 13 & 5 \\ 23 & 15 \end{bmatrix} \qquad \text{MEWO}$$

$$\begin{bmatrix} 2 & -1 \\ -7 & 4 \end{bmatrix} \begin{bmatrix} 92 & 59 \\ 166 & 107 \end{bmatrix} = \begin{bmatrix} 18 & 11 \\ 20 & 15 \end{bmatrix} \qquad \text{RKTO}$$

$$\begin{bmatrix} 2 & -1 \\ -7 & 4 \end{bmatrix} \begin{bmatrix} 63 & 44 \\ 112 & 79 \end{bmatrix} = \begin{bmatrix} 14 & 9 \\ 7 & 8 \end{bmatrix} \qquad \text{NIGH}$$

$$\begin{bmatrix} 2 & -1 \\ -7 & 4 \end{bmatrix} \begin{bmatrix} 104 & 120 \\ 188 & 216 \end{bmatrix} = \begin{bmatrix} 20 & 24 \\ 24 & 24 \end{bmatrix} \qquad \text{TXXX}$$

Using the decoder matrix given, decode each of the following messages.

(a) $\begin{bmatrix} 7 & 12 \\ 13 & 21 \end{bmatrix}$ decoder matrix $\begin{bmatrix} 2 & -1 \\ -5 & 3 \end{bmatrix}$

(b) $\begin{bmatrix} 35 & 20 \\ -42 & -25 \end{bmatrix}, \begin{bmatrix} 76 & 51 \\ -95 & -60 \end{bmatrix}$ decoder matrix $\begin{bmatrix} -1 & -1 \\ 4 & 3 \end{bmatrix}$

(c) $\begin{bmatrix} 133 & 80 \\ 55 & 36 \end{bmatrix}, \begin{bmatrix} 120 & 41 \\ 53 & 18 \end{bmatrix}, \begin{bmatrix} 113 & 145 \\ 49 & 62 \end{bmatrix}, \begin{bmatrix} 123 & 118 \\ 54 & 52 \end{bmatrix}$

decoder matrix $\begin{bmatrix} 1 & -2 \\ -2 & 5 \end{bmatrix}$

(d) $\begin{bmatrix} 0 & -24 & -1 \\ -36 & 66 & -8 \\ 97 & -59 & 33 \end{bmatrix}, \begin{bmatrix} -16 & -3 & 19 \\ 15 & -2 & -81 \\ 36 & 27 & 129 \end{bmatrix}$

decoder matrix $\begin{bmatrix} 14 & 8 & 3 \\ 8 & 5 & 2 \\ 3 & 2 & 1 \end{bmatrix}$

C **20.** The decoding matrix is the matrix that multiplies with the coding matrix to give the identity matrix $\begin{bmatrix} 1 & 0 \\ 0 & 1 \end{bmatrix}$. The matrix used to code the following message was $\begin{bmatrix} 5 & 2 \\ 7 & 3 \end{bmatrix}$.

(a) Find the decoding matrix.

(b) Decode

$$\begin{bmatrix} 43 & 89 \\ 63 & 126 \end{bmatrix}, \begin{bmatrix} 130 & 47 \\ 186 & 70 \end{bmatrix}, \begin{bmatrix} 100 & 23 \\ 144 & 34 \end{bmatrix}, \begin{bmatrix} 113 & 118 \\ 162 & 170 \end{bmatrix}$$

8.3   APPLICATIONS TO COMMERCIAL EXAMPLES

Matrix multiplication is one of the most widely applicable tools of mathematics. In the examples that follow, it might be argued that the problems could have been solved just as easily without the use of matrices. The convenience of the matrix approach becomes apparent only in practical situations that are much more complex than the examples we present. Our examples will produce matrices with dimensions like 1 × 4 and 3 × 3. In practice, it is not uncommon to have matrices with hundreds if not thousands of rows and columns. However, the general approach is the same. The difference is that, in the first case, the calculations can be done by hand or by using a calculator; in the second case, the calculations require the aid of a computer.

Example 1   A recording company produces singles, albums, cassette tapes, and compact discs. The production costs for these can be divided into two categories: raw materials and labour. This information is stored in the following form. Entries are in dollars.

	Raw Materials	Labour
Singles	0.27	0.76
Albums	0.89	2.87
Cassette Tapes	1.63	2.18
Compact Discs	5.37	5.52

Assume that the company plans to produce 20 000 singles, 80 000 albums, 95 000 cassette tapes, and 10 000 compact discs. What is the total cost of raw materials and the total cost of labour for production of these quantities?

Solution   To find the total cost for raw materials we must multiply the quantity of each item (singles, albums, ...) with the unit cost of raw materials for that item, then add the products.

(20 000)(0.27) + (80 000)(0.89) + (95 000)(1.63) + (10 000)(5.37)
= 285 150

This reminds us of matrix multiplication. In particular,

$$\begin{array}{cccc} \text{Singles} & \text{Albums} & \text{Tapes} & \text{Discs} \\ [20\ 000 & 80\ 000 & 95\ 000 & 10\ 000] \end{array} \begin{bmatrix} 0.27 \\ 0.89 \\ 1.63 \\ 5.37 \end{bmatrix} \begin{array}{l} \text{Singles} \\ \text{Albums} \\ \text{Tapes} \\ \text{Discs} \end{array}$$

$$= [(20\ 000)(0.27) + (80\ 000)(0.89) + (95\ 000)(1.63) + (10\ 000)(5.37)]$$

$$= [285\ 150]$$

Similarly, to find the total cost for labour, we multiply the quantity of each item with the labour cost per unit for that item and add the products. In matrix form this would be

$$
\begin{array}{cccc}
\text{Singles} & \text{Albums} & \text{Tapes} & \text{Discs} \\
[20\ 000 & 80\ 000 & 95\ 000 & 10\ 000]
\end{array}
\begin{bmatrix} 0.76 \\ 2.87 \\ 2.18 \\ 5.52 \end{bmatrix}
\begin{array}{l}
\text{Singles} \\
\text{Albums} \\
\text{Tapes} \\
\text{Discs}
\end{array}
$$

$$
\begin{aligned}
&= [(20\ 000)(0.76) + (80\ 000)(2.87) + (95\ 000)(2.18) \\
&\quad + (10\ 000)(5.52)] \\
&= [507\ 100]
\end{aligned}
$$

These could have been combined into the single matrix multiplication

$$
[20\ 000 \quad 80\ 000 \quad 95\ 000 \quad 10\ 000]
\begin{bmatrix}
0.27 & 0.76 \\
0.89 & 2.87 \\
1.63 & 2.18 \\
5.37 & 5.52
\end{bmatrix}
$$
$$
= [285\ 150 \quad 507\ 100]
$$

From the product matrix we can determine that the cost for raw materials is $285 150 and the cost for labour is $507 100.

Example 2   A computer software firm has three outlets in Branton: the main, the west end, and the east end branches. Each outlet sells three types of software that we designate as business, scientific, and entertainment. The head office uses a matrix to record the following information concerning the number of each type of software sold by each outlet in a given month.

	Business	Scientific	Entertainment
Main	32	24	230
West	15	10	140
East	10	18	150

If, on the average, a piece of business software costs $400, a piece of scientific software costs $200, and a piece of entertainment software costs $50, find the total receipts for each store in the given month.

Solution   The given information can be written in the following matrix form.

$$
\begin{array}{l}
 \begin{array}{ccc} \text{Bus} & \text{Sci} & \text{Ent} \end{array} \\
\begin{array}{l} \text{Main} \\ \text{West} \\ \text{East} \end{array}
\begin{bmatrix}
32 & 24 & 230 \\
15 & 10 & 140 \\
10 & 18 & 150
\end{bmatrix}
\end{array}
$$

To find the total receipts for each outlet, the number of each type (business, scientific, entertainment) sold at that outlet is multiplied by the unit price for that item; then the products are added. For the main outlet, the calculation would be

$$(32)(400) + (24)(200) + (230)(50) = 29\ 100$$

If we use matrices, to obtain this calculation we must construct a column matrix of prices and multiply in the following way.

$$
\begin{array}{c}
\text{Bus}\ \ \text{Sci}\ \ \text{Ent} \\
\begin{array}{c}\text{Main}\\\text{West}\\\text{East}\end{array}
\begin{bmatrix} 32 & 24 & 230 \\ 15 & 10 & 140 \\ 10 & 18 & 150 \end{bmatrix}
\begin{bmatrix} 400 \\ 200 \\ 50 \end{bmatrix}
\begin{array}{c}\text{Bus}\\\text{Sci}\\\text{Ent}\end{array}
\end{array}
$$

$$
= \begin{bmatrix} (32)(400) + (24)(200) + (230)(50) \\ (15)(400) + (10)(200) + (140)(50) \\ (10)(400) + (18)(200) + (150)(50) \end{bmatrix}
$$

$$
= \begin{bmatrix} 29\ 100 \\ 15\ 000 \\ 15\ 100 \end{bmatrix}
$$

Therefore, the total receipts from the main outlet is \$29 100; the west outlet is \$15 000; and the east outlet is \$15 100.

When using matrices to solve questions like these, it is essential to make sure the matrices are set up in such a way that the required product is obtained. In Example 2, it would make no sense to set up the prices in a row matrix and multiply as follows.

$$
\begin{array}{c}
\text{Bus}\ \ \text{Sci}\ \ \text{Ent} \\
\begin{array}{c}\text{Bus}\ \ \ \text{Sci}\ \ \ \text{Ent}\\ \lbrack 400\ \ \ 200\ \ \ 50\ \rbrack\end{array}
\begin{bmatrix} 32 & 24 & 230 \\ 15 & 10 & 140 \\ 10 & 18 & 150 \end{bmatrix}
\end{array}
$$

Although the multiplication is defined, it does not yield the solution to the problem asked. In fact, the products are meaningless.

Example 3   A subsidiary of an automobile corporation makes engines for its cars. It makes three types: four-cylinder, six-cylinder, and eight-cylinder. The production of each engine (although mostly mechanized) requires the services of a skilled mechanic to do some of the more intricate work and an inspection officer to check all the work after production. The following table gives a breakdown of the number of work-hours needed for each type of engine.

	Mechanic	Inspector
Four-cylinder	20	3
Six-cylinder	25	4
Eight-cylinder	30	5

(a) If the plant produced 300 four-cylinder, 500 six-cylinder, and 100 eight-cylinder engines in a given month, determine the number of hours needed by mechanics and by inspectors.

(b) If a mechanic gets $16.75 an hour and an inspector gets $13.50 an hour, determine the total labour costs.

Solution   The information given in the chart can be written in the following matrix form.

$$\begin{array}{c} \\ \text{Four-cylinder} \\ \text{Six-cylinder} \\ \text{Eight-cylinder} \end{array} \begin{array}{cc} \text{Mechanic} & \text{Inspector} \\ \left[\begin{array}{cc} 20 & 3 \\ 25 & 4 \\ 30 & 5 \end{array} \right] \end{array}$$

(a) To determine the total number of mechanic work-hours needed, the quantity of each type (four-cylinder, six-cylinder, eight-cylinder) must be multiplied by the number of mechanic work-hours required for that type. To achieve the correct multiplications we construct a row matrix consisting of the quantities and multiply in the following way.

$$[300 \quad 500 \quad 100] \begin{bmatrix} 20 & 3 \\ 25 & 4 \\ 30 & 5 \end{bmatrix}$$

$$= [(300)(20) + (500)(25) + (100)(30) \quad (300)(3) + (500)(4) + (100)(5)]$$
$$= [21\ 500 \quad 3400]$$

Therefore there are 21 500 mechanic work-hours and 3400 inspector work-hours needed.

(b) To determine the total labour expenses, the number of mechanic work-hours must be multiplied by the wage per hour and the number of inspector work-hours must be multiplied by the wage per hour, and the resulting products must be added. This can be achieved by constructing a column matrix of the wages per hour and multiplying in the following way.

$$[21\ 500 \quad 3400] \begin{bmatrix} 16.75 \\ 13.50 \end{bmatrix} = [(21\ 500)(16.75) + (3400)(13.50)]$$

$$= [406\ 025]$$

Therefore the total labour cost is $406 025.

EXERCISE 8.3

B **1.** Supermarkets, in an attempt to attract customers, advertise the sale of certain products. Advertisers hope that once the customers are in the store they will do all their shopping there, even for items not on sale. In an attempt to determine which supermarket is actually the cheapest place to shop, a consumer advocate keeps weekly records of the prices of certain items. The chart shows a typical weekly survey. Entries are in dollars.

	Store A	Store B	Store C
Bread (one loaf)	1.39	1.27	1.33
Milk (one litre)	1.07	1.05	1.15
Eggs (one dozen)	1.33	1.39	1.39
Corn (one can)	0.89	0.79	0.73

Note: This is an abbreviated list. There are actually over 100 items.

If, during an average week, a family of four requires three loaves of bread, fourteen litres of milk, one dozen eggs, and two cans of corn, determine the total expenditure for these items at each of the three stores. Based on these data, which store has the cheapest prices?

2. A Finite Mathematics teacher uses the following formula to determine her students' final marks: 20 percent of the first term, 25 percent of the first exam, 20 percent of the second term, and 35 percent of the final exam. Some of her students' marks are listed below.

	First Term	First Exam	Second Term	Final Exam
	20	25	20	35
Anderson N.	68	63	71	57
Anthony P.	82	77	84	73
Bellavia D.	55	48	59	50
Curic A.	95	92	94	83

Find each of the four students' final marks.

3. Suppose the Finite Mathematics teacher in Question 2 listed her students' marks in the following way.

	Anderson N.	Anthony P.	Bellavia D.	Curic A.
First Term	68	82	55	95
First Exam	63	77	48	92
Second Term	71	84	59	94
Final Exam	57	73	50	83

How would we now find each of the four students' final marks?

4. A firm produces four types of computer printers: a laser printer, a graphics printer, a high quality printer, and a budget printer.

Each of these printers requires four different raw materials. These requirements are shown in the table.

	Raw Material			
	A	B	C	D
Laser	6	8	4	9
Graphics	8	6	9	7
High Quality	5	5	4	4
Budget	3	3	4	4

(a) If there are 12 laser, 10 graphics, 25 high quality, and 30 budget printers scheduled for production next month, determine the amount of each raw material needed.

(b) If the per unit cost of the raw materials is $3.00 for raw material A, $10.00 for raw material B, $20.00 for raw material C, and $6.00 for raw material D, find the cost of producing each type of printer.

5. A sociological survey was conducted to determine the relationship between education and income in a large Canadian city. The following chart shows income brackets for each level of education.

	Under $20 000	$20 000–$40 000	Over $40 000
Less than High School	60%	30%	10%
High School	45%	40%	15%
College	30%	50%	20%
University	15%	40%	45%

In a randomly selected sample of 1000 people: 150 have less than a high school education; 300 have a high school diploma; 350 have a college education; and 200 have a university education. How many of the 1000 people do you expect there would be in each of the three income brackets?

6. A company specializing in custom-made shirts produces four different sizes: small, medium, large, and extra-large. The amount of material and labour needed to produce each type is listed in the chart below.

	Material (m^2)	labour (h)
Small	1	2
Medium	1.3	2
Large	1.7	3
Extra-Large	2	3

(a) If the company made 230 small, 450 medium, 300 large, and 75 extra-large shirts last month, find the total amount of material used and the total number of hours required.

(b) If material costs \$11.30 per m^2 and wages are \$10.70 an hour, find the cost of making a small, medium, large, or extra-large shirt.

(c) What was the total cost of making all the shirts last month?

Questions 7 and 8 are exercises in setting up a mathematical model. You decide how the data could be represented in matrix form. No actual figures will be given.

7. Four companies sell three similar products. The quantity of each product sold by each company is known. Represent this data by a matrix B. Represent the price of each product by a second matrix P and find the total amount earned by each of the four companies. Assuming that the manufacturing cost for each product is the same for each company, represent these data by a matrix and find the total spent on manufacturing each product.

8. Repeat Question 7 using a different way of setting up the matrices. [Hint: See Questions 2 and 3.]

8.4 MARKOV CHAINS

As was mentioned in Section 5.7, one area in which matrices are widely used is in the branch of Applied Mathematics called Stochastic Processes. Let us first recall a few of the important facts needed in this section.

When a fair coin is tossed, the probability of a head or tail turning up is $\frac{1}{2}$. If this process (of tossing a coin) is repeated a second time, the probability of a head or a tail is still $\frac{1}{2}$. The result of the first toss of the coin has no effect on the second toss; the trials are *independent*. Similarly, a third or fourth toss of the coin is unaffected by the results of the previous trials.

This is not always the case. In many (if not most) situations in real life, the results of a trial can affect the probabilities of future trials. In this section we limit our discussion to trials in which the outcome of a trial may be affected by the outcome of the immediately preceding trial (but not by any other). This kind of stochastic process is called a **Markov chain**.

Example 1 There are two cola distributors in a northern region of the country. Research has shown that if a person buys Brand A there is a 90 percent chance the person will buy Brand A the next time. If a person buys Brand B there is a 70 percent chance the person will buy Brand B the next time. Brand B has just finished an extensive advertising campaign and it is predicted that initially there is an 80 percent chance that a person will buy Brand B. Find the probabilities that a person will buy Brand A or Brand B on the second try.

Solution   If someone buys Brand A, since there is a 90 percent chance the person will buy it the next time, there is a 10 percent chance the person will buy Brand B. If someone buys Brand B, since there is a 70 percent chance the person will buy Brand B the next time, there is a 30 percent chance the person will buy Brand A. Initially, there is an 80 percent chance that a person will buy Brand B and therefore a 20 percent chance a person will buy Brand A.

As in Section 5.7, we use a tree diagram to illustrate these probabilities. Note that probabilities placed on the second set of branches of the tree are the conditional probabilities based on the outcome of the previous trial.

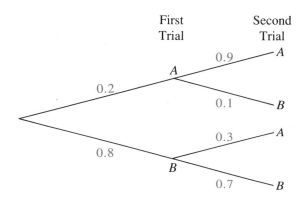

As we see from the diagram, there are two branches that will result in a person using Brand A the second time. We calculate the probability in the following way.

$P(A \text{ the 2nd time})$
$= P(A \text{ the 1st time}) \times P(A \text{ the 2nd time} \mid A \text{ the 1st time})$
$\quad + P(B \text{ the 1st time}) \times P(A \text{ the 2nd time} \mid B \text{ the 1st time})$
$= (0.2)(0.9) + (0.8)(0.3)$
$= 0.42$

Similarly, there are two branches that will result in a person using Brand B the second time.

$P(B \text{ the 2nd time})$
$= P(A \text{ the 1st time}) \times P(B \text{ the 2nd time} \mid A \text{ the 1st time})$
$\quad + P(B \text{ the 1st time}) \times P(B \text{ the 2nd time} \mid B \text{ the 1st time})$
$= (0.2)(0.1) + (0.8)(0.7)$
$= 0.58$

Therefore there is a 42 percent chance a person will buy Brand A the second time and a 58 percent chance a person will buy Brand B. ◁▷

The kinds of multiplications used in Example 1 remind us of matrix multiplication. For example,

$$[0.2 \quad 0.8] \begin{bmatrix} 0.9 \\ 0.3 \end{bmatrix} = [(0.2)(0.9) + (0.8)(0.3)]$$

$$= [0.42]$$

and

$$[0.2 \quad 0.8] \begin{bmatrix} 0.1 \\ 0.7 \end{bmatrix} = [(0.2)(0.1) + (0.8)(0.7)]$$

$$= [0.58]$$

These two matrix multiplications could have been written as one, in the following way. Transution

$$S^0$$
$$[0.2 \quad 0.8] \begin{bmatrix} 0.9 & 0.1 \\ 0.3 & 0.7 \end{bmatrix} = [0.42 \quad 0.58]$$

The matrix, $\begin{bmatrix} 0.9 & 0.1 \\ 0.3 & 0.7 \end{bmatrix}$, contains the conditional probabilities and is called the **transition matrix** or the **matrix of transition probabilities**. It is denoted by P and is characterized by the following properties.

---

1. A transition matrix is square. "P"
2. The entries are probabilities, so they are always between 0 and 1, inclusive.
3. The sum of the entries in any row is always 1.

The matrix, $[0.2 \quad 0.8]$, contains the initial probabilities and hence is called the **initial probability vector**. It is denoted by $S^{(0)}$. [S is an abbreviation for *state* and the zero indicates this is the initial state.]

The matrix, $[0.42 \quad 0.58]$, contains the probabilities of buying Brand A or Brand B after the first trial (for the second trial) and is called the **first-step probability vector**. It is denoted by $S^{(1)}$.

A **probability vector** is characterized by the following properties.

---

1. A probability vector is a row matrix.
2. The entries are probabilities, so they are always between 0 and 1, inclusive.
3. The sum of the entries is 1.

Example 2 Bob and Jim are extremely competitive tennis players. Every Tuesday night at 8:00 sharp they show up at the tennis courts to continue their life-long rivalry. Over the years a pattern has developed. Whenever Bob wins, his confidence increases and the probability of his winning the next week is 0.7. However, when he loses, the probability of his winning the next week is only 0.4.
(a) Find the matrix of transition probabilities, P, for this Markov chain.
(b) If the initial probability of either Bob or Jim winning is 0.5, what is the probability of each player winning the next week?

(c) What is the probability of each player winning the third match played in two weeks?

Solution   (a) If Bob wins, the probability of his winning the next week is 0.7. Therefore, if Bob wins, the probability of Jim winning the next week is $1 - 0.7 = 0.3$. These conditional probabilities give us the first row in the matrix of transition probabilities.

$$\begin{array}{c} \\ \text{BOB} \\ \text{JIM} \end{array} \begin{array}{cc} \text{BOB} & \text{JIM} \\ \left[\begin{array}{cc} 0.7 & 0.3 \\ & \end{array} \right] \end{array}$$

If Bob loses (Jim wins), the probability of his winning the next week is 0.4. Therefore if Bob loses (Jim wins), the probability of Jim winning is $1 - 0.4 = 0.6$. This gives us the second row in the matrix of transition probabilities.

$$\begin{array}{c} \\ \text{BOB} \\ \text{JIM} \end{array} \begin{array}{cc} \text{BOB} & \text{JIM} \\ \left[\begin{array}{cc} 0.7 & 0.3 \\ 0.4 & 0.6 \end{array} \right] \end{array}$$

Note: The entries in each row of the transition matrix always add up to 1.

(b) If the initial probability of either player winning is 0.5, the initial probability vector is

$$\begin{array}{cc} \text{BOB} & \text{JIM} \\ S^{(0)} = [\, 0.5 & 0.5 \,] \end{array}$$

The probabilities of the players winning the second week are given by

$$S^{(1)} = S^{(0)}P$$

$$= [0.5 \quad 0.5] \begin{bmatrix} 0.7 & 0.3 \\ 0.4 & 0.6 \end{bmatrix}$$

$$= [0.55 \quad 0.45]$$

Therefore the probability Bob will win the second week is 0.55 and the probability Jim will win is 0.45.

(c) The probabilities of the players winning the match in the third week is given by

$$S^{(2)} = S^{(1)}P$$

$$= [0.55 \quad 0.45] \begin{bmatrix} 0.7 & 0.3 \\ 0.4 & 0.6 \end{bmatrix}$$

$$= [0.565 \quad 0.435]$$

Therefore the probability Bob will win the third week is 0.565 and the probability Jim will win is 0.435. [$S^{(2)}$ is called the **second-**

step probability vector and gives the probabilities of each player winning the third match.]   ◇

In the preceding example, the second-step probability vector, $S^{(2)}$, was obtained by multiplying the first-step probability vector, $S^{(1)}$, with P. However,

$$S^{(2)} = S^{(1)}P$$
$$= (S^{(0)}P)P$$
$$= S^{(0)}(PP) \qquad \text{(associative property)}$$
$$= S^{(0)}P^2$$

This suggests an alternative method for finding the second-step probability vector without actually finding the first-step probabilities.

Similarly,

$$S^{(3)} = S^{(2)}P$$
$$= (S^{(0)}P^2)P$$
$$= S^{(0)}(P^2P)$$
$$= S^{(0)}P^3$$

and the third-step probabilities can be calculated in this way. In general,

$$S^{(n)} = S^{(0)}P^n$$

We will use this property to calculate probabilities in the following example.

Example 3   The transition matrix, P, of a Markov chain is $\begin{bmatrix} 0.5 & 0.5 \\ 0.4 & 0.6 \end{bmatrix}$ and the initial probability vector, $S^{(0)}$, is $[0.4 \quad 0.6]$. Find the first-, second-, and third-step probability vectors.

Solution   First we find P^2 and P^3.

$$P^2 = PP \qquad\qquad\qquad P^3 = PP^2$$

$$= \begin{bmatrix} 0.5 & 0.5 \\ 0.4 & 0.6 \end{bmatrix}\begin{bmatrix} 0.5 & 0.5 \\ 0.4 & 0.6 \end{bmatrix} \qquad = \begin{bmatrix} 0.5 & 0.5 \\ 0.4 & 0.6 \end{bmatrix}\begin{bmatrix} 0.45 & 0.55 \\ 0.44 & 0.56 \end{bmatrix}$$

$$= \begin{bmatrix} 0.45 & 0.55 \\ 0.44 & 0.56 \end{bmatrix} \qquad\qquad = \begin{bmatrix} 0.445 & 0.555 \\ 0.444 & 0.556 \end{bmatrix}$$

The first-step probability vector, $S^{(1)}$, is given by

$$S^{(1)} = S^{(0)}P$$

$$= [0.4 \quad 0.6]\begin{bmatrix} 0.5 & 0.5 \\ 0.4 & 0.6 \end{bmatrix}$$

$$= [0.44 \quad 0.56]$$

The second-step probability vector, $S^{(2)}$, is given by

$$S^{(2)} = S^{(0)}P^2$$

$$= [0.4 \quad 0.6] \begin{bmatrix} 0.45 & 0.55 \\ 0.44 & 0.56 \end{bmatrix}$$

$$= [0.444 \quad 0.556]$$

The third-step probability vector, $S^{(3)}$, is given by

$$S^{(3)} = S^{(0)}P^3$$

$$= [0.4 \quad 0.6] \begin{bmatrix} 0.445 & 0.555 \\ 0.444 & 0.556 \end{bmatrix}$$

$$= [0.4444 \quad 0.5556]$$

Example 4   Atlas Weather Services describes a day's weather as sunny, cloudy, or rainy. According to previous information, they have determined that following a sunny day there is a 60 percent chance of having another sunny day, a 30 percent chance of having a cloudy day, and a 10 percent chance of rain. Following a cloudy day there is a 50 percent chance of having another cloudy day, a 20 percent chance of rain, and a 30 percent chance of having a sunny day. If it was raining, then there is a 40 percent chance of rain the next day, a 50 percent chance of cloudy cover, and a 10 percent chance of sun.

(a) Construct the transition matrix, P, Atlas Weather Services would use to predict future weather patterns.

(b) Find P^2 and P^3.

(c) If it rains on Monday, what is the probability it will rain on Tuesday?

(d) If it is sunny on Monday, what is the probability it will be sunny on Wednesday?

(e) If it is cloudy on Monday, what is the probability it will be sunny on Thursday?

Solution   (a) The transition matrix, P, is

$$\begin{array}{c c} & \begin{array}{ccc} \text{Sun} & \text{Cloud} & \text{Rain} \end{array} \\ \begin{array}{c} \text{Sun} \\ \text{Cloud} \\ \text{Rain} \end{array} & \begin{bmatrix} 0.6 & 0.3 & 0.1 \\ 0.3 & 0.5 & 0.2 \\ 0.1 & 0.5 & 0.4 \end{bmatrix} \end{array}$$

(b) $P^2 = PP$

$$= \begin{bmatrix} 0.6 & 0.3 & 0.1 \\ 0.3 & 0.5 & 0.2 \\ 0.1 & 0.5 & 0.4 \end{bmatrix} \begin{bmatrix} 0.6 & 0.3 & 0.1 \\ 0.3 & 0.5 & 0.2 \\ 0.1 & 0.5 & 0.4 \end{bmatrix}$$

$$= \begin{bmatrix} 0.46 & 0.38 & 0.16 \\ 0.35 & 0.44 & 0.21 \\ 0.25 & 0.48 & 0.27 \end{bmatrix}$$

$$P^3 = P^2P$$

$$= \begin{bmatrix} 0.46 & 0.38 & 0.16 \\ 0.35 & 0.44 & 0.21 \\ 0.25 & 0.48 & 0.27 \end{bmatrix} \begin{bmatrix} 0.6 & 0.3 & 0.1 \\ 0.3 & 0.5 & 0.2 \\ 0.1 & 0.5 & 0.4 \end{bmatrix}$$

$$= \begin{bmatrix} 0.406 & 0.408 & 0.186 \\ 0.363 & 0.430 & 0.207 \\ 0.321 & 0.450 & 0.229 \end{bmatrix}$$

(c) If it rains on Monday then the initial probability vector (or state) is

$$S^{(0)} = [0 \quad 0 \quad 1]$$

To predict the weather for Tuesday we find the first-step probability vector.

$$S^{(1)} = S^{(0)}P$$

$$= [0 \quad 0 \quad 1] \begin{bmatrix} 0.6 & 0.3 & 0.1 \\ 0.3 & 0.5 & 0.2 \\ 0.1 & 0.5 & 0.4 \end{bmatrix}$$

$$= [0.1 \quad 0.5 \quad 0.4]$$

Therefore, there is a probability of 0.4 or a 40 percent chance it will rain on Tuesday.

(d) If it is sunny on Monday then the initial state is

$$S^{(0)} = [1 \quad 0 \quad 0]$$

To predict the weather for Wednesday we find the second-step probability vector.

$$S^{(2)} = S^{(0)}P^2$$

$$= [1 \quad 0 \quad 0] \begin{bmatrix} 0.46 & 0.38 & 0.16 \\ 0.35 & 0.44 & 0.21 \\ 0.25 & 0.48 & 0.27 \end{bmatrix}$$

$$= [0.46 \quad 0.38 \quad 0.16]$$

Therefore, there is a probability of 0.46 or a 46 percent chance it will be sunny on Wednesday.

(e) If it is cloudy on Monday then we have

$$S^{(0)} = [0 \quad 1 \quad 0]$$

To predict the weather for Thursday we find the third-step probability vector.

$$S^{(3)} = S^{(0)}P^3$$

$$= [0 \quad 1 \quad 0] \begin{bmatrix} 0.406 & 0.408 & 0.186 \\ 0.363 & 0.430 & 0.207 \\ 0.321 & 0.450 & 0.229 \end{bmatrix}$$

$$= [0.363 \quad 0.430 \quad 0.207]$$

Therefore there is a probability of 0.363 or a 36.3 percent chance it will be sunny on Thursday.   ◇

EXERCISE 8.4

A **1.** Which of the following is the transition matrix for a Markov chain? For those that are not, give a reason.

(a) $\begin{bmatrix} 0.9 & 0.1 \\ 0.7 & 0.3 \end{bmatrix}$
(b) $\begin{bmatrix} \frac{1}{2} & \frac{1}{2} \\ \frac{1}{4} & \frac{3}{4} \end{bmatrix}$

(c) $\begin{bmatrix} 0.65 & 0.35 \\ 0.5 & 0.45 \end{bmatrix}$
(d) $\begin{bmatrix} 0.73 & 0.27 \\ 1.36 & -0.36 \end{bmatrix}$

(e) $\begin{bmatrix} \frac{1}{3} & \frac{1}{3} & \frac{1}{3} \\ \frac{1}{4} & \frac{1}{2} & \frac{1}{4} \\ \frac{2}{5} & \frac{1}{5} & \frac{1}{5} \end{bmatrix}$
(f) $\begin{bmatrix} 0.43 & 0.28 & 0.29 \\ 0.75 & 0 & 0.25 \end{bmatrix}$

2. Which of the following are probability vectors? For those that are not, give a reason.

(a) $\begin{bmatrix} 0.8 & 0.2 \\ 0.4 & 0.6 \end{bmatrix}$
(b) $[0.9 \quad 0.1]$

(c) $[0.3 \quad 0.3 \quad 0.3]$
(d) $[0 \quad 0 \quad 1 \quad 0]$

3. Global Rent-A-Car has four distribution locations. A rented car may be returned to any of the four locations. From past statistics the management has determined that the following transition matrix can be used to describe the return of their vehicles.

$$\begin{array}{c} \\ A \\ B \\ C \\ D \end{array} \begin{array}{cccc} A & B & C & D \end{array} \\ \begin{bmatrix} 0.8 & 0.2 & 0 & 0 \\ 0.2 & 0.7 & 0.1 & 0 \\ 0 & 0.1 & 0.8 & 0.1 \\ 0 & 0 & 0.3 & 0.7 \end{bmatrix}$$

(a) For a car rented at A, give the probability of being returned to B.

(b) For a car rented at C, give the probability of being returned to A.

(c) For a car rented at D, give the probability of being returned to C.

B **4.** In Silicon Falls, Alberta, there are two pocket calculator distributors. We will call them A and B. Distributor A has been in the business for some time and its name has become well known. For this reason it is assumed that, for first-time buyers, there is a 70 percent chance they will choose calculator A. Unfortunately, it has been found that after being used the buttons on calculator A have a tendency to stick when pressed. Therefore, if a person bought calculator A, there is only a 60 percent chance she or he will choose A for a second calculator. On the other hand, it has been found that most first-time buyers of calculator B are very satisfied and there is a 90 percent chance they will buy B as their second calculator.

(a) Find the transition matrix P.

(b) Find the initial probability vector $S^{(0)}$.

(c) Find P^2 and P^3.

(d) Find the first step probability vector, $S^{(1)}$, and hence determine the probabilities of a person buying calculator A or B for a second calculator.

(e) Find the second step probability vector, $S^{(2)}$, and hence determine the probabilities of a person buying calculator A or B for a third calculator.

(f) Find the third step probability vector, $S^{(3)}$, and hence determine the probabilities of a person buying calculator A or B for a fourth calculator.

5. CKTV Weather Services describes a day's weather as sunny, cloudy, or rainy. According to previous information, they have determined that following a sunny day there is a 50 percent chance of having another sunny day, a 35 percent chance of having a cloudy day, and a 15 percent chance of rain. Following a cloudy day there is a 45 percent chance of having another cloudy day, a 25 percent chance of rain, and a 30 percent chance of sun. If it was raining, then there is a 40 percent chance of rain the next day, a 45 percent chance of cloud cover, and a 15 percent chance of sun.

(a) Construct the transition matrix CKTV Weather Services would use to predict future weather patterns.

(b) If it rains on Monday, what is the probability it will rain on Tuesday?

(c) If it is cloudy on Thursday, what is the probability it will be sunny on Saturday?

6. In a particular area the regional government is in the habit of studying the movement patterns of its population. They classify communities as city, suburban, or rural. They have determined that each year, of people living in the city, 12 percent will move to the suburbs and 2 percent will move to a rural area. Of people living in the suburbs, 8 percent will move to the city and 3 percent will move to the country. Of rural residents, 15 percent will move to the city and 6 percent will move to the suburbs. The rest remain where they are.

(a) Construct the matrix of transition probabilities describing the patterns of movement.

(b) If a person is living in the city today, what is the probability the person will be living in the city a year from now?

(c) For a person living in the country what is the probability the person will still be living in a rural area three years from now?

7. A mouse is placed in one of the compartments of the maze shown. A transition takes place when the mouse moves through one of the doors available into another compartment. It is assumed that these moves are made with equal probability. The probability of moving from a compartment into itself is zero.

(a) Construct the transition matrix P for this Markov chain.

(b) Compute P^2, P^3, and P^4.

(c) If a mouse starts in compartment 1, what is the probability it will be in compartment 3 after two transitions? after three transitions?

(d) If a mouse starts in compartment 2, what is the probability it will be in compartment 1 after two transitions? after four transitions?

8. Repeat Question 7 using the following maze.

9. Zeljko tries not to be late for his dates with Vesna too often. Whenever he is late, there is a 90 percent chance he will be on time for the next date. However, whenever he is on time, there is only a

70 percent chance he will be on time for the next date.
(a) Construct the transition matrix P for this Markov chain.
(b) Determine P^2, P^3, and P^4.
(c) If there is an 80 percent chance of Zeljko being on time for the first date, what are the chances of him being on time for the second, third, fourth, and fifth dates?

10. A survey indicates that if at least one of the parents of a child has a university degree then there is a 75 percent chance of that child obtaining one. If neither parent has a university degree then there is only a 33 percent chance that the child will graduate from university.
(a) Construct the matrix of transition probabilities P for this Markov chain.
(b) What is the probability that the grandchild of parents without a university degree will graduate from university?
(c) What is the probability that the great-grandchild of a parent with a degree will also obtain one?

11. In a northern community there are only two courier services, Northstar and Red Lake. It has been determined that if a person tries Northstar there is only a 40 percent chance the person will try it the next time. If a person tries Red Lake, there is a 60 percent chance the person will use their services the next time.
(a) Construct the transition matrix P for the two companies.
(b) Calculate P^2, P^3, and P^4.
(c) For a person trying Northstar for the first time, what is the probability the person will use their services the second time, the third time, the fourth time?

12. The transition matrix, P, for a Markov chain is given.

	STATE 1	STATE 2	STATE 3
STATE 1	0.6	0.3	0.1
STATE 2	0.4	0.4	0.2
STATE 3	0.3	0.4	0.3

(a) If the system starts in state 2, what is the initial probability vector?
(b) If the system starts in state 3, what is the initial probability vector?
(c) Compute P^2, P^3, and P^4.
(d) What is the probability that the system moves from state 3 to state 2 in one transition?
(e) What is the probability that the system moves from state 1 to state 3 in three transitions?
(f) If the system begins in state 2, what is the probability it will be in state 2 after four transitions?

8.5 REGULAR MARKOV CHAINS AND STEADY STATE VECTORS

In a competitive market that follows a Markov chain pattern, it is especially useful to be able to predict long-term trends. Companies may want to know if the market will keep changing or if there is some state, $S^{(n)}$, after which the market settles down; that is, remains steady. In this section we investigate *regular* Markov chains that move toward some *steady* state. It turns out that such processes are characterized by the following definition.

> A Markov chain is said to be **regular** if the transition matrix P, or some power of P, has only positive entries.

Example 1 Which of the following are transition matrices of a regular Markov chain?

(a) $\begin{bmatrix} 0.8 & 0.2 \\ 0.5 & 0.5 \end{bmatrix}$

(b) $\begin{bmatrix} 0.5 & 0.5 & 0 \\ 0.4 & 0.4 & 0.2 \\ 0.3 & 0.3 & 0.4 \end{bmatrix}$

(c) $\begin{bmatrix} 1 & 0 \\ 0 & 1 \end{bmatrix}$

(d) $\begin{bmatrix} 0.4 & 0.4 & 0.2 \\ 0.6 & 0.2 & 0.2 \\ 0.8 & 0.2 & 0.3 \end{bmatrix}$

Solution

(a) Since all entries are greater than or equal to zero and each row adds to one, this is the transition matrix for some Markov chain. Since every entry in the transition matrix is positive, the Markov chain is regular.

(b) Since all entries are greater than or equal to zero and each row adds to one, this is the transition matrix for some Markov chain. The given matrix has a zero entry. However,

$$\begin{bmatrix} 0.5 & 0.5 & 0 \\ 0.4 & 0.4 & 0.2 \\ 0.3 & 0.3 & 0.4 \end{bmatrix}^2 = \begin{bmatrix} 0.5 & 0.5 & 0 \\ 0.4 & 0.4 & 0.2 \\ 0.3 & 0.3 & 0.4 \end{bmatrix}\begin{bmatrix} 0.5 & 0.5 & 0 \\ 0.4 & 0.4 & 0.2 \\ 0.3 & 0.3 & 0.4 \end{bmatrix}$$

$$= \begin{bmatrix} 0.45 & 0.45 & 0.10 \\ 0.42 & 0.42 & 0.16 \\ 0.39 & 0.39 & 0.22 \end{bmatrix}$$

Since this matrix has only positive entries, the Markov chain is regular.

(c) Since all entries are greater than or equal to zero and each row adds to one, this is the transition matrix for some Markov chain. The transition matrix has zero entries, so we consider powers of this matrix.

$$\begin{bmatrix} 1 & 0 \\ 0 & 1 \end{bmatrix}^2 = \begin{bmatrix} 1 & 0 \\ 0 & 1 \end{bmatrix} \begin{bmatrix} 1 & 0 \\ 0 & 1 \end{bmatrix}$$

$$= \begin{bmatrix} 1 & 0 \\ 0 & 1 \end{bmatrix}$$

Every power of the transition matrix is the same and contains zero entries. Therefore this is not the transition matrix of a regular Markov chain.

(d) Since the third row does not add to one, this is not a transition matrix of a Markov chain.   ⬦

The importance of *regular Markov chains* is that, in the long run, the probability vectors, $S^{(n)}$, remain virtually unchanged. We illustrate this with the following example.

Example 2   In the town of Quinton there are two supermarkets: Henry's and Morton's. It has been found that if a person shops at Henry's there is an 80 percent chance the person will return to Henry's the next time. If a person shops at Morton's there is only a 60 percent chance the person will return to Morton's the next time. Assume Quinton residents shop only at Henry's or Morton's.

(a) Construct the transition matrix, P, for this Markov chain.

(b) If there is initially a 50 percent chance of a person shopping at either store, find the probability vectors $S^{(1)}$, $S^{(2)}$, $S^{(3)}$, $S^{(4)}$, $S^{(5)}$, $S^{(6)}$, and $S^{(7)}$.

(c) What long-term trend becomes apparent?

Solution   (a) The transition matrix, P, is

$$\begin{array}{cc} & \text{Henry's} \quad \text{Morton's} \\ \begin{array}{c} \text{Henry's} \\ \text{Morton's} \end{array} & \begin{bmatrix} 0.8 & 0.2 \\ 0.4 & 0.6 \end{bmatrix} \end{array}$$

Note: Since the transition matrix contains only positive entries, the Markov chain is regular.

(b) The initial probability vector is

$$\begin{array}{c} \text{Henry's} \quad \text{Morton's} \\ S^{(0)} = \quad [0.5 \quad 0.5] \end{array}$$

$$S^{(1)} = S^{(0)}P = [0.5 \quad 0.5] \begin{bmatrix} 0.8 & 0.2 \\ 0.4 & 0.6 \end{bmatrix} = [0.6 \quad 0.4]$$

$$S^{(2)} = S^{(1)}P = [0.6 \quad 0.4] \begin{bmatrix} 0.8 & 0.2 \\ 0.4 & 0.6 \end{bmatrix} = [0.64 \quad 0.36]$$

$$S^{(3)} = S^{(2)}P = [0.64 \quad 0.36] \begin{bmatrix} 0.8 & 0.2 \\ 0.4 & 0.6 \end{bmatrix} = [0.656 \quad 0.344]$$

$$S^{(4)} = S^{(3)}P = [0.656 \quad 0.344] \begin{bmatrix} 0.8 & 0.2 \\ 0.4 & 0.6 \end{bmatrix} = [0.6624 \quad 0.3376]$$

$$S^{(5)} = S^{(4)}P = [0.6624 \quad 0.3376] \begin{bmatrix} 0.8 & 0.2 \\ 0.4 & 0.6 \end{bmatrix} = [0.66496 \quad 0.33504]$$

$$S^{(6)} = S^{(5)}P = [0.66496 \quad 0.33504] \begin{bmatrix} 0.8 & 0.2 \\ 0.4 & 0.6 \end{bmatrix} = [0.665984 \quad 0.334016]$$

$$S^{(7)} = S^{(6)}P = [0.665984 \quad 0.334016] \begin{bmatrix} 0.8 & 0.2 \\ 0.4 & 0.6 \end{bmatrix} = [0.6663936 \quad 0.3336064]$$

(c) In the long run, it appears that there is approximately a 67 percent chance a person will shop at Henry's and a 33 percent chance a person will shop at Morton's.

In the preceding example, we started with the initial probability vector $S^{(0)} = [0.5 \quad 0.5]$. In fact, the same long-term results would have been obtained regardless of what initial probability vector we use.

Example 3 Repeat Example 2 using the initial probability vector $S^{(0)} = [1 \quad 0]$

Solution

$$S^{(1)} = S^{(0)}P = [1 \quad 0] \begin{bmatrix} 0.8 & 0.2 \\ 0.4 & 0.6 \end{bmatrix} = [0.8 \quad 0.2]$$

$$S^{(2)} = S^{(1)}P = [0.8 \quad 0.2] \begin{bmatrix} 0.8 & 0.2 \\ 0.4 & 0.6 \end{bmatrix} = [0.72 \quad 0.28]$$

$$S^{(3)} = S^{(2)}P = [0.72 \quad 0.28] \begin{bmatrix} 0.8 & 0.2 \\ 0.4 & 0.6 \end{bmatrix} = [0.688 \quad 0.312]$$

$$S^{(4)} = S^{(3)}P = [0.688 \quad 0.312] \begin{bmatrix} 0.8 & 0.2 \\ 0.4 & 0.6 \end{bmatrix} = [0.6752 \quad 0.3248]$$

$$S^{(5)} = S^{(4)}P = [0.6752 \quad 0.3248] \begin{bmatrix} 0.8 & 0.2 \\ 0.4 & 0.6 \end{bmatrix} = [0.67008 \quad 0.32992]$$

$$S^{(6)} = S^{(5)}P = [0.67008 \quad 0.32992] \begin{bmatrix} 0.8 & 0.2 \\ 0.4 & 0.6 \end{bmatrix} = [0.668032 \quad 0.331968]$$

$$S^{(7)} = S^{(6)}P = [0.668032 \quad 0.331968] \begin{bmatrix} 0.8 & 0.2 \\ 0.4 & 0.6 \end{bmatrix} = [0.6672128 \quad 0.3327872]$$

Again, in the long run, it appears that there is a 67 percent chance a person will shop at Henry's and a 33 percent chance a person will shop at Morton's.

When a regular Markov chain reaches the point where the probability vectors stabilize, the Markov chain is close to a *steady state*. We make the following definition.

A probability vector which remains unchanged upon multiplication with the transition matrix is called a **steady state vector**.

Example 4   Find the steady state vector of the regular Markov chain with transition matrix

$$P = \begin{bmatrix} 0.8 & 0.2 \\ 0.6 & 0.4 \end{bmatrix}$$

We illustrate two methods.

Solution   **Method 1**   As has been mentioned, the same steady state will be approached regardless of the initial probability vector used. So we choose $S^{(0)} = [0.5 \quad 0.5]$.

$$S^{(1)} = S^{(0)}P = [0.5 \quad 0.5] \begin{bmatrix} 0.8 & 0.2 \\ 0.6 & 0.4 \end{bmatrix} = [0.7 \quad 0.3]$$

$$S^{(2)} = S^{(1)}P = [0.7 \quad 0.3] \begin{bmatrix} 0.8 & 0.2 \\ 0.6 & 0.4 \end{bmatrix} = [0.74 \quad 0.26]$$

$$S^{(3)} = S^{(2)}P = [0.74 \quad 0.26] \begin{bmatrix} 0.8 & 0.2 \\ 0.6 & 0.4 \end{bmatrix} = [0.748 \quad 0.252]$$

$$S^{(4)} = S^{(3)}P = [0.748 \quad 0.252] \begin{bmatrix} 0.8 & 0.2 \\ 0.6 & 0.4 \end{bmatrix} = [0.7496 \quad 0.2504]$$

$$S^{(5)} = S^{(4)}P = [0.7496 \quad 0.2504] \begin{bmatrix} 0.8 & 0.2 \\ 0.6 & 0.4 \end{bmatrix} = [0.74992 \quad 0.25008]$$

$$S^{(6)} = S^{(5)}P = [0.74992 \quad 0.25008] \begin{bmatrix} 0.8 & 0.2 \\ 0.6 & 0.4 \end{bmatrix} = [0.749984 \quad 0.250016]$$

$$S^{(7)} = S^{(6)}P = [0.749984 \quad 0.250016] \begin{bmatrix} 0.8 & 0.2 \\ 0.6 & 0.4 \end{bmatrix} = [0.7499968 \quad 0.2500032]$$

Thus the steady state vector seems to be $[0.75 \quad 0.25]$.

Method 2   The first method is quite tedious. We now use the definition of the steady state vector and illustrate a shorter and more direct method.

Let the steady state vector be $[a \quad b]$. Then, by definition

$$[a \quad b] \begin{bmatrix} 0.8 & 0.2 \\ 0.6 & 0.4 \end{bmatrix} = [a \quad b]$$

Multiplying, we obtain

$$[0.8a + 0.6b \quad 0.2a + 0.4b] = [a \quad b]$$

This yields two equations

$$0.8a + 0.6b = a \qquad \text{and} \qquad 0.2a + 0.4b = b$$

Collecting like terms we see that the two equations are equivalent to the single equation.

$$a = 3b$$

There is one fact we must not forget: $[a \quad b]$ is a probability vector; therefore

$$a + b = 1$$

We solve the two equations

$$a = 3b \qquad ①$$
$$a + b = 1 \qquad ②$$

Substituting for a in ②, we get

$$3b + b = 1$$
$$b = \tfrac{1}{4}$$

Substituting in (1), we obtain

$$a = \tfrac{3}{4}$$

Therefore the steady state vector is $\begin{bmatrix} \tfrac{3}{4} & \tfrac{1}{4} \end{bmatrix}$ or [0.75   0.25].

The second method that was illustrated gives a direct procedure for predicting the long-term trends for competitive markets that follow a Markov chain pattern.

Example 5   Moi is the goalkeeper for her school soccer team. Every time she stops a penalty shot, her confidence increases and it is anticipated that there is a 70 percent chance she will make a save on the next shot. However, if the other team scores on a penalty shot, she gets nervous and there is only a 40 percent chance of her stopping the next penalty shot. Find the steady state vector and hence determine, in the long run, the chances of Moi making a save.

Solution   The transition matrix for this Markov chain is

$$\begin{array}{cc} & \begin{array}{cc} \text{Save} & \text{Goal} \end{array} \\ \begin{array}{c} \text{Save} \\ \text{Goal} \end{array} & \begin{bmatrix} 0.7 & 0.3 \\ 0.4 & 0.6 \end{bmatrix} \end{array}$$

Since the transition matrix has no zero entries, the chain is regular and we look for a steady state vector. Let the steady state vector be $[a \quad b]$. Then

$$[a \quad b] \begin{bmatrix} 0.7 & 0.3 \\ 0.4 & 0.6 \end{bmatrix} = [a \quad b]$$

Multiplying, we obtain

$$[0.7a + 0.4b \quad 0.3a + 0.6b] = [a \quad b]$$

This gives two equations

$$0.7a + 0.4b = a \qquad \text{and} \qquad 0.3a + 0.6b = b$$

Which simplify to $a = \tfrac{4}{3}b$

We use the fact that $a + b = 1$ and solve the two equations

$$a = \tfrac{4}{3}b \qquad \text{①}$$
$$a + b = 1 \qquad \text{②}$$

Substituting for a in ②, we obtain

$$\tfrac{4}{3}b + b = 1$$
$$b = \tfrac{3}{7}$$

Substituting in ①, we get

$$a = \tfrac{4}{7}$$

Therefore the steady state vector is $\left[\tfrac{4}{7} \ \tfrac{3}{7}\right]$ and, in the long-run, there is a probability of $\tfrac{4}{7}$ Moi will make the save.

EXERCISE 8.5

B **1.** Determine which of the following is a transition matrix of a regular Markov chain. For those that are not, give a reason.

(a) $\begin{bmatrix} 0.3 & 0.7 \\ 0.8 & 0.2 \end{bmatrix}$

(b) $\begin{bmatrix} 0 & 1 \\ 1 & 0 \end{bmatrix}$

(c) $\begin{bmatrix} 0.6 & 0.2 & 0.2 \\ 0.3 & 0.5 & 0.2 \\ 0.4 & 0.4 & 0.2 \end{bmatrix}$

(d) $\begin{bmatrix} 0.5 & 0.5 & 0 \\ 0.5 & 0 & 0.5 \\ 0 & 0.5 & 0.5 \end{bmatrix}$

(e) $\begin{bmatrix} 0.7 & 0.3 \\ 0.4 & 0.5 \end{bmatrix}$

(f) $\begin{bmatrix} \tfrac{1}{2} & \tfrac{1}{2} & 0 \\ \tfrac{1}{3} & \tfrac{1}{3} & \tfrac{1}{3} \end{bmatrix}$

2. In each of the following, the transition matrix, P, for a regular Markov chain is given. Determine the steady state vector by
   (i) choosing an initial probability vector, $S^{(0)}$, and finding successive values for $S^{(n)}$, $n = 1, 2, 3, 4, 5, 6, 7$.
   (ii) letting the steady state vector be $[a \ \ b]$ and solving the matrix equation $[a \ \ b] P = [a \ \ b]$.

(a) $\begin{bmatrix} 0.7 & 0.3 \\ 0.3 & 0.7 \end{bmatrix}$

(b) $\begin{bmatrix} 0.9 & 0.1 \\ 0.3 & 0.7 \end{bmatrix}$

3. Two soft drink companies, A and B, make non-alcoholic coolers. Statistics have shown that of people who try company A's cooler, there is an 80 percent chance they will buy it the next time. There is only a 50 percent chance that people will buy company B's cooler if they bought it the last time.

(a) Determine the transition matrix, P, for this Markov chain. Note that this chain is regular.

(b) By finding the steady state vector, determine the long-term trends in this competitive market.

4. Natural Foods and Poco's are two health food stores located in the same general area. Market research has shown that, after shopping at Natural Foods, there is a 90 percent chance a person will return. However, there is only a 60 percent chance a person will return to Poco's after shopping there.

(a) Determine the transition matrix, P, for this Markov chain.

(b) Determine the long-term trends in this market.

5. Hargrove Collegiate is considering the purchase of a new photocopying machine. The school has narrowed their choices to two: Machine A and Machine B. On a daily basis each machine can be in one of two states: working properly, or not working properly and in need of repair. The transition matrices for the machines are

Machine A

	Working	Not Working
Working	0.8	0.2
Not Working	0.4	0.6

Machine B

	Working	Not Working
Working	0.9	0.1
Not Working	0.7	0.3

Based on long-term performance, which photocopier should the school buy?

6. Parkview Rent-A-Car has three distribution locations. A rented car may be returned to any of the three locations. From past experience, the management has determined that the following transition matrix can be used to describe the return of their vehicles.

Returned to

		A	B	C
Rented from	A	0.6	0.4	0
	B	0.3	0.4	0.3
	C	0	0.7	0.3

(a) Show that this is the transition matrix of a regular Markov chain.

(b) Choose an initial probability vector, $S^{(0)}$, and find $S^{(n)}$ for $n = 1, 2, 3, 4, 5, 6$.

(c) From your results in part (b), what appears to be the most efficient way the company can distribute its cars?

(d) Check your prediction by multiplying your steady state vector by P.

7. A particle is located on a circle at one of three possible points: A, B, or C. A trial takes place when the particle moves from one point to another point. The particle moves clockwise 60 percent of the time and counter-clockwise 40 percent of the time.
   (a) Determine the transition matrix, P.
   (b) Show that this Markov chain is regular.
   (c) Assuming the particle starts at position A, find $S^{(n)}$ for $n = 1, 2, 3, 4, 5, 6$.
   (d) To what steady state do the probability vectors seem to be tending?
   (e) Check your prediction by multiplying your steady state vector by P.

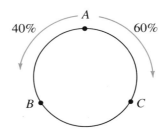

C 8. Let $P = \begin{bmatrix} p & 1-p \\ q & 1-q \end{bmatrix}$, where $p, q > 0$, be the transition matrix of a regular Markov chain. Show that the steady state vector is
$$\left[\frac{q}{1 + q - p} \quad \frac{1-p}{1 + q - p} \right]$$

8.6   REVIEW EXERCISE

1. State the value of (i) a_{13} (ii) a_{43} (iii) a_{32}, where possible.
   (a) $\begin{bmatrix} -5 & 4 & 17 & -1 \\ 2 & 21 & -5 & 0 \\ 3 & -3 & 6 & 16 \\ 7 & -8 & 9 & 10 \end{bmatrix}$
   (b) $\begin{bmatrix} 0.2 & 0.8 & 1.9 \\ -0.4 & 0.7 & 2.5 \\ 8.2 & 5.1 & -6.9 \\ 1.2 & 0.4 & 1.0 \end{bmatrix}$

   (c) $\begin{bmatrix} 4 & -5 & 0 \\ 34 & -9 & -12 \end{bmatrix}$

2. State the dimensions of each matrix in Question 1.
3. For the matrix given, state each of the following entries in the form a_{ij}.
   (a) -32 (b) 14   (c) 1   (d) -10
   $$\begin{bmatrix} 24 & -32 & -5 & 19 \\ -9 & 2 & -10 & 6 \\ 0 & 14 & -3 & 1 \end{bmatrix}$$

4. In the following matrix, we let $a_{ij} = 1$ if individual i is older than individual j and 0 otherwise.

$$
\begin{array}{cc}
 & \text{Individual} \\
\text{Individual} &
\begin{array}{c}
\;\;\;\;1\;\;2\;\;3\;\;4\;\;5 \\
\begin{array}{c} 1 \\ 2 \\ 3 \\ 4 \\ 5 \end{array}
\left[
\begin{array}{ccccc}
0 & 0 & 1 & 0 & 0 \\
1 & 0 & 1 & 0 & 1 \\
0 & 0 & 0 & 0 & 0 \\
1 & 1 & 1 & 0 & 1 \\
0 & 0 & 1 & 0 & 0
\end{array}
\right]
\end{array}
\end{array}
$$

In this group,
(a) who is the oldest individual?
(b) who is the youngest individual?
(c) what can we conclude about individuals 1 and 5?

5. (a) Construct the corresponding matrix, A, for the following network. Recall: The element in the ith row and jth column gives the number of direct paths from i to j.

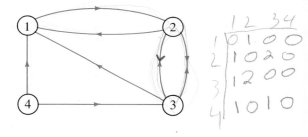

(b) Calculate A^2.

(c) Locate the paths that the entries in A^2 represent.

6. Perform the indicated operations, where possible, in each of the following.

(a) $\begin{bmatrix} -2 & 3 \\ 8 & -8 \\ 6 & -5 \end{bmatrix} - 7 \begin{bmatrix} 5 & -9 \\ 12 & -6 \\ -7 & 1 \end{bmatrix}$

(b) $-0.4 \begin{bmatrix} 3 & -7 & 9 \\ -2 & -8 & -1 \end{bmatrix} + 1.2 \begin{bmatrix} -4 & 3 & 2 \\ -6 & 10 & -5 \end{bmatrix}$

(c) $[2 \;\; -3 \;\; -5] \begin{bmatrix} -3 & 4 & 1 \\ -1 & -2 & 3 \\ 4 & -6 & -1 \end{bmatrix}$

(d) $\begin{bmatrix} -2 & -4 \\ -7 & 0 \\ 2 & 10 \end{bmatrix} \begin{bmatrix} 9 & -8 & 3 \\ -4 & -6 & 1 \end{bmatrix}$

(e) $\begin{bmatrix} 3 \\ -5 \end{bmatrix} \begin{bmatrix} -3 & 1 \\ -8 & 10 \end{bmatrix}$

(f) $\begin{bmatrix} -2 & 6 & -3 & 1 \\ -1 & 4 & -6 & 8 \\ 3 & -5 & 1 & 0 \\ -2 & -3 & 6 & -8 \end{bmatrix} \begin{bmatrix} 2 \\ -2 \\ 4 \\ -6 \end{bmatrix}$

(g) $-4 \begin{bmatrix} -3 & -6 \\ 1 & -2 \\ 5 & 8 \end{bmatrix} + \begin{bmatrix} 1 & -2 & 1 \\ -1 & 1 & -1 \\ -2 & -1 & 1 \end{bmatrix} \begin{bmatrix} 3 & -3 \\ 4 & -1 \\ -2 & 9 \end{bmatrix}$

7. If

$$A = \begin{bmatrix} -2 & 6 \\ 12 & -25 \end{bmatrix} \quad B = \begin{bmatrix} -5 & -3 \\ 4 & 9 \end{bmatrix}$$

$$C = \begin{bmatrix} 1 & -7 \\ 7 & -13 \end{bmatrix} \quad D = \begin{bmatrix} -2 & 0 \\ 1 & -4 \\ 6 & 3 \end{bmatrix}$$

find, where possible, each of the following.

(a) $A + B - C$ (b) $3A - 4B$ (c) $A(BC)$

(d) $D(BC)$ (e) $(AC)^2$ (f) $(DA)^2$

8. The workers at a meat packing plant are paid $10.50 an hour for an eight-hour day. For any additional hours they are paid time-and-a-half. The tables below show the hours worked by three of the employees for the week Oct. 9 to Oct. 13.

		Oct. 9	Oct. 10	Oct. 11	Oct. 12	Oct. 13
	1	8.0	8.5	8.5	8.0	9.0
Worker	2	8.0	8.0	8.5	8.0	8.5
	3	8.0	8.5	9.0	8.5	9.0

(a) Construct two matrices, one showing the regular hours worked and the other showing the overtime hours worked each day by each worker.

(b) Use these matrices to determine the daily pay due each worker.

9. Three courier companies specialize in same-day service. The rates they charge (in dollars) are summarized in the following table.

Mass	Company I	II	III
0–100 g	6.50	7.00	7.50
100–200 g	7.50	7.50	8.00
200–300 g	8.50	8.00	8.00
300–400 g	9.50	8.50	8.50

If each company increases its rates by 10 percent, find a matrix representing the new rates for each company.

10. Decode each of the following messages.

(a) $\begin{bmatrix} 103 & 56 \\ 56 & 31 \end{bmatrix}$ decoding matrix $\begin{bmatrix} 4 & -7 \\ -1 & 2 \end{bmatrix}$

(b) $\begin{bmatrix} 66 & 103 \\ 39 & 64 \end{bmatrix}, \begin{bmatrix} 85 & 55 \\ 50 & 29 \end{bmatrix}, \begin{bmatrix} 64 & 62 \\ 40 & 41 \end{bmatrix}, \begin{bmatrix} 67 & 72 \\ 43 & 42 \end{bmatrix}, \begin{bmatrix} 70 & 84 \\ 45 & 54 \end{bmatrix}$

decoding matrix $\begin{bmatrix} 2 & -3 \\ -1 & 2 \end{bmatrix}$

11. A company produces three types of V.C.R.s. We refer to them as A, B, and C. Each of these V.C.R.s requires three different raw materials. These requirements are shown in the following table.

		Raw Material		
		I	II	III
	A	7	6	5
V.C.R.	B	5	4	3
	C	4	3	3

(a) If there are 100, 300, and 250 of models A, B, and C, respectively, scheduled for production next month, determine the amount of each raw material needed.

(b) If the per-unit cost of the raw materials is $8.00 for raw material I, $10.00 for raw material II, and $15.00 for raw material III, find the cost of producing each type of V.C.R.

12. An English teacher uses the following formula to determine his students' essay marks: 40 percent for style and 60 percent for content. Some of his students' marks are listed in the following chart.

	Style	Content
Adderly L.	73	68
Campbell U.	91	85
Denton T.	55	50
Lee F.	62	58

Find each of the four students' final essay marks.

13. Which of the following is a transition matrix for a Markov chain? For those which are not, give a reason. For those which are, is the chain regular?

(a) $\begin{bmatrix} 0.5 & 0.5 \\ 0.2 & 0.8 \end{bmatrix}$ (b) $\begin{bmatrix} 1 & 0 \\ 0.2 & 0.7 \end{bmatrix}$

(c) $\begin{bmatrix} 0.6 & 0.4 \\ 1 & 0 \\ 0.1 & 0.9 \end{bmatrix}$ (d) $\begin{bmatrix} 0.5 & 0.4 & 0.1 \\ 0 & 0.5 & 0.5 \\ 0 & 0.5 & 0.5 \end{bmatrix}$

14. Nancy and Kevin Winters play two-handed euchre every night. Over the years a pattern has developed. Whenever Nancy wins, her confidence increases and the probability of her winning the next night is 0.6. However, when she loses, the probability of her winning the next night is only 0.3.

(a) Find the matrix of transition probabilities, P, for this Markov chain.

(b) If the initial probability of either Nancy or Kevin winning is 0.5, what is the probability of each player winning the next night?

(c) If Kevin wins on Tuesday night, what is the probability he will win on Thursday night?

(d) Find the steady state vector for this Markov chain.

15. There are three video-game arcades located in the downtown area of Weston. We refer to them as A, B, and C. Statistics show that

     (1) after going to arcade A, people will return there 60 percent of the time, will try arcade B 20 percent of the time, and will try arcade C 20 percent of the time.

     (2) after going to arcade B, people will return there 50 percent of the time, will try arcade A 25 percent of the time, and will try arcade C 25 percent of the time.

     (3) after going to arcade C, people will return there 80 percent of the time, will try arcade A 10 percent of the time, and will try arcade B 10 percent of the time.

(a) Find the transition matrix P.

(b) If the initial probabilities of a person attending arcades A, B, and C are 30 percent, 30 percent, and 40 percent, respectively, find the first- and second-step probability vectors.

(c) If a person initially went to arcade B, what is the probability the person will return to arcade B on his or her fourth time?

16. P is the transition matrix of a Markov chain.

$$P = \begin{bmatrix} 0.5 & 0.5 & 0 \\ 0 & 0.5 & 0.5 \\ 0.5 & 0 & 0.5 \end{bmatrix}$$

(a) Show that the Markov chain is regular.

(b) Choose an initial probability vector, $S^{(0)}$, and find $S^{(n)}$ for $n = 1, 2, 3, 4, 5, 6$.

(c) From your results in part (b), what appears to be the steady state vector for this chain?

(d) Check your prediction by showing that the vector remains unchanged when multiplied with P.

8.7 CHAPTER 8 TEST

1. Perform the indicated operations, where possible, in each of the following. Where the operation is not possible, explain why.

   (a)
   $$5 \begin{bmatrix} 3 & -5 \\ -2 & -1 \\ 6 & 0 \end{bmatrix} - 3 \begin{bmatrix} -3 & 8 \\ 10 & -5 \\ -7 & 1 \end{bmatrix}$$

   (b)
   $$\begin{bmatrix} 2 & -2 & 3 \\ -1 & -2 & 5 \end{bmatrix} \begin{bmatrix} 4 & -9 \\ 7 & 10 \\ -8 & 9 \end{bmatrix}$$

   (c)
   $$\begin{bmatrix} -5 & 12 & 15 \end{bmatrix} \begin{bmatrix} -5 & -2 & 4 \\ 8 & -1 & 6 \end{bmatrix}$$

2. If
   $$A = \begin{bmatrix} -1 & 4 & -2 \\ 1 & -3 & 2 \\ 5 & -2 & -1 \end{bmatrix} \qquad B = \begin{bmatrix} 3 & -3 & 1 \\ 6 & 2 & -2 \\ 0 & 2 & 1 \end{bmatrix}$$
   $$C = \begin{bmatrix} 7 & 0 \\ -4 & 2 \\ 1 & -1 \end{bmatrix}$$

   find, where possible, each of the following.

   (a) AC (b) $2B - 3A$ (c) $4C + 5B$

3. Riverside Collegiate, Holbrook High, and Westview S.S. share one administrative assistant. Every Monday she takes an inventory of the amount of paper (packages of 500 sheets) available for the photocopying machine at each school. The following charts show her records for two consecutive Mondays.

   Mon. Sept. 7

Paper Type	Riverside	Holbrook	Westview
216 mm × 279 mm	300	200	250
216 mm × 279 mm (punched)	300	200	250
216 mm × 356 mm	300	200	250

   Mon. Sept. 14

Paper Type	Riverside	Holbrook	Westview
216 mm × 279 mm	282	188	235
216 mm × 279 mm (punched)	279	185	232
216 mm × 356 mm	288	193	244

   (a) Construct a matrix showing the amount of each type of paper used at each school during the week.
   (b) Assuming that the same amount of paper is used each week, predict the inventory at the end of eight weeks.
   (c) Assuming that the same amount of paper is used each week, will the supply of paper last for the semester (19 weeks)?

4. Using the coding method of this chapter, decode the following message.

$$\begin{bmatrix} -47 & -53 \\ -27 & -35 \end{bmatrix}, \begin{bmatrix} -6 & -54 \\ -1 & -35 \end{bmatrix} \qquad \text{decoding matrix} \qquad \begin{bmatrix} -2 & 3 \\ -1 & 1 \end{bmatrix}$$

5. A subsidiary of an automobile corporation makes chassis for its cars. It makes three types: A, B, and C. The production of chassis requires the services of a skilled mechanic and an inspection officer to check the work after production. The following table gives a breakdown of the number of work-hours needed for each type of chassis.

	Chassis		
	A	**B**	**C**
Mechanic	10	15	20
Inspector	1	1.5	2

(a) If the plant produced 250, 400, and 200 of chassis A, B, and C respectively, determine the number of hours needed by mechanics and inspectors.

(b) If a mechanic gets $18.00 an hour and an inspector gets $15.00 an hour, determine the total labour costs.

6. A local television station describes a day's weather as sunny, cloudy, or rainy. According to previous information, they have determined that following a sunny day there is a 60 percent chance of having another sunny day, a 30 percent chance of having a cloudy day, and a 10 percent chance of rain. Following a cloudy day, there is a 40 percent chance of having another cloudy day, a 30 percent chance of rain, and a 30 percent chance of having a sunny day. If it was raining, then there is a 40 percent chance of rain the next day, a 40 percent chance of cloud cover, and a 20 percent chance of sun.

(a) Construct the transition matrix the television station uses to predict future weather patterns.

(b) If it is sunny on Monday, what is the probability of sun for Wednesday?

(c) If it is cloudy on Tuesday, what is the probability of rain for Friday?

7. In an eastern Canadian city there are two taxi companies: Hillside Cab Co. and Garden Taxi. Market surveys have shown, that when people call Hillside Cab, there is an 80 percent chance they will call Hillside the next time. Whereas, there is only a 60 percent chance they would call Garden Taxi if they called Garden the last time.

(a) Construct the transition matrix, P, for this Markov chain.

(b) If a person called Hillside Cab their first time, what is the probability the person will call Hillside the third time a taxi is needed?

(c) Determine the long-term trends of this competitive market by finding the steady state vector.

CHAPTER 9

SYSTEMS OF LINEAR EQUATIONS

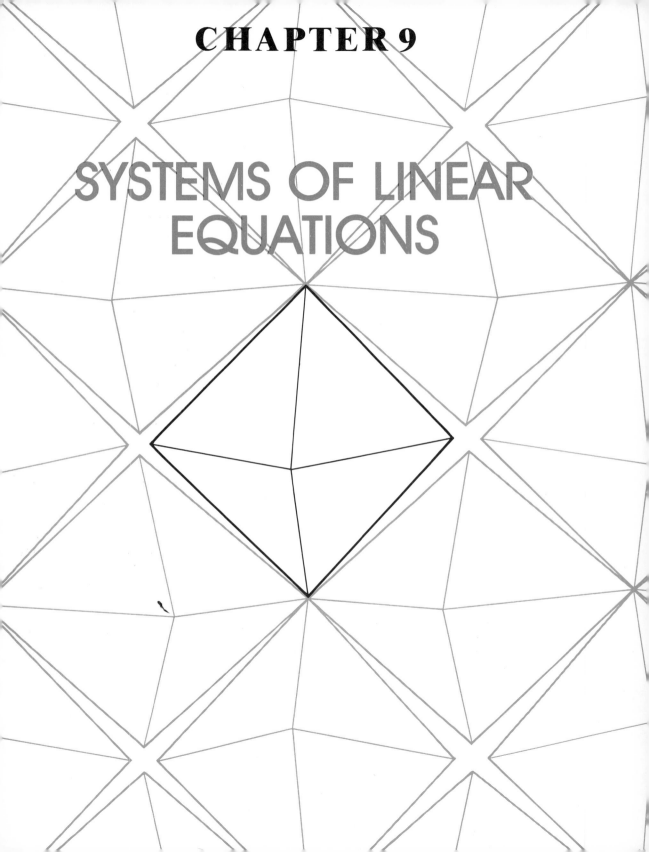

REVIEW AND PREVIEW TO
CHAPTER 9

EXERCISE 1   **Solving Systems of Equations by Graphing**

---

1. Graph the lines defined by the following equations.

   (a) $y = 3x - 4$ (b) $y = -\frac{2}{5}x + 1$

   (c) $3x + 2y = 7$ (d) $5x - 8y = 10$

2. Solve each of the following systems of equations by graphing the corresponding lines.

   (a) $\begin{cases} y = 2x - 3 \\ y = -x + 6 \end{cases}$ (b) $\begin{cases} 3x + 2y = -4 \\ x - 3y = -5 \end{cases}$

   (c) $\begin{cases} 2x - y = 6 \\ -4x + 2y = -12 \end{cases}$ (d) $\begin{cases} 3x + y = 7 \\ 6x + 2y = 10 \end{cases}$

   (e) $\begin{cases} x - y = -3 \\ x + y = 1 \\ 2x + 3y = 4 \end{cases}$ (f) $\begin{cases} 2x - y = 5 \\ x + y = 4 \\ -3x + y = 8 \end{cases}$

Supply and Demand

In a free market, the price of an item is determined by two factors: **supply** and **demand**. If the demand for an item is high, then manufacturers may try to raise the price. If the demand for an item is low, manufacturers may lower the price. If the price is high, then the manufacturer may wish to produce more items than if the price were lower. When supply and demand are in balance, we say that the market is in **equilibrium** and the price at which this occurs is called the **equilibrium price**.

Example 1   The supply and demand for a particular item are given the following linear equations

$$S = \tfrac{1}{2}x - 105$$
$$D = -2x + 1430$$

where x is the price in dollars, and S and D are the quantity supplied and demanded, respectively.

(a) Find the equilibrium price and the quantity produced at the price.

(b) Graph the supply and demand functions on the same set of axes. Label this equilibrium point.

Solution   (a) The equilibrium point will be attained when supply equals demand.

$$S = D$$
$$\tfrac{1}{2}x - 105 = -2x + 1430$$
$$x - 210 = -4x + 2860$$
$$5x = 3070$$
$$x = 614$$

When $x = 614$, $S = 202$.

Therefore, the equilibrium price is \$614, and 202 items would be produced at this price.

(b)

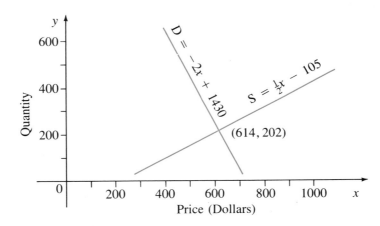

EXERCISE 2

For each of the following pairs of supply and demand functions,

(a) determine the equilibrium price and the quantity supplied at that price.

(b) graph the two functions on the same set of axes and indicate this equilibrium point.

1. $\begin{cases} S = 3x - 210 \\ D = -\tfrac{1}{3}x + 480 \end{cases}$ 2. $\begin{cases} S = 4x - 480 \\ D = -\tfrac{2}{3}x + 640 \end{cases}$

3. $\begin{cases} S = 3x - 1130 \\ D = -\tfrac{42}{5}x + 4000 \end{cases}$ 4. $\begin{cases} S = \tfrac{5}{3}x - 372 \\ D = -\tfrac{2}{7}x + 284 \end{cases}$

INTRODUCTION

In real-world applications, the solution to a problem may require the simultaneous solution of thousands of equations. In this chapter we see how the method of *elimination* can be generalized to an algorithmic process that can be programmed into a computer.

9.1 SOLVING LINEAR SYSTEMS BY ELIMINATION

A system of linear equations consists of one or more linear equations. To *solve* a system of linear equations, we determine the values of the variables that satisfy all of the equations in the system simultaneously. For instance: $x = 3$ and $y = 4$ is a solution to the system

$$\begin{cases} x + 2y = 11 \\ x - y = -1 \end{cases}$$

because $3 + 2(4) = 11$ and $3 - 4 = -1$.

One technique for solving a system of linear equations is the method usually referred to as **elimination**. The idea behind the method is to use one equation to *eliminate* a variable from the remaining equations. To do this there are two rules we can apply.

---

1. We can multiply any equation by a non-zero real number.
2. We can add (or subtract) a multiple of one equation to (or from) any other equation.

The application of these rules does not change the solution of the system. The following examples illustrate the use of these rules.

Example 1   (a) Solve the following system of equations by elimination.

(b) Verify your solution.

$$\begin{cases} 3x - 4y = 10 & \textcircled{1} \\ 2x + 5y = 7 & \textcircled{2} \end{cases}$$

Solution   (a) First we multiply Equation 1 by 2 to obtain

$$6x - 8y = 20$$

and multiply Equation 2 by 3 to obtain

$$6x + 15y = 21$$

The system can now be written as

$$\begin{cases} 6x - 8y = 20 & \text{③} \\ 6x + 15y = 21 & \text{④} \end{cases}$$

We use Equation 3 to eliminate x from Equation 4.

Equation 4 minus Equation 3 gives

$$23y = 1$$

or $y = \frac{1}{23}$

Substituting $y = \frac{1}{23}$ in Equation 3, we get

$$6x - 8\left(\tfrac{1}{23}\right) = 20$$

or $x = \frac{78}{23}$

Therefore, $x = \frac{78}{23}$ and $y = \frac{1}{23}$.

(b) To verify our solution we check that the values for x and y satisfy both equations.

Check for Equation 1   Check for Equation 2

$$3\left(\tfrac{78}{23}\right) - 4\left(\tfrac{1}{23}\right) = \tfrac{234}{23} - \tfrac{4}{23} \qquad 2\left(\tfrac{78}{23}\right) + 5\left(\tfrac{1}{23}\right) = \tfrac{156}{23} + \tfrac{5}{23}$$

$$= \tfrac{230}{23} \qquad\qquad\qquad\qquad = \tfrac{161}{23}$$

$$= 10 \qquad\qquad\qquad\qquad\quad = 7$$

We can interpret this result geometrically. When graphed, the lines corresponding to the equations intersect at the point whose coordinates are $\left(\frac{78}{23}, \frac{1}{23}\right)$.

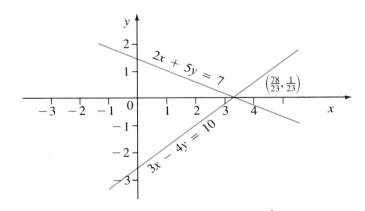

Example 2   Use elimination to solve the following system of three equations in three unknowns.

$$\begin{cases} x + 3y - z = -14 & \text{①} \\ 4x - 2y - 5z = 11 & \text{②} \\ 7x + 6y + z = 1 & \text{③} \end{cases}$$

Solution   When solving three equations in three unknowns, the technique is to use one of the equations to eliminate the same variable from the other two equations. In this case we use Equation 1 to eliminate x from Equations 2 and 3:

$$\text{②} - 4 \times \text{①} \text{ gives} \qquad -14y - z = 67 \qquad \text{④}$$
$$\text{③} - 7 \times \text{①} \text{ gives} \qquad -15y + 8z = 99 \qquad \text{⑤}$$

The system can now be written as

$$\begin{cases} x + 3y - z = -14 & \text{①} \\ -14y - z = 67 & \text{④} \\ -15y + 8z = 99 & \text{⑤} \end{cases}$$

Equations 4 and 5 are two equations in two unknowns and we solve them in the usual way. We use Equation 4 to eliminate z from Equation 5.

$$\text{⑤} + 8 \times \text{④} \text{ gives} \qquad -127y = 635 \qquad \text{⑥}$$

The system can now be written as

$$\begin{cases} x + 3y - z = -14 & \text{①} \\ -14y - z = 67 & \text{④} \\ -127y = 635 & \text{⑥} \end{cases}$$

From Equation 6, we obtain

$$y = -5$$

Substituting $y = -5$ in Equation 4, we get

$$-14(-5) - z = 67$$

or $z = 3$

Substituting $y = -5$ and $z = 3$ in Equation 1, we obtain

$$x + 3(-5) - 3 = -14$$

or $x = 4$

Therefore, $x = 4$, $y = -5$, and $z = 3$.

Example 3   Use elimination to solve the following system of four equations in four unknowns.

$$\begin{cases} 2w - x + y - z = 5 & \text{①} \\ w - 2x - 3y + z = -1 & \text{②} \\ 3w - 2x + y + 2z = 4 & \text{③} \\ w + x + 2y - 2z = 4 & \text{④} \end{cases}$$

Solution   When solving a system of four equations in four unknowns, we begin by choosing one equation and one variable in that equation to eliminate that variable from the other three equations. In this case, we use Equation 2 to eliminate w from the other three equations. Since we are using Equation 2, we write it first.

$$\begin{cases} w - 2x - 3y + z = -1 & \text{②} \\ 2w - x + y - z = 5 & \text{①} \\ 3w - 2x + y + 2z = 4 & \text{③} \\ w + x + 2y - 2z = 4 & \text{④} \end{cases}$$

① $-$ 2 $\times$ ② gives	$3x + 7y - 3z = 7$	⑤
③ $-$ 3 $\times$ ② gives	$4x + 10y - z = 7$	⑥
④ $-$ ② gives	$3x + 5y - 3z = 5$	⑦

The system of equations can now be written as

$$\begin{cases} w - 2x - 3y + z = -1 & \text{②} \\ 3x + 7y - 3z = 7 & \text{⑤} \\ 4x + 10y - z = 7 & \text{⑥} \\ 3x + 5y - 3z = 5 & \text{⑦} \end{cases}$$

Equations 5, 6, and 7 are three equations in three unknowns and we solve them in the usual way. We use Equation 6 to eliminate z from Equations 5 and 7. Before doing this we write Equation 6 before Equations 5 and 7.

$$\begin{cases} w - 2x - 3y + z = -1 & \text{②} \\ 4x + 10y - z = 7 & \text{⑥} \\ 3x + 7y - 3z = 7 & \text{⑤} \\ 3x + 5y - 3z = 5 & \text{⑦} \end{cases}$$

| ⑤ $-$ 3 $\times$ ⑥ gives | $-9x - 23y = -14$ | ⑧ |
| ⑦ $-$ 3 $\times$ ⑥ gives | $-9x - 25y = -16$ | ⑨ |

The system of equations can now be written as

$$\begin{cases} w - 2x - 3y + z = -1 & \text{②} \\ 4x + 10y - z = 7 & \text{⑥} \\ -9x - 23y = -14 & \text{⑧} \\ -9x - 25y = -16 & \text{⑨} \end{cases}$$

Equations 8 and 9 are two equations in two unknowns and we solve them in the usual way. We use Equation 8 to eliminate x from Equation 9.

$$⑨ - ⑧ \text{ gives} \quad -2y = -2 \quad ⑩$$

The system can now be written as

$$\begin{cases} w - 2x - 3y + z = -1 & ② \\ 4x + 10y - z = 7 & ⑥ \\ -9x - 23y = -14 & ⑧ \\ -2y = -2 & ⑩ \end{cases}$$

From Equation 10, we get

$$y = 1$$

Substituting $y = 1$ in Equation 8, we get

$$-9x - 23(1) = -14$$

or
$$x = -1$$

Substituting $y = 1$ and $x = -1$ in Equation 6, we get

$$4(-1) + 10(1) - z = 7$$

or
$$z = -1$$

Substituting $y = 1$, $x = -1$, and $z = -1$ in Equation 2, we get

$$w - 2(-1) - 3(1) + (-1) = -1$$

or
$$w = 1$$

Therefore, $w = 1$, $x = -1$, $y = 1$, and $z = -1$.

Sometimes some equations in a system have variables missing. The same procedure can be followed.

Example 4   Solve the following system of equations by using the methods of this section.

$$\begin{cases} w - y + z = 1 & ① \\ x - z = 3 & ② \\ w - x + y = 0 & ③ \\ w + 2x + 2z = 0 & ④ \end{cases}$$

Solution   We use Equation 1 to eliminate y from the other equations since y does not appear in Equations 2 and 4.

$$③ + ① \text{ gives} \quad 2w - x + z = 1 \quad ⑤$$

The system can now be written as

$$\begin{cases} w - y + z = 1 & ① \\ x - z = 3 & ② \\ 2w - x + z = 1 & ⑤ \\ w + 2x + 2z = 0 & ④ \end{cases}$$

Equations 2, 5, and 4 are three equations in three unknowns and we solve them in the usual way. We use Equation 2 to eliminate x from Equations 5 and 4.

⑤ + ② gives $\qquad$ $2w = 4$ $\qquad$ ⑥
④ − 2 × ② gives $\qquad$ $w + 4z = -6$ $\qquad$ ⑦

The system can now be written as

$$\begin{cases} w & - y + & z = 1 & \text{①} \\ & x & - z = 3 & \text{②} \\ 2w & & = 4 & \text{⑥} \\ w & & + 4z = -6 & \text{⑦} \end{cases}$$

From Equation 6, we get

$$w = 2$$

Substituting $w = 2$ in Equation 7, we get

$$2 + 4z = -6$$
or $\qquad z = -2$

Substituting $z = -2$ in Equation 2, we get

$$x - (-2) = 3$$
or $\qquad x = 1$

Substituting $w = 2$ and $z = -2$ in Equation 1, we get

$$2 - y + (-2) = 1$$
or $\qquad y = -1$

Therefore $w = 2$, $x = 1$, $y = -1$, and $z = -2$.

EXERCISE 9.1

B **1.** Solve each of the following systems of equations by elimination. Verify your solutions.

(a) $\begin{cases} 2x + y = -6 \\ 3x - 4y = 2 \end{cases}$ $\qquad$ (b) $\begin{cases} 5x - 3y = -1 \\ 4x - 6y = 16 \end{cases}$

(c) $\begin{cases} -7x + 3y = 12 \\ 2x + 5y = 10 \end{cases}$ $\qquad$ (d) $\begin{cases} 9x - 4y = -26 \\ x - 8y = -8 \end{cases}$

2. Solve each of the following systems of equations by elimination.

(a) $\begin{cases} x - 2y + z = 7 \\ 2x + y - z = 1 \\ 3x + y + 2z = 6 \end{cases}$ $\qquad$ (b) $\begin{cases} 2x - 3y - 2z = -1 \\ 2x + 4y + z = 1 \\ x - y + z = 5 \end{cases}$

(c) $\begin{cases} -2x + 2y - z = -11 \\ x - 3y + 4z = 13 \\ 5x + 4y + z = 8 \end{cases}$ $\qquad$ (d) $\begin{cases} 2x - y + z = 6 \\ x + 2y - z = 3 \\ -x + y - 2z = 3 \end{cases}$

(e) $\begin{cases} -x + 3y + z = 0 \\ 3x + 2y + 2z = 23 \\ 5x - 4y - 2z = 27 \end{cases}$ (f) $\begin{cases} 4x - y - 2z = 4 \\ 3x + 4y - z = -13 \\ -2x + 3y + 2z = -6 \end{cases}$

3. Solve each of the following systems of equations.

(a) $\begin{cases} w + x - y + z = -4 \\ 2w - x + 3y - z = 11 \\ -w - 2x + 2y - z = 7 \\ 3w + x - y - 2z = 4 \end{cases}$

(b) $\begin{cases} -w + 2x + y - z = -2 \\ 2w + 3x - 2y + z = -4 \\ 3w - x - y + 3z = 7 \\ -4w + x + y - 2z = -8 \end{cases}$

(c) $\begin{cases} w - x + y - 4z = 14 \\ -4w + 2x - y + 3z = -19 \\ 2w - x + y - 2z = 12 \\ -w + 3x + 4y + z = 5 \end{cases}$

4. Solve each of the following systems of equations.

(a) $\begin{cases} x \quad\quad + 2z = 20 \\ \quad -3y - z = 7 \\ 4x - 2y \quad\quad = 26 \end{cases}$ (b) $\begin{cases} w + x \quad\quad + z = -3 \\ \quad x + y + z = -2 \\ w + x + y \quad\quad = 2 \\ w \quad\quad + y + z = 0 \end{cases}$

(c) $\begin{cases} w - x \quad\quad\quad = -1 \\ \quad x - y \quad\quad = -1 \\ \quad\quad y - z = -1 \\ w + x + y + z = 10 \end{cases}$

9.2 DEPENDENT AND INCONSISTENT SYSTEMS

In the last section, all of the systems of equations had a *unique* (exactly one) *solution* for the variables involved. Such a system of equations is said to be **independent**. Not all systems of equations have a unique solution. Some have many solutions. When a system of linear equations has more than one solution, it is said to be **dependent**. It turns out that any dependent system has an infinite number of solutions. Finally, some systems of equations have no solution. Such a system is said to be **inconsistent**.

Types of Systems	
Independent:	a unique solution
Dependent:	more than one solution
Inconsistent:	no solution

In this section we give examples of the latter two types of systems and show how they can be solved. We begin with a system that is inconsistent.

Example 1   Solve the following system of equations by elimination.

$$\begin{cases} x + 3y = 12 & \text{①} \\ -3x - 9y = 25 & \text{②} \end{cases}$$

Solution   We use Equation 1 to eliminate x from Equation 2.

$$\text{②} + 3 \times \text{①} \text{ gives} \quad 0y = -11$$

There is no value for y that satisfies this equation. Therefore, the system has no solution and so is inconsistent.

We can interpret this result geometrically. When graphed, the lines corresponding to the equations are parallel and do not intersect.

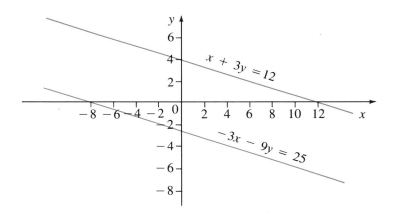

The preceding example was quite easy but it shows us the kind of result we obtain when we solve an inconsistent system. We now consider a system of three equations in three unknowns.

Example 2   Solve the following system by elimination.

$$\begin{cases} -3x + 8y - 3z = -6 & \text{①} \\ 2x - 3y + z = 0 & \text{②} \\ x + 2y - z = 3 & \text{③} \end{cases}$$

Solution   We use Equation 3 to eliminate x from Equations 1 and 2. Hence, let us write Equation 3 first.

$$\begin{cases} x + 2y - z = 3 & \text{③} \\ 2x - 3y + z = 0 & \text{②} \\ -3x + 8y - 3z = -6 & \text{①} \end{cases}$$

$$② - 2 \times ③ \text{ gives } \quad -7y + 3z = -6 \quad ④$$
$$① + 3 \times ③ \text{ gives } \quad 14y - 6z = 3 \quad ⑤$$

The system of equations can now be written as

$$\begin{cases} x + 2y - z = 3 & ③ \\ -7y + 3z = -6 & ④ \\ 14y - 6z = 3 & ⑤ \end{cases}$$

Equations 4 and 5 are two equations in two unknowns and are solved in the usual way. We use Equation 4 to eliminate y from Equation 5.

$$⑤ + 2 \times ④ \text{ gives } \quad 0z = -9$$

As in the last example, there is no value for z that will satisfy this equation. Therefore, the system has no solution and, so, is inconsistent.

Until this point all the systems of equations contained the same number of equations as unknowns; that is, two equations in two unknowns, or three equations in three unknowns and so on. This is not always the case. A system may contain more equations than unknowns or it may contain more unknowns than equations. We now give an example of a system with four equations in three unknowns.

Example 3 Solve the following system of equations by using elimination.

$$\begin{cases} 2x - 3y + z = -8 & ① \\ x + y - z = 0 & ② \\ -4x + 5y - z = 14 & ③ \\ x + 3y + z = 0 & ④ \end{cases}$$

Solution We solve a system like this in exactly the same way we solved the others. We choose one equation and use it to eliminate the same variable from the other equations. In this case, we use Equation 1 to eliminate z from the other equations.

$$② + ① \text{ gives } \quad 3x - 2y = -8 \quad ⑤$$
$$③ + ① \text{ gives } \quad -2x + 2y = 6 \quad ⑥$$
$$④ - ① \text{ gives } \quad -x + 6y = 8 \quad ⑦$$

The system of equations can now be written as

$$\begin{cases} 2x - 3y + z = -8 & ① \\ 3x - 2y = -8 & ⑤ \\ -2x + 2y = 6 & ⑥ \\ -x + 6y = 8 & ⑦ \end{cases}$$

We now use Equation 5 to eliminate y from Equations 6 and 7.

$$⑥ + ⑤ \text{ gives} \qquad x = -2 \qquad ⑧$$
$$⑦ + 3 \times ⑤ \text{ gives} \qquad 8x = -16$$
$$\text{or} \qquad x = -2 \qquad ⑨$$

The system of equations can now be written as

$$\begin{cases} 2x - 3y + z = -8 & ① \\ 3x - 2y \quad\;\; = -8 & ⑤ \\ \quad x \qquad\quad = -2 & ⑧ \\ \quad x \qquad\quad = -2 & ⑨ \end{cases}$$

Substituting $x = -2$ in Equation 5, we get

$$3(-2) - 2y = -8$$
$$\text{or} \qquad\qquad y = 1$$

Substituting $x = -2$ and $y = 1$ in Equation 1, we get

$$2(-2) - 3(1) + z = -8$$
$$\text{or} \qquad\qquad z = -1$$

Therefore $x = -2$, $y = 1$, $z = -1$. Notice that the system has a unique solution, so it is independent. ◁▷

Now we turn our attention to systems that are dependent; that is, systems that have an infinite number of solutions.

Example 4 Solve the following system of equations by elimination.

$$\begin{cases} 3x - 9y = 6 & ① \\ -2x + 6y = -4 & ② \end{cases}$$

Solution First we multiply Equation 1 by 2 to obtain

$$6x - 18y = 12 \qquad ③$$

and we multiply Equation 2 by 3 to obtain

$$-6x + 18y = -12 \qquad ④$$

The system can now be written as

$$\begin{cases} 6x - 18y = 12 & ③ \\ -6x + 18y = -12 & ④ \end{cases}$$

We use Equation 3 to eliminate x from Equation 4.

$$④ + ③ \text{ gives} \qquad 0y = 0 \qquad ⑤$$

The system of equations can be written as

$$\begin{cases} 6x - 18y = 12 & ③ \\ 0y = 0 & ⑤ \end{cases}$$

Any real number will satisfy Equation 5. Thus the solution(s) to the system are the solution(s) to the remaining Equation 3. There are infinitely many solutions to Equation 3. We express these solutions by introducing a **parameter**, k.

Let $y = k$

Substituting $y = k$ in Equation 3, we obtain

$$6x - 18(k) = 12$$

or $$x = 2 - 3k$$

Thus, the solution is given by the pair of **parametric equations**

$$x = 2 - 3k$$
$$y = k$$

where $k \in R$.

In the system of equations solved in Example 4, there is an infinite number of solutions. Every different value for k will yield a different solution to the system. If we desire to know some of the solutions, we need only choose values for k and substitute to find x and y. We give two such solutions.

When $k = 0, x = 2 - 3(0) = 2$
$$y = 0$$

When $k = 1, x = 2 - 3(1) = -1$
$$y = 1$$

Again we can interpret this result geometrically. When graphed, the lines corresponding to the two equations are the same.

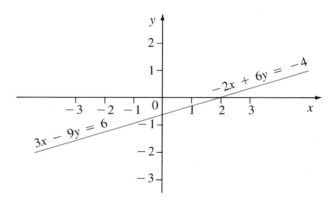

Earlier in this section we mentioned that a system of equations may contain more variables than equations. We now give an example of such a system and show how to solve it.

Example 5 Solve the following system of equations by using elimination.

$$\begin{cases} 2x - y + 2z = -6 & ① \\ 3x + 4y - 2z = 4 & ② \end{cases}$$

Solution We use Equation 1 to eliminate y from Equation 2.

$$② + 4 \times ① \text{ gives } \qquad 11x + 6z = -20 \qquad ③$$

The system can be written.

$$\begin{cases} 2x - y + 2z = -6 & ① \\ 11x \quad + 6z = -20 & ③ \end{cases}$$

There is no more elimination we can do that would further simplify the system. The solutions to these equations are the solution to the system. We express the solution by introducing the parameter k.

Let $z = k$
Substituting $z = k$ in Equation 3, we obtain

$$11x + 6(k) = -20$$

or $$x = \frac{-20 - 6k}{11}$$

Substituting $x = \dfrac{-20 - 6k}{11}$ and $z = k$ in Equation 1, we get

$$2\left(\frac{-20 - 6k}{11}\right) - y + 2(k) = -6$$

or $$y = \frac{26 + 10k}{11}$$

Therefore, $x = \dfrac{-20 - 6k}{11}$, $y = \dfrac{26 + 10k}{11}$, and $z = k$; $k \in R$. ◇

The system in Example 5 is dependent and we can find particular solutions by substituting values for k and solving for x, y, and z. We give two such solutions.

$$\text{When } k = 0, x = \frac{-20 - 6(0)}{11} = -\frac{20}{11}$$

$$y = \frac{26 + 10(0)}{11} = \frac{26}{11}$$

$$z = 0$$

$$\text{When } k = 1, x = \frac{-20 - 6(1)}{11} = -\frac{26}{11}$$

$$y = \frac{26 + 10(1)}{11} = \frac{36}{11}$$

$$z = 1$$

Example 6   Solve the following system of equations using elimination.

$$\begin{cases} 3x - y + z = 10 & ① \\ x + 3y - z = 7 & ② \\ 13x + 9y - z = 58 & ③ \end{cases}$$

Solution   We use Equation 1 to eliminate z from Equations 2 and 3.

$$② + ① \text{ gives} \qquad 4x + 2y = 17 \qquad ④$$
$$③ + ① \text{ gives} \qquad 16x + 8y = 68 \qquad ⑤$$

The system can now be written as

$$\begin{cases} 3x - y + z = 10 & ① \\ 4x + 2y = 17 & ④ \\ 16x + 8y = 68 & ⑤ \end{cases}$$

We now use Equation 4 to eliminate y from Equation 5.

$$⑤ - 4 \times ④ \text{ gives} \qquad 0x = 0 \qquad ⑥$$

The system can be written as

$$\begin{cases} 3x - y + z = 10 & ① \\ 4x + 2y = 17 & ④ \\ 0x = 0 & ⑥ \end{cases}$$

Any real number will satisfy Equation 6. Thus the solutions to the system are the solutions to the remaining Equations 1 and 4. We express the solutions by introducing a parameter k.

Let $y = k$

Substituting $y = k$ in Equation 4, we get

$$4x + 2(k) = 17$$

or $x = \dfrac{17 - 2k}{4}$

Substituting $y = k$ and $x = \dfrac{17 - 2k}{4}$ in Equation 1, we get

$$3\left(\frac{17 - 2k}{4}\right) - k + z = 10$$

or $\qquad z = \dfrac{-11 + 10k}{4}$

Therefore, $x = \dfrac{17 - 2k}{4}$, $y = k$, and $z = \dfrac{-11 + 10k}{4}$; $k \in R$.   ◇

In some dependent systems of equations it becomes necessary to introduce more than one parameter, as we now illustrate.

Example 7   Solve the following system by elimination.

$$\begin{cases} 3w - x + y - z = 4 & ① \\ w + x - y + 2z = 1 & ② \\ 9w + x - y + 4z = 11 & ③ \end{cases}$$

Solution   We use Equation 1 to eliminate y from Equations 2 and 3.

$$② + ① \text{ gives } \qquad 4w + z = 5 \qquad ④$$
$$③ + ① \text{ gives } \qquad 12w + 3z = 15 \qquad ⑤$$

The system can be written as

$$\begin{cases} 3w - x + y - z = 4 & ① \\ 4w \qquad\qquad + z = 5 & ④ \\ 12w \qquad\qquad + 3z = 15 & ⑤ \end{cases}$$

Equations 4 and 5 are two equations in two unknowns. We use Equation 4 to eliminate z from Equation 5.

$$⑤ - 3 \times ④ \text{ gives } \qquad 0w = 0 \qquad ⑥$$

The system can be written as

$$\begin{cases} 3w - x + y - z = 4 & ① \\ 4w \qquad\qquad + z = 5 & ④ \\ 0w \qquad\qquad = 0 & ⑥ \end{cases}$$

All real numbers are solutions in Equation 6. Therefore, the solutions to the system are the solutions to Equations 1 and 4.

Let $\qquad z = s$

Substituting $z = s$ in Equation 4, we get

$$4w + s = 5$$

or $\qquad w = \dfrac{5 - s}{4}$

Substituting $w = \dfrac{5 - s}{4}$ and $z = s$ in Equation 1, we still cannot solve for x or y.

Therefore, we introduce another parameter. Let $y = t$.

$$3\left(\frac{5 - s}{4}\right) - x + t - s = 4$$

or $$x = \frac{-1 - 7s + 4t}{4}$$

Therefore $w = \dfrac{5 - s}{4}$, $x = \dfrac{-1 - 7s + 4t}{4}$, $y = t$, and $z = s$.

When two parameters have been used to express the solutions to a system of equations, we obtain particular solutions by choosing values for both parameters and by substituting to find w, x, y, and z. We show two solutions.

$$\text{Let } s = 0 \text{ and } t = 0, \ w = \frac{5 - 0}{4} = \frac{5}{4}$$

$$x = \frac{-1 - 7(0) + 4(0)}{4} = -\frac{1}{4}$$

$$y = 0$$
$$z = 0$$

$$\text{Let } s = 0 \text{ and } t = 1, \ w = \frac{5 - 0}{4} = \frac{5}{4}$$

$$x = \frac{-1 - 7(0) + 4(1)}{4} = \frac{3}{4}$$

$$y = 1$$
$$z = 0$$

EXERCISE 9.2

B   The systems of equations in this exercise are a mixture of independent, dependent, and inconsistent systems. Solve each system by using the method of elimination. If the system is dependent, describe the solution in parametric form and find two particular solutions.

1. $\begin{cases} -7x + 3y = 4 \\ 14x - 6y = -8 \end{cases}$ **2.** $\begin{cases} 2x - 5y = 10 \\ 7x + 2y = -14 \end{cases}$

3. $\begin{cases} 12x - 9y = 7 \\ 16x - 12y = 15 \end{cases}$ **4.** $\begin{cases} 6x + 9y = -15 \\ 4x + 6y = -10 \end{cases}$

5. $\begin{cases} x - 3y = 0 \\ 2x + 2y = 3 \\ 5x - y = 1 \end{cases}$ **6.** $\begin{cases} 2x + y = 5 \\ x + y = 3 \\ x + 3y = 5 \end{cases}$

7. $\begin{cases} 2x - y + 2z = -3 \\ 3x + 2y - z = -2 \\ 5x + 8y - 7z = 0 \end{cases}$

8. $\begin{cases} 2x - 2y + z = 0 \\ -x + 3y + 2z = -3 \\ 2x + 6y + 11z = 10 \end{cases}$

9. $\begin{cases} -4x + 5y + 2z = -1 \\ 3x - 2y + 2z = -1 \\ x - y + z = -1 \end{cases}$

10. $\begin{cases} -x + 2y - 3z = -12 \\ 3x - 2y + z = 8 \\ x + 6y - 13z = -44 \end{cases}$

11. $\begin{cases} 2x + y + z = 5 \\ 9x + 5y + 3z = 19 \\ 6x + 5y - 2z = 3 \end{cases}$

12. $\begin{cases} x + 2y + 3z = 4 \\ 4x + 3y + 2z = 1 \\ 6x + 7y + 8z = 9 \end{cases}$

13. $\begin{cases} 4x + 3y + 7z = 30 \\ 2x \pm 4y + 3z = 20 \end{cases}$

14. $\begin{cases} w + 2x + 3z = -4 \\ y - 5z = 6 \\ -7w - 14x - 21z = 28 \\ 8y - 40z = 48 \end{cases}$

15. $\begin{cases} w + x - y - z = -5 \\ w - x + y - z = 1 \\ w + x + y + z = 5 \\ w - x - y - z = -3 \end{cases}$

16. $\begin{cases} w - x = -1 \\ x - y = -1 \\ y - z = -1 \\ -w + z = 3 \end{cases}$

17. $\begin{cases} w + x = 2 \\ x + y = 2 \\ y + z = 2 \\ w + z = 2 \end{cases}$

18. $\begin{cases} 2w - 3x + y - z = 6 \\ 3w + x + 2y - z = -1 \end{cases}$

C **19.** Consider the following system of equations.

$$\begin{cases} x + y + z = 4 \\ 2x - y + z = 4 \end{cases}$$

(a) Verify that $x = 2$, $y = 1$, and $z = 1$ is a solution to the system.

(b) Verify that $x = 4$, $y = 2$, and $z = -2$ is another solution to the system.

(c) Show that the average; $x = \dfrac{2 + 4}{2} = 3$, $y = \dfrac{1 + 2}{2} = \dfrac{3}{2}$, and $z = \dfrac{1 + (-2)}{2} = -\dfrac{1}{2}$ is also a solution to the system.

(d) Show that the average of the solutions in parts (a) and (c) is also a solution to the system.

PROBLEMS PLUS

Mike gives Marcel as many dollars as Marcel has and Alana as many dollars as Alana has. Marcel gives Mike and Alana as many dollars as each then has. Alana gives Mike and Marcel as many dollars as each then has. Each of them ends up with forty dollars. How many dollars did each of them have to start with?

9.3 ELEMENTARY ROW OPERATIONS

The method of elimination has served us very well in the solution of systems of equations. Unfortunately, in practice a system may involve hundreds, if not thousands, of equations and unknowns. To solve such a system by hand would be somewhat time-consuming. With the technology available to us today, it is reasonable to use the resources of a computer to aid us in the solution of such a large system. It is the purpose of this and the following sections to develop a programmable method of solving systems of linear equations. Matrices provide an approach that is adaptable to a computer-based algorithm.

We first define some terms. In the system $\begin{cases} 3x - 5y = 14 \\ x + 2y = 1 \end{cases}$ we define the **matrix of coefficients** to be

$$\begin{bmatrix} 3 & -5 \\ 1 & 2 \end{bmatrix}$$

The entries in the first row are the coefficients of x and y, respectively, in the first equation. The entries in the second row are the coefficients of x and y, respectively, in the second equation.
The matrix

$$\begin{bmatrix} 3 & -5 & | & 14 \\ 1 & 2 & | & 1 \end{bmatrix}$$

is called the **augmented coefficient matrix**, or simply the **augmented matrix**, because the column of constants *augments* the matrix of coefficients. Although it is not necessary to include the broken line in the augmented matrix, we will, for it serves to remind us that 14 and 1 are constants that appear on the right side of the equations.

Example 1　Write the matrix of coefficients and the augmented matrix for each of the following systems of equations.

(a) $\begin{cases} 4x - y = 0 \\ 5x + 7y = 12 \end{cases}$　　　　(b) $\begin{cases} 3x - y = -8 \\ 5y = 12 \end{cases}$

(c) $\begin{cases} 2x + 3y - z = 4 \\ -x + 5z = 10 \\ 2x + 5y = 7 \end{cases}$

Solution　(a)　The matrix of coefficients is

$$\begin{bmatrix} 4 & -1 \\ 5 & 7 \end{bmatrix}$$

If we augment this with the column of constants we obtain the augmented matrix

$$\begin{bmatrix} 4 & -1 & | & 0 \\ 5 & 7 & | & 12 \end{bmatrix}$$

(b) The matrix of coefficients is

$$\begin{bmatrix} 3 & -1 \\ 0 & 5 \end{bmatrix}$$

Notice that x does not appear in the second equation; therefore, its coefficient is 0. In the matrix of coefficients we must insert this 0. The augmented matrix is

$$\begin{bmatrix} 3 & -1 & | & -8 \\ 0 & 5 & | & 12 \end{bmatrix}$$

(c) The matrix of coefficients is

$$\begin{bmatrix} 2 & 3 & -1 \\ -1 & 0 & 5 \\ 2 & 5 & 0 \end{bmatrix}$$

The augmented matrix is

$$\begin{bmatrix} 2 & 3 & -1 & | & 4 \\ -1 & 0 & 5 & | & 10 \\ 2 & 5 & 0 & | & 7 \end{bmatrix}$$

We return to the original system of equations $\begin{cases} 3x - 5y = 14 \\ x + 2y = 1 \end{cases}$

The following steps might be used when solving this system by elimination.

System		Augmented Matrix
$\begin{cases} 3x - 5y = 14 \\ x + 2y = 1 \end{cases}$	① ②	$\begin{bmatrix} 3 & -5 & | & 14 \\ 1 & 2 & | & 1 \end{bmatrix}$

We use Equation 2 to eliminate x from Equation 1.

Step 1: Since we are using Equation 2, we write it first.

$$\begin{cases} x + 2y = 1 \\ 3x - 5y = 14 \end{cases} \quad \begin{matrix} ② \\ ① \end{matrix} \quad \begin{bmatrix} 1 & 2 & | & 1 \\ 3 & -5 & | & 14 \end{bmatrix}$$

Step 2: ① $-$ $3 \times$ ② gives $-11y = 11$ ③

The system can now be written.

$$\begin{cases} x + 2y = 1 \\ -11y = 11 \end{cases} \quad \begin{matrix} ② \\ ③ \end{matrix} \quad \begin{bmatrix} 1 & 2 & | & 1 \\ 0 & -11 & | & 11 \end{bmatrix}$$

Step 3: We divide Equation 3 by -11 to obtain

$$\begin{cases} x + 2y = 1 \\ y = -1 \end{cases} \qquad \begin{matrix} ② \\ ④ \end{matrix} \qquad \begin{bmatrix} 1 & 2 & | & 1 \\ 0 & 1 & | & -1 \end{bmatrix}$$

Substituting $y = -1$ in Equation 2, we obtain

$$x + 2(-1) = 1$$

or $\qquad\qquad\qquad x = 3$

Therefore, $x = 3$ and $y = -1$.

Solving the preceding system of equations involved three operations that we can perform with equations without changing the solution of the system.

1. We can switch the order of the equations. [Step 1]
2. We can add (or subtract) multiples of one equation to (or from) another equation. [Step 2]
3. We can multiply any equation by a non-zero real number. [Step 3]

Since equations in the system correspond to rows in the augmented matrix, if we translate these operations into their corresponding matrix operations, they become the following.

Elementary Row Operations

1. We can interchange the rows of the matrix.
2. We can add (or subtract) multiples of one row to (or from) another row.
3. We can multiply any row by a non-zero real number.

Because these are operations on the rows of the augmented matrix, they are called the **elementary row operations** or, in short, **row operations**. Whenever a matrix can be obtained from another by one or more elementary row operations, we say that the matrices are **equivalent**. If A and B are two equivalent matrices, we write A~B.

The following example illustrates the notation we use when applying each of these operations to a matrix.

Example 2 Perform each of the following row operations on the given matrix.
(a) Interchange row 1 with row 3.
(b) Subtract two times row 1 from row 2.
(c) Multiply row 3 by -2.

$$\begin{bmatrix} 2 & -1 & | & 3 \\ 4 & 2 & | & -3 \\ 1 & -2 & | & 5 \end{bmatrix}$$

Solution (a) $\begin{bmatrix} 2 & -1 & | & 3 \\ 4 & 2 & | & -3 \\ 1 & -2 & | & 5 \end{bmatrix} \sim \begin{bmatrix} 1 & -2 & | & 5 \\ 4 & 2 & | & -3 \\ 2 & -1 & | & 3 \end{bmatrix} \begin{matrix} R_3 \\ \\ R_1 \end{matrix}$

(b) $\begin{bmatrix} 2 & -1 & | & 3 \\ 4 & 2 & | & -3 \\ 1 & -2 & | & 5 \end{bmatrix} \sim \begin{bmatrix} 2 & -1 & | & 3 \\ 0 & 4 & | & -9 \\ 1 & -2 & | & 5 \end{bmatrix} R_2 - 2R_1$

(c) $\begin{bmatrix} 2 & -1 & | & 3 \\ 4 & 2 & | & -3 \\ 1 & -2 & | & 5 \end{bmatrix} \sim \begin{bmatrix} 2 & -1 & | & 3 \\ 4 & 2 & | & -3 \\ -2 & 4 & | & -10 \end{bmatrix} -2R_3$

Notice that the operation performed is written on the right side of the matrix beside the row or rows that change. R_i is an abbreviation for row i.

Example 3 Perform the following row operations in succession on the given matrix.
(a) Subtract row 1 from row 2.
(b) Interchange row 1 and row 2.
(c) Subtract three times row 1 from row 2.
(d) Multiply row 2 by $-\frac{1}{23}$.

$$\begin{bmatrix} 3 & -2 & | & 5 \\ 4 & 5 & | & -1 \end{bmatrix}$$

Solution $\begin{bmatrix} 3 & -2 & | & 5 \\ 4 & 5 & | & -1 \end{bmatrix} \sim \begin{bmatrix} 3 & -2 & | & 5 \\ 1 & 7 & | & -6 \end{bmatrix} R_2 - R_1$

$\sim \begin{bmatrix} 1 & 7 & | & -6 \\ 3 & -2 & | & 5 \end{bmatrix} \begin{matrix} R_2 \\ R_1 \end{matrix}$

$\sim \begin{bmatrix} 1 & 7 & | & -6 \\ 0 & -23 & | & 23 \end{bmatrix} R_2 - 3R_1$

$\sim \begin{bmatrix} 1 & 7 & | & -6 \\ 0 & 1 & | & -1 \end{bmatrix} -\frac{1}{23}R_2$

Example 4 Perform the following row operations in succession on the given matrix.
(a) Interchange row 1 and row 3.
(b) Subtract three times row 1 from row 2.
(c) Subtract two times row 1 from row 3.
(d) Interchange row 2 and row 3.
(e) Multiply row 2 by -1.
(f) Add row 2 to row 1.
(g) Subtract five times row 2 from row 3.
(h) Multiply row 3 by $-\frac{1}{47}$.

(i) Subtract ten times row 3 from row 1.

(j) Subtract eight times row 3 from row 2.

$$\begin{bmatrix} 2 & -3 & -4 & | & -3 \\ 3 & 2 & -1 & | & 10 \\ 1 & -1 & 2 & | & -4 \end{bmatrix}$$

Solution

$$\begin{bmatrix} 2 & -3 & -4 & | & -3 \\ 3 & 2 & -1 & | & 10 \\ 1 & -1 & 2 & | & -4 \end{bmatrix} \sim \begin{bmatrix} 1 & -1 & 2 & | & -4 \\ 3 & 2 & -1 & | & 10 \\ 2 & -3 & -4 & | & -3 \end{bmatrix} \begin{matrix} R_3 \\ \\ R_1 \end{matrix}$$

$$\sim \begin{bmatrix} 1 & -1 & 2 & | & -4 \\ 0 & 5 & -7 & | & 22 \\ 2 & -3 & -4 & | & -3 \end{bmatrix} R_2 - 3R_1$$

$$\sim \begin{bmatrix} 1 & -1 & 2 & | & -4 \\ 0 & 5 & -7 & | & 22 \\ 0 & -1 & -8 & | & 5 \end{bmatrix} R_3 - 2R_1$$

$$\sim \begin{bmatrix} 1 & -1 & 2 & | & -4 \\ 0 & -1 & -8 & | & 5 \\ 0 & 5 & -7 & | & 22 \end{bmatrix} \begin{matrix} \\ R_3 \\ R_2 \end{matrix}$$

$$\sim \begin{bmatrix} 1 & -1 & 2 & | & -4 \\ 0 & 1 & 8 & | & -5 \\ 0 & 5 & -7 & | & 22 \end{bmatrix} -R_2$$

$$\sim \begin{bmatrix} 1 & 0 & 10 & | & -9 \\ 0 & 1 & 8 & | & -5 \\ 0 & 5 & -7 & | & 22 \end{bmatrix} R_1 + R_2$$

$$\sim \begin{bmatrix} 1 & 0 & 10 & | & -9 \\ 0 & 1 & 8 & | & -5 \\ 0 & 0 & -47 & | & 47 \end{bmatrix} R_3 - 5R_2$$

$$\sim \begin{bmatrix} 1 & 0 & 10 & | & -9 \\ 0 & 1 & 8 & | & -5 \\ 0 & 0 & 1 & | & -1 \end{bmatrix} -\frac{1}{47}R_3$$

$$\sim \begin{bmatrix} 1 & 0 & 0 & | & 1 \\ 0 & 1 & 8 & | & -5 \\ 0 & 0 & 1 & | & -1 \end{bmatrix} R_1 - 10R_3$$

$$\sim \begin{bmatrix} 1 & 0 & 0 & | & 1 \\ 0 & 1 & 0 & | & 3 \\ 0 & 0 & 1 & | & -1 \end{bmatrix} R_2 - 8R_3$$

EXERCISE 9.3

A **1.** For each of the following systems of equations, give the matrix of coefficients and the augmented matrix.

(a) $\begin{cases} 2x - 4y = 18 \\ x + 3y = -4 \end{cases}$

(b) $\begin{cases} 2x - 5y + 7z = 23 \\ -3x \qquad - 4z = 12 \end{cases}$

(c) $\begin{cases} 2x - 4y + 6z = -12 \\ \qquad 3y + 2z = 6 \\ -x - 3y \qquad = 9 \end{cases}$

(d) $\begin{cases} 2x + y = 0 \\ 4x - 5y = 0 \\ x + y = 0 \end{cases}$

(e) $\begin{cases} 2x + 5y - 2z = 4 \\ -3x - 2y + z = 18 \\ x + y + z = 21 \\ -9x \qquad - 3z = 13 \end{cases}$

(f) $\begin{cases} 2w - x + 7y - 4z = 24 \\ w + 3x - 5y + 3z = 16 \\ -6w \qquad + 9y \qquad = 10 \\ 2w \qquad\qquad + 7z = 28 \end{cases}$

2. For each of the following augmented matrices give the corresponding system of equations.

(a) $\begin{bmatrix} 3 & 8 & | & -4 \\ 4 & 0 & | & 7 \end{bmatrix}$

(b) $\begin{bmatrix} -2 & 4 & | & 6 \\ 0 & 7 & | & 14 \\ 3 & -5 & | & 12 \end{bmatrix}$

(c) $\begin{bmatrix} 4 & -3 & 1 & | & 0 \\ 3 & 0 & -1 & | & 6 \end{bmatrix}$

(d) $\begin{bmatrix} 0 & 1 & 2 & | & -4 \\ 2 & 1 & 0 & | & 3 \\ 3 & -3 & 1 & | & 10 \\ 1 & 0 & -1 & | & 12 \end{bmatrix}$

B **3.** Perform each of the following row operations on the given matrix.

(a) Interchange row 3 and row 2.
$$\begin{bmatrix} 1 & 2 & | & -4 \\ 0 & -3 & | & 5 \\ 0 & 1 & | & -7 \end{bmatrix}$$

(b) Subtract three times row 1 from row 2.
$$\begin{bmatrix} 1 & -3 & | & 5 \\ 3 & -5 & | & -4 \end{bmatrix}$$

(c) Add two times row 1 to row 3.
$$\begin{bmatrix} 1 & -8 & 4 & | & -1 \\ 0 & 2 & -5 & | & 6 \\ -2 & 3 & -2 & | & 1 \end{bmatrix}$$

(d) Multiply row 2 by $-\frac{1}{2}$.
$$\begin{bmatrix} 1 & -3 & | & 7 \\ 0 & -2 & | & 3 \end{bmatrix}$$

In Questions 4 through 9, inclusive, perform the indicated elementary row operations in succession on the given matrix.

4.
$$\begin{bmatrix} 5 & -3 & | & -7 \\ 1 & -4 & | & 2 \end{bmatrix}$$

(a) Interchange row 1 and row 2.

(b) Subtract five times row 1 from row 2.

(c) Multiply row 2 by $\frac{1}{17}$.

5.
$$\begin{bmatrix} 4 & -2 & -1 & | & 12 \\ 3 & -1 & 0 & | & 9 \\ 1 & 1 & 1 & | & 5 \end{bmatrix}$$

(a) Interchange row 1 and row 3.

(b) Subtract three times row 1 from row 2.

(c) Subtract four times row 1 from row 3.

(d) Subtract row 3 from row 2.

(e) Multiply row 2 by $\frac{1}{2}$.

(f) Add six times row 2 to row 3.

6.
$$\begin{bmatrix} 2 & 3 & 4 & | & 6 \\ -5 & -3 & 2 & | & 7 \end{bmatrix}$$

(a) Multiply row 1 by $\frac{1}{2}$.

(b) Add five times row 1 to row 2.

(c) Multiply row 2 by $\frac{2}{9}$.

7.
$$\begin{bmatrix} 2 & 3 & | & 5 \\ -1 & 2 & | & -6 \\ 5 & 11 & | & 10 \end{bmatrix}$$

(a) Interchange row 1 and row 2.

(b) Multiply row 1 by -1.

(c) Subtract two times row 1 from row 2.

(d) Subtract five times row 1 from row 3.

(e) Multiply row 2 by $\frac{1}{7}$.

(f) Add two times row 2 to row 1.

(g) Subtract 21 times row 2 from row 3.

(h) Subtract four times row 3 from row 1.

(i) Add row 3 to row 2.

8.
$$\begin{bmatrix} -4 & -13 & 9 & | & 4 \\ 2 & 3 & -1 & | & -2 \\ 1 & -2 & 3 & | & 4 \end{bmatrix}$$

(a) Interchange row 1 and row 3.

(b) Subtract two times row 1 from row 2.

(c) Add four times row 1 to row 3.

(d) Multiply row 2 by $\frac{1}{7}$.

(e) Add two times row 2 to row 1.

(f) Add 21 times row 2 to row 3.

(g) Multiply row 3 by $-\frac{1}{10}$.

(h) Subtract eight-sevenths times row 3 from row 1.

(i) Add ten-sevenths times row 3 to row 2.

9.
$$\begin{bmatrix} 2 & -3 & 4 & -1 & | & 10 \\ 1 & 3 & 1 & -4 & | & 3 \\ 1 & -6 & 3 & 3 & | & 7 \\ 1 & -15 & 5 & 10 & | & 11 \end{bmatrix}$$

(a) Interchange row 1 and row 2.

(b) Subtract two times row 1 from row 2.

(c) Subtract row 1 from row 3.

(d) Subtract row 1 from row 4.

(e) Subtract row 2 from row 3.

(f) Subtract two times row 2 from row 4.

(g) Multiply row 2 by $-\frac{1}{9}$.

10. On the matrix in Question 9, perform the following row operations in succession.

(a) Interchange row 1 and row 3.

(b) Subtract row 1 from row 2.

(c) Subtract two times row 1 from row 3.

(d) Subtract row 1 from row 4.

(e) Subtract row 2 from row 3.

(f) Add row 2 to row 4.

(g) Multiply row 2 by $\frac{1}{9}$.

C **11.** Find a sequence of row operations that will transform
$$\begin{bmatrix} 4 & -5 & | & 13 \\ -1 & 3 & | & -5 \end{bmatrix}$$
to the form
$$\begin{bmatrix} 1 & -3 & | & 5 \\ 0 & 1 & | & -1 \end{bmatrix}$$

12. Find a sequence of row operations that will transform
$$\begin{bmatrix} 2 & -3 & | & -1 \\ -3 & 4 & | & 0 \\ 1 & 2 & | & 10 \end{bmatrix}$$
to the form
$$\begin{bmatrix} 1 & 0 & | & 4 \\ 0 & 1 & | & 3 \\ 0 & 0 & | & 0 \end{bmatrix}$$

13. Find a sequence of row operations that will transform

$$\begin{bmatrix} 3 & -1 & 1 & | & 10 \\ 1 & 3 & -1 & | & 7 \\ 13 & 9 & -1 & | & 58 \end{bmatrix}$$

to the form

$$\begin{bmatrix} 1 & 3 & -1 & | & 7 \\ 0 & 1 & -\frac{2}{5} & | & \frac{11}{10} \\ 0 & 0 & 0 & | & 0 \end{bmatrix}$$

14. Find a sequence of row operations that will transform

$$\begin{bmatrix} 3 & 2 & 0 & | & -2 \\ 2 & -3 & -6 & | & -8 \\ 1 & 1 & -3 & | & 1 \end{bmatrix}$$

to the form

$$\begin{bmatrix} 1 & 0 & 0 & | & -2 \\ 0 & 1 & 0 & | & 2 \\ 0 & 0 & 1 & | & -\frac{1}{3} \end{bmatrix}$$

9.4 ECHELON FORM OF A MATRIX

In Section 9.3 we introduced the augmented matrix corresponding to a system of linear equations. The matrix method for solving a system of equations involves applying row operations to **reduce** the augmented matrix to an equivalent form in which the solution to the system is easily obtained. In this section we introduce one such form and show how the elementary row operations are used to obtain it.

A matrix is said to be in **echelon form** if the following conditions are satisfied.

Echelon Form
1. The first non-zero entry in any row is a 1.
2. Each row contains more leading zeros than the preceding row.
3. All zero rows are at the bottom.

The word *echelon* is an old navy term. Warships of a fleet are said to be in echelon form if they are arranged in a slanting line relative to their direction of travel. We give some examples of matrices in echelon form.

$$\begin{bmatrix} 1 & 5 & | & -4 \\ 0 & 1 & | & 9 \end{bmatrix} \qquad \begin{bmatrix} 1 & 7 & -8 & | & 2 \\ 0 & 1 & -3 & | & -6 \\ 0 & 0 & 1 & | & -1 \end{bmatrix} \qquad \begin{bmatrix} 1 & -7 & | & -3 \\ 0 & 0 & | & 1 \end{bmatrix}$$

$$\begin{bmatrix} 1 & -5 & | & 7 \\ 0 & 0 & | & 0 \end{bmatrix} \qquad \begin{bmatrix} 0 & 1 & | & 9 \\ 0 & 0 & | & 1 \\ 0 & 0 & | & 0 \end{bmatrix} \qquad \begin{bmatrix} 1 & \frac{1}{2} & | & 6 \\ 0 & 1 & | & -4 \\ 0 & 0 & | & 0 \\ 0 & 0 & | & 0 \end{bmatrix}$$

Example 1   Which of the following matrices are in echelon form? If a matrix is not, give a reason.

(a) $\begin{bmatrix} 1 & -4 & | & 5 \\ 0 & 8 & | & -2 \\ 0 & 0 & | & 0 \end{bmatrix}$ (b) $\begin{bmatrix} 1 & 2 & | & 3 \\ 0 & 1 & | & 5 \\ 0 & 1 & | & -2 \\ 0 & 0 & | & 1 \end{bmatrix}$

(c) $\begin{bmatrix} 1 & 4 & -9 & | & 18 \\ 0 & 0 & 1 & | & 3 \\ 0 & 0 & 0 & | & 0 \\ 0 & 0 & 0 & | & 1 \end{bmatrix}$ (d) $\begin{bmatrix} 0 & 1 & 5 & | & -23 \\ 0 & 0 & 1 & | & 4 \\ 0 & 0 & 0 & | & 0 \end{bmatrix}$

Solution   (a)   The first non-zero entry in the second row is 8, so the matrix is not in echelon form.

(b)   The third row does not contain more leading zeros than the second row, so the matrix is not in echelon form.

(c)   The third row contains all zeros and is not at the bottom, so the matrix is not in echelon form.

(d)   The first non-zero entry in every row is 1. Each row contains more leading zeros than the preceding row. The zero row is at the bottom. Therefore, the matrix is in echelon form.

The following two examples show how row operations can be applied to a matrix to reduce it to echelon form.

Example 2   Use a sequence of row operations to reduce the following matrix to echelon form.

$$\begin{bmatrix} 2 & -1 & -4 & | & -7 \\ 1 & -1 & -3 & | & -4 \\ 1 & 1 & -1 & | & -2 \end{bmatrix}$$

Solution   We proceed in the following way.

Step 1:   We try to obtain a 1 in the a_{11} position.

Interchange row 1 and row 2.

$$\begin{bmatrix} 1 & -1 & -3 & | & -4 \\ 2 & -1 & -4 & | & -7 \\ 1 & 1 & -1 & | & -2 \end{bmatrix} \begin{matrix} R_2 \\ R_1 \\ \, \end{matrix}$$

Step 2:   We next try to obtain zeros below this 1 in the a_{21} and a_{31} positions.

Subtract two times row 1 from row 2.

$$\begin{bmatrix} 1 & -1 & -3 & | & -4 \\ 0 & 1 & 2 & | & 1 \\ 1 & 1 & -1 & | & -2 \end{bmatrix} \quad R_2 - 2R_1$$

Subtract row 1 from row 3.

$$\begin{bmatrix} 1 & -1 & -3 & | & -4 \\ 0 & 1 & 2 & | & 1 \\ 0 & 2 & 2 & | & 2 \end{bmatrix} \quad R_3 - R_1$$

Step 3: We now obtain a 1 in the a_{22} position.

We already have the required 1.

$$\begin{bmatrix} 1 & 1 & -3 & | & -4 \\ 0 & 1 & 2 & | & 1 \\ 0 & 2 & 2 & | & 2 \end{bmatrix}$$

Step 4: Following the suggested pattern, we now obtain a zero below this 1 in the a_{32} position.

Subtract two times row 2 from row 3.

$$\begin{bmatrix} 1 & 1 & -3 & | & -4 \\ 0 & 1 & 2 & | & 1 \\ 0 & 0 & -2 & | & 0 \end{bmatrix} \quad R_3 - 2R_2$$

Step 5: Try to obtain a 1 in the a_{33} position.

Multiply row 3 by $-\frac{1}{2}$.

$$\begin{bmatrix} 1 & 1 & -3 & | & -4 \\ 0 & 1 & 2 & | & 1 \\ 0 & 0 & 1 & | & 0 \end{bmatrix} \quad -\frac{1}{2}R_3$$

The matrix is now in echelon form.

Notice the algorithmic pattern. First, we obtain an appropriate 1, then we use the 1 to obtain the needed zeros in that particular column.

Example 3   Reduce the following matrix to echelon form.

$$\begin{bmatrix} 2 & 1 & 1 & | & 2 \\ -1 & 10 & 13 & | & -19 \\ 3 & -2 & -3 & | & 9 \end{bmatrix}$$

Solution   We obtain a 1 in the a_{11} position. To avoid fractions we will not divide row 1 by 2. Instead, we will add row 2 to row 1.

$$\begin{bmatrix} 1 & 11 & 14 & | & -17 \\ -1 & 10 & 13 & | & -19 \\ 3 & -2 & -3 & | & 9 \end{bmatrix} \begin{matrix} R_1 + R_2 \\ \\ \\ \end{matrix}$$

We now use this 1 to obtain the needed zeros in this column.

$$\begin{bmatrix} 1 & 11 & 14 & | & -17 \\ 0 & 21 & 27 & | & -36 \\ 3 & -2 & -3 & | & 9 \end{bmatrix} \begin{matrix} \\ R_2 + R_1 \\ \\ \end{matrix}$$

$$\begin{bmatrix} 1 & 11 & 14 & | & -17 \\ 0 & 21 & 27 & | & -36 \\ 0 & -35 & -45 & | & 60 \end{bmatrix} \begin{matrix} \\ \\ R_3 - 3R_1 \end{matrix}$$

We next obtain a 1 in the a_{22} position.

$$\begin{bmatrix} 1 & 11 & 14 & | & -17 \\ 0 & 1 & \frac{9}{7} & | & -\frac{12}{7} \\ 0 & -35 & -45 & | & 60 \end{bmatrix} \begin{matrix} \\ \frac{1}{21}R_2 \\ \\ \end{matrix}$$

We now use this 1 to obtain the required zero in the a_{32} position.

$$\begin{bmatrix} 1 & 11 & 14 & | & -17 \\ 0 & 1 & \frac{9}{7} & | & -\frac{12}{7} \\ 0 & 0 & 0 & | & 0 \end{bmatrix} \begin{matrix} \\ \\ R_3 + 35R_2 \end{matrix}$$

The last row is all zeros, so the matrix is in echelon form.

It is now a simple matter to solve a system of linear equations by using this method. The following two examples illustrate how this is done.

Example 4   Solve the following system of equations by reducing the corresponding augmented matrix to echelon form.

$$\begin{cases} 2x - 3y + z = -2 \\ 2x + y - z = 4 \\ x - y - z = 1 \end{cases}$$

Solution   The augmented matrix corresponding to this system of equations is

$$\begin{bmatrix} 2 & -3 & 1 & | & -2 \\ 2 & 1 & -1 & | & 4 \\ 1 & -1 & -1 & | & 1 \end{bmatrix}$$

We now use row operations to reduce the augmented matrix to echelon form. To save space we perform some operations in the same step.

$$\begin{bmatrix} 2 & -3 & 1 & | & -2 \\ 2 & 1 & -1 & | & 4 \\ 1 & -1 & -1 & | & 1 \end{bmatrix} \sim \begin{bmatrix} 1 & -1 & -1 & | & 1 \\ 2 & 1 & -1 & | & 4 \\ 2 & -3 & 1 & | & -2 \end{bmatrix} \begin{matrix} R_3 \\ \\ R_1 \end{matrix}$$

$$\sim \begin{bmatrix} 1 & -1 & -1 & | & 1 \\ 0 & 3 & 1 & | & 2 \\ 0 & -1 & 3 & | & -4 \end{bmatrix} \begin{matrix} \\ R_2 - 2R_1 \\ R_3 - 2R_1 \end{matrix}$$

$$\sim \begin{bmatrix} 1 & -1 & -1 & | & 1 \\ 0 & -1 & 3 & | & -4 \\ 0 & 3 & 1 & | & 2 \end{bmatrix} \begin{matrix} \\ R_3 \\ R_2 \end{matrix}$$

$$\sim \begin{bmatrix} 1 & -1 & -1 & | & 1 \\ 0 & 1 & -3 & | & 4 \\ 0 & 3 & 1 & | & 2 \end{bmatrix} -R_2$$

$$\sim \begin{bmatrix} 1 & -1 & -1 & | & 1 \\ 0 & 1 & -3 & | & 4 \\ 0 & 0 & 10 & | & -10 \end{bmatrix} \begin{matrix} \\ \\ R_3 - 3R_2 \end{matrix}$$

$$\sim \begin{bmatrix} 1 & -1 & -1 & | & 1 \\ 0 & 1 & -3 & | & 4 \\ 0 & 0 & 1 & | & -1 \end{bmatrix} \frac{1}{10}R_3$$

The augmented matrix is now in echelon form. The system of equations corresponding to this is

$$\begin{cases} x - y - z = 1 \\ \quad\; y - 3z = 4 \\ \qquad\quad z = -1 \end{cases}$$

Substituting $z = -1$ in the second equation, we get

$$y - 3(-1) = 4$$

or $y = 1$

Substituting $y = 1$ and $z = -1$ in the first equation, we get

$$x - 1 - (-1) = 1$$

or $x = 1$

Therefore $x = 1$, $y = 1$, and $z = -1$.   ◇

Example 5 Solve the following system by reducing the corresponding augmented matrix to echelon form.

$$\begin{cases} -w + x + y + 2z = -4 \\ 2w + 3x - y - z = 0 \\ w + 9x + y + 4z = -12 \end{cases}$$

Solution   The augmented matrix corresponding to this system of equations is

$$\begin{bmatrix} -1 & 1 & 1 & 2 & | & -4 \\ 2 & 3 & -1 & -1 & | & 0 \\ 1 & 9 & 1 & 4 & | & -12 \end{bmatrix}$$

We now perform a sequence of row operations to reduce this matrix to echelon form.

$$\begin{bmatrix} -1 & 1 & 1 & 2 & | & -4 \\ 2 & 3 & -1 & -1 & | & 0 \\ 1 & 9 & 1 & 4 & | & -12 \end{bmatrix} \sim \begin{bmatrix} 1 & -1 & -1 & -2 & | & 4 \\ 2 & 3 & -1 & -1 & | & 0 \\ 1 & 9 & 1 & 4 & | & -12 \end{bmatrix} \begin{matrix} -R_1 \\ \\ \\ \end{matrix}$$

$$\sim \begin{bmatrix} 1 & -1 & -1 & -2 & | & 4 \\ 0 & 5 & 1 & 3 & | & -8 \\ 0 & 10 & 2 & 6 & | & -16 \end{bmatrix} \begin{matrix} \\ R_2 - 2R_1 \\ R_3 - R_1 \end{matrix}$$

$$\sim \begin{bmatrix} 1 & -1 & -1 & -2 & | & 4 \\ 0 & 1 & \frac{1}{5} & \frac{3}{5} & | & -\frac{8}{5} \\ 0 & 10 & 2 & 6 & | & -16 \end{bmatrix} \begin{matrix} \\ \frac{1}{5}R_2 \\ \\ \end{matrix}$$

$$\sim \begin{bmatrix} 1 & -1 & -1 & -2 & | & 4 \\ 0 & 1 & \frac{1}{5} & \frac{3}{5} & | & -\frac{8}{5} \\ 0 & 0 & 0 & 0 & | & 0 \end{bmatrix} \begin{matrix} \\ \\ R_3 - 10R_2 \end{matrix}$$

The last row is all zeros, so the matrix is in echelon form. The system of equations corresponding to this reduced matrix is

$$\begin{cases} w - x - y - 2z = 4 \\ \quad x + \frac{1}{5}y + \frac{3}{5}z = -\frac{8}{5} \\ \quad \quad 0 = 0 \end{cases}$$

This is a dependent system of equations and we introduce two parameters to express the solution.

Let $y = s$ and $z = t$. Substituting in the second equation, we obtain

$$x + \frac{1}{5}s + \frac{3}{5}t = -\frac{8}{5}$$

or $x = \dfrac{-8 - s - 3t}{5}$

Substituting in the first equation, we get

$$w - \frac{-8 - s - 3t}{5} - s - 2t = 4$$

or $w = \dfrac{12 + 4s + 7t}{5}$

Therefore, $w = \dfrac{12 + 4s + 7t}{5}$, $x = \dfrac{-8 - s - 3t}{5}$, $y = s$, and $z = t$.

In the preceding example, we can obtain particular solutions by choosing values for s and t and by solving for w, x, y, and z. We give two such solutions.

Let $s = 0$ and $t = 0$, then

$$w = \frac{12 + 4(0) + 7(0)}{5} = \frac{12}{5}$$

$$x = \frac{-8 - 0 - 3(0)}{5} = -\frac{8}{5}$$

$$y = 0$$
$$z = 0$$

Let $s = 1$ and $t = 0$, then

$$w = \frac{12 + 4(1) + 7(0)}{5} = \frac{16}{5}$$

$$x = \frac{-8 - 1 - 3(0)}{5} = -\frac{9}{5}$$

$$y = 1$$
$$z = 0$$

EXERCISE 9.4

A 1. State which of the following matrices are in echelon form. For those that are not, give a reason.

(a) $\begin{bmatrix} 1 & -6 & | & 10 \\ 0 & -1 & | & 1 \end{bmatrix}$

(b) $\begin{bmatrix} 1 & 4 & -2 & | & 5 \\ 0 & 1 & 2 & | & -9 \\ 0 & 1 & 10 & | & -4 \end{bmatrix}$

(c) $\begin{bmatrix} 0 & 1 & | & -3 \\ 0 & 0 & | & 1 \\ 0 & 0 & | & 0 \end{bmatrix}$

(d) $\begin{bmatrix} 1 & 12 & -10 & | & 3 \\ 0 & 1 & -6 & | & 4 \\ 0 & 0 & 1 & | & 1 \\ 0 & 0 & 0 & | & 0 \end{bmatrix}$

(e) $\begin{bmatrix} 1 & -4 & | & 3 \\ 0 & 1 & | & -3 \\ 0 & 0 & | & 0 \end{bmatrix}$

(f) $\begin{bmatrix} 1 & 3 & | & 0 \\ 0 & 0 & | & 0 \end{bmatrix}$

(g) $\begin{bmatrix} 1 & -2 & 7 & | & 3 \\ 0 & 0 & 1 & | & 5 \\ 0 & 0 & 0 & | & 0 \end{bmatrix}$

(h) $\begin{bmatrix} 1 & -6 & | & 8 \\ 0 & 1 & | & -1 \\ 0 & 0 & | & 1 \\ 0 & 0 & | & 0 \end{bmatrix}$

2. Each of the following is the augmented matrix corresponding to a system of linear equations reduced to echelon form. In each case, state whether the system is independent, dependent, or inconsistent. If the system is dependent, state the number of parameters needed to express the solution.

(a) $\begin{bmatrix} 1 & -7 & | & 3 \\ 0 & 1 & | & 4 \end{bmatrix}$

(b) $\begin{bmatrix} 1 & 2 & | & -9 \\ 0 & 0 & | & 0 \end{bmatrix}$

(c) $\begin{bmatrix} 1 & -4 & 6 & | & 2 \\ 0 & 0 & 1 & | & 3 \\ 0 & 0 & 0 & | & 0 \end{bmatrix}$

(d) $\begin{bmatrix} 1 & -3 & 1 & | & 5 \\ 0 & 1 & 2 & | & -5 \\ 0 & 0 & 0 & | & 1 \end{bmatrix}$

(e) $\begin{bmatrix} 1 & 3 & -3 & | & 1 \\ 0 & 1 & 2 & | & -4 \end{bmatrix}$

(f) $\begin{bmatrix} 1 & 3 & -5 & -3 & | & 2 \\ 0 & 0 & 1 & -2 & | & 1 \\ 0 & 0 & 0 & 1 & | & -2 \end{bmatrix}$

B **3.** Use a sequence of elementary row operations to reduce each of the following matrices to echelon form.

(a) $\begin{bmatrix} 3 & -5 & | & 4 \\ -1 & 7 & | & -5 \end{bmatrix}$

(b) $\begin{bmatrix} 5 & 7 & | & -6 \\ 4 & -2 & | & 4 \end{bmatrix}$

(c) $\begin{bmatrix} 2 & 8 & | & -6 \\ 3 & -2 & | & 10 \end{bmatrix}$

(d) $\begin{bmatrix} 2 & 3 & -7 & | & 1 \\ 5 & -3 & 0 & | & 1 \end{bmatrix}$

(e) $\begin{bmatrix} 3 & -2 & | & 1 \\ -1 & 3 & | & 9 \\ 2 & -4 & | & -7 \end{bmatrix}$

(f) $\begin{bmatrix} 2 & -4 & 5 & | & 3 \\ 1 & -2 & 6 & | & -3 \\ 1 & -4 & 1 & | & 2 \end{bmatrix}$

(g) $\begin{bmatrix} -4 & -4 & 4 & | & 8 \\ 2 & -3 & 5 & | & 0 \\ -3 & 0 & 1 & | & -9 \end{bmatrix}$

(h) $\begin{bmatrix} 0 & 1 & 0 & -1 & | & 1 \\ 1 & 1 & 0 & -1 & | & 0 \\ 0 & -1 & 1 & 0 & | & -1 \\ -1 & 1 & 0 & 1 & | & 0 \end{bmatrix}$

4. Each of the following is the augmented matrix corresponding to a system of linear equations reduced to echelon form. In each case determine the solution to the system. If the system is dependent, determine two particular solutions.

(a) $\begin{bmatrix} 1 & -5 & | & 4 \\ 0 & 1 & | & 2 \end{bmatrix}$

(b) $\begin{bmatrix} 1 & -2 & | & 3 \\ 0 & 0 & | & 0 \end{bmatrix}$

(c) $\begin{bmatrix} 1 & -9 & 3 & | & 2 \\ 0 & 1 & -3 & | & 2 \\ 0 & 0 & 1 & | & -1 \end{bmatrix}$

(d) $\begin{bmatrix} 1 & -8 & 3 & | & 1 \\ 0 & 1 & -2 & | & 4 \\ 0 & 0 & 0 & | & 0 \end{bmatrix}$

(e) $\begin{bmatrix} 0 & 1 & 2 & | & -3 \\ 0 & 0 & 0 & | & 1 \end{bmatrix}$

(f) $\begin{bmatrix} 1 & -6 & 0 & 2 & | & -5 \\ 0 & 0 & 1 & -3 & | & 1 \\ 0 & 0 & 0 & 0 & | & 0 \end{bmatrix}$

5. Solve each of the following systems of equations by reducing the corresponding augmented matrix to echelon form.

(a) $\begin{cases} 3x - 4y = 7 \\ x + 3y = 11 \end{cases}$

(b) $\begin{cases} 2x + 3y = 1 \\ -x + 3y = -3 \end{cases}$

(c) $\begin{cases} 5x - 3y = 8 \\ 4x + 2y = 5 \end{cases}$

(d) $\begin{cases} 3x - 4y = 9 \\ -6x + 8y = -18 \end{cases}$

6. Solve each of the following systems of equations by reducing the corresponding augmented matrix to echelon form.

(a)
$$\begin{cases} 2x - y + z = 9 \\ x + 2y - z = -5 \\ 3x + y - 2z = -2 \end{cases}$$

(b)
$$\begin{cases} 2x + y - z = 8 \\ 2x - y - z = 2 \\ -x + y - 2z = 3 \end{cases}$$

(c)
$$\begin{cases} 3x - y + 2z = 4 \\ x + 2y + z = 4 \\ 3x - 8y + z = -4 \end{cases}$$

(d)
$$\begin{cases} 3x + 2y - z = 5 \\ 2x + 2y + z = 9 \end{cases}$$

(e)
$$\begin{cases} x - y + z = 2 \\ 2x + y - z = 4 \\ -x + 2y + z = -8 \end{cases}$$

(f)
$$\begin{cases} x - y + z = 1 \\ x + y - z = 1 \\ -x + y + z = 1 \\ x + y + z = 3 \end{cases}$$

(g)
$$\begin{cases} w - x + y - z = -2 \\ w + x + y + z = 4 \\ -w + x - y - z = -2 \\ 2w - x + y + z = 4 \end{cases}$$

(h)
$$\begin{cases} 2w - x + y - z = 3 \\ -w + x - y - z = 0 \\ 3w - 2x + y - z = 3 \end{cases}$$

(i)
$$\begin{cases} 2x + y - z = 4 \\ -x + 2y - z = -1 \\ 3x + 4y - 3z = 5 \end{cases}$$

(j)
$$\begin{cases} 2w + x - y + z = 4 \\ w - x + y - z = 0 \end{cases}$$

9.5 ROW-REDUCED ECHELON FORM OF A MATRIX

In Section 9.4 we introduced the echelon form of a matrix and used row operations to reduce the augmented matrix corresponding to a system of equations to this form. In this section we introduce the *row-reduced echelon form* of the augmented matrix and show how it can be used in solving a system of linear equations.

A matrix is said to be in **row-reduced echelon form** if the following conditions are true.

Row-Reduced Echelon Form

1   The matrix is in echelon form.
2   When a column contains the leading 1 of any row, then all other entries in that column are zero.

We give some examples of matrices in row-reduced echelon form.

$$\begin{bmatrix} 1 & 0 & | & -4 \\ 0 & 1 & | & 8 \end{bmatrix} \qquad \begin{bmatrix} 1 & 0 & 0 & | & 3 \\ 0 & 1 & 0 & | & -1 \\ 0 & 0 & 1 & | & 7 \end{bmatrix} \qquad \begin{bmatrix} 1 & -3 & 0 & | & 0 \\ 0 & 0 & 1 & | & 0 \\ 0 & 0 & 0 & | & 0 \end{bmatrix}$$

$$\begin{bmatrix} 1 & 2 & | & 0 \\ 0 & 0 & | & 1 \end{bmatrix} \qquad \begin{bmatrix} 1 & 0 & 5 & | & 0 \\ 0 & 1 & 3 & | & 0 \\ 0 & 0 & 0 & | & 0 \\ 0 & 0 & 0 & | & 0 \end{bmatrix} \qquad \begin{bmatrix} 0 & 1 & | & 0 \\ 0 & 0 & | & 1 \\ 0 & 0 & | & 0 \end{bmatrix}$$

Example 1   Determine which of the following matrices are in row-reduced echelon form. For those that are not, give a reason.

(a) $\begin{bmatrix} 1 & 0 & | & 2 \\ 0 & 1 & | & 0 \\ 0 & 0 & | & 1 \end{bmatrix}$

(b) $\begin{bmatrix} 1 & 3 & 0 & | & 0 \\ 0 & 0 & 1 & | & 0 \\ 0 & 0 & 0 & | & 1 \end{bmatrix}$

(c) $\begin{bmatrix} 1 & 2 & 0 & | & 0 \\ 0 & 0 & 2 & | & 0 \\ 0 & 0 & 0 & | & 1 \\ 0 & 0 & 0 & | & 0 \end{bmatrix}$

(d) $\begin{bmatrix} 1 & 0 & | & -5 \\ 0 & 1 & | & 0 \end{bmatrix}$

Solution   (a)   The matrix is in echelon form. The leading 1 in the third row appears in column three. Since the first entry in column three is not zero, the matrix in not in row-reduced echelon form.

(b)   The matrix is in echelon form. Since every column containing a leading 1 has zeros everywhere else, the matrix is in row-reduced echelon form.

(c)   The first non-zero entry in the second row is not 1, so the matrix is not in echelon form. Hence it is not in row-reduced echelon form.

(d)   The matrix is in echelon form. Since every column containing the first 1 in a row has zeros everywhere else, the matrix is in row-reduced echelon form.

Example 2   Use a sequence of row operations to find the row-reduced echelon form of

$$\begin{bmatrix} 2 & -3 & | & 3 \\ 1 & 4 & | & 7 \end{bmatrix}$$

Solution   We proceed in the following way.

Step 1:   We try to obtain a 1 in the a_{11} position.

Interchange row 1 and row 2.

$$\begin{bmatrix} 1 & 4 & | & 7 \\ 2 & -3 & | & 3 \end{bmatrix} \begin{matrix} R_2 \\ R_1 \end{matrix}$$

Step 2:   We next try to obtain a zero in the a_{21} position.

Subtract two times row 1 from row 2.

$$\begin{bmatrix} 1 & 4 & | & 7 \\ 0 & -11 & | & -11 \end{bmatrix} \begin{matrix} \\ R_2 - 2R_1 \end{matrix}$$

Step 3:   We now obtain a 1 in the a_{22} position.

Multiply row 2 by $-\frac{1}{11}$.

$$\begin{bmatrix} 1 & 4 & | & 7 \\ 0 & 1 & | & 1 \end{bmatrix} \begin{matrix} \\ -\frac{1}{11}R_2 \end{matrix}$$

Step 4: We now obtain a zero in the a_{12} position.

Subtract four times row 2 from row 1.

$$\begin{bmatrix} 1 & 0 & | & 3 \\ 0 & 1 & | & 1 \end{bmatrix} \begin{matrix} R_1 - 4R_2 \\ \end{matrix}$$

The matrix is now in row-reduced echelon form.

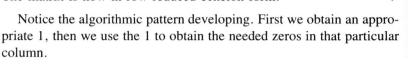

Notice the algorithmic pattern developing. First we obtain an appropriate 1, then we use the 1 to obtain the needed zeros in that particular column.

Example 3   Reduce the following matrix to row-reduced echelon form.

$$\begin{bmatrix} 2 & -1 & 1 & | & 4 \\ 1 & 1 & 2 & | & 2 \\ -1 & 2 & -1 & | & -4 \end{bmatrix}$$

Solution   We obtain a 1 in the a_{11} position. We interchange row 1 and row 2.

$$\begin{bmatrix} 1 & 1 & 2 & | & 2 \\ 2 & -1 & 1 & | & 4 \\ -1 & 2 & -1 & | & -4 \end{bmatrix} \begin{matrix} R_2 \\ R_1 \\ \end{matrix}$$

We now use this 1 to obtain the needed zeros in this column.

$$\begin{bmatrix} 1 & 1 & 2 & | & 2 \\ 0 & -3 & -3 & | & 0 \\ -1 & 2 & -1 & | & -4 \end{bmatrix} \begin{matrix} \\ R_2 - 2R_1 \\ \end{matrix}$$

$$\begin{bmatrix} 1 & 1 & 2 & | & 2 \\ 0 & -3 & -3 & | & 0 \\ 0 & 3 & 1 & | & -2 \end{bmatrix} \begin{matrix} \\ \\ R_3 + R_1 \end{matrix}$$

We next obtain a 1 in the a_{22} position.

$$\begin{bmatrix} 1 & 1 & 2 & | & 2 \\ 0 & 1 & 1 & | & 0 \\ 0 & 3 & 1 & | & -2 \end{bmatrix} \begin{matrix} \\ -\frac{1}{3}R_2 \\ \end{matrix}$$

We now use this 1 to obtain the required zeros in the a_{12} and a_{32} positions.

$$\begin{bmatrix} 1 & 0 & 1 & | & 2 \\ 0 & 1 & 1 & | & 0 \\ 0 & 3 & 1 & | & -2 \end{bmatrix} \begin{matrix} R_1 - R_2 \\ \\ \end{matrix}$$

$$\begin{bmatrix} 1 & 0 & 1 & | & 2 \\ 0 & 1 & 1 & | & 0 \\ 0 & 0 & -2 & | & -2 \end{bmatrix} \begin{matrix} \\ \\ R_3 - 3R_2 \end{matrix}$$

We obtain a 1 in the a_{33} position.

$$\begin{bmatrix} 1 & 0 & 1 & | & 2 \\ 0 & 1 & 1 & | & 0 \\ 0 & 0 & 1 & | & 1 \end{bmatrix} \quad -\tfrac{1}{2}R_3$$

Finally, we use this 1 to obtain zeros in the a_{13} and a_{23} positions.

$$\begin{bmatrix} 1 & 0 & 0 & | & 1 \\ 0 & 1 & 1 & | & 0 \\ 0 & 0 & 1 & | & 1 \end{bmatrix} \begin{matrix} R_1 - R_3 \\ \\ \\ \end{matrix}$$

$$\begin{bmatrix} 1 & 0 & 0 & | & 1 \\ 0 & 1 & 0 & | & -1 \\ 0 & 0 & 1 & | & 1 \end{bmatrix} \begin{matrix} \\ R_2 - R_3 \\ \\ \end{matrix}$$

The matrix is now in row-reduced echelon form.

We now use the row-reduced echelon form of the augmented matrix to solve systems of equations.

Example 4   Solve the following system of equations by reducing the corresponding augmented matrix to row-reduced echelon form.

$$\begin{cases} 2x - y + z = 6 \\ -x + y - z = -4 \\ x + y + 2z = 3 \end{cases}$$

Solution   The augmented matrix corresponding to this system of equations is

$$\begin{bmatrix} 2 & -1 & 1 & | & 6 \\ -1 & 1 & -1 & | & -4 \\ 1 & 1 & 2 & | & 3 \end{bmatrix}$$

We apply a sequence of row operations to reduce this matrix to row-reduced echelon form.

$$\begin{bmatrix} 2 & -1 & 1 & | & 6 \\ -1 & 1 & -1 & | & -4 \\ 1 & 1 & 2 & | & 3 \end{bmatrix} \sim \begin{bmatrix} 1 & 1 & 2 & | & 3 \\ -1 & 1 & -1 & | & -4 \\ 2 & -1 & 1 & | & 6 \end{bmatrix} \begin{matrix} R_3 \\ \\ R_1 \end{matrix}$$

$$\sim \begin{bmatrix} 1 & 1 & 2 & | & 3 \\ 0 & 2 & 1 & | & -1 \\ 0 & -3 & -3 & | & 0 \end{bmatrix} \begin{matrix} \\ R_2 + R_1 \\ R_3 - 2R_1 \end{matrix}$$

$$\sim \begin{bmatrix} 1 & 1 & 2 & | & 3 \\ 0 & -3 & -3 & | & 0 \\ 0 & 2 & 1 & | & -1 \end{bmatrix} \begin{matrix} \\ R_3 \\ R_2 \end{matrix}$$

$$\sim \begin{bmatrix} 1 & 1 & 2 & | & 3 \\ 0 & 1 & 1 & | & 0 \\ 0 & 2 & 1 & | & -1 \end{bmatrix} \quad -\tfrac{1}{3}R_2$$

$$\sim \begin{bmatrix} 1 & 0 & 1 & | & 3 \\ 0 & 1 & 1 & | & 0 \\ 0 & 0 & -1 & | & -1 \end{bmatrix} \begin{matrix} R_1 - R_2 \\ \\ R_3 - 2R_2 \end{matrix}$$

$$\sim \begin{bmatrix} 1 & 0 & 1 & | & 3 \\ 0 & 1 & 1 & | & 0 \\ 0 & 0 & 1 & | & 1 \end{bmatrix} \quad -R_3$$

$$\sim \begin{bmatrix} 1 & 0 & 0 & | & 2 \\ 0 & 1 & 0 & | & -1 \\ 0 & 0 & 1 & | & 1 \end{bmatrix} \begin{matrix} R_1 - R_3 \\ R_2 - R_3 \\ \end{matrix}$$

The augmented matrix is now in row-reduced echelon form. The corresponding system of equations is

$$\begin{cases} x & = 2 \\ \quad y & = -1 \\ \quad\quad z = 1 \end{cases}$$

Therefore $x = 2$, $y = -1$, and $z = 1$.

Example 5 Solve the following system of linear equations by reducing the corresponding augmented matrix to row-reduced echelon form.

$$\begin{cases} w - x + y - z = -4 \\ w + x + y + z = 0 \\ w - 3x + y - 3z = -8 \\ -w + x + y - z = 0 \end{cases}$$

Solution The corresponding augmented matrix is

$$\begin{bmatrix} 1 & -1 & 1 & -1 & | & -4 \\ 1 & 1 & 1 & 1 & | & 0 \\ 1 & -3 & 1 & -3 & | & -8 \\ -1 & 1 & 1 & -1 & | & 0 \end{bmatrix}$$

We now perform a sequence of row operations to reduce the augmented matrix to row-reduced echelon form.

$$\begin{bmatrix} 1 & -1 & 1 & -1 & | & -4 \\ 1 & 1 & 1 & 1 & | & 0 \\ 1 & -3 & 1 & -3 & | & -8 \\ -1 & 1 & 1 & -1 & | & 0 \end{bmatrix} \sim \begin{bmatrix} 1 & -1 & 1 & -1 & | & -4 \\ 0 & 2 & 0 & 2 & | & 4 \\ 0 & -2 & 0 & -2 & | & -4 \\ 0 & 0 & 2 & -2 & | & -4 \end{bmatrix} \begin{matrix} \\ R_2 - R_1 \\ R_3 - R_1 \\ R_4 + R_1 \end{matrix}$$

$$\sim \begin{bmatrix} 1 & -1 & 1 & -1 & | & -4 \\ 0 & 1 & 0 & 1 & | & 2 \\ 0 & -2 & 0 & -2 & | & -4 \\ 0 & 0 & 2 & -2 & | & -4 \end{bmatrix} \begin{array}{l} \\ \frac{1}{2}R_2 \\ \\ \\ \end{array}$$

$$\sim \begin{bmatrix} 1 & 0 & 1 & 0 & | & -2 \\ 0 & 1 & 0 & 1 & | & 2 \\ 0 & 0 & 0 & 0 & | & 0 \\ 0 & 0 & 2 & -2 & | & -4 \end{bmatrix} \begin{array}{l} R_1 + R_2 \\ \\ R_3 + 2R_2 \\ \\ \end{array}$$

$$\sim \begin{bmatrix} 1 & 0 & 1 & 0 & | & -2 \\ 0 & 1 & 0 & 1 & | & 2 \\ 0 & 0 & 2 & -2 & | & -4 \\ 0 & 0 & 0 & 0 & | & 0 \end{bmatrix} \begin{array}{l} \\ \\ R_4 \\ R_3 \end{array}$$

$$\sim \begin{bmatrix} 1 & 0 & 1 & 0 & | & -2 \\ 0 & 1 & 0 & 1 & | & 2 \\ 0 & 0 & 1 & -1 & | & -2 \\ 0 & 0 & 0 & 0 & | & 0 \end{bmatrix} \begin{array}{l} \\ \\ \frac{1}{2}R_3 \\ \end{array}$$

$$\sim \begin{bmatrix} 1 & 0 & 0 & 1 & | & 0 \\ 0 & 1 & 0 & 1 & | & 2 \\ 0 & 0 & 1 & -1 & | & -2 \\ 0 & 0 & 0 & 0 & | & 0 \end{bmatrix} \begin{array}{l} R_1 - R_3 \\ \\ \\ \end{array}$$

The matrix is now in row-reduced echelon form. The corresponding system of equations is

$$\begin{cases} w & + z = 0 \\ & x & + z = 2 \\ & & y - z = -2 \\ & & 0 = 0 \end{cases}$$

This is a dependent system of equations.

Let $z = k$. Substituting in the third equation, we get

$$y - k = -2$$

or $\qquad y = -2 + k$

Substituting in the second equation, we get

$$x + k = 2$$

or $\qquad x = 2 - k$

Substituting in the first equation, we get

$$w + k = 0$$

or $\qquad w = -k$

Therefore $w = -k$, $x = 2 - k$, $y = -2 + k$, and $z = k$.

EXERCISE 9.5

A **1.** State which of the following matrices are in row-reduced echelon form. For those that are not, give a reason.

(a) $\begin{bmatrix} 1 & 0 & | & -2 \\ 0 & 1 & | & 3 \end{bmatrix}$

(b) $\begin{bmatrix} 1 & 3 & 0 & | & 4 \\ 0 & 1 & 0 & | & -7 \\ 0 & 0 & 1 & | & 0 \end{bmatrix}$

(c) $\begin{bmatrix} 1 & -3 & | & 0 \\ 0 & 0 & | & 1 \\ 0 & 0 & | & 0 \end{bmatrix}$

(d) $\begin{bmatrix} 1 & 0 & 4 & | & 0 \\ 0 & 1 & 0 & | & 0 \\ 0 & 0 & 0 & | & 1 \\ 0 & 0 & 0 & | & 0 \end{bmatrix}$

(e) $\begin{bmatrix} 1 & 0 & 2 & | & 0 \\ 0 & 1 & 0 & | & -5 \\ 0 & 0 & 1 & | & 3 \end{bmatrix}$

(f) $\begin{bmatrix} 0 & 1 & -2 & | & 0 \\ 0 & 0 & 0 & | & 2 \end{bmatrix}$

2. Each of the following is the augmented matrix, in row-reduced echelon form, corresponding to a system of equations. In each case, identify the system as independent, dependent, or inconsistent. If the system is dependent, state how many parameters are needed to describe the solutions.

(a) $\begin{bmatrix} 1 & 0 & | & 5 \\ 0 & 1 & | & -3 \end{bmatrix}$

(b) $\begin{bmatrix} 1 & -4 & | & -6 \\ 0 & 0 & | & 1 \end{bmatrix}$

(c) $\begin{bmatrix} 1 & 2 & | & -4 \\ 0 & 0 & | & 0 \end{bmatrix}$

(d) $\begin{bmatrix} 1 & 0 & -1 & | & 2 \\ 0 & 1 & 5 & | & -6 \end{bmatrix}$

(e) $\begin{bmatrix} 1 & 0 & | & -2 \\ 0 & 1 & | & 3 \\ 0 & 0 & | & 0 \end{bmatrix}$

(f) $\begin{bmatrix} 1 & 0 & 2 & | & 5 \\ 0 & 1 & -9 & | & 3 \\ 0 & 0 & 0 & | & 0 \end{bmatrix}$

(g) $\begin{bmatrix} 1 & -2 & 0 & | & 2 \\ 0 & 0 & 1 & | & 2 \\ 0 & 0 & 0 & | & 0 \\ 0 & 0 & 0 & | & 0 \end{bmatrix}$

(h) $\begin{bmatrix} 1 & 5 & 0 & 2 & | & -3 \\ 0 & 0 & 1 & 4 & | & -1 \\ 0 & 0 & 0 & 0 & | & 0 \\ 0 & 0 & 0 & 0 & | & 0 \end{bmatrix}$

B **3.** Reduce each of the following matrices to row-reduced echelon form.

(a) $\begin{bmatrix} 3 & 4 & | & -5 \\ 1 & -2 & | & 3 \end{bmatrix}$

(b) $\begin{bmatrix} 5 & -2 & | & 1 \\ 2 & -1 & | & 4 \end{bmatrix}$

(c) $\begin{bmatrix} -1 & 2 & 1 & | & 2 \\ 1 & 3 & -2 & | & 1 \\ 2 & 1 & -1 & | & 2 \end{bmatrix}$

(d) $\begin{bmatrix} 2 & 1 & | & 3 \\ 1 & -2 & | & 1 \\ 1 & -4 & | & 3 \end{bmatrix}$

(e) $\begin{bmatrix} -1 & 1 & 0 & | & 2 \\ 2 & 3 & -4 & | & 1 \\ -1 & 6 & -4 & | & 7 \end{bmatrix}$

(f) $\begin{bmatrix} 1 & -1 & 1 & | & -1 \\ 2 & 1 & -1 & | & 2 \\ 1 & 2 & -2 & | & -1 \\ 2 & -2 & -2 & | & 0 \end{bmatrix}$

4. Solve each of the following systems of equations by reducing the corresponding augmented matrix to row-reduced echelon form.

(a) $\begin{cases} x + 3y = 1 \\ 5x + 6y = 8 \end{cases}$
(b) $\begin{cases} 5x + 7y = -4 \\ -x + 3y = 3 \end{cases}$

(c) $\begin{cases} -4x + 8y = -16 \\ x - 2y = 4 \end{cases}$
(d) $\begin{cases} 2x - 6y = -8 \\ -3x + 9y = 12 \end{cases}$

(e) $\begin{cases} -3x + 9y = 6 \\ x - 3y = 2 \end{cases}$

5. Solve each of the following systems of equations by reducing the corresponding augmented matrix to row-reduced echelon form.

(a) $\begin{cases} 4x - 2y - z = 12 \\ 3x - y = 9 \\ x + y + z = 5 \end{cases}$
(b) $\begin{cases} 2x + y + z = 2 \\ -x + 10y + 13z = -19 \\ 3x - 2y - 3z = 9 \end{cases}$

(c) $\begin{cases} x + y + z = 2 \\ x + 9y + 3z = 4 \\ 2x - 2y + z = 3 \end{cases}$
(d) $\begin{cases} 2x + y - z = 0 \\ x - 2y + 3z = 0 \\ 4x - 4y + z = 0 \end{cases}$

(e) $\begin{cases} 2x - y = 5 \\ x - 2y + z = 0 \\ 3y - 2z = 4 \end{cases}$
(f) $\begin{cases} 4x - 3y = 2 \\ 3x - y + 2z = 9 \\ 2y - z = -9 \end{cases}$

6. Solve each of the following by reducing the corresponding augmented matrix to row-reduced echelon form.

(a) $\begin{cases} 2w - x + y + 2z = 1 \\ w + 2x + y - z = 0 \\ w + x - z = 1 \\ 3w - x + y = 6 \end{cases}$
(b) $\begin{cases} w - 2x + y + z = -3 \\ 3w + x - y - z = 10 \\ x + y + z = -2 \\ w + x + y = 2 \end{cases}$

(c) $\begin{cases} 2w - x + z = 7 \\ 3x + y - z = -4 \\ 2w + 2x + y = 3 \\ 2w - 7x - 2y + 3z = 15 \end{cases}$

7. Solve each of the following systems by using matrices.

(a) $\begin{cases} 2x - y + 3z = 4 \\ 3x + y - z = 6 \end{cases}$
(b) $\begin{cases} 2w + x - y + z = 6 \\ w - x + y + z = 10 \end{cases}$

(c) $\begin{cases} -w + x - y + z = 0 \\ 2w + x + y = 0 \\ w + x - 2y + z = 0 \end{cases}$
(d) $\begin{cases} 2x + y = 5 \\ x - y = 4 \\ -x + 4y = -7 \\ -x - 5y = 2 \end{cases}$

(e) $\begin{cases} 3w - x + y - z = 10 \\ 2w + x + y - 2z = 15 \end{cases}$
(f) $\begin{cases} w + x + y + z = 5 \\ 2w - x + y - z = 7 \\ -w + 5x + y + 5z = 1 \end{cases}$

C **8.**   Solve each of the following by using matrices.

(a) $\begin{cases} 0.8x - 0.2y + 1.2z = -0.2 \\ 0.5x + 1.3y + 2.8z = 0.9 \\ 0.3x - 0.4y - 0.5z = -0.1 \end{cases}$

(b) $\begin{cases} 0.25x + 0.55y - 0.15z = -0.45 \\ 0.65x - 0.35y + 0.25z = 2.25 \\ -0.15x + 1.45y - 0.55z = -3.15 \end{cases}$

9.6   APPLICATIONS OF SYSTEMS OF EQUATIONS

The known and unknown quantities in a real-world problem may be related by a linear system of equations. If they are, and if we can determine their relationship, then the matrix methods of this chapter can be used to solve the equations. The solutions to the system must then be examined to determine their suitability to the problem. We give two examples of how this is done.

Example 1   In a national park there are two species of caribou that can be distinguished only by close inspection. The authorities have devised an ingenious method to determine the population of each species. It is known that species I reproduces at a rate of 10 percent a year and species II reproduces at a rate of 15 percent a year. An aerial survey by bush planes has shown a total adult population of 1184 and 147 new offspring. Show how the authorities use this information to determine the population of each species.

Solution   Let x be the number of adult species I caribou.
Let y be the number of adult species II caribou.
Since the total number of adult caribou is 1184,

$$x + y = 1184$$

Species I reproduces at a rate of 10 percent a year, so there are $0.10x$ new species I offspring. Similarly, species II reproduces at a rate of 15 percent a year, so there are $0.15y$ new species II offspring. Since the total number of offspring is 147,

$$0.10x + 0.15y = 147$$

We solve the following system of equations.

$$\begin{cases} x + y = 1184 \\ 0.10x + 0.15y = 147 \end{cases}$$

The corresponding augmented matrix is

$$\begin{bmatrix} 1 & 1 & | & 1184 \\ 0.10 & 0.15 & | & 147 \end{bmatrix}$$

We reduce this matrix to row-reduced echelon form.

$$\begin{bmatrix} 1 & 1 & | & 1184 \\ 0.10 & 0.15 & | & 147 \end{bmatrix} \sim \begin{bmatrix} 1 & 1 & | & 1184 \\ 0 & 0.05 & | & 28.6 \end{bmatrix} R_2 - 0.1R_1$$

$$\sim \begin{bmatrix} 1 & 1 & | & 1184 \\ 0 & 1 & | & 572 \end{bmatrix} 20R_2$$

$$\sim \begin{bmatrix} 1 & 0 & | & 612 \\ 0 & 1 & | & 572 \end{bmatrix} R_1 - R_2$$

The system of equations corresponding to this matrix is

$$\begin{cases} x = 612 \\ y = 572 \end{cases}$$

Therefore, there are 612 adult species I caribou and 572 adult species II caribou. There are 0.10(612) or approximately 61 species I offspring and 0.15(572) or approximately 86 species II offspring. In total, there are 673 species I and 658 species II caribou.   ⬧

Example 2   Peter Findley has just re-mortgaged his house and plans to invest in mutual funds the $100 000 he obtained. His broker has recommended three such funds to him. The prospective growth rate and dividend yield for each fund is given in the following chart.

	Mutual Fund		
	A	B	C
Performance			
Growth Rate	10%	12%	18%
Dividend	12%	11%	8%

(a) If Peter decides he wants his portfolio to have an average growth rate of 14 percent and an average dividend yield of 10 percent, how should he divide his money among the three mutual funds?

(b) Some of Peter's friends have invested in Fund C, so Peter decides to invest $40 000 of the $100 000 in this fund. How should the remainder of the money be invested in Fund A and Fund B so that he still meets the desired 14 percent growth rate and 10 percent dividend yield?

(c) What is the maximum amount of money Peter can invest in Fund C and still meet his desired 14 percent growth rate and 10 percent dividend yield?

Solution   (a) Let x be the amount of money in dollars Peter should invest in Fund A.
Let y be the amount of money in dollars Peter should invest in Fund B.
Let z be the amount of money in dollars Peter should invest in Fund C.

Since Peter has $100 000 to invest,

$$x + y + z = 100\ 000$$

Since Peter wants an average growth rate of 14 percent,

$$0.10x + 0.12y + 0.18z = 0.14(100\ 000)$$

or

$$0.10x + 0.12y + 0.18z = 14\ 000$$

Since Peter wants an average dividend yield of 10 percent,

$$0.12x + 0.11y + 0.08z = 0.10(100\ 000)$$

or

$$0.12x + 0.11y + 0.08z = 10\ 000$$

We solve the following system of equations.

$$\begin{cases} x + y + z = 100\ 000 \\ 0.10x + 0.12y + 0.18z = 14\ 000 \\ 0.12x + 0.11y + 0.08z = 10\ 000 \end{cases}$$

The augmented matrix corresponding to this system is

$$\begin{bmatrix} 1 & 1 & 1 & | & 100\ 000 \\ 0.10 & 0.12 & 0.18 & | & 14\ 000 \\ 0.12 & 0.11 & 0.08 & | & 10\ 000 \end{bmatrix}$$

We perform a series of row operations to reduce the augmented matrix.

$$\begin{bmatrix} 1 & 1 & 1 & | & 100\ 000 \\ 0.10 & 0.12 & 0.18 & | & 14\ 000 \\ 0.12 & 0.11 & 0.08 & | & 10\ 000 \end{bmatrix}$$

$$\sim \begin{bmatrix} 1 & 1 & 1 & | & 100\ 000 \\ 0 & 0.02 & 0.08 & | & 4\ 000 \\ 0 & -0.01 & -0.04 & | & -2\ 000 \end{bmatrix} \begin{matrix} \\ R_2 - 0.10R_1 \\ R_3 - 0.12R_1 \end{matrix}$$

$$\sim \begin{bmatrix} 1 & 1 & 1 & | & 100\ 000 \\ 0 & 1 & 4 & | & 200\ 000 \\ 0 & -0.01 & -0.04 & | & -2\ 000 \end{bmatrix} \begin{matrix} \\ 50R_2 \\ \ \end{matrix}$$

$$\sim \begin{bmatrix} 1 & 0 & -3 & | & -100\ 000 \\ 0 & 1 & 4 & | & 200\ 000 \\ 0 & 0 & 0 & | & 0 \end{bmatrix} \begin{matrix} R_1 - R_2 \\ \\ R_3 + 0.01R_2 \end{matrix}$$

The matrix is in row-reduced echelon form. The system of equations corresponding to it is

$$x\qquad - 3z = -100\ 000$$
$$y + 4z = 200\ 000$$
$$0 = 0$$

This is a dependent system. Let $z = k$.

Substituting in the second equation, we get

$$y + 4k = 200\ 000$$
or $\qquad y = 200\ 000 - 4k$

Substituting in the first equation, we get

$$x - 3k = -100\ 000$$
or $\qquad x = -100\ 000 + 3k$

Therefore, the solution is given by the parametric equations

$$x = -100\ 000 + 3k$$
$$y = 200\ 000 - 4k$$
$$z = k$$

Since x, y, and z represent the amounts of money invested, they cannot be negative.

$$-100\ 000 + 3k \geqslant 0 \quad \text{and} \quad 200\ 000 - 4k \geqslant 0 \quad \text{and} \quad k \geqslant 0$$

$$k \geqslant \tfrac{100\ 000}{3} \qquad\qquad\qquad k \leqslant 50\ 000$$

Therefore,

$$\tfrac{100\ 000}{3} \leqslant k \leqslant 50\ 000$$

(b) If Peter invests \$40 000 in Fund C, then $k = 40\ 000$. Substituting, we obtain

$$x = -100\ 000 + 3(40\ 000)$$
$$= 20\ 000$$
and
$$y = 200\ 000 - 4(40\ 000)$$
$$= 40\ 000$$

Therefore, Peter should invest \$20 000 in Fund A and \$40 000 in Fund B.

(c) Peter is investing k dollars in Fund C. Since $k \leqslant 50\ 000$, the maximum he can invest in Fund C is \$50 000.

PROBLEMS PLUS

Solve the following system of equations.
$$w + 2x + 3y + 4z = 8$$
$$3w + 9x + 7y + 5z = -8$$
$$5w + 7x + 9y + 3z = 8$$
$$4w + 3x + 2y + \ z = -8$$
[Hint: Look for patterns in the equations.]

EXERCISE 9.6

Use matrix methods in solving each of the following problems.

B **1.** Moi Lee has decided to invest $40 000 in mutual funds. Her broker has recommended three funds to her. The prospective growth rate and dividend yield for each fund is given in the chart below.

| | **Mutual Fund** | | |
	A	**B**	**C**
Performance			
Growth Rate	18%	12%	20%
Dividend	9%	12%	8%

(a) If Moi decides she wants her portfolio to have an average growth rate of 16 percent and an average dividend yield of 10 percent, how should she divide her money among the three mutual funds?

(b) Moi read a financial article concerning Fund B and has decided to invest half her money in that fund. Can she do this and still maintain her 16 percent growth rate and 10 percent dividend yield? If so, how would the other half of her money be split between Fund A and Fund C? If not, what is the maximum amount she can invest in Fund B and maintain her goals?

2. B. C. Logging, Ltd. has obtained the federal government's permission to cut the trees on 20 000 hectares of crown land (provided they replant 40 000 hectares of previously cut land with seedlings). Of the 20 000 hectares, one-quarter contains high quality redwood and the remainder is a mixture of lesser-grade woods. B. C. Logging supplies furniture manufacturers and construction companies with their needed lumber. The furniture manufacturers require 70 percent of their lumber to be of high quality; whereas, the lumber companies require only 10 percent of their lumber to be of high quality. Determine the number of hectares of land that will supply the furniture manufacturers and the construction companies so that all the lumber will be sold.

3. The cancer patients at Lakeview Hospital are to take part in the testing of three new experimental drugs. Each patient is to receive a daily dosage of exactly 12 units of drug A, 22 units of drug B, and 10 units of drug C. The hospital purchases two solutions. Solution 1 contains 2 units of drug A, 3 units of drug B, and 1 unit of drug C per 100 mL. Solution 2 contains 1 unit of drug A, 2 units of drug B, and 1 unit of drug C per 100 mL. Determine if there is a combination of the two solutions that will meet the required daily dosages of all three drugs. If so, find it.

4. Refer to Example 1 of this section. In the following year a similar survey was conducted and the adult population was found to number 936 with 125 new offspring. By determining the population of each species, what significant information can be deduced?

5. A dietician is trying to prescribe a well-balanced meal from three foods for people who wish to lose weight. Thirty grams of food I provides 3 units of iron, 1 unit of calcium, and 1 unit of carbohydrates. Thirty grams of food II provides 1 unit of iron, 3 units of calcium, and 1 unit of carbohydrates. Thirty grams of food III provides 2 units of iron, 1 unit of calcium, and 4 units of carbohydrates. If a well-balanced meal consists of 20 units of iron, 18 units of calcium, and 16 units of carbohydrates, determine the number of grams of each food that should go into the meal.

6. Four types of transport trucks are equipped to haul three different types of machines per load. The number of each machine that each truck can carry on one load is given in the following chart.

	Truck 1	Truck 2	Truck 3	Truck 4
Machine A	2	1	1	1
Machine B	1	1	2	1
Machine C	1	2	1	1

(a) Find the general solution to this question: how many trucks of each type should be sent to haul exactly 30 of each type of machine? (Assume that each truck is fully loaded.)

(b) If there are only ten Truck 4's available, find all the particular solutions that satisfy this condition.

(c) If there are only six Truck 3's available, find all the particular solutions that satisfy this condition.

7. A small manufacturing company employs three carpenters, seven electronic technicians, and one person to do the packing. The company is equipped to assemble three products: console televisions, portable televisions, and stereos. Each console television requires 4 h carpentry work, 8 h electrical work, and 1 h for packing. Each portable television requires 1 h carpentry work, 4 h electrical work, and $\frac{1}{2}$ h for packing. Each stereo requires 3 h carpentry work, 6 h electrical work, and 1 h for packing. If the company wishes to keep everybody working 40 h a week, how many of each product should they manufacture weekly?

9.7 REVIEW EXERCISE

1. Solve each of the following systems of equations by the method of elimination.

   (a) $\begin{cases} 3x - 9y = 10 \\ 4x + y = 7 \end{cases}$

   (b) $\begin{cases} 5x + 2y = 40 \\ -10x - 4y = -20 \end{cases}$

   (c) $\begin{cases} x + 2y - z = 0 \\ 2x - 3y + z = 11 \\ -2x + 4y - 3z = -11 \end{cases}$

   (d) $\begin{cases} 4x - y + 2z = 4 \\ 2x + 3y - z = -11 \\ 4x - 15y + 10z = 56 \end{cases}$

   (e) $\begin{cases} 2x + y = 1 \\ 2y + z = -1 \\ x + 2z = 3 \end{cases}$

   (f) $\begin{aligned} 2x - y &= -7 \\ x + y &= -2 \\ 5x - 7y &= -22 \end{aligned}$

   (g) $\begin{cases} w - 2x - 3y + z = -16 \\ 2w + 2x - y + 3z = -9 \\ -w + x - 3y + 2z = 14 \end{cases}$

   (h) $\begin{cases} w - x + 2y - 2z = 2 \\ -2w - x - y + 2z = -2 \\ 2w + x + y + 2z = 4 \\ w + 2x + 2y + z = 2 \end{cases}$

   (i) $\begin{cases} w + 2x = 5 \\ x + 2y = 8 \\ y + 2z = 11 \\ 2w + z = 6 \end{cases}$

   (j) $\begin{cases} w - 2x + 2y - z = 4 \\ 2w - x + y - z = 7 \end{cases}$

2. For each of the following matrices, perform the indicated row operations in succession.

   (a) $\begin{bmatrix} 2 & 1 & | & 4 \\ 3 & -3 & | & 7 \end{bmatrix}$

   (i) Subtract row 2 from row 1.

   (ii) Multiply row 1 by -1.

   (iii) Subtract three times row 1 from row 2.

   (vi) Multiply row 2 by $\dfrac{1}{9}$.

   (v) Add four times row 2 to row 1.

   (b) $\begin{bmatrix} 2 & -3 & 1 & | & -1 \\ -3 & 4 & -1 & | & 1 \\ 1 & -2 & 1 & | & 3 \end{bmatrix}$

   (i) Interchange row 1 and row 3.

   (ii) Add three times row 1 to row 2.

   (iii) Subtract two times row 1 from row 3.

(iv) Interchange row 2 and row 3.

  (v) Add two times row 2 to row 1.

(vi) Add two times row 2 to row 3.

(vii) Multiply row 3 by $-\frac{1}{4}$.

(viii) Add 11 times row 3 to row 1.

(xi) Add seven times row 3 to row 2.

3. State which of the following matrices are in echelon form. For those that are not, give a reason.

(a) $\begin{bmatrix} 1 & -6 & | & 5 \\ 0 & 1 & | & -9 \end{bmatrix}$
    (b) $\begin{bmatrix} 1 & 2 & | & 4 \\ 0 & 0 & | & 1 \end{bmatrix}$

(c) $\begin{bmatrix} 1 & 0 & | & 0 \\ 0 & 0 & | & 2 \\ 0 & 0 & | & 0 \end{bmatrix}$
    (d) $\begin{bmatrix} 0 & 1 & 3 & | & -5 \\ 0 & 0 & 1 & | & 7 \\ 0 & 0 & 1 & | & 0 \end{bmatrix}$

(e) $\begin{bmatrix} 1 & 2 & | & -9 \\ 0 & 1 & | & 4 \\ 0 & 0 & | & 0 \\ 0 & 0 & | & 1 \end{bmatrix}$
    (f) $\begin{bmatrix} 1 & 0 & 0 & 0 & | & 1 \\ 0 & 0 & 1 & 0 & | & 3 \\ 0 & 0 & 0 & 1 & | & 0 \\ 0 & 0 & 0 & 0 & | & 0 \end{bmatrix}$

4. For the matrices in Question 3, determine which are in row-reduced echelon form. For those that are not, give a reason why.

5. Use a sequence of row operations to reduce each of the following matrices to echelon form.

(a) $\begin{bmatrix} -2 & 5 & | & 2 \\ -1 & -4 & | & -6 \end{bmatrix}$
    (b) $\begin{bmatrix} 8 & -6 & | & 7 \\ -2 & 4 & | & 3 \end{bmatrix}$

(c) $\begin{bmatrix} 3 & 4 & 5 & 2 & | & 8 \\ 6 & 7 & 7 & 4 & | & 7 \\ 4 & 4 & 3 & 3 & | & 3 \end{bmatrix}$
    (d) $\begin{bmatrix} 3 & 1 & -1 & | & 5 \\ 4 & -5 & -2 & | & 7 \end{bmatrix}$

6. Use a sequence of row operations to reduce each of the following matrices to row-reduced echelon form.

(a) $\begin{bmatrix} 2 & -1 & | & 3 \\ -1 & 2 & | & 1 \\ 4 & 3 & | & -2 \end{bmatrix}$
    (b) $\begin{bmatrix} 2 & -2 & 0 & | & 2 \\ -4 & 2 & 4 & | & 5 \\ -2 & 3 & -5 & | & -6 \end{bmatrix}$

(c) $\begin{bmatrix} 3 & | & -4 \\ 4 & | & -1 \\ 1 & | & -3 \\ 2 & | & -6 \end{bmatrix}$
    (d) $\begin{bmatrix} 1 & 2 & 1 & | & 2 \\ 4 & -7 & -5 & | & 2 \\ 2 & -1 & -1 & | & 2 \\ 1 & -5 & -6 & | & 0 \end{bmatrix}$

7. Solve each of the following systems of equations by reducing the augmented matrix to echelon form.

(a) $\begin{cases} 2x - 3y = 5 \\ -x + 2y = 7 \end{cases}$
    (b) $\begin{cases} 2x - 6y = 8 \\ -3x + 9y = 12 \end{cases}$

(c) $\begin{cases} 2x - y + 2z = 2 \\ 3x + 2y + z = 0 \end{cases}$
    (d) $\begin{cases} 3x - 2y + 4z = 16 \\ x - 4y + z = 15 \\ x + 2y + 3z = -2 \end{cases}$

(e)
$$\begin{cases} x - 4y + 5z = -11 \\ 3x + y + z = 7 \\ 2x + 2y - z = 9 \end{cases}$$

(f)
$$\begin{cases} 6y - 5z = 1 \\ 2x - 2y + 3z = 3 \\ x + 2y - z = 2 \end{cases}$$

8. Solve each of the following systems of equations by reducing the corresponding augmented matrix to row-reduced echelon form.

(a)
$$\begin{cases} w - 2x - y + z = 4 \\ 2w + x + 2y - z = 5 \\ 3w + 2x - 3y + 2z = 25 \end{cases}$$

(b)
$$\begin{cases} 3w - x + y - 2z = 12 \\ w + x - 2y + z = 4 \end{cases}$$

(c)
$$\begin{cases} 2w + x - 2y + z = -2 \\ -w + 2x + y - z = -1 \\ w + x - y + z = -1 \\ -2w + 2x + y + 2z = -1 \end{cases}$$

(d)
$$\begin{cases} w + x + y = 1 \\ x + y + z = -1 \\ w + y + z = 1 \\ w - 2x + z = 2 \end{cases}$$

(e)
$$\begin{cases} 2x - 3y + z = 10 \\ x + y - z = -2 \\ -x + 2y - 2z = -10 \\ -2x + 2y + z = 4 \end{cases}$$

(f)
$$\begin{cases} -w + 2x - y + z = -5 \\ 2w - x + 2y + 2z = 17 \\ w + 4x + y + 7z = 19 \\ 4w + x + 4y + 8z = 41 \end{cases}$$

9. A chemist has been asked to create a 1500 mL solution that is 35 percent acid, by mixing two solutions together. One solution is 50 percent acid and the other is 10 percent acid. Determine the amounts of each solution that should be added to obtain the desired result.

10. The daily requirements of three vitamins are 18 units each. One hundred grams of Food I contains four units of vitamin A, eight units of vitamin B, and four units of vitamin C. One hundred grams of Food II contains three units of vitamin A, six units of vitamin B, and four units of vitamin C. One hundred grams of Food III contains one unit of vitamin A, two units of vitamin B, and six units of vitamin C. Determine the amounts of each food that must be eaten to meet exactly the daily requirements.

11. Carole Mason has decided to invest $50 000 in the stock market. Her broker has recommended three stocks that he thinks show future potential. The present growth rate and dividend yield for each stock are listed in the following table.

	Stock		
	A	**B**	**C**
Growth Rate	13%	7%	15%
Dividend	7%	10%	6%

(a) If Carole decides she wants her portfolio to have an average growth rate of 11 percent and an average dividend yield of 8 percent, determine how she should divide her money among the three stocks to reach this goal?

(b) If Carole decides to invest $20 000 in stock B, how should the remainder of her money be invested to maintain the average growth rate and dividend yield she wants?

9.8 CHAPTER 9 TEST

1. Solve the following system of equations by elimination.
$$\begin{cases} 2x - y + 3z = 1 \\ x + 2y - z = 3 \\ 3x + y - 2z = 16 \end{cases}$$

2. Perform the indicated row operations on the given matrix in succession.
$$\begin{bmatrix} 4 & 3 & 3 & | & -5 \\ 3 & 2 & -1 & | & 0 \\ -2 & -3 & 1 & | & 4 \end{bmatrix}$$
   (a) Subtract row 2 from row 1.
   (b) Subtract three times row 1 from row 2.
   (c) Add two times row 1 to row 3.
   (d) Multiply row 2 by -1.
   (e) Add row 2 to row 3.
   (f) Multiply row 3 by $\frac{1}{22}$.

3. Which of the following matrices are in echelon form? For those that are not, give a reason.
   (a) $\begin{bmatrix} 1 & -3 & 0 & | & 0 \\ 0 & 0 & 1 & | & 6 \\ 0 & 0 & 0 & | & 1 \end{bmatrix}$ (b) $\begin{bmatrix} 1 & 0 & | & 7 \\ 0 & 1 & | & 4 \\ 0 & 0 & | & 2 \\ 0 & 0 & | & 0 \end{bmatrix}$

4. Which of the following matrices are in row-reduced echelon form? For those that are not, give a reason.
   (a) $\begin{bmatrix} 0 & 1 & 0 & 0 & | & 0 \\ 0 & 0 & 0 & 1 & | & 0 \end{bmatrix}$ (b) $\begin{bmatrix} 1 & -1 & 2 & | & 0 \\ 0 & 0 & 0 & | & 1 \\ 0 & 0 & 0 & | & 1 \\ 0 & 0 & 0 & | & 0 \end{bmatrix}$

5. Use a series of row operations to reduce the following matrix to row-reduced echelon form.
$$\begin{bmatrix} 3 & -1 & | & 4 \\ -2 & 1 & | & 0 \\ 1 & -2 & | & 1 \\ 1 & -1 & | & 1 \end{bmatrix}$$

6. Solve each of the following systems of equations using matrices. If the system is dependent, find two particular solutions.
   (a) $\begin{cases} 2x - y - z = 4 \\ x + 2y - 3z = -3 \\ 4x - 7y + 3z = 18 \end{cases}$

   (b) $\begin{cases} 2x - 3y = 9 \\ 3x + y = 8 \\ -2x - 8y = 2 \end{cases}$

(c) $\begin{cases} w + x & = 0 \\ \quad\ x + y & = 0 \\ \qquad\quad y + z = 0 \\ w & \quad\ \ + z = 0 \end{cases}$

7. A chemist has two solutions on hand. The first is 90 percent acid and the second is 50 percent acid. How much of each solution should be mixed together to create a 5000 mL solution that is 65 percent acid.

8. Mario Marino is going to invest $60 000 in mutual funds. His broker has recommended three funds. The growth rate and dividend yield for each fund are listed in the chart below.

	Mutual Fund		
	A	**B**	**C**
Growth Rate	16%	18%	10%
Dividend	9%	8%	12%

(a) If Mario decides he wants his portfolio to have an average growth rate of 14 percent and an average dividend yield of 10 percent, how should he divide his money among the three funds?

(b) If Mario decides to put $25 000 in Fund C, how should the remainder of the money be invested so that he still meets the desired 14 percent growth rate and 10 percent dividend yield?

(c) What is the maximum amount of money Mario can invest in Fund C?

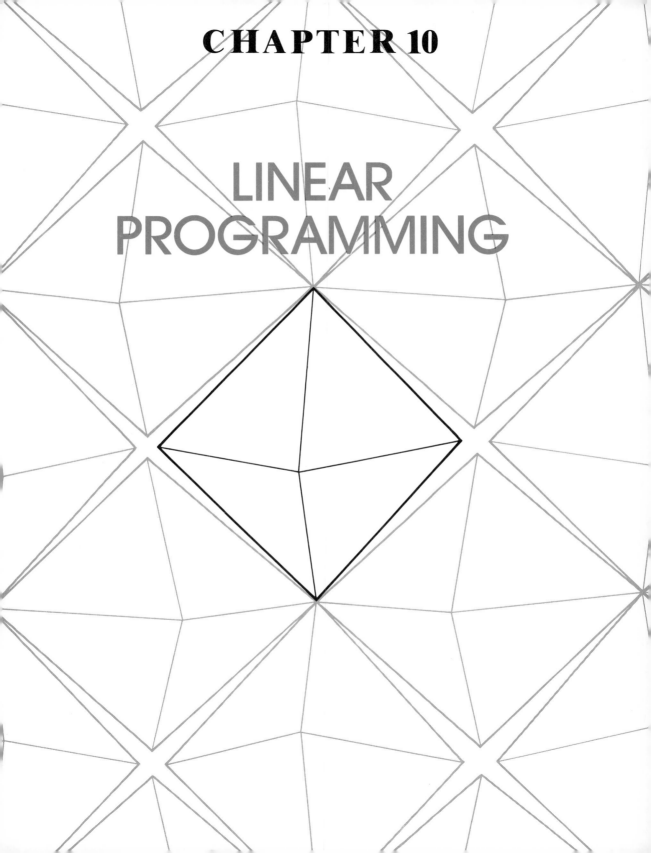

CHAPTER 10

LINEAR PROGRAMMING

REVIEW AND PREVIEW TO
CHAPTER 10

Graphing Linear Equations

The graph of a linear equation in the plane is a straight line. The graph of a straight line can be determined by finding any two points on the line. Usually the most convenient pair of points to use are found by determining the intercepts. Linear equations are often written in the slope-intercept form $y = mx + b$, and the y-intercept b can be read directly from the equation.

Example 1 Draw the graph of the linear equation $3x + 5y = 15$.

Solution To find the x-intercept, we substitute $y = 0$ into the equation.

$$3x + 5(0) = 15$$
$$x = 5$$

The x-intercept is 5.

Similarly, to find the y-intercept we substitute $x = 0$ into the equation.

$$3(0) + 5y = 15$$
$$y = 3$$

The y-intercept is 3.

The graph of the line follows.

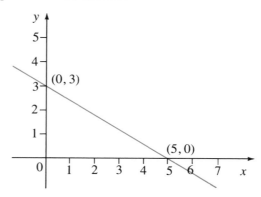

EXERCISE 1

1. Draw the graphs of the following linear equations.
    (a) $2x + 4y = 8$
    (b) $4x + 3y = 12$
    (c) $-2x + 3y = 9$

(d) $5x - 2y = 10$

(e) $y = 3x - 2$

(f) $y = \frac{3}{2}x + 6$

(g) $y = -2x + 11$

(h) $y = -0.3x + 2.1$

Graphing Inequalities

A linear inequality defines a region of the plane bounded by a straight line. To graph the region, we draw the *boundary line* (which is obtained by changing the inequality sign to an equality sign) and shade one side of the line. Whether to shade above or below a non-vertical line can be determined by the inequality sign, once the inequality has been expressed in the form $y < mx + b$ (*below*) or $y > mx + b$ (*above*). Boundary lines that are vertical have the equation form $x = k,\ k \in R$. The shading of the corresponding regions $x < k$ and $x > k$ are *left* and *right* of the boundary line, respectively.

If the boundary line is to be included in the region ($\leq$ or $\geq$) the graph of the boundary line is *solid*. If the boundary line is not included ($<$ or $>$) then the graph of the boundary line is *broken*.

Example 1 Graph the region defined by $3x - 4y < 12$.

Solution The boundary line is $3x - 4y = 12$, which has x-intercept 4 and y-intercept -3. The inequality sign is $<$ so the boundary line is dotted.

To determine the region to shade, rewrite in the form $y < mx + b$ or $y > mx + b$.

Dividing by a negative number changes the direction of the inequality sign.

$$3x - 4y < 12$$
$$-4y < 3x + 12$$
$$y > -\tfrac{3}{4}x - 3$$

The sign is $>$ so we shade above the boundary line.

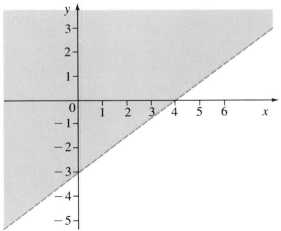

Example 2   Graph the intersection set of the regions defined by the following set of inequalities.

$$3x + 6y < 9$$
$$x \geqslant 0$$
$$y \geqslant 0$$

Solution   The boundary line for the region defined by $3x + 6y < 9$ is $3x + 6y = 9$ and its graph is dotted. The x-intercept is 3 and the y-intercept is $\frac{3}{2}$. To determine the region to shade we rewrite the inequality into the form $y < mx + b$ or $y > mx + b$.

$$3x + 6y < 9$$
$$6y < -3x + 9$$
$$y < -\tfrac{1}{2}x + \tfrac{3}{2}$$

The sign is $<$ so we shade below the boundary line.

The region $x \geqslant 0$ has a vertical boundary line $x = 0$ (which is the y-axis) and its graph is solid. The inequality sign is $\geqslant$ so we shade to the right of the boundary line.

The region $y \geqslant 0$ has the boundary line $y = 0$ (which is the x-axis) and its graph is solid. The inequality sign is $\geqslant$ so we shade above the boundary line.

The intersection set is the part of the plane where the three shaded regions overlap, as indicated in colour in the graph.

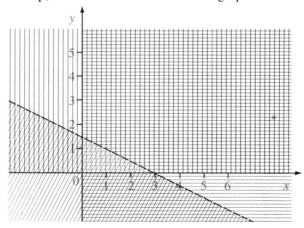

EXERCISE 2

1.   Graph the following regions.
   (a) $3x - y > 6$
   (b) $2x + 4y \leqslant 8$
   (c) $5x - 3y > 5$

(d) $0.2x + 0.6y < 0.9$
(e) $y \geqslant 3x - 2$
(f) $y < -2x + 5$
(g) $y \leqslant -x + \frac{3}{2}$

2. Graph the intersection set of the regions defined by the following sets of inequalities.

(a) $x + y \leqslant 6$
     $x + 2y \leqslant 8$
     $x \geqslant 0$
     $y \geqslant 0$

(b) $2x + 3y \leqslant 12$
     $3x + 2y \leqslant 12$
     $x \geqslant 0$
     $y \geqslant 0$

(c) $x + y \leqslant 9$
     $x + 2y \leqslant 15$
     $2x + y \leqslant 15$
     $x \geqslant 0$
     $y \geqslant 0$

Family of Lines

A linear equation of the form $ax + by = k$, where k is a parameter generates a family of lines. For example, the equation $x + y = k$, $k \in R$ represents the set of lines

$$x + y = -2$$
$$x + y = 1.1$$
$$x + y = \sqrt{2}$$

$x + y = 13$, and so on, where the value k can be any real number. The common characteristic of this family of lines is that each member has exactly the same slope.

$$x + y = k$$
$$y = -x + k \qquad \text{(of the form } y = mx + b)$$

For any value of k, the slope of the line $y = -x + k$ is -1. The graph of this family of lines is the set of parallel lines with slope -1.

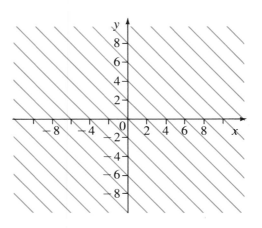

EXERCISE 3

1. Graph five members of the following families of lines.
   (a) $2x + 3y = k, k \in R$
   (b) $9x - y = k, k \in R$
   (c) $y = 3x + k, k \in R$
   (d) $y = -\dfrac{1}{2}x + \dfrac{k}{2}, k \in R$
   (e) $P = 3x + 2y, P \in R$

INTRODUCTION

When you shop for a stereo component, you usually consider price, features, specifications, design, and so forth. Once the decision to purchase has been made, you might not always choose the cheapest product or the one with the most features. The one that you choose is the product that best meets your requirements. We call a problem in which we need to determine a ''best'' solution an **optimization problem**.

Optimization problems are solved in business to maximize profits, and in transportation to minimize distance. In many other fields optimization problems must be solved. This form of decision-making has become so important that a branch of Mathematics called Optimization Theory has emerged to develop techniques to solve these problems.

Linear programming is a process for solving optimization problems.

10.1   LINEAR MODELS

In this section we practise translating described situations into their mathematical models. The techniques used to solve the problems are developed in Sections 2 through 5 of this chapter.

Example 1   A bicycle manufacturer makes two types of bicycles, racing and touring. The profit per bicycle is $50 and $35, respectively. The racing bicycles require two hours to assemble and 30 min for fine adjustment. The touring models can be assembled in one-and-a-half hours and 15 min are needed for adjustment. If there are 90 labour hours available for assembly and 20 labour hours for adjustment per week, how many of each type of bicycle should be produced to maximize profits?

Solution   We must maximize profit, so we construct a profit equation.
Let P be the profit in dollars.
Let r be the number of racing bicycles made per week.
Let t be the number of touring bicycles made per week.
Then,

$$P = 50r + 35t$$

The information pertaining to the labour hours leads to the following equations.
The total assembly time must be less than or equal to 90 h. Each racer requires 2 h and each touring bicycle is 1.5 h, so

$$2r + 1.5t \leq 90$$

The total adjustment time must be less than or equal to 20 h and each racer requires $\frac{1}{2}$ h and each touring bicycle $\frac{1}{4}$ h, so

$$\tfrac{1}{2}r + \tfrac{1}{4}t \leq 20$$

The number of bicycles of either type cannot be negative, so

$$r \geq 0$$
and $t \geq 0$

Our linear programming problem is to

Maximize: $P = 50r + 35t$

Subject to: $2r + 1.5t \leq 90$

$$\tfrac{1}{2}r + \tfrac{1}{4}t \leq 20$$

$$r \geq 0$$
and $t \geq 0$

This example illustrates the form that all linear programming problems will take. There is a function that must be optimized (either maximized or minimized) and this function is called the **objective function**. The variables upon which the objective function depend have restrictions and these are called **constraints**. So our bicycle example has become the following.

Maximize: $P = 50r + 35t$ (*objective function*)

Subject to: $2r + 1.5t \leq 90$

$$\tfrac{1}{2}r + \tfrac{1}{4}t \leq 20$$ (*constraints*)

$$r \geq 0$$
and $t \geq 0$

Our objective function, together with the constraints, is called a **linear model** (since the function and the inequalities in the model are linear). The standard form for linear models is to have all of the constraints (except for the non-negativity constraints) written with the variables on the left of a $\leq$ sign. Numerical examples of linear models in standard form follow.

(a) Maximize: $P = 12s + 8t$
Subject to: $3s + 2t \leq 101$
$$5s + \quad t \leq 93$$
$$s \geq 0$$
$$t \geq 0$$

(b) Minimize: $A = 40a + 45b + 50c$

Subject to:
$$a + b + c \leqslant 25$$
$$-a + 2c \leqslant 0$$
$$-a + b - c \leqslant 0$$
$$a \geqslant 0$$
$$b \geqslant 0$$
$$c \geqslant 0$$

Our strategy to translate described situations into linear models is to:

> 1. Identify the variable that is to be optimized. Look for key-words like maximum, minimum, maximize, minimize, the largest, the smallest, the least, the greatest, and so on.
> 2. Define the variables upon which the objective function is dependent.
> 3. Construct the constraints in terms of the defined variables.

Example 2   A financial speculator wants to get the highest return for her investments. She estimates that investing in real estate yields a 13 percent annual return on the investment, and the stock market a 17 percent return. She has been advised to invest at least as much in real estate as in stocks. If she has $20 000 to invest, how should she invest it?

Solution   We are asked to maximize the return (objective function).
Let R be the investment return in dollars.
Let r be the amount invested in real estate, in dollars.
Let s be the amount invested in stocks, in dollars.

Then, $R = 0.13r + 0.17s$

There is to be at least as much invested in real estate as in stocks, so,

$$r \geqslant s$$
$$s - r \leqslant 0 \qquad \text{(constraint–standard form)}$$

The total investment can be, at most, $20 000, so

$$r + s \leqslant 20\ 000 \qquad \text{(constraint)}$$

Investment amounts cannot be negative, so

$$r \geqslant 0$$
$$s \geqslant 0$$

Our linear model is:

Maximize: $R = 0.13r + 0.17s$

Subject to: $-r + s \leqslant 0$
$$r + s \leqslant 20\ 000$$
$$r \geqslant 0$$
$$s \geqslant 0$$

Example 3   A Niagara region grape farmer has 100 hectares in which to plant Concord, Riesling, or Chardonnay grape vines. Each hectare of Concord grapes yields 12 t of grapes. Riesling yields 15 t per hectare and Chardonnay yields 20 t per hectare. The labour required to tie and prune the vines averages 50, 60, and 70 respectively. The profits per hectare are $360, $900, and $1300, respectively. Given that the farmer has a quota that limits total production at 2000 t of grapes, and there are 10 000 labour hours available, how many hectares of each grape should be planted to make the most profit?

Solution   We must maximize profit (objective function).
Let P be the profit.
Let c be the number of hectares of Concord grapes.
Let r be the number of hectares of Riesling grapes.
Let y be the number of hectares of Chardonnay grapes.

Then, $P = 360c + 900r + 1300y$

The tonnage quota leads to a constraint.

$$12c + 15r + 20y \leqslant 2000$$

The labour hours available lead to another constraint.

$$50c + 60r + 70y \leqslant 10\ 000$$

The number of hectares per variety cannot be negative, so

$$c \geqslant 0$$
$$r \geqslant 0$$
$$y \geqslant 0$$

Our linear model is

Maximize: $P = 360c + 900r + 1300y$
Subject to: $12c + 15r + 20y \leqslant 2000$
$$50c + 60r + 70y \leqslant 10\ 000$$
$$c \geqslant 0$$
$$r \geqslant 0$$
$$y \geqslant 0$$

EXERCISE 10.1

A **1.** Let s be the number of squash balls manufactured and let t be the number of tennis balls manufactured by a company. Translate the following sentences into linear constraints in terms of s and t.
   (a)   The total number of balls is less than 500.
   (b)   There are more squash balls produced than tennis balls.
   (c)   There are fewer tennis balls produced than squash balls.
   (d)   There are at least twice as many squash balls produced as tennis balls.
   (e)   The cost of each squash ball is $0.75 and the cost of a tin of three tennis balls is $2.95, and the total cost cannot exceed $100.00.

2.   Introduce the necessary variables and translate the following sentences into objective functions.
   (a)   A vegetable retailer wishes to maximize her profits in the sale of corn and beets in which she makes a profit of $0.50 per dozen and $0.35 per bunch, respectively.
   (b)   If a publisher makes $0.75 profit per paperback copy of a novel and $2.25 per textbook, what number of each should be produced to reap the greatest returns?
   (c)   If a farmer makes $300 profit per hectare of apples and $250 profit per hectare of peaches, how many hectares of each fruit should he plant to make the most money?
   (d)   A journalist receives $250 for a short article and $400 for a long article. How many of each should she write to receive the greatest amount of money for her writing?
   (e)   Travelling by bus costs approximately $10 per 100 km, and by train, $15 per 100 km. What distance should be travelled by each mode of transportation if the total cost is to be minimum?

B   Translate the following situations into linear models. Do not attempt to solve them.

3.   A factory makes baseball bats and hockey sticks. A bat takes ten minutes of machining and five minutes of a craftsman's time, while a hockey stick requires 15 min of machining and three minutes of a craftsman's time. There are, at most, ten hours of machine time available per day and four hours of a craftsman's time. The profits on the bats and the sticks are $1.20 and $1.75, respectively. Determine the maximum profit that the factory can make in a day.

4. Dawson Forge intends to buy two types of machines: punches and shears. The specific requirements of each machine are detailed in the following table.

	Shop Floor Space (m²)	Labour Needed per Machine (Workers)	Output per Week (units)
Punches	400	8	250
Shears	500	4	175

The forge has 4000 m² of floor space available and 44 skilled workers to work the machines. How many machines of each type should be purchased to achieve maximum output?

5. Research has been extensive in energy conservation. It has been estimated that the annual cost of heating a building is $2.25 for every square metre of window and $0.50 for every square metre of wall or roof. A building code requires that the area of the windows must be at least one-sixth the area of the walls and roof. If annual heating costs are not to exceed $900, what is the largest surface area a building can have?

6. A farmer intends to use a 20 hectare field to plant potatoes and corn. The labour per hectare is three working days and two working days, respectively. The profits per hectare are $175 and $140, respectively. If there are only 42 working days available, how many hectares of each vegetable should be planted to give the greatest profit?

7. A promoter measures the "marketing success" of a concert by using an index number that he devised. The number is a weighted sum of the number of old songs and the number of new songs sung during the concert. The old songs are weighted with a three and the new with a seven. A performer sings, at most, 30 songs during a concert and intends to sing at least as many old songs as new. How many of each should be sung to maximize the "marketing success" of the performance?

8. A law firm offers three services: tax planning, real estate transactions, and preparing wills. The time required for each task and the average fee per client are summarized in the following table.

	Initial Consulting (hours)	Research (hours)	Document Preparation (hours)	Fee (dollars)
Tax Planning	3	2	1	500
Real Estate	$\frac{1}{2}$	8	2	900
Wills	2	1	4	150

The tasks are divided among the partners of the firm and the total available time per week for consulting, research, and document preparation are 22 h, 30 h, and 26 h, respectively. How many clients for each service would be optimal (bring the most money into the firm)?

C **9.** Given the general linear model:

Maximize: $f = a_1x_1 + a_2x_2 + \ldots + a_nx_n$ (objective function)

Subject to: $a_{11}x_1 + a_{12}x_2 + \ldots + a_{1n}x_n \leqslant c_1$

$$\vdots \qquad\qquad\qquad\qquad \vdots \quad \text{(constraints)}$$

$$a_{m1}x_1 + a_{m2}x_2 + \ldots + a_{mn}x_n \leqslant c_m$$

and $x_1, x_2, \ldots, x_n \geqslant 0$

Rewrite this general model by using sigma notation.

10. An engineering manufacturer has a limited capacity for welding, for machining, and for storing finished products, and also a limited sales force. The manufacturer makes six products, each of which uses different proportions of these limited resources. The manager will have to decide what amounts of each product to make to achieve as large a profit as possible. The relevant information is contained in the following table.

	Hours Welding	Hours Machining	Hours Selling	m³ Storing	Dollars Profit
Product 1	5	3	2	0.22	12
Product 2	3	6	5	0.07	9
Product 3	8	1	3	0.15	15
Product 4	2	2	4	0.04	9
Product 5	6	5	1	0.11	12
Product 6	6	0	4	0.22	18
Approximate Total Daily Capacity	120	70	80	3.70	

Determine the linear model that could be used to help the manager make his or her decision.

10.2   GRAPHICAL SOLUTIONS

We now develop techniques to solve the linear programming problems for the optimum solution.

As long as our constraints are expressed in *only two variables*, we can graph each constraint on a set of axes. In this section we will consider only those linear models that have two variables in the constraints.

Example 1   We return to the bicycle model problem of Section 10.1, Example 1, in which we want to determine the number of racing and touring bicycles to build to maximize profits. The linear model is:

Maximize: $P = 50r + 35t$
Subject to: $2r + 1.5t \leqslant 90$
$$\tfrac{1}{2}r + \tfrac{1}{4}t \leqslant 20$$
$$r \geqslant 0$$
$$t \geqslant 0$$

Solution   Let us graph the constraints.
The first constraint is $2r + 1.5t \leqslant 90$.
Rewrite the equation in the slope-intercept form $y = mx + b$.

$$2r + \tfrac{3}{2}t \leqslant 90$$

$$\tfrac{3}{2}t \leqslant -2r + 90$$

$$t \leqslant -\tfrac{4}{3}r + 60$$

The graph of this region would be below ($\leqslant$) the boundary line $t = -\tfrac{4}{3}r + 60$. The graph of the boundary line $t = -\tfrac{4}{3}r + 60$ has t-intercept 60 and we find the r-intercept to be 45 (substitute $t = 0$ into the equation). The graph of the region defined by the first constraint follows.

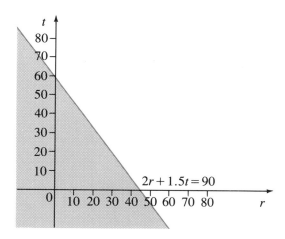

Now we graph the second constraint, $\tfrac{1}{2}r + \tfrac{1}{4}t \leqslant 20$.

$$\tfrac{1}{2}r + \tfrac{1}{4}t \leqslant 20$$

$$\tfrac{1}{4}t \leqslant -\tfrac{1}{2}r + 20$$

$$t \leqslant -2r + 80$$

So the region is below ($\leqslant$) the boundary line $t = -2r + 80$.
The boundary line has t-intercept 80, and r-intercept 40.

The graph follows.

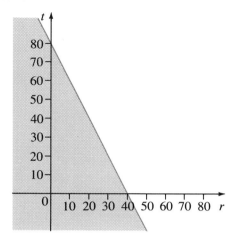

The two constraints $r \geqslant 0$ and $t \geqslant 0$ combine to restrict us to the first quadrant.

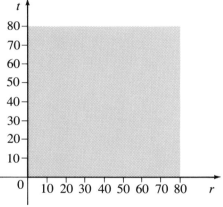

Since all of these constraints must be satisfied, the region of interest will be the intersection of all four regions. That region is now graphed.

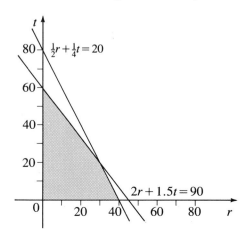

This shaded region represents all of the possible combinations of the variables r and t that will satisfy the given constraints. This set of all possible solutions to the constraints of the linear model is called **the feasible region**.

It is our task now to determine which one of these points in the feasible region maximizes the objective function,

$$P = 50r + 35t$$

We notice that the objective function is in the form of a linear equation describing a "family of lines", that is, of the form $ax + by = k$ where $k \in R$. A family of lines of this form is a family of parallel lines. The slope of the parallel lines in our objective function's family of lines can be found.

$$P = 50r + 35t$$
$$-50r + P = 35t$$
$$t = -\tfrac{10}{7}r + \tfrac{1}{35}P \qquad \text{(of the form } y = mx + b\text{)}$$

So the slope of the objective function's family of lines is $-\tfrac{10}{7}$. Let us superimpose this family of lines on the feasible region.

Slope of the objective function is $-\tfrac{10}{7}$.

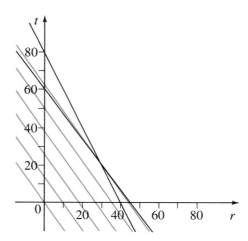

As we move further from the origin along this family of lines, the t-intercept increases. From the equation in which we found the slope of the family of lines,

$$t = -\tfrac{10}{7}r + \tfrac{1}{35}P$$

we see that the t-intercept is $\tfrac{P}{35}$. So as the t-intercept increases, $\tfrac{P}{35}$ and hence P increases. This suggests that to find the point that maximizes P we look for the point in the feasible region and on the objective function's family of lines that is *farthest away from the origin*. In our example this occurs at the intersection point of the constraint lines $2r + 1.5t = 90$ and $\frac{1}{2}r + \frac{1}{4}t = 20$. We solve for this point.

$$2r + 1.5t = 90 \qquad ①$$
$$\tfrac{1}{2}r + \tfrac{1}{4}t = 20 \qquad ②$$

$① - 4 \times ②$ gives: $\qquad 0.5t = 10$
$$t = 20$$

Substitute into $①$: $\quad 2r + 1.5(20) = 90$
$$2r = 60$$
$$r = 30$$

The maximum value of P occurs when $r = 30$ and $t = 20$ and this maximum value is

$$P = 50r + 35t$$
$$= 50(30) + 35(20)$$
$$= 2200$$

The manufacturer should make 30 racing model bicycles and 20 touring model bicycles to get a maximum profit of $2200.

The corners of the feasible region are called **corner points**. It can be proved (as Example 1 suggests) that the following is true.

> An optimal solution to a linear programming problem always occurs at a corner point.

The corner points are formed by the intersection of two constraint lines. From now on, we determine the corner points and decide which point gives the optimal solution upon substitution into the objective function.

To summarize, the optimal solution of a linear model may be determined by following these steps:

> 1. Draw the feasible region determined by the constraints.
> 2. Determine the coordinates of the corner points algebraically.
> 3. Calculate the value of the objective function at each corner point and select the maximum value and the points that give that maximum.

Let us illustrate these steps by solving Example 1 a second time.

Alternative Solution to
Example 1   We graph the feasible region dictated by the constraints:

$$2r + 1.5t \leqslant 90$$
$$\tfrac{1}{2}r + \tfrac{1}{4}t \leqslant 20$$
$$r \geqslant 0$$
$$t \geqslant 0$$

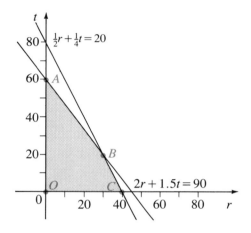

The corner points are labelled O, A, B, C.

The corner points O, A, and C are found by inspection.

The corner point B is the intersection point of the two constraint lines $2r + 1.5t = 90$ and $\tfrac{1}{2}r + \tfrac{1}{4}t = 20$. Solving the system of equations, we found B to be $(30, 20)$.

We evaluate the objective function at each corner point.

Corner Point	(r, t)	$P = 50r + 35t$	
O	$(0, 0)$	$P = 50(0) + 35(0)$	$= 0$
A	$(0, 60)$	$P = 50(0) + 35(60)$	$= 2100$
B	$(30, 20)$	$P = 50(30) + 35(20)$	$= 2200$
C	$(40, 0)$	$P = 50(40) + 35(0)$	$= 2000$

We conclude that the corner point B, that is, when $r = 30$ and $t = 20$, gives the maximum value for P, which is \$2200. The manufacturer's optimal production quantities for the two bicycle models are 30 racing models and 20 touring models.

The following example illustrates a situation in which the feasible region is more complex.

Example 2   Determine the optimal solution of the linear model:

$$\text{Maximize: } Z = 5x + 6y$$
$$\text{Subject to: } x + y \leqslant 9$$
$$x + 2y \leqslant 15$$
$$2x + y \leqslant 15$$
$$x \geqslant 0$$
$$y \geqslant 0$$

Solution   We determine the feasible region dictated by the constraints.

The region defined by $x + y \leqslant 9$ is the region below the line $y = -x + 9$ which has x-intercept 9 and y-intercept 9. The region defined by $x + 2y \leqslant 15$ is the region below the line $y = -\frac{1}{2}x + \frac{15}{2}$, which has y-intercept $\frac{15}{2}$, and x-intercept 15. The region defined by $2x + y \leqslant 15$ is the region below the line $y = -2x + 15$, which has y-intercept 15 and x-intercept $\frac{15}{2}$. The constraints $x \geqslant 0$ and $y \geqslant 0$ restrict us to the first quadrant. The feasible region is now graphed.

Slope of the objective function is $-\dfrac{5}{6}$.

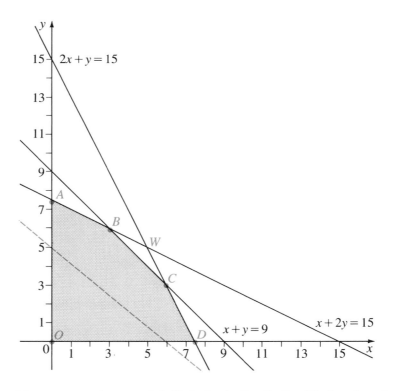

The corner points are labelled O, A, B, C, D. (Notice that the intersection point of two of the constraint lines, labelled W, is not a corner point.) By inspection, the points O, A, and D are $(0,0)$,

$\left(0, \frac{15}{2}\right)$ and $\left(\frac{15}{2}, 0\right)$, respectively. The corner point B is the intersection point of the two constraint lines $x + y = 9$ and $x + 2y = 15$. We solve for B.

$$x + y = 9 \qquad \text{①}$$
$$x + 2y = 15 \qquad \text{②}$$

$$\text{② } - \text{①:} \qquad y = 6$$
Substitute into ①: $\quad x + (6) = 9$
$$x = 3$$

The point B is $(3, 6)$.

Similarly, the corner point C is the intersection point of the constraint lines $x + y = 9$ and $2x + y = 15$. The point C is $(6, 3)$.

We now evaluate the objective function at the corner points.

Corner Point	(x, y)	$Z = 5x + 6y$	
O	$(0, 0)$	$Z = 5(0) + 6(0)$	$= 0$
A	$\left(0, \frac{15}{2}\right)$	$Z = 5(0) + 6\left(\frac{15}{2}\right)$	$= 45$
B	$(3, 6)$	$Z = 5(3) + 6(6)$	$= 51$
C	$(6, 3)$	$Z = 5(6) + 6(3)$	$= 48$
D	$\left(\frac{15}{2}, 0\right)$	$Z = 5\left(\frac{15}{2}\right) + 6(0)$	$= 37.5$

Z attains a maximum value of 51 when $x = 3$ and $y = 6$. This is the optimal solution to the linear model. ◇

When solving a *minimization problem*, we look for the corner point that gives the *minimum value* to the objective function. The next example illustrates this point.

Example 3   Determine the optimal solution of the linear model:

$$\text{Minimize:} \quad N = 5x + 6y$$
$$\text{Subject to:} \quad x + 2y \geqslant 6$$
$$2x + y \geqslant 5$$
$$2x + 3y \geqslant 10$$
$$x \geqslant 0$$
$$y \geqslant 0$$

Solution   We determine the feasible region dictated by the constraints.

The region defined by $x + 2y \geqslant 6$ is the region above the line $y = -\frac{1}{2}x + 3$ which has x-intercept 6 and y-intercept 3. The region defined by $2x + y \geqslant 5$ is the region above the line $y = -2x + 5$, which has x-intercept $\frac{5}{2}$ and y-intercept 5. The region defined by $2x + 3y \geqslant 10$ is the region above the line $y = -\frac{2}{3}x + \frac{10}{3}$, which has x-intercept 5 and y-intercept $\frac{10}{3}$. The constraints $x \geqslant 0$ and $y \geqslant 0$ restrict us to the first quadrant. The feasible region is now graphed.

Slope of the objective function is $-\frac{5}{6}$.

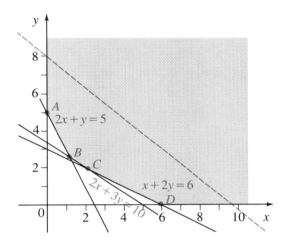

The corner points are labelled A, B, C, and D. By inspection, points A and D are $(0, 5)$ and $(6, 0)$, respectively. The corner point B is the intersection point of the two constraint lines $2x + y = 5$ and $2x + 3y = 10$. Solving the system

$$\left.\begin{array}{r} 2x + y = 5 \\ 2x + 3y = 10 \end{array}\right\}$$

we find the point B to be $(1.25, 2.5)$. Similarly, the corner point C is the intersection point of the constraint lines $2x + 3y = 10$ and $x + 2y = 6$. The point C is $(2, 2)$.

We now evaluate the objective function at the corner points.

Corner Point	(x, y)	$N = 5x + 6y$	
A	$(0, 5)$	$N = 5(0) + 6(5)$	$= 30$
B	$(1.25, 2.5)$	$N = 5(1.25) + 6(2.5)$	$= 21.25$
C	$(2, 2)$	$N = 5(2) + 6(2)$	$= 22$
D	$(6, 0)$	$N = 5(6) + 6(0)$	$= 30$

N attains a minimum value of 21.25 when $x = 1.25$ and $y = 2.5$. This is the optimal solution to the linear model.

EXERCISE 10.2

A **1.** Each of the following graphs represents the feasible region of a linear model. The line indicated in red is a member of the objective function's family of lines.

    (a) Use a straight edge to aid you in deciding which corner point yields the maximum solution to the objective function.

(i)

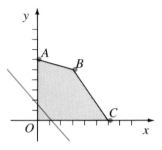

(ii)

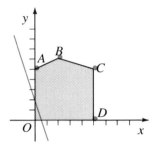

(iii)

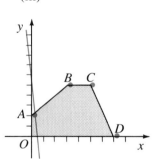

(iv)

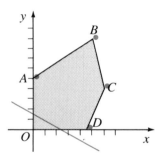

    (b) Use a straight edge to aid you in deciding which corner point yields the minimum solution to the objective function.

(i)

(ii)

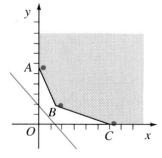

B **2.** (a) Given the following feasible regions and their corner points,
determine the corner point that maximizes the indicated
objective function.

(i)   Maximize: $T = 3s + 4t$ (ii) Maximize:
$$Z = 0.3w + 1.2v$$

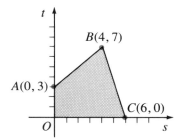

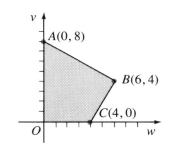

(iii) Maximize:
$$N = 35x + 17y$$

(iv) Maximize:
$$P = 1.25r + 1.79s$$

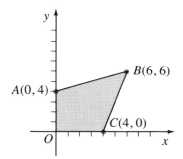

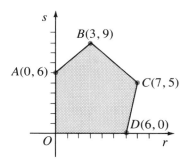

(b) Given the following feasible regions and their corner points,
determine the corner point that minimizes the indicated
objective function.

(i)   Minimize:
$$B = 1.3a + 2.1b$$

(ii) Minimize:
$$Z = 0.3f + 1.2g$$

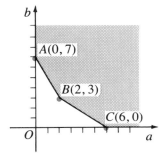

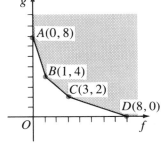

3. Determine the optimal solutions of the following linear models.

(a) Maximize: $K = 3m + 2n$
Subject to: $m + n \leqslant 3$
$m + 2n \leqslant 4$
$m \geqslant 0$
$n \geqslant 0$

(b) Maximize: $R = 3h + 4k$
Subject to: $2h + 3k \leqslant 6$
$6h + 4k \leqslant 12$
$h \geqslant 0$
$k \geqslant 0$

(c) Minimize: $R = 3s + 3t$
Subject to: $5s + 3t \geqslant 27$
$s + 3t \geqslant 15$
$s \geqslant 0$
$t \geqslant 0$

(d) Maximize: $M = 3u + v$
Subject to: $u + 2v \leqslant 7$
$4u + 2v \leqslant 10$
$2u + 3v \leqslant 12$
$u \geqslant 0$
$v \geqslant 0$

(e) Maximize: $N = 4w + 4z$
Subject to: $3w + 8z \leqslant 24$
$4w + 5z \leqslant 20$
$6w + 4z \leqslant 24$
$w \geqslant 0$
$z \geqslant 0$

(f) Minimize: $W = 2x + 5y$
Subject to: $3x + 2y \geqslant 16$
$x + y \geqslant 7$
$x + 5y \geqslant 15$
$x \geqslant 0$
$y \geqslant 0$

(g) Maximize: $V = 12p + 3q$
Subject to: $p + 4q \leqslant 26$
$p + 2q \leqslant 14$
$p + q \leqslant 11$
$p \geqslant 0$
$q \geqslant 0$

(h) Maximize: $P = 16r + 20s$
Subject to: $r - 3s \leqslant 15$
$r + 3s \leqslant 21$
$r + s \leqslant 11$
$r \geqslant 0$
$s \geqslant 0$

C 4. Given a feasible region similar to the one in the diagram with line l_1 having slope m_1, and line l_2 having slope m_2, what is the necessary condition on the slope of the objective function if
(a) the corner point A is the optimal solution?
(b) the corner point B is the optimal solution?
(c) the corner point C is the optimal solution?

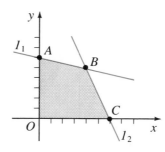

10.3 LINEAR PROGRAMMING PROBLEMS

We now put together the ideas of the two previous sections to solve a linear programming problem. In Section 10.1 we translated a described problem into a linear model. In Section 10.2 we learned a graphical technique of solving linear models. We now solve the problems in their entirety by first translating the problem into its linear model and then solving for the optimal solution by using the graphical technique.

Example 1 A manufacturer is developing a new fishing rod made from carbon and boron fibres. The strength of the rod is measured by an index number that is a weighted sum of the amounts of each material, with carbon having a weighting coefficient of 3.2 and boron a weighting of 3.6. The cost of materials for the rod must not exceed $20.00 and the costs per gram are $0.35 and $0.45 for carbon and boron fibres, respectively. The mass of the rod should not exceed 50 g. Determine the composition of the rod that gives it the greatest strength.

Solution We must maximize strength, so we construct a strength equation as the objective function.
Let S be the strength index of the rod.
Let c be the amount of carbon (in grams) in the rod.
Let b be the amount of boron (in grams) in the rod.
Then,

$$S = 3.2c + 3.6b$$

The cost (in cents) of the rod leads to one constraint.

$$35c + 45b \leqslant 2000$$

The mass (in grams) leads to another constraint.

$$c + b \leqslant 50$$

The rod is to be made of these two materials, so

$$c \geqslant 0$$
$$b \geqslant 0$$

Our linear model is

Maximize: $S = 3.2c + 3.6b$
Subject to: $35c + 45b \leqslant 2000$
$c + b \leqslant 50$
$c \geqslant 0$
$b \geqslant 0$

Because there are *only two variables* in the constraints, we can solve this linear model by using the graphical method. We need to graph the feasible region. The region defined by the constraint line $35c + 45b \leq 2000$ is below the boundary line $b = -\frac{7}{9}c + \frac{400}{9}$, which has b-intercept $\frac{400}{9}$ and c-intercept $\frac{400}{7}$.

The region defined by the constraint $c + b \leq 50$ is below the constraint line $b = -c + 50$, which has b-intercept 50 and c-intercept 50. The constraints $c \geq 0$ and $b \geq 0$ restrict us to the first quadrant.

The feasible region is graphed.

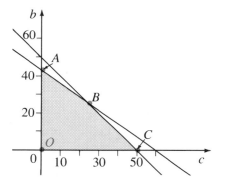

The corner points of the feasible region are labelled O, A, B, C. By inspection, we see that O is $(0, 0)$, A is $(0, \frac{400}{9})$, and C is $(50, 0)$. The corner point B is the intersection point of the two constraint lines.

$$35c + 45b = 2000$$
$$c + b = 50$$

Solving this system gives the ordered pair $(25, 25)$.

We evaluate the objective function at each corner point.

Corner Point	(c, b)	$S = 3.2c + 3.6b$
O	$(0, 0)$	0
A	$\left(0, \frac{400}{9}\right)$	160
B	$(25, 25)$	170
C	$(50, 0)$	160

We note that the maximum value of S is 170 and it occurs when $c = 25$ and $b = 25$. We conclude that the optimal composition of the rod is 25 g of carbon ($c = 25$) and 25 g of boron ($b = 25$), which will give the rod the greatest strength with an index value of 170.

EXERCISE 10.3

B   Determine the optimal solution for each of the following linear
       programming problems.

1. A financial speculator wants to get the highest return for her
    investments. She estimates that investing in real estate yields a 13
    percent annual return on the investment, and the stock market a 17
    percent return. She has been advised to invest at least as much in
    real estate as in stocks. If she has $20 000 to invest, how should she
    invest it?

2. A food processing company develops two products, Nutrifood and
    Omnidiet, and claims that the foods are sufficient for a nutritional
    diet. The daily nutritional requirements of a person are 2 units of
    carbohydrates, 1.3 units of proteins, and 1.1 units of fats. Each
    kilogram of Nutrifood contains 10, 6, and 10 units of carbohydrates,
    proteins, and fats, respectively; each kilogram of Omnidiet contains
    4, 4, and 2 units of carbohydrates, proteins, and fats, respectively.
    The cost per kilogram of Nutrifood and Omnidiet is $4.00 and
    $2.10, respectively. How many kilograms of each should a person
    purchase per month (assume 30 days) to minimize costs while
    meeting the minimum nutritional requirements?

3. A factory makes baseball bats and hockey sticks. A bat takes 10 min
    of machining and 5 min of a craftsman's time, while a hockey stick
    requires 15 min of machining and 3 min of a craftsman's time. There
    are no more than ten hours of machine time available per day and
    four hours of a craftsman's time. The profits on the bats and the
    sticks are $1.20 and $1.75, respectively. Determine the maximum
    profit that the factory can make in a day.

4. Dawson Forge intends to buy two types of machines: punches and
    shears. The specific requirements of each machine are detailed in the
    following table.

	Shop Floor Space (m²)	Labour Needed Per Machine (Workers)	Output per Week (units)
Punches	400	8	250
Shears	500	4	175

    The forge has 4000 m² of floor space available and 44 skilled
    workers to work the machines. How many machines of each type
    should be purchased to achieve maximum output?

5. Research has been extensive in energy conservation. It has been
    estimated that the annual cost of heating a building is $2.25 for
    every square metre of window and $0.50 for every square metre of

wall or roof. A building code requires that the area of the windows must be at least one-sixth the area of the walls and roof. If annual heating costs are not to exceed $900, what is the largest surface area a building can have?

6. A farmer intends to use a 20 hectare field to plant potatoes and corn. The labour per hectare is three working days and two working days, respectively. The profits per hectare are $175 and $140, respectively. If there are only 42 working days available, how many hectares of each vegetable should be planted to give the greatest profit?

7. A promoter measures the "marketing success" of a concert by using an index number that he devised. The number is a weighted sum of the number of old songs and the number of new songs sung during the concert. The old songs are weighted with a three and the new with a seven. A performer sings, at most, 30 songs during a concert and intends to sing at least as many old songs as new. How many of each should be sung to maximize the "marketing success" of the performance?

*10.4   THE SIMPLEX METHOD

When the constraints of a linear model are expressed in *three or more variables* the graphical solution to the problem is not appropriate. We now introduce a technique, called the **simplex method**, that will allow us to solve linear programming problems without restriction. This technique was developed by G. B. Dantzig in 1941 and is widely used today because its algorithm can be readily converted into a computer program.

The simplex method relies heavily on matrices and row operations as seen in Chapter 9. We proceed through examples.

Example 1   Determine the optimum solution to the linear model:

$$\text{Maximize: } H = 4x + 6y + 5z$$
$$\text{Subject to: } x + y + z \leq 27$$
$$2z \leq x$$
$$y \leq x + z$$
$$x \geq 0$$
$$y \geq 0$$
$$z \geq 0$$

Solution   The first step is to write all of the constraint inequalities in standard form (variables on the left of a $\leq$ sign). We then express them as equalities. To do this, we add new variables to the system, called **slack variables**. These make up the differences so that the inequalities become equalities. So the constraint

$$x + y + z \leqslant 27$$

becomes

$$x + y + z + s_1 = 27$$

The constraint

$$2z \leqslant x$$
$$-x + 2z \leqslant 0$$

becomes

$$-x + 2z + s_2 = 0$$

The constraint

$$y \leqslant z + x$$
$$-x + y - z \leqslant 0$$

becomes

$$-x + y - z + s_3 = 0$$

Our constraints with the three slack variables, s_1, s_2, s_3, have now become:

$$
\begin{aligned}
x + y + z + s_1 \quad\quad\quad &= 27 \\
-x \quad\quad + 2z + \quad s_2 \quad\quad &= 0 \\
-x + y - z + \quad\quad\quad s_3 &= 0
\end{aligned}
$$

And we also write the objective function with all of the variables on one side.

$$H = 4x + 6y + 5z$$

becomes $-4x - 6y - 5z + H = 0$

We now have a linear system of equations

$$
\begin{aligned}
x \;+ y + z + s_1 \quad\quad\quad\quad &= 27 \\
-x \quad\quad + 2z + \quad s_2 \quad\quad\quad &= 0 \\
-x \;+ y - z + \quad\quad s_3 \quad\quad &= 0 \\
-4x - 6y - 5z + \quad\quad\quad\quad H &= 0
\end{aligned}
$$

which can be written in a matrix form:

x	y	z	s_1	s_2	s_3	H	constant	
1	1	1	1	0	0	0	27	}
−1	0	2	0	1	0	0	0	} (constraints)
−1	1	−1	0	0	1	0	0	}
−4	−6	−5	0	0	0	1	0	} (objective function)

↑

This matrix organization of the linear model is called the **simplex tableau**.

In the graphical solution of a linear programming problem we looked at each corner point of the feasible region and determined which corner point optimized the objective function. The simplex method is an algorithm to do just that. We move from corner point to corner point, evaluating the objective function at each point and stop when it has been optimized.

The algorithm is developed now. We perform a sequence of row operations on the simplex tableau to reduce it to a form in which all of the entries in the last row (the objective function row) are non-negative (≥ 0). The rationale for doing this is to maximize the objective function, so we would want all of the coefficients of the variables to be positive and as large as possible.

We proceed by identifying a **pivot element** (or just pivot) in the simplex tableau. The pivot is found by following these steps.

1. The **pivot column** is the one in which the last entry is *the most negative*. In our example the pivot column is the y-column since -6 is the most negative of all of the entries in the bottom row. We indicate the pivot column with an arrow.

$$
\begin{array}{cccccccc}
x & y & z & s_1 & s_2 & s_3 & H & \text{constant}
\end{array}
$$

$$
\left[
\begin{array}{ccccccc|c}
1 & 1 & 1 & 1 & 0 & 0 & 0 & 27 \\
-1 & 0 & 2 & 0 & 1 & 0 & 0 & 0 \\
-1 & 1 & -1 & 0 & 0 & 1 & 0 & 0 \\
\hline
-4 & -6 & -5 & 0 & 0 & 0 & 1 & 0
\end{array}
\right]
\begin{array}{l}
\left.\vphantom{\begin{array}{c}1\\1\\1\end{array}}\right\} \text{(constraints)}\\[1.2em]
\} \text{(objective function)}
\end{array}
$$

2. The pivot is the positive element in the pivot column *whose ratio of (constant entry): (pivot column entry) is the smallest*. We ignore negative and undefined ratios. In our example we check the ratios $\frac{27}{1} = 27$, $\frac{0}{1} = 0$. The smallest ratio 0 identifies the 1 in the third row (circled) as the pivot.

$$
\begin{array}{cccccccc}
x & y & z & s_1 & s_2 & s_3 & H & \text{constant}
\end{array}
$$

$$
\left[
\begin{array}{ccccccc|c}
1 & 1 & 1 & 1 & 0 & 0 & 0 & 27 \\
-1 & 0 & 2 & 0 & 1 & 0 & 0 & 0 \\
-1 & ① & -1 & 0 & 0 & 1 & 0 & 0 \\
\hline
-4 & -6 & -5 & 0 & 0 & 0 & 1 & 0
\end{array}
\right]
\begin{array}{l}
\left.\vphantom{\begin{array}{c}1\\1\\1\end{array}}\right\} \text{(constraints)}\\[1.2em]
\} \text{(objective function)}
\end{array}
$$

We now use appropriate row operations on the tableau to reduce the pivot column to: a 1 at the pivot, and 0's in the rest of the column.

That is, the pivot column in our example should look like the following.

$$
\begin{array}{ccccccc}
x & y & z & s_1 & s_2 & s_3 & H \quad \text{constant}
\end{array}
$$

$$
\left.\begin{bmatrix}
- & 0 & - & - & - & - & - \mid - \\
- & 0 & - & - & - & - & - \mid - \\
- & 1 & - & - & - & - & - \mid - \\
\hline
- & 0 & - & - & - & - & - \mid -
\end{bmatrix}\right.
$$

$\left.\begin{array}{c} \\ \\ \\ \end{array}\right\}$ (constraints)

$\Big\}$ (objective function)

We proceed.

$$
\begin{bmatrix}
2 & 0 & 2 & 1 & 0 & -1 & 0 \mid 27 \\
-1 & 0 & 2 & 0 & 1 & 0 & 0 \mid 0 \\
-1 & 1 & -1 & 0 & 0 & 1 & 0 \mid 0 \\
\hline
-4 & -6 & -5 & 0 & 0 & 0 & 1 \mid 0
\end{bmatrix}
\qquad R_1 - R_3
$$

$$
\begin{bmatrix}
2 & 0 & 2 & 1 & 0 & -1 & 0 \mid 27 \\
-1 & 0 & 2 & 0 & 1 & 0 & 0 \mid 0 \\
-1 & 1 & -1 & 0 & 0 & 1 & 0 \mid 0 \\
\hline
-10 & 0 & -11 & 0 & 0 & 6 & 1 \mid 0
\end{bmatrix}
\qquad R_4 + 6R_3
$$

Our pivot column has been reduced to the required form. We now select a new pivot based on exactly the same steps as before.

1. The pivot column is the third column (-11 is the most negative).

2. The pivot is the entry 2 in the second row (since $\frac{27}{2} > \frac{0}{2}$; $\frac{0}{-1}$ is ignored because -1 is not positive.)

$$
\begin{bmatrix}
2 & 0 & 2 & 1 & 0 & -1 & 0 \mid 27 \\
-1 & 0 & ② & 0 & 1 & 0 & 0 \mid 0 \\
-1 & 1 & -1 & 0 & 0 & 1 & 0 \mid 0 \\
\hline
-10 & 0 & -11 & 0 & 0 & 6 & 1 \mid 0
\end{bmatrix}
$$

We now reduce this pivot column.

$$
\begin{bmatrix}
2 & 0 & 2 & 1 & 0 & -1 & 0 \mid 27 \\
-\frac{1}{2} & 0 & 1 & 0 & \frac{1}{2} & 0 & 0 \mid 0 \\
-1 & 1 & -1 & 0 & 0 & 1 & 0 \mid 0 \\
\hline
-10 & 0 & -11 & 0 & 0 & 6 & 1 \mid 0
\end{bmatrix}
\qquad \frac{1}{2}R_2
$$

$$\begin{bmatrix} 3 & 0 & 0 & 1 & -1 & -1 & 0 & | & 27 \\ -\frac{1}{2} & 0 & 1 & 0 & \frac{1}{2} & 0 & 0 & | & 0 \\ -1 & 1 & -1 & 0 & 0 & 1 & 0 & | & 0 \\ \hline -10 & 0 & -11 & 0 & 0 & 6 & 1 & | & 0 \end{bmatrix} \quad R_1 - 2R_2$$

$$\begin{bmatrix} 3 & 0 & 0 & 1 & -1 & -1 & 0 & | & 27 \\ -\frac{1}{2} & 0 & 1 & 0 & \frac{1}{2} & 0 & 0 & | & 0 \\ -\frac{3}{2} & 1 & 0 & 0 & \frac{1}{2} & 1 & 0 & | & 0 \\ \hline -10 & 0 & -11 & 0 & 0 & 6 & 1 & | & 0 \end{bmatrix} \quad R_3 + R_2$$

$$\begin{bmatrix} 3 & 0 & 0 & 1 & -1 & -1 & 0 & | & 27 \\ -\frac{1}{2} & 0 & 1 & 0 & \frac{1}{2} & 0 & 0 & | & 0 \\ -\frac{3}{2} & 1 & 0 & 0 & \frac{1}{2} & 1 & 0 & | & 0 \\ \hline -\frac{31}{2} & 0 & 0 & 0 & \frac{11}{2} & 6 & 1 & | & 0 \end{bmatrix} \quad R_4 + 11R_2$$

The second pivot column has been reduced. We choose the next pivot.

1.   The next pivot column is column 1 (the negative entry $-\frac{31}{2}$).

2.   The pivot is the 3 (the only positive ratio).

$$\begin{bmatrix} ③ & 0 & 0 & 1 & -1 & -1 & 0 & | & 27 \\ -\frac{1}{2} & 0 & 1 & 0 & \frac{1}{2} & 0 & 0 & | & 0 \\ -\frac{3}{2} & 1 & 0 & 0 & \frac{1}{2} & 1 & 0 & | & 0 \\ \hline -\frac{31}{2} & 0 & 0 & 0 & \frac{11}{2} & 6 & 1 & | & 0 \end{bmatrix}$$

We reduce this pivot column.

$$\begin{bmatrix} 1 & 0 & 0 & \frac{1}{3} & -\frac{1}{3} & -\frac{1}{3} & 0 & | & 9 \\ -\frac{1}{2} & 0 & 1 & 0 & \frac{1}{2} & 0 & 0 & | & 0 \\ -\frac{3}{2} & 1 & 0 & 0 & \frac{1}{2} & 1 & 0 & | & 0 \\ \hline -\frac{31}{2} & 0 & 0 & 0 & \frac{11}{2} & 6 & 1 & | & 0 \end{bmatrix} \quad \frac{1}{3}R_1$$

$$\begin{bmatrix} 1 & 0 & 0 & \frac{1}{3} & -\frac{1}{3} & -\frac{1}{3} & 0 & | & 9 \\ 0 & 0 & 1 & \frac{1}{6} & \frac{2}{6} & -\frac{1}{6} & 0 & | & \frac{9}{2} \\ -\frac{3}{2} & 1 & 0 & 0 & \frac{1}{2} & 1 & 0 & | & 0 \\ \hline -\frac{31}{2} & 0 & 0 & 0 & \frac{11}{2} & 6 & 1 & | & 0 \end{bmatrix} \quad R_2 + \frac{1}{2}R_1$$

$$\begin{bmatrix} 1 & 0 & 0 & \frac{1}{3} & -\frac{1}{3} & -\frac{1}{3} & 0 & | & 9 \\ 0 & 0 & 1 & \frac{1}{6} & \frac{2}{6} & -\frac{1}{6} & 0 & | & \frac{9}{2} \\ 0 & 1 & 0 & \frac{1}{2} & 0 & \frac{1}{2} & 0 & | & \frac{27}{2} \\ \hline -\frac{31}{2} & 0 & 0 & 0 & \frac{11}{2} & 6 & 1 & | & 0 \end{bmatrix} \quad R_3 + \frac{3}{2}R_1$$

$$\begin{bmatrix} 1 & 0 & 0 & \frac{1}{3} & -\frac{1}{3} & -\frac{1}{3} & 0 & | & 9 \\ 0 & 0 & 1 & \frac{1}{6} & \frac{2}{6} & -\frac{1}{6} & 0 & | & \frac{9}{2} \\ 0 & 1 & 0 & \frac{1}{2} & 0 & \frac{1}{2} & 0 & | & \frac{27}{2} \\ \hline 0 & 0 & 0 & \frac{31}{6} & \frac{1}{3} & \frac{5}{6} & 1 & | & \frac{279}{2} \end{bmatrix} \quad R_4 + \frac{31}{2}R_1$$

There are no more negative entries in the bottom row, so our reduction is complete.

Now, we interpret the final simplex tableau. The bottom row tells us that the objective function is

$$0x + 0y + 0z + \tfrac{31}{6}s_1 + \tfrac{1}{3}s_2 + \tfrac{5}{6}s_3 + (1)H = \tfrac{279}{2}$$

or,

$$H = \tfrac{279}{2} - \tfrac{31}{6}s_1 - \tfrac{1}{3}s_2 + \tfrac{5}{6}s_3$$

The slack variables are all non-negative, so the objective function H will attain a maximum value of $\frac{279}{2}$ when all of the slack variables equal zero. The values of x, y, and z that achieve this optimum can be obtained by translating the final simplex tableau back into equation form (remembering that the slack variables are now all zero).

$$\left. \begin{array}{l} (1)x + 0y + 0z = 9 \\ 0x + 0y + (1)z = \frac{9}{2} \\ 0x + (1)y + 0z = \frac{27}{2} \end{array} \right\} \qquad \begin{array}{l} x = 9 \\ z = \frac{9}{2} \\ y = \frac{27}{2} \end{array}$$

To summarize, the simplex method of solving a linear model consists of the following steps:
1. Construct the simplex tableau using slack variables.
2. Identify the pivot.
3. Reduce the pivot column by using matrix row operations.
4. Repeat steps (2) and (3) until there are no negative entries in the bottom row.
5. Allow the slack variables to be zero and translate the matrix back into equation form to obtain the optimal solution.

For practice, let us solve one of the linear models from Section 10.2 by using the simplex method.

Example 2   (same as Example 2, Section 10.2)

Using the simplex method, determine the optimal solution of the linear model.

$$\text{Maximize: } Z = 5x + 6y$$
$$\text{Subject to: } x + y \leqslant 9$$
$$x + 2y \leqslant 15$$
$$2x + y \leqslant 15$$
$$x \geqslant 0$$
$$y \geqslant 0$$

Solution   Introducing slack variables, we obtain

$$\left. \begin{array}{l} x + y + s_1 \qquad\qquad = 9 \\ x + 2y + \quad s_2 \qquad\quad = 15 \\ 2x + y + \qquad s_3 \quad = 15 \end{array} \right\} \text{(constraints)}$$
$$\left. -5x - 6y + \qquad\qquad Z = 0 \right\} \text{(objective function)}$$

The simplex tableau follows.

x	y	s_1	s_2	s_3	Z		constant
1	1	1	0	0	0		9
1	2	0	1	0	0		15
2	1	0	0	1	0		15
-5	-6	0	0	0	1		0

The first pivot is the 2 in the second column (since -6 is the most negative entry in the bottom row and $\frac{15}{2} < \frac{9}{1} < \frac{15}{1}$).

$$\begin{bmatrix} 1 & 1 & 1 & 0 & 0 & 0 & | & 9 \\ 1 & ② & 0 & 1 & 0 & 0 & | & 15 \\ 2 & 1 & 0 & 0 & 1 & 0 & | & 15 \\ \hline -5 & -6 & 0 & 0 & 0 & 1 & | & 0 \end{bmatrix}$$

We reduce the pivot column.

$$\begin{bmatrix} 1 & 1 & 1 & 0 & 0 & 0 & | & 9 \\ \frac{1}{2} & 1 & 0 & \frac{1}{2} & 0 & 0 & | & \frac{15}{2} \\ 2 & 1 & 0 & 0 & 1 & 0 & | & 15 \\ \hline -5 & -6 & 0 & 0 & 0 & 1 & | & 0 \end{bmatrix} \quad \frac{1}{2}R_2$$

$$\begin{bmatrix} \frac{1}{2} & 0 & 1 & -\frac{1}{2} & 0 & 0 & | & \frac{3}{2} \\ \frac{1}{2} & 1 & 0 & \frac{1}{2} & 0 & 0 & | & \frac{15}{2} \\ 2 & 1 & 0 & 0 & 1 & 0 & | & 15 \\ \hline -5 & -6 & 0 & 0 & 0 & 1 & | & 0 \end{bmatrix} \quad R_1 - R_2$$

$$\begin{bmatrix} \frac{1}{2} & 0 & 1 & -\frac{1}{2} & 0 & 0 & | & \frac{3}{2} \\ \frac{1}{2} & 1 & 0 & \frac{1}{2} & 0 & 0 & | & \frac{15}{2} \\ \frac{3}{2} & 0 & 0 & -\frac{1}{2} & 1 & 0 & | & \frac{15}{2} \\ \hline -5 & -6 & 0 & 0 & 0 & 1 & | & 0 \end{bmatrix} \quad R_3 - R_2$$

$$\begin{bmatrix} \frac{1}{2} & 0 & 1 & -\frac{1}{2} & 0 & 0 & | & \frac{3}{2} \\ \frac{1}{2} & 1 & 0 & \frac{1}{2} & 0 & 0 & | & \frac{15}{2} \\ \frac{3}{2} & 0 & 0 & -\frac{1}{2} & 1 & 0 & | & \frac{15}{2} \\ \hline -2 & 0 & 0 & 3 & 0 & 1 & | & 45 \end{bmatrix} \quad R_4 + 6R_2$$

The pivot column has been reduced. The next pivot is the $\frac{1}{2}$ in the first row, first column since -2 is negative in the bottom row, and

$$\frac{\frac{3}{2}}{\frac{1}{2}} < \frac{\frac{15}{2}}{\frac{3}{2}} < \frac{\frac{15}{2}}{\frac{1}{2}}$$

$$\begin{bmatrix} \boxed{\frac{1}{2}} & 0 & 1 & -\frac{1}{2} & 0 & 0 & | & \frac{3}{2} \\ \frac{1}{2} & 1 & 0 & \frac{1}{2} & 0 & 0 & | & \frac{15}{2} \\ \frac{3}{2} & 0 & 0 & -\frac{1}{2} & 1 & 0 & | & \frac{15}{2} \\ \hline -2 & 0 & 0 & 3 & 0 & 1 & | & 45 \end{bmatrix}$$
$\uparrow$

We reduce the pivot column.

$$\begin{bmatrix} 1 & 0 & 2 & -1 & 0 & 0 & | & 3 \\ \frac{1}{2} & 1 & 0 & \frac{1}{2} & 0 & 0 & | & \frac{15}{2} \\ \frac{3}{2} & 0 & 0 & -\frac{1}{2} & 1 & 0 & | & \frac{15}{2} \\ \hline -2 & 0 & 0 & 3 & 0 & 1 & | & 45 \end{bmatrix} \quad 2R_1$$
$\uparrow$

$$\begin{bmatrix} 1 & 0 & 2 & -1 & 0 & 0 & | & 3 \\ 0 & 1 & -1 & 1 & 0 & 0 & | & 6 \\ \frac{3}{2} & 0 & 0 & -\frac{1}{2} & 1 & 0 & | & \frac{15}{2} \\ \hline -2 & 0 & 0 & 3 & 0 & 1 & | & 45 \end{bmatrix} \quad R_2 - \frac{1}{2}R_1$$
$\uparrow$

$$\begin{bmatrix} 1 & 0 & 2 & -1 & 0 & 0 & | & 3 \\ 0 & 1 & -1 & 1 & 0 & 0 & | & 6 \\ 0 & 0 & -3 & 1 & 1 & 0 & | & 3 \\ \hline -2 & 0 & 0 & 3 & 0 & 1 & | & 45 \end{bmatrix} \quad R_3 - \frac{3}{2}R_1$$
$\uparrow$

$$\begin{bmatrix} 1 & 0 & 2 & -1 & 0 & 0 & | & 3 \\ 0 & 1 & -1 & 1 & 0 & 0 & | & 6 \\ 0 & 0 & -3 & 1 & 1 & 0 & | & 3 \\ \hline 0 & 0 & 4 & 1 & 0 & 1 & | & 51 \end{bmatrix} \quad R_4 + 2R_1$$
$\uparrow$

There are no more negative values in the bottom row, so this is the final simplex tableau. Allowing the slack variables to be zero, we conclude that the optimal solution is

$x = 3$ (from row 1)
$y = 6$ (from row 2)

yielding a maximum

$Z = 51$ (from row 4)

EXERCISE 10.4

A **1.** Given the following initial simplex tableaux, determine first the pivot column and then the pivot.

(a) $$\begin{bmatrix} 2 & 3 & 1 & 0 & 0 & | & 12 \\ 3 & 5 & 0 & 1 & 0 & | & 9 \\ \hline -4 & -7 & 0 & 0 & 0 & | & 0 \end{bmatrix}$$

(b) $$\begin{bmatrix} 35 & 23 & 1 & 0 & 0 & | & 154 \\ 13 & 19 & 0 & 1 & 0 & | & 79 \\ \hline -24 & -13 & 0 & 0 & 1 & | & 0 \end{bmatrix}$$

(c) $$\begin{bmatrix} 2 & 5 & 1 & 0 & 0 & 0 & | & 17 \\ 4 & 7 & 0 & 1 & 0 & 0 & | & 31 \\ -1 & 5 & 0 & 0 & 1 & 0 & | & 2 \\ \hline -9 & -6 & 0 & 0 & 0 & 1 & | & 0 \end{bmatrix}$$

(d) $$\begin{bmatrix} 35 & 23 & 1 & 0 & 0 & 0 & | & 73 \\ 45 & 8 & 0 & 1 & 0 & 0 & | & 11 \\ 13 & 19 & 0 & 0 & 1 & 0 & | & 19 \\ \hline -11 & -17 & 0 & 0 & 0 & 1 & | & 0 \end{bmatrix}$$

(e) $$\begin{bmatrix} 8 & 4 & 3 & 1 & 0 & 0 & 0 & | & 24 \\ 1 & 3 & 4 & 0 & 1 & 0 & 0 & | & 41 \\ -1 & -5 & 1 & 0 & 0 & 1 & 0 & | & 31 \\ 7 & 3 & 9 & 0 & 0 & 0 & 1 & | & 21 \\ \hline -4 & -9 & -7 & 0 & 0 & 0 & 1 & | & 0 \end{bmatrix}$$

(f) $$\begin{bmatrix} 25 & 26 & 0 & 1 & 0 & 0 & 0 & 0 & | & 12 \\ 47 & 0 & 12 & 0 & 1 & 0 & 0 & 0 & | & 37 \\ 63 & 13 & 5 & 0 & 0 & 1 & 0 & 0 & | & 41 \\ 0 & 15 & 0 & 0 & 0 & 0 & 1 & 0 & | & 9 \\ \hline -21 & -17 & -31 & 0 & 0 & 0 & 0 & 1 & | & 0 \end{bmatrix}$$

(g) $$\begin{bmatrix} 3 & 2 & 1 & 4 & 1 & 0 & 0 & 0 & 0 & | & 8 \\ 2 & 2 & 4 & 0 & 0 & 1 & 0 & 0 & 0 & | & 6 \\ 0 & 4 & 3 & 4 & 0 & 0 & 1 & 0 & 0 & | & 10 \\ 4 & 4 & 2 & 2 & 0 & 0 & 0 & 1 & 0 & | & 9 \\ \hline -3 & -6 & -8 & -4 & 0 & 0 & 0 & 0 & 1 & | & 0 \end{bmatrix}$$

2. Given the following final simplex tableaux, state the optimal solutions.

(a)

x	y	s_1	s_2	R		const
0	1	3	0	0		4
1	0	7	1	0		7
0	0	2	5	1		23

(b)

x	y	s_1	s_2	A		const
1	0	11	-4	0		$\frac{7}{2}$
0	1	-6	6	0		9
0	0	21	5	1		53

(c)

x	y	z	w	s_1	s_2	s_3	s_4	M		const
0	0	1	0	3	-4	3	9	0		24
1	0	0	0	2	2	-4	-8	0		7
0	1	0	0	7	7	7	2	0		$\frac{5}{2}$
0	0	0	1	-5	-1	2	6	0		13
0	0	0	0	14	9	11	8	1		123

(d)

x	y	z	w	s_1	s_2	s_3	s_4	P		const
0	0	0	1	3	4	-6	0	0		23
0	1	0	0	2	8	5	1	0		11
0	0	1	0	$\frac{1}{2}$	2	7	2	0		$\frac{9}{2}$
1	0	0	0	-5	1	-3	-7	0		5
0	0	0	0	3	12	19	31	1		201

B 3. Given the following initial simplex tableaux, use the simplex method to reduce them to their final tableaux, and then state the optimal solution.

(a)

x	y	s_1	s_2	P		const
3	-2	1	0	0		12
1	1	0	1	0		8
-5	-2	0	0	1		0

(b)

x	y	s_1	s_2	P		const
7	2	1	0	0		42
-7	8	0	1	0		28
-2	-3	0	0	1		0

(c)

$$
\begin{array}{ccccccccc}
 & x & y & z & s_1 & s_2 & s_3 & P & \text{const} \\
\left[\begin{array}{c}\\ \\ \\ \end{array}\right. & \begin{array}{c} 2 \\ -3 \\ -5 \end{array} & \begin{array}{c} 2 \\ 0 \\ 5 \end{array} & \begin{array}{c} 2 \\ 6 \\ -5 \end{array} & \begin{array}{c} 1 \\ 0 \\ 0 \end{array} & \begin{array}{c} 0 \\ 1 \\ 0 \end{array} & \begin{array}{c} 0 \\ 0 \\ 1 \end{array} & \begin{array}{c} 0 \\ 0 \\ 0 \end{array} & \left.\begin{array}{c} 54 \\ 0 \\ 0 \end{array}\right] \\
\hline
 & -4 & -6 & -5 & 0 & 0 & 0 & 1 & 0
\end{array}
$$

4. Determine the optimal solution to the following linear models.

   (a) Maximize: $C = 50x + 30y + 20z$
   Subject to: $x + y + z \leqslant 24$
   $$y \leqslant x + z$$
   $$2z \leqslant x$$
   $$x \geqslant 0$$
   $$y \geqslant 0$$
   $$z \geqslant 0$$

   (b) Maximize: $P = 3x + 4y + 2z$
   Subject to: $7x \leqslant 3y + 30$
   $$9y \leqslant 5x + 34$$
   $$x + y \leqslant z + 7$$
   $$x \geqslant 0$$
   $$y \geqslant 0$$
   $$z \geqslant 0$$

C **5.** Given an objective function in n variables and subject to m constraints, determine the dimensions of the simplex tableau that would be used to find the optimal solution.

*10.5 LINEAR PROGRAMMING PROBLEMS (SIMPLEX METHOD)

Optimization problems may be concerned with a minimization process or a maximization process. The solution of linear models in three or more variables (requiring the simplex method) dealing with minimization is similar but slightly more complicated than the solution of maximization problems and will not be developed in this text. For interested students, *An Introduction to Linear Programming* by Paul R. Thie presents a thorough treatment of all aspects of linear programming.

We complete this chapter with one final example requiring a rather large simplex tableau and an unusual twist in the interpretation of the final tableau.

Example 1 A tennis manufacturer makes three qualities of tennis racquets, beginner, intermediate, and expert. The profits per racquet are $4, $6, and $8, respectively. The labour (in hours) per week required to manufacture the racquets as well as the total labour available per week for each stage of the making of a racquet is presented in the following table.

Task	Type of Racquet: Beginner	Type of Racquet: Intermediate	Type of Racquet: Expert	Total Available Labour Hours
Construction	5	5	4	96
Finishing	3	2	8	72
Stringing	3	3	2	40

It has been determined from a marketing analysis that if four more intermediate racquets were sold per week, the intermediate model would sell at least twice as many as the combined beginner and expert models. Determine the optimum number of each racquet model to produce in order to maximize profits.

Solution   We must maximize profits. We construct a profit equation as the objective function.

Let P be the profits per week in dollars.

Let x be the number of beginner racquets made per week.

Let y be the number of intermediate racquets made per week.

Let z be the number of expert racquets made per week.

Then, $P = 4x + 6y + 8z$

Three constraints arise out of the labour restrictions:

$$5x + 5y + 4z \leqslant 96$$
$$3x + 2y + 8z \leqslant 72$$
$$3x + 3y + 2z \leqslant 40$$

The final constraint arises out of the market analysis, which can be translated into the following inequality.

$$y + 4 \geqslant 2(x + z)$$
or $$2x - y + 2z \leqslant 4$$

And since the number of racquets of each type must be non-negative, $x \geqslant 0$, $y \geqslant 0$, and $z \geqslant 0$.

Our linear model is

Maximize: $P = 4x + 6y + 8z$
Subject to: $5x + 5y + 4z \leqslant 96$
$3x + 2y + 8z \leqslant 72$
$3x + 3y + 2z \leqslant 40$
$2x - \ y + 2z \leqslant 4$
$x \geqslant 0, \ y \geqslant 0, \ z \geqslant 0$

Introducing slack variables, we obtain

$$5x + 5y + 4z + s_1 \qquad\qquad\qquad = 96$$
$$3x + 2y + 8z + \quad s_2 \qquad\qquad = 72$$
$$3x + 3y + 2z + \qquad s_3 \qquad\quad = 40$$
$$2x - y + 2z + \qquad\quad s_4 \quad = 4$$
$$-4x - 6y - 8z + \qquad\qquad\quad P = 0$$

The simplex tableau follows.

$$
\begin{array}{ccccccccc}
x & y & z & s_1 & s_2 & s_3 & s_4 & P & \text{constant}
\end{array}
$$

$$
\left[
\begin{array}{cccccccc|c}
5 & 5 & 4 & 1 & 0 & 0 & 0 & 0 & 96 \\
3 & 2 & 8 & 0 & 1 & 0 & 0 & 0 & 72 \\
3 & 3 & 2 & 0 & 0 & 1 & 0 & 0 & 40 \\
2 & -1 & 2 & 0 & 0 & 0 & 1 & 0 & 4 \\
\hline
-4 & -6 & -8 & 0 & 0 & 0 & 0 & 1 & 0
\end{array}
\right]
\begin{array}{l}
\left.\rule{0pt}{40pt}\right\} \text{ (constraints)} \\[10pt]
\} \text{ (objective function)}
\end{array}
$$

The first pivot is the number 2 in the third column. (-8 is the most negative entry in the bottom row and $\frac{4}{2} < \frac{72}{8} < \frac{40}{2} < \frac{96}{4}$).

$$
\left[
\begin{array}{cccccccc|c}
5 & 5 & 4 & 1 & 0 & 0 & 0 & 0 & 96 \\
3 & 2 & 8 & 0 & 1 & 0 & 0 & 0 & 72 \\
3 & 3 & 2 & 0 & 0 & 1 & 0 & 0 & 40 \\
2 & -1 & ② & 0 & 0 & 0 & 1 & 0 & 4 \\
\hline
-4 & -6 & -8 & 0 & 0 & 0 & 0 & 1 & 0
\end{array}
\right]
$$

We reduce the pivot column.

$$
\left[
\begin{array}{cccccccc|c}
5 & 5 & 4 & 1 & 0 & 0 & 0 & 0 & 96 \\
3 & 2 & 8 & 0 & 1 & 0 & 0 & 0 & 72 \\
3 & 3 & 2 & 0 & 0 & 1 & 0 & 0 & 40 \\
1 & -\frac{1}{2} & 1 & 0 & 0 & 0 & \frac{1}{2} & 0 & 4 \\
\hline
-4 & -6 & -8 & 0 & 0 & 0 & 0 & 1 & 0
\end{array}
\right]
\qquad \frac{1}{2}R_4
$$

$$
\left[
\begin{array}{cccccccc|c}
1 & 7 & 0 & 1 & 0 & 0 & -2 & 0 & 88 \\
-5 & 6 & 0 & 0 & 1 & 0 & -4 & 0 & 54 \\
1 & 4 & 0 & 0 & 0 & 1 & -1 & 0 & 36 \\
1 & -\frac{1}{2} & 1 & 0 & 0 & 0 & \frac{1}{2} & 0 & 2 \\
\hline
4 & -10 & 0 & 0 & 0 & 0 & 4 & 1 & 16
\end{array}
\right]
\qquad
\begin{array}{l}
R_1 - 4R_4 \\
R_2 - 8R_4 \\
R_3 - 3R_4 \\
\\
R_5 + 8R_4
\end{array}
$$

The next pivot is the number 4 in the second column (-10 is the only negative entry in the bottom row and $\frac{36}{4} = \frac{54}{6} \leqslant \frac{88}{7}$).

$$
\begin{bmatrix}
1 & 7 & 0 & 1 & 0 & 0 & -2 & 0 & | & 88 \\
-5 & 6 & 0 & 0 & 1 & 0 & -4 & 0 & | & 54 \\
1 & ④ & 0 & 0 & 0 & 1 & -1 & 0 & | & 36 \\
1 & -\frac{1}{2} & 1 & 0 & 0 & 0 & \frac{1}{2} & 0 & | & 2 \\
\hline
4 & -10 & 0 & 0 & 0 & 0 & 4 & 1 & | & 16
\end{bmatrix}
$$

We reduce this pivot column.

$$
\begin{bmatrix}
1 & 7 & 0 & 1 & 0 & 0 & -2 & 0 & | & 88 \\
-5 & 6 & 0 & 0 & 1 & 0 & -4 & 0 & | & 54 \\
\frac{1}{4} & 1 & 0 & 0 & 0 & \frac{1}{4} & -\frac{1}{4} & 0 & | & 9 \\
1 & -\frac{1}{2} & 1 & 0 & 0 & 0 & \frac{1}{2} & 0 & | & 2 \\
\hline
4 & -10 & 0 & 0 & 0 & 0 & 4 & 1 & | & 16
\end{bmatrix}
\quad \frac{1}{4}R_3
$$

$$
\begin{bmatrix}
-\frac{3}{4} & 0 & 0 & 1 & 0 & -\frac{7}{4} & -\frac{1}{4} & 0 & | & 25 \\
-\frac{13}{2} & 0 & 0 & 0 & 1 & 0 & -\frac{5}{2} & 0 & | & 2 \\
\frac{1}{4} & 1 & 0 & 0 & 0 & \frac{1}{4} & -\frac{1}{4} & 0 & | & 9 \\
\frac{9}{8} & 0 & 1 & 0 & 0 & \frac{1}{8} & \frac{3}{8} & 0 & | & \frac{13}{2} \\
\hline
\frac{13}{2} & 0 & 0 & 0 & 0 & \frac{5}{2} & \frac{3}{2} & 1 & | & 106
\end{bmatrix}
\quad
\begin{matrix}
R_1 - 7R_3 \\
R_2 - 6R_3 \\
\\
R_4 + \frac{1}{2}R_3 \\
\\
R_5 + 10R_3
\end{matrix}
$$

There are no more negative entries in the bottom row so this is the final simplex tableau.

Now, we interpret the final tableau. We have a somewhat different situation in that the first column was not reduced to zeros and ones. However, when we allow the slack variables to be zero and translate the bottom row back into the objective function we obtain

$$\frac{13}{2}x + P = 106$$

or $$P = 106 - \frac{13}{2}x$$

This will clearly be a maximum when $x = 0$ (since x must be $\geqslant 0$). The values of the other variables for the optimal solution are

$$y = 9 \qquad \text{(from row 2)}$$
$$z = \tfrac{13}{2} \qquad \text{(from row 4)}$$

and these values yield a maximum value for P of

$$P = 106 \qquad \text{(from row 5)}$$

We conclude that the maximum profit may be made if no beginners' racquets, nine intermediate racquets, and six and a half expert racquets are made per week. The maximum profit would be $106.

EXERCISE 10.5

B   Determine the optimal solution for each of the following linear programming problems.

1. (a) A cassette tape manufacturer makes two qualities of tapes, normal and chromium dioxide. The machine that produces the normal tapes can spool no more than 5000 tapes in a day and the machine that makes the chromium dioxide tapes can do no more than 3000 per day. The packaging machine that handles both types of tapes can package a maximum of 6000 tapes a day. The profit is $0.35 on the normal tapes and $0.55 on the chromium dioxide tapes. How many of each type of cassette tape should be made to maximize profits?

   (b) The same manufacturer decides to introduce a third quality of tape, metal. Its machine can produce 2500 per day. The same machine packages all three types of tapes, again to a maximum of 6000 tapes per day. The profit per tape is $0.45. How many of each tape should be produced now?

2. A manufacturer of stereo components wants to introduce compact disc players to his product line of turntables and cassette players. The following table lists relevant production information.

	No. of Hours Assembling	No. of Hours Testing	No. of Hours Packaging	Profit($) per Unit
CD Players	2	1	$\frac{1}{3}$	35
Turntables	$\frac{1}{2}$	1	$\frac{1}{2}$	15
Cassette Decks	$\frac{3}{2}$	$\frac{3}{2}$	$\frac{1}{4}$	25
Available Working Hours per Task	18	12	5	

The manufacturer's sales force recommends that more cassette players should be produced than CD players. How many units of each component should be manufactured to maximize profits?

3. A stock broker offers three investment options to her client. Option 1 offers a return of 11 percent per annum. Option 2 offers a return of 13 percent per annum. Option 3 offers a return of 17 percent. The client has $50 000 to invest. The broker also advises that no more than $20 000 should be invested in Option 2, and the combined amounts invested in Option 1 and Option 2 should be greater than the money invested in Option 3. How much should the client invest in each option if he wants to maximize return?

4. A foundry makes three grades of steel from the raw materials coke, coal, and iron. One tonne of grade X requires one tonne of coke, one tonne of coal, and one tonne of iron. Grade XX requires 1.0 t, 0.8 t, and 1.0 t, respectively, of the raw materials to produce one tonne of the steel. And grade XXX requires two tonnes of coke, one tonne of coal, and one tonne of iron to produce a tonne of steel. The profits per tonne of the grades of steel are $20, $50, and $10 for the grades X, XX, and XXX, respectively. How many tonnes of each grade of steel should be produced to maximize profits if the raw materials available to the foundry are 200 t of coke, 200 t of coal, and 100 t of iron?

10.6 REVIEW EXERCISE

1. Given the following feasible regions and their corner points, determine the corner point that maximizes the indicated objective function.

(a) Maximize: $P = 35x + 40y$

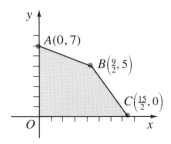

(b) Maximize: $Z = 200x + 325y$

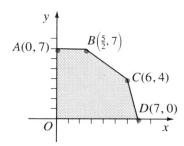

2. Using the graphical technique, determine the optimal solutions of the following linear models.
    (a) Maximize: $G = 9x + 3y$
         Subject to: $x + y \leqslant 10$
                      $x + 2y \leqslant 15$
                      $2x + y \leqslant 12$
                      $x \geqslant 0$
                      $y \geqslant 0$
    (b) Minimize: $W = 4x + 8y$
         Subject to: $x + y \geqslant 8$
                      $-3x + y \geqslant -12$
                      $x - 3y \geqslant -12$
                      $x \geqslant 0$
                      $y \geqslant 0$

*3. Given the following initial simplex tableaux, use the simplex method to reduce them to their final tableaux, and then state the optimal solution.

(a)

	x	y	s_1	s_2	s_3	P	const
	1	1	1	0	0	0	10
	1	2	0	1	0	0	15
	2	1	0	0	1	0	12
	-9	-3	0	0	0	1	0

(b)

	x	y	z	s_1	s_2	s_3	P	const
	3	3	3	1	0	0	0	81
	-2	0	4	0	1	0	0	0
	-1	1	-1	0	0	1	0	0
	-5	-4	-6	0	0	0	1	0

4. Determine the optimal solutions to the following linear models.
    (a) Maximize: $C = 40x + 50y$
         Subject to: $x + 2y \leqslant 720$
                      $5x + 4y \leqslant 1800$
                      $3x + y \leqslant 900$
                      $x \geqslant 0$
                      $y \geqslant 0$

*(b) Maximize: $P = 16x + 24y + 32z$
Subject to: $10x + 10y + 8z \leq 192$
$9x + 6y + 24z \leq 216$
$6x + 6y + 4z \leq 80$
$4x - 2y + 4z \leq 8$
$x \geq 0$
$y \geq 0$
$z \geq 0$

5. A tire manufacturer makes two qualities of tires, regular and radial. The machine that produces the regular tires can make up to 200 tires in a day and the machine that makes the radial tires can make no more than 125 per day. The finishing machine that handles both types of tires can finish, at best, 225 tires in a day. The profit on the regular tires is $27 and $42 on the radial tires. How many of each type of tire should be made to maximize profits?

*6. The following table organizes production information pertaining to the manufacturing of one unit of each of four products.

	Time Required in Hours on:				Profit $
	Machine A	Machine B	Machine C	Machine D	per Unit
Product X	5	3	2	3	12
Product Y	3	6	5	2	9
Product Z	8	1	3	4	15
Product W	2	2	4	1	9
Availability of the Machines in hours	120	70	80	100	

Determine the production quantities of each of these products to maximize profits.

10.7 CHAPTER 10 TEST

1. Translate the following situation into a linear model. Do not attempt to solve it.

A farmer intends to plant wheat and corn in a 400 hectare farm. She finds that she can plant 25 hectares a day of wheat and 20 hectares a day of corn. The wheat produces a profit of $220 per hectare and the corn $260 per hectare. How many hectares of each crop should be planted to maximize profits if there are only 18 days available for planting?

2. (a) Using the graphical technique, determine the optimal solution of the following linear model.

Maximize: $K = 4x + 9y$
Subject to: $3x + 3y \leqslant 9$
$x + 2y \leqslant 4$
$x \geqslant 0$
$y \geqslant 0$

*(b) Using the simplex method, determine the optimal solution of the following linear model.

Maximize: $M = 2x + 7y$
Subject to: $2x + 3y \leqslant 7$
$4x + 2y \leqslant 10$
$x \geqslant 0$
$y \geqslant 0$

3. A manufacturer of mufflers makes two qualities of muffler, one using 10-gauge steel and one using 12-gauge steel. The following table lists relevant daily production information.

	No. of Hours Assembling	No. of Hours Inspecting	Profit ($) per Unit
10-gauge muffler	2	$\frac{1}{4}$	7
12-gauge muffler	$\frac{5}{2}$	$\frac{1}{3}$	12
Available working hours per task	18	8	

The manufacturer knows he will sell more 10-gauge mufflers than 12-gauge and so production should reflect this fact. How many of each should be produced to maximize profits?

*4. A company called Safetee manufactures three styles of infant car seats: economy, deluxe, and executive. The manufacturing of the seats is a three-stage process in which the seats are assembled, upholstered, and tested. The production stage times for assembling, upholstering, and testing the economy seat are two, one-half, and one hours, respectively. For the deluxe seat the times are $\frac{5}{2}$, $\frac{3}{4}$, and one hour for the assembling, upholstering, and testing, respectively. The times for assembling, upholstering, and testing the executive seat are $\frac{5}{2}$, one, and one hour respectively. The company allows 20 h for assembling car seats, eight hours for upholstering, and six hours for testing. From past sales analysis, the economy seat outsells both the deluxe and executive models combined and production must take this into account. How many of each model should be produced to yield the maximum profit, if the profits per seat are $10 for the economy, $15 for the deluxe, and $17 for the executive?

CUMULATIVE REVIEW FOR CHAPTERS 8 TO 10

1. For the matrix
$$\begin{bmatrix} 2 & -5 & 6 & -3 \\ 7 & 0 & 1 & -1 \\ -6 & 4 & -10 & -4 \end{bmatrix}$$
   answer the following questions.
   (a) State the dimensions of the matrix.
   (b) State the value of a_{23} and a_{32}.
   (c) Which entry, in the form a_{ij}, is -6?

2. For the following network

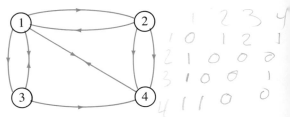

   (a) Construct the corresponding matrix, A.
   (b) Determine A^2.
   (c) Explain the meaning of the entries in A^2.

3. Perform the indicated operations, where possible, in each of the following.
   (a)
   $$1.2 \begin{bmatrix} 5 & -2 \\ 7 & 14 \\ -5 & 1 \end{bmatrix} + 0.4 \begin{bmatrix} -3 & 80 \\ -7 & -8 \\ 12 & -9 \end{bmatrix}$$

   (b) $\frac{1}{2} \begin{bmatrix} 4 & -12 & 3 \\ -5 & 2 & -6 \end{bmatrix} - \frac{1}{3} \begin{bmatrix} 6 & -9 & 3 \\ -8 & 2 & 12 \end{bmatrix}$

   (c)
   $$\begin{bmatrix} 2 & -6 & 5 \end{bmatrix} \begin{bmatrix} -1 & -7 \\ 3 & -5 \\ 1 & -12 \end{bmatrix}$$

   (d)
   $$\begin{bmatrix} 2 & -3 & 1 \\ 4 & -7 & -2 \end{bmatrix} \begin{bmatrix} 1 & 3 & -1 \\ 8 & 10 & -5 \\ 9 & -7 & -6 \end{bmatrix}$$

   (e)
   $$\begin{bmatrix} -2 & 3 \\ 1 & 7 \\ -8 & 12 \\ 8 & -9 \end{bmatrix} \begin{bmatrix} -3 & -5 & 4 \\ 10 & -13 & -7 \end{bmatrix}$$

   (f) $-3 \begin{bmatrix} 6 & -3 \\ -3 & 6 \end{bmatrix} + \begin{bmatrix} 4 & -3 \\ 2 & -1 \end{bmatrix} \begin{bmatrix} 5 & 1 \\ -1 & -4 \end{bmatrix}$

   (g)
   $$\begin{bmatrix} 2 & -1 & -1 \\ 2 & 3 & -7 \end{bmatrix} \begin{bmatrix} -1 & 8 \\ -8 & 4 \\ -4 & 5 \end{bmatrix} - \begin{bmatrix} 1 \\ 1 \end{bmatrix} \begin{bmatrix} 3 & -3 \end{bmatrix}$$

4. If
$$A = \begin{bmatrix} -2 & 3 \\ 4 & -7 \end{bmatrix} \quad B = \begin{bmatrix} 1.2 & -3.4 & 2.1 \\ 5.3 & 1.7 & -0.3 \end{bmatrix}$$
$$C = \begin{bmatrix} 0.4 & -1.1 & -3.6 \\ 2.5 & -1.8 & 2.2 \end{bmatrix}$$
find (where possible)
(a) $0.7B - 1.3C$ (b) A^2
(c) C^2 (d) $AB + C$

5. Decode the following message.
$$\begin{bmatrix} 58 & 13 \\ 82 & 19 \end{bmatrix}, \begin{bmatrix} 62 & 36 \\ 83 & 49 \end{bmatrix}, \begin{bmatrix} 63 & 85 \\ 89 & 118 \end{bmatrix} \qquad \text{decoding matrix } \begin{bmatrix} 3 & -2 \\ -4 & 3 \end{bmatrix}$$

6. The weekly hours for four workers at a small manufacturing plant are given in the following table.

	\multicolumn{4}{c}{Worker}			
	1	**2**	**3**	**4**
Monday	8.5	8.0	8.5	9.0
Tuesday	8.5	8.5	8.5	9.0
Wednesday	8.0	8.0	8.5	8.5
Thursday	9.0	9.0	9.5	10.0
Friday	8.0	8.0	8.0	8.5

The workers are paid $12 an hour for an eight-hour working day. For any additional time worked in a single day the workers receive time-and-a-half.
(a) Construct two matrices, one showing regular hours and the other showing overtime hours for the four workers.
(b) Use matrix methods to determine the weekly pay due each worker.

7. A Finite Mathematics teacher uses the following formula to determine her students' final marks: 20 percent of the first term, 20 percent of the first exam, 20 percent of the second term, and 40 percent of the final exam. Some of her students' marks are listed below.

	First Term	First Exam	Second Term	Final Exam
Anchors, J.	72	67	75	69
Bettram, T.	88	85	91	83
Gallo, B.	43	41	55	52
Hutton, B.	63	59	51	64

Find each of the four students' final marks.

8. Which of the following can be the transition matrix for a Markov chain? For those that cannot, give a reason why.
(a) $\begin{bmatrix} 0.4 & 0.6 \\ 0.1 & 0.9 \end{bmatrix}$ (b) $\begin{bmatrix} \frac{3}{4} & \frac{1}{4} \\ \frac{1}{2} & \frac{1}{3} \end{bmatrix}$

(c) $\begin{bmatrix} 0.3 & 0.4 & 0.3 \\ 0.2 & 0.4 & 0.4 \\ 0.6 & 0.1 & 0.3 \end{bmatrix}$ (d) $\begin{bmatrix} \frac{1}{2} & 0 & \frac{1}{2} \\ 0 & 1 & 0 \\ \frac{3}{2} & 0 & -\frac{1}{2} \end{bmatrix}$

9. Which of the following could be the transition matrix of a regular Markov chain? For those that cannot, give a reason.

(a) $\begin{bmatrix} 0.4 & 0.6 \\ 0.9 & 0.1 \end{bmatrix}$ (b) $\begin{bmatrix} 0.5 & 0.5 \\ 0 & 1 \end{bmatrix}$

(c) $\begin{bmatrix} 0.2 & 0.3 & 0.5 \\ 0.6 & 0.4 & 0 \\ 0.3 & 0.2 & 0.5 \end{bmatrix}$ (d) $\begin{bmatrix} 0.3 & 0.6 & 0.1 \\ 0.8 & 0.1 & 0.1 \end{bmatrix}$

10. The transition matrix, P, of a Markov chain is $\begin{bmatrix} 0.7 & 0.3 \\ 0.8 & 0.2 \end{bmatrix}$ and the initial probability vector, $S^{(0)}$, is $[0.5 \quad 0.5]$.

   (a) Find P^2 and P^3.
   (b) Find the first, second, and third step probability vectors.
   (c) Find the steady state vector.

11. Located near Walker's Beach are two camping grounds: one is provincially operated and the other is privately owned. Statistics have shown that, of the people who camp at the provincial camp grounds, 80 percent will return there the next time and 20 percent will try the privately owned camp. Of the people who camp at the private grounds, 60 percent will return the next time and 40 percent will camp at the provincial grounds.

   (a) Find the transition matrix P.
   (b) Find P^2 and P^3.
   (c) If the initial probability of a person trying the provincial camp is 65 percent and the privately owned camp is 35 percent, what is the probability of a person camping at the provincial grounds on the second and third times?
   (d) Given that a person camped on the privately owned grounds the first time out, what is the probability he or she will return there on the third camping excursion?
   (e) Determine the long-term trends of the campers by finding the steady state vector.

12. A rat is placed in one of the compartments of the maze shown. A transition takes place when the rat moves through one of the doors available to it into another compartment. It is assumed that these moves are made with equal probability. The probability of moving from one compartment into itself is zero.

   (a) Construct the transition matrix P for this Markov chain.
   (b) Compute P^2, P^3, and P^4.

(c) If a rat starts in compartment 1, what is the probability it will be in compartment 3 after two transitions?

(d) If a rat starts in compartment 4, what is the probability it will be in compartment 1 after three transitions?

(e) If a rat starts in compartment 2, what is the probability it will be back in compartment 2 after four transitions?

13. In the west end of a major Canadian city, three supermarkets compete for the local business. A study of the local shopping patterns produced the following transition matrix.

$$\begin{array}{c} \\ A \\ B \\ C \end{array} \begin{array}{ccc} A & B & C \\ \left[\begin{array}{ccc} 0.8 & 0.2 & 0 \\ 0.2 & 0.6 & 0.2 \\ 0.1 & 0.2 & 0.7 \end{array}\right] \end{array}$$

(a) Show that this Markov chain is regular.

(b) Find the steady state vector and, hence, determine the long-term trends of the local shoppers.

14. Solve each of the following systems of equations by elimination.

(a) $\begin{cases} 2x - y + z = 11 \\ -2x + 3y - 2z = -15 \\ 3x + 2y - z = 8 \end{cases}$

(b) $\begin{cases} -4x + y - 3z = 10 \\ -x - 2y + z = -12 \end{cases}$

15. Perform the indicated row operations on the given matrix in succession.

$$\left[\begin{array}{ccc} 2 & -1 & 3 \\ -1 & 4 & 1 \\ 3 & 2 & -1 \end{array}\right]$$

(a) row 1 + row 2

(b) row 2 + row 1

(c) row 3 − 3 row 1

(d) row 3 + row 2

(e) $\frac{1}{7}$ row 2

(f) $-\frac{1}{8}$ row 3

16. State which of the following matrices are in row-reduced echelon form. For those that are not, give a reason why.

(a) $\begin{bmatrix} 0 & 1 & 3 & -4 \\ 0 & 0 & 0 & 1 \end{bmatrix}$

(b) $\begin{bmatrix} 1 & 2 & 0 & 0 \\ 0 & 0 & 2 & 0 \\ 0 & 0 & 0 & 1 \\ 0 & 0 & 0 & 0 \end{bmatrix}$

(c) $\begin{bmatrix} 0 & 1 & 0 \\ 0 & 0 & 1 \\ 0 & 0 & 0 \\ 0 & 0 & 0 \end{bmatrix}$

17. Use a sequence of row operations to reduce each of the following matrices to echelon form.

(a) $\begin{bmatrix} -3 & 9 & -12 \\ 2 & 5 & -4 \end{bmatrix}$

(b) $\begin{bmatrix} 3 & -2 & 1 & 0 \\ -1 & 4 & -4 & 2 \\ 2 & -2 & -3 & 1 \\ -1 & -2 & 1 & -1 \end{bmatrix}$

(c) $\begin{bmatrix} 3 & 5 & 7 \\ 4 & 2 & 6 \\ 0 & 1 & -2 \\ 3 & -3 & 6 \end{bmatrix}$

18. Solve each of the following systems of equations by using matrices.

(a) $\begin{cases} 5x + 2y = 14 \\ 2x - 6y = -15 \end{cases}$

(b) $\begin{cases} 3x - 4y + 2z = 19 \\ 2x + 2y - z = -6 \\ x - y + z = 6 \end{cases}$

(c) $\begin{cases} 2x - y + z = 4 \\ -x + y - 2z = -8 \\ 2x + y - 5z = -20 \end{cases}$

(d) $\begin{cases} 2w - 2x - y + z = 4 \\ 3w + x - y + 2z = 4 \\ w - 5x - y = 4 \end{cases}$

(e) $\begin{cases} w - x + y = 0 \\ x - y + z = 3 \\ w + y - z = 0 \\ -w + x + z = 3 \end{cases}$

19. A druggist has been asked to create 1500 mL of a solution that is 65 percent acid. She has two solutions on hand. The first is 50 percent acid and the second is 90 percent acid. How much of each solution should she mix together to obtain the required solution?

20. A dietician is trying to prescribe a well-balanced meal from three foods. Fifty grams of food I provides six units of protein, two units of carbohydrates, and three units of vitamins. Fifty grams of food II contains one unit of protein, three units of carbohydrates, and four units of vitamins. Fifty grams of food III contains five units of protein, two units of carbohydrates, and two units of vitamins. If a well-balanced meal consists of 20 units of protein, 15 units of carbohydrates, and 20 units of vitamins, determine the number of grams of each food that should go into each meal.

21. Gary Daniels has decided to invest $20 000 in mutual funds. His broker has recommended four funds to him. The prospective growth rate and dividend yield for each fund is given in the following chart.

	Mutual Fund			
	A	**B**	**C**	**D**
Growth Rate	10%	12%	16%	18%
Dividend	12%	10%	6%	4%

(a) If Gary wishes an average growth rate of 13 percent and an average dividend yield of 9 percent on his investments, determine how he should divide his money among the four funds.

(b) Gary decides to invest $10 000 in Fund B and $5000 in Fund C. Determine how the remainder of the money should be split among Fund A and Fund D so that the average 13 percent growth rate and 9 percent dividend yield are still achieved.

22. Given the following feasible regions and their corner points, determine the corner point that maximizes the indicated objective function.

(a) Maximize: $P = 20x + 25y$

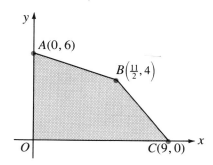

(b) Maximize: $R = 300x + 400y$

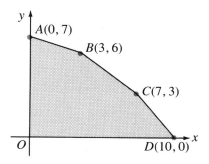

23. Using the graphical technique, determine the optimal solutions of the following linear models.

(a) Maximize: $S = 4x + 5y$
   Subject to: $x + y \leqslant 12$
               $3x + y \leqslant 30$
               $x + 2y \leqslant 18$
               $x \geqslant 0$
               $y \geqslant 0$

(b) Maximize: $T = 6x + 3y$
   Subject to: $x + y \leqslant 15$
               $x - 2y \leqslant -18$
               $2x + y \leqslant 25$
               $x \geqslant 0$
               $y \geqslant 0$

24. Given the following initial simplex tableaux, use the simplex method to reduce them to their final tableaux, and hence, state the optimal solution.

(a)

	x	y	s_1	s_2	P	constant
	3	2	1	0	0	10
	1	1	0	1	0	12
	-3	-4	0	0	1	0

(b)

	x	y	z	s_1	s_2	s_3	P	constant
	1	1	2	1	0	0	0	20
	1	1	1	0	1	0	0	30
	1	2	-3	0	0	1	0	10
	-2	-6	-4	0	0	0	1	0

*25. Determine the optimal solution to the following linear model.
Maximize: $P = 2x + 4y + 5z$
Subject to: $x + y + z \leqslant 12$
         $x - y + z \leqslant 8$
         $x \leqslant z$
         $x \geqslant 0$
         $y \geqslant 0$
         $z \geqslant 0$

*26. Nicole Bertrand is planning to invest up to $20 000 in three stocks. Stock A is a gold mining stock and this investment must be less than one half of the other two investments combined. The company issuing Stock B owns an abundance of undeveloped land and Nicole does not want her investment in this stock to exceed $8000. The dividend yields of the three stocks are given in the following chart.

	Stock A	Stock B	Stock C
Dividend	8%	10%	6%

How should Nicole invest in the three stocks so as to maximize her dividend yield?

TWENTIETH CENTURY MATHEMATICIANS

Professor Albert W. Tucker (of Princeton University) was born in Oshawa, Ontario in 1905 and grew up in small towns nearby. He is best known for his work in mathematical programming (an extension of linear programming) and the theory of games. He did so well in high school geometry that his school principal (one of the three teachers in the school!) declared that he must be a ''mathematical genius'' and could have a promising career as an actuary.

He also impressed his professors at the University of Toronto where he graduated in 1928. From there he went to Princeton University, in Princeton, New Jersey to work on a Ph.D. in topology. For 20 years he contributed to topology (the study of shapes and deformation). Then in 1947, the simplex method of linear programming (Chapter 10 in this text) was invented and Professor Tucker became interested in extending the ideas and methods to non-linear programming. He did this by relating the concepts to Kirchoff's laws of electrical networks. (These concepts were also used by the provers of the four-colour theorem).

He says, ''For me it was a revelation to see an algorithm which, if you let it, would develop the theory for you. Ever since that time, it has been my aim to make theory and the numerical methods of solving problems as unified as possible.''

In the '50s, Dr. Tucker was involved in a problems seminar at the IBM Research Centre at which, among other things, the participants tried to agree on what combinatorial mathematics was. They knew combinatorics (as it is now called) was useful and important, but what was it? They agreed that networks and graphs belonged there, as well as many aspects of matrices. Of course the traditional combinatorics of permutations and combinations belonged there too. Since they couldn't decide or agree on limits to combinatorics, they decided to develop it and see what they came up with. Professor Tucker is a major contributor to this development.

PROBLEMS PLUS

Duality

A bakery has two machines, a mixer and a kneader, with which it can prepare large batches of ingredients for three products—bread, cakes, and pastries. The following table displays the machine time required for the making of the respective foods:

	Bread	Cake	Pastry	Machine Capacity (hours/day)
Mixer	3	3	2	19
Kneader	2	0	3	21
Profit $/batch	120	90	90	

The optimization problem might be: how many batches of the respective units should be prepared in order to realize a maximum daily profit? The solution of this problem requires the Simplex method because we are dealing in three variables. However if we consider a closely related *dual problem* in which we minimize the total amount of machine time used per day, we obtain a linear model in two dimensions which we can solve graphically. The two models are presented below. Solve them both and verify that their optimal solutions are identical.

Maximization:

Let b be the number of batches of bread.

Let c be the number of batches of cake.

Let p be the number of batches of pastries.

Maximize: $P = 120b + 90c + 90p$

Subject to:

$$3b + 3c + 2p \leq 19$$
$$2b + 3p \leq 21$$
$$b, c, p \geq 0$$

Minimization:

Let m be the number of hours on the mixer

Let k be the number of hours on the kneader

Minimize: $P = 19m + 21k$

Subject to:

$$3m + 2k \geq 120$$
$$3m \geq 90$$
$$2m + 3k \geq 90$$
$$m, k \geq 0$$

APPENDIX A

TABLE 1
AREAS UNDER THE NORMAL CURVE $N(0, 1)$

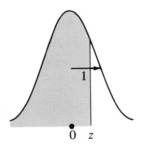

z	area	z	area
−4.0	0.0001		
−3.0	0.0013	0.1	0.5398
−2.9	0.0019	0.2	0.5793
−2.8	0.0026	0.3	0.6179
−2.7	0.0035	0.4	0.6554
−2.6	0.0047	0.5	0.6915
−2.5	0.0062	0.6	0.7257
−2.4	0.0082	0.7	0.7580
−2.3	0.0108	0.8	0.7881
−2.2	0.0139	0.9	0.8159
−2.1	0.0179	1.0	0.8413
−2.0	0.0227	1.1	0.8643
−1.9	0.0287	1.2	0.8849
−1.8	0.0359	1.3	0.9032
−1.7	0.0446	1.4	0.9192
−1.6	0.0548	1.5	0.9332
−1.5	0.0668	1.6	0.9452
−1.4	0.0808	1.7	0.9554
−1.3	0.0968	1.8	0.9641
−1.2	0.1151	1.9	0.9713
−1.1	0.1357	2.0	0.9773
−1.0	0.1587	2.1	0.9821
−0.9	0.1841	2.2	0.9861
−0.8	0.2119	2.3	0.9892
−0.7	0.2420	2.4	0.9918
−0.6	0.2743	2.5	0.9938
−0.5	0.3085	2.6	0.9953
−0.4	0.3446	2.7	0.9965
−0.3	0.3821	2.8	0.9974
−0.2	0.4207	2.9	0.9981
−0.1	0.4602	3.0	0.9987
0.0	0.5000	4.0	0.9999

ANSWERS

CHAPTER 1 PERMUTATIONS

EXERCISE 1.1

1. (a) Sum   (b) Product   (c) Product   (d) Sum
(e) Product

2. (a)

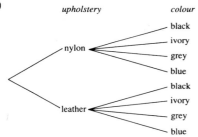

(b) 8

3. 6

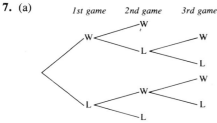

4. 21   **5.** (a) 25   (b) 20   **6.** 60

7. (a)

1st game   2nd game   3rd game

(b) 2

8. 47   **9.** 28   **10.** 1296   **11.** 24
12. 36   **13.** 208 860
14. (a) 4   (b) 13   (c) 16   (d) No   **15.** 12

16. (a)

1st child   2nd child   3rd child

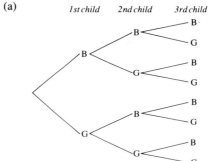

(b) 3   (c) 3   (d) No

EXERCISE 1.2

1. No
2. (a) – (v),   (b) – (iii),   (c) – (i),   (d) – (vi),
(e) – (iv),   (f) – (ii)
3. (a) 336   (b) 19 535 040   (c) 5985   (d) 36
(e) 3 652 110   (f) 2 919 735
4. (a) 30 240   (b) 586 051 200   (c) 84   (d) 495
(e) 56   (f) 8008   (g) 20   (h) 990
6. (a) 720   (b) 6!   **7.** 7!
8. (a) $n!$ (b) $(n+1)!$ (c) $(n+1)!$ (d) $(n+2)!$
(e) $n(n-1)$ or n^2-n (f) $(n+2)(n+1)n$
9. (a) 8   (b) 5   (c) 6   (d) 8

EXERCISE 1.3

1. (a) 60   (b) 15 120   (c) 1 663 200   (d) 120
(e) 1680   (f) 1 814 400
3. 24   **4.** (a) 60   (b) 125   (c) 12   (d) 50
5. 336   **6.** 40 320   **7.** 997 002 000
8. 1440   **9.** (a) 95 040   (b) 7920
10. (a) 6840   (b) 8000
12. (a) 40 320   (b) 5040   (c) 24   (d) 720

14. (a) (i) 20, 60 (ii) 336, 6720 (iii) 3 991 680, 95 040 (c) (i) 1 663 200 (ii) 3024

15. (a) 20 (b) 10

EXERCISE 1.4

2. (a) 840 (b) 120 (c) 39 916 800
(d) 2 494 800 (e) 129 729 600 (f) 415 800

3. 44666 46466 46646 46664 64664 66464 66644
66446 64646 64466

4. (a) 210 (b) 35   **5.** 12 600   **6.** 84

7. 1287   **8.** 10   **9.** 369 600   **10.** 13 860

11. 45 045

12. (a) 453 600 (b) 45 360 (c) 90 720
(d) 90 720

13. 210   **14.** 39 916 800 $\times$ cost of stamp

15. (a) 7 484 400 (b) 369 600

EXERCISE 1.5

1. 39 916 800   **2.** 720   **3.** 35 280

4. (a) 4096 (b) 3584 (c) 625 (d) 4500
(e) 4500

5. 127   **6.** 14.400   **7.** 32 659 200   **8.** 60

9. 3439   **10.** 480   **11.** 239 500 800

12. 40 319   **13.** 90 720   **14.** 144

15. 33   **16.** 26   **17.** 7200

1.6 REVIEW EXERCISE

3. (a) 5 (b) 1 (c) 1 (d) 6

4.

5. (a) 180 (b) 1120 (c) 72 (d) 1260

6. 676, 17 576   **7.** 5039

8. (a) 5040 (b) 45 360 (c) 25 200

9. 2520   **10.** 5040

11. (a) 120 (b) 24 (c) 48 (d) 72   **13.** 6

1.7 CHAPTER 1 TEST

1. -46

2.

3. 210   **4.** 5040   **5.** (a) 42 (b) 252

6. (a) 420 (b) 120

7. 320   **8.** (a) 24 (b) 12 (c) 36

CHAPTER 2 COMBINATIONS

REVIEW AND PREVIEW TO CHAPTER 2

EXERCISE 1

1. (a) $\dfrac{m^2}{n^2}$ (b) $\dfrac{1}{2}$ (c) $\dfrac{y^2}{x^2}$ (d) $\dfrac{x+3}{x+4}$ (e) 1

(f) $\dfrac{x+y}{y}$

2. (a) $\dfrac{x(x-2)}{4(x+2)}$ or $\dfrac{x^2-2x}{4x+8}$ (b) $x(4x+1)$ or $4x^2+x$

(c) $\dfrac{1}{a^2+b^2}$

EXERCISE 2

1. (a) $\dfrac{x^2-x-7}{6}$ (b) $\dfrac{7x+3}{x-4}$

2. (a) 420 (b) x^2-1 (c) $8+4x-2x^2-x^3$

3. (a) $\dfrac{53a}{36}$ (b) $\dfrac{2y-3x-2x^2}{xy}$ (c) $\dfrac{19ab-2b^2+24a^2}{18ab}$

(d) $\dfrac{10x+2}{12+x-x^2}$ (e) $\dfrac{2a-ab+2b}{a-ab}$

EXERCISE 2.1

2. 0

3. (a) {DEER, EDER, EEDR, EERD, DERE, EDRE, ERDE, ERED, DREE, RDEE, REDE, REED} (b) $\{\frac{2}{3}, \frac{2}{5}, \frac{3}{2}, \frac{3}{5}, \frac{5}{3}, \frac{5}{2}\}$

(c) $\{J\heartsuit, Q\heartsuit, K\heartsuit, J\diamondsuit, Q\diamondsuit, K\diamondsuit\}$

4. (b) 37

5. (a) $\varnothing$, {green} (b) $\varnothing$, {H}, {T}, {H,T}

(c) $\varnothing$, {yes}, {no}, {maybe}, {yes, no}, {yes, maybe}, {no, maybe}, {yes, no, maybe}

(d) $\varnothing$, {3}, {5}, {7}, {9}, {3, 5}, {3, 7}, {3, 9}, {5, 7}, {5, 9}, {7, 9}, {3, 5, 7}, {3, 5, 9}, {3, 7, 9}, {5, 7, 9}, {3, 5, 7, 9}

6. (a) 2 (b) 4 (c) 8 (d) 16 (e) 32 (f) 2^{13} (g) 2^{105} (h) 2^{n}

7. (a) $F' = \{0, 1, 4, 6, 7, 8, 9, 11, 12, 13, 14, 16, 17, 18, 19, 21, 22, 23, 24\}$

(b) $G' = \{1, 2, 3, 4, 5, 6, 7\}$

(c) $C' = \{a, e, i, o, u\}$

(d) $B' = \{12, 13, 14, \ldots, 19, 20\}$

8. (a) I is a subset of R. (b) R and C are disjoint. (c) T is a subset of E. (d) N and W are disjoint sets. (e) N and P are equal sets.

9. (a)

(b)

10. possible, but not the only possibility

11. (a) set of whole numbers which are not perfect squares

(b) set of odd numbers

(c) set including all even numbers and all perfect squares

(d) set of even perfect squares

(e) set including all odd numbers and all numbers which are not perfect squares

(f) set of odd numbers which are not perfect squares

(g) set of numbers which are neither even nor perfect squares

(h) set of numbers which are not even perfect squares

12. (a) {K, Y, B, R, D} (b) {K, E, Y} (c) {E, B, O, A, R, D} (d) {O, A} (e) {K, E, Y, B, R, D} (f) {K, Y} (g) {K, Y} (h) {K, E, Y, B, R, D}

13. (b)

A'∪B'   (A∩B)'

(c)

A'∪B'   (A∩B)'

14. (b)

A'∩B'   (A∩B)'

(c)

A'∩B'   (A∪B)'

15. (a) (i) 5   (ii) 2   (iii) 3   (iv) 3   (v) 2   (vi) 5
(vii) 0
(b) (i) 5   (ii) 2   (iii) 2   (iv) 3   (v) 3   (vi) 4
(vii) 0
(c) (i) 5   (ii) 3   (iii) 3   (iv) 2   (v) 2   (vi) 5
(vii) 1

16. (c) S (d) A (e) A (f) A (g) $A \cup A' = S$,
$A \cap A' = \varnothing$

17. (a) $A' \cap B'$ (b) $A' \cup B'$

18. $n(A \cup B) = n(A) + n(B) - n(A \cap B)$

20.

| 1st element | 2nd element | 3rd element |

```
                                          in
                             in
               in                         out
                                          in
                   out
                                          out
                                          in
                             in
               out                        out
                                          in
                   out
                                          out
```

EXERCISE 2.2

2. (a) number of arrangements   (b) number of lists

3. (a) 15   (b) 495   (c) 1   (d) 56   (e) 120
(f) 120   (g) 120   (h) 1   (i) 60   (j) 126
(k) 4950   (l) 700

5. 792   **6.** (a) 2300   (b) 13 800   **7.** 56

8. 2 598 960

9. (a) (i) 1   (ii) 1   (iii) 1   (iv) 1   (b) $\binom{n}{n} = 1$

10. $\binom{n}{0} = 1$

11. (a) (i) 5   (ii) 9   (iii) 11   (iv) 17   (b) $\binom{n}{1} = n$

12. (a) 210   (b) 5   (c) 50   (d) 100   (e) 50   (f) 5

13. 16 380   **14.** (a) 252   (b) 140   (c) 72

15. 4 484 480   **16.** 24   **17.** $\frac{13!}{5!8!} \frac{13!}{2!11!} \frac{13!}{3!10!} \frac{13!}{3!10!}$

18. (a) (i) 184   (ii) 330   (iii) 28   (iv) 10
(b) $\binom{n}{r} = \binom{n}{n-r}$

19. (c) $\binom{n+1}{r+1} = \binom{n+1}{r+1}\binom{n}{r}$

20. (a) 5   (b) 7 or 2   (c) 2   (d) 10

22. $\frac{13!}{5!8!} \frac{39!}{8!31!}$

23. (a) 924   (b) 34 650   (c) 554 400

EXERCISE 2.3

1. (a) 64   (b) 6   **2.** (a) 2^n (b) n **3.** 127

4. 31   **5.** (a) 2300   (b) 276   (c) 2024

6. 66   **7.** (a) 7   (b) 11   **8.** 225 765

9. (a) 16   (b) 256   (c) at least 6

10. 28 561   **11.** 5   **12.** 23   **13.** 924

14. 71   **15.** 3   **16.** 728   **17.** 8514

18. (a) 2520   (b) 2430

19. if Josie chooses biography

20. 330 × 12! × 8!

22. (a) 5   (b) 47

23. (a) 11   (b) 12   (c) 19   (d) 16

24. (a) 9   (b) 10   **25.** 320

26. (a)

	1st element	2nd element	3rd element	nth element
no. entries in column	(2 = 2^1)	(4 = 2^2)	(8 = 2^3) ...	(2^n)

```
                              in
                   in
                              out
        in
                              in
                   out
                              out
                              in
                   in
        out                   out
                              in
                   out
                              out
```

EXERCISE 2.4

1. (a) 14   (b) 12

2. $n(X \cap Y) = n(X) + n(Y) - n(X \cup Y)$

3. (a) $n(P) + n(Q)$ (b) 0

4. D and E are disjoint.

5. (a) 10
(b)

7. (a) 22 (b) 19

8. 3

9. (a) 90 (b) 10 (c) 20 (d) 50

11. 400   **12.** 2

13. $n(A \cup B \cup C \cup D) = n(A) + n(B) + n(C)$
$+ n(D) - n(A \cap B) - n(A \cap C) - n(A \cap D)$
$- n(B \cap C) - n(B \cap D) - n(C \cap D)$
$+ n(A \cap B \cap C) + n(A \cap B \cap D) + n(B \cap C \cap D)$
$- n(A \cap B \cap C \cap D)$

15. 8   **16.** 2

2.5 REVIEW EXERCISE

1. (a) yes (b) yes (c) yes (d) no (e) no
(f) no (g) yes

2. (a) $X' = \{b, c, d, g, n, t\}$
(b) $Y' = \{b, d, e, i, n, o, t, u\}$
(c) $X \cup Y = \{a, e, i, o, u, c, g\}$
(d) $X \cap Y = \{a\}$

3. (a) $\binom{7}{4}$ (b) the number of 3-subsets of a set of
10 objects   (c) the number of ways of choosing
for the triple scoop

4. (a) 1 (b) 9 (c) 1 (d) 8

5. (a) $n(Q) + n(R)$ (b) $n(Q) + n(R) - n(Q \cap R)$

6. (a) $+ - \times, + \times -, \times + -, - + \times, - \times +,$
$\times - +$
(b) $\varnothing, \{+\}, \{-\}, \{\times\}, \{+, -\}, \{+, \times\}, \{-, \times\}, \{+, -, \times\}$

7. (a) as ad af ag sa sd sf sg da ds df dg fa fs fd fg
ga gs gd gf
(b) $\{a, s\}, \{a, d\}, \{a, f\}, \{a, g\}, \{s, d\}, \{s, f\}, \{s, g\},$
$\{d, f\}, \{d, g\}, \{f, g\}$

8. (a) 5! (b) $\frac{12!}{7!}$ (c) $\frac{9!}{5!4!}$

9. (a) 84 (b) 45 (c) 55 440 (d) 2520
(e) 10 080

10. (a) 4! (b) 28! (c) 15 (d) 9900 (e) 6!
(f) $P(7, 4)$ (g) $\binom{8}{5}$ (h) $\binom{7}{4}$

11. 210   **12.** 16   **13.** 12   **14.** 3360

15. (a) 5040 (b) 95

16. 56   **17.** 2186   **18.** 360   **19.** 40

20. (a) 177 100 (b) 55 055 (c) 8855 (d) 80 200

21. 2100   **22.** (a) 74 (b) 1   **24.** (a) 8 (b) 5

2.6 CHAPTER 2 TEST

1. 43   **2.** 66   **3.** 63

4. (a) $P(n, r) = r! \binom{n}{r}$

5. 35   **6.** $2! \dfrac{71!}{67!4!} \dfrac{21!}{16!5!}$ **7.** 14 378

8. (a) 185 (b) 71

CHAPTER 3 THE BINOMIAL THEOREM

REVIEW AND PREVIEW TO CHAPTER 3

EXERCISE 1

1. (a) $-1 + 1 + 3 + 5$
(b) $\frac{1}{6} + \frac{1}{7} + \frac{1}{8} + \frac{1}{9} + \frac{1}{10}$
(c) $0 + 2 + 6 + 12 + 20 + 30$
(d) $\frac{1}{2} + 1 + 2 + 4 + 8 + 16 + 32$
(e) $1 + 4 + 6 + 4 + 1$
(f) $1 - 49 + 441 - 1225 + 1225 - 441 + 49 - 1$

2. (a) $\sum_{i=0}^{7} 2^i$ (b) $\sum_{k=3}^{7} kx$ (c) $\sum_{i=1}^{7} a^i$
(d) $\sum_{i=1}^{6} (-1)^{i-1} x^i$ (e) $\sum_{r=0}^{7} \binom{7}{r}$
(f) $\sum_{r=0}^{10} \binom{10}{r}^2$ (g) $\sum_{r=0}^{9} (-1)^r \binom{9}{r}$
(h) $\sum_{r=0}^{n} \binom{n}{r}$ (i) $\sum_{r=0}^{n} (-1)^r \binom{n}{r}^2$

EXERCISE 2

1. (a) x^{-1} (b) x^{-2} (c) $-x^{-3}$ (d) $2x^{-2}$
   (e) $-3x^{-1}$ (f) $x^{\frac{1}{2}}$ (g) $x^{-\frac{1}{2}}$ (h) $x^{-\frac{1}{3}}$

2. (a) $27x^{22}$ (b) $-2x^2$ (c) $-x^{17}$ (d) x^{16-r}
   (e) a^{11-2r} (f) $(-1)^r 2^{5-r} x^{10-3r}$ (g) $2^{n-r} x^{3r-n}$
   (h) $(-1)^r x^{n-3r}$

EXERCISE 3

1. (a) $4x^2 - 12x + 9$ (b) $x^4 + 6x^3 + 9x^2$
   (c) $x^3 + 3x^2 + 3x + 1$
   (d) $a^6 - 12a^4 + 48a^2 - 64$
   (e) $12x^3 + 40x^2 - 25x - 125$
   (f) $a^4 - 2a^3b + 2ab^3 - b^4$
   (g) $x^4 - 8x^3 + 24x^2 - 32x + 16$
   (h) $225p^4 - 60p^3q - 236p^2q^2 + 32pq^3 + 64q^4$

EXERCISE 3.1

1. (a) $\binom{9}{7}$ (b) $\binom{13}{8}$ (c) $\binom{46}{7}$ (d) $\binom{26}{0}$

2. (a) $\binom{9}{4}$ (b) $\binom{18}{7}$ (c) $\binom{29}{5}$ (d) $\binom{n}{r}$

3. (a) $\binom{25}{5} = 53\,130$ (b) $\binom{24}{4} = 10\,626$
   (c) $\binom{24}{5} = 42\,504$ (d) $\binom{25}{5} = \binom{24}{4} + \binom{24}{5}$

4. (a) $\binom{n}{r}$ (b) $\binom{n-1}{r-1}$ (c) $\binom{n-1}{r}$
   (d) $\binom{n}{r} = \binom{n-1}{r-1} + \binom{n-1}{r}$

5. $n = 12$: 1 12 66 220 495 792 924 792 495 220 66 12 1

6. (b) 128 (c) (i) 256 (ii) 512 (iii) 1024
   (d) 2^n

7. $128, 2^n$ 8. 8 9. 7 10. 9

11. (c) $\binom{12}{6} = 924$ (d) (i) $\binom{4}{2}$ (ii) $\binom{6}{3}$
    (iii) $\binom{8}{4}$ (iv) $\binom{10}{5}$ (v) $\binom{12}{6}$ (e) $\binom{2n}{n}$
    (f) $\sum_{r=0}^{n} \binom{n}{r}^2$

12. (a) $\binom{2n}{n}$ (b) $\binom{n}{0}\binom{n}{n}$, $\binom{n}{1}\binom{n}{n-1}$, $\binom{n}{2}\binom{n}{n-2}$,
    $\binom{n}{3}\binom{n}{n-3}$, ..., $\binom{n}{n}\binom{n}{0}$
    (c) $\sum_{r=0}^{n} \binom{n}{r}\binom{n}{n-r} = \binom{2n}{n}$
    (d) $\sum_{r=0}^{n} \binom{n}{r}^2 = \binom{2n}{n}$

13. (b) 0 (c) (i) 0 (ii) 0 (d) $\begin{cases} 1 & \text{if } n = 0 \\ 0 & \text{if } n \neq 0 \end{cases}$

15. (a) 10, 15, 21
    (c) $\binom{2}{2}, \binom{3}{2}, \binom{4}{2}, \binom{5}{2}, \binom{6}{2}, \binom{7}{2}$
    (d) $\binom{8}{2}, \binom{9}{2}$ (e) $\binom{n+1}{2}$

16. (a) 5050 (b) 500 500 (c) 20 200

17. (a) 20, 35, 56
    (c) $\binom{3}{3}, \binom{4}{3}, \binom{5}{3}, \binom{6}{3}, \binom{7}{3}, \binom{8}{3}$
    (d) $\binom{9}{3}, \binom{10}{3}$ (e) $\binom{n+2}{3}$

EXERCISE 3.2

1. (a) 32 (b) 20 (c) 4
2. 3,0,6,0,3   3. 2,0,3,0,1   4. 9,16,19,16,9
5. 0,9,0,7,0,3   6. 210
7. (a) $a^9 + 9a^8b + 36a^7b^2 + 84a^6b^3 + 126a^5b^4$
   $+ 126a^4b^5 + 84a^3b^6 + 36a^2b^7 + 9ab^8 + b^9$
   (b) $a^{10} + 10a^9b + 45a^8b^2 + 120a^7b^3$
   $+ 210a^6b^4 + 252a^5b^5 + 210a^4b^6 + 120a^3b^7$
   $+ 45a^2b^8 + 10ab^9 + b^{10}$ (c) $a^{11} + 11a^{10}b$
   $+ 55a^9b^2 + 165a^8b^3 + 330a^7b^4 + 462a^6b^5$
   $+ 462a^5b^6 + 330a^4b^7 + 165a^3b^8 + 55a^2b^9$
   $+ 11ab^{10} + b^{11}$

8. (a) $\binom{3}{0} a^3 + \binom{3}{1} a^2b + \binom{3}{2} ab^2 + \binom{3}{3} b^3$
   (b) $\binom{4}{0} a^4 + \binom{4}{1} a^3b + \binom{4}{2} a^2b^2 + \binom{4}{3} ab^3$
   $+ \binom{4}{4} b^4$
   (c) $\binom{5}{0} a^5 + \binom{5}{1} a^4b + \binom{5}{2} a^3b^2 + \binom{5}{3} a^2b^3$
   $+ \binom{5}{4} ab^4 + \binom{5}{5} b^5$

9. $\binom{n}{0} a^n + \binom{n}{1} a^{n-1}b + \binom{n}{2} a^{n-2}b^2$
   $+ \binom{n}{3} a^{n-3}b^3 + \dots + \binom{n}{n} b^n$

EXERCISE 3.3

1. (a) $\binom{5}{0} a^5 + \binom{5}{1} a^4b + \binom{5}{2} a^3b^2 + \binom{5}{3} a^2b^3$
   $+ \binom{5}{4} ab^4 + \binom{5}{5} b^5$ (b) $\binom{3}{0} x^3 + \binom{3}{1} x^2y +$
   $\binom{3}{2} xy^2 + \binom{3}{3} y^3$ (c) $\binom{4}{0}\left(\frac{1}{4}\right)^4 + \binom{4}{1}\left(\frac{1}{4}\right)^3\left(\frac{3}{4}\right)$
   $+ \binom{4}{2}\left(\frac{1}{4}\right)^2\left(\frac{3}{4}\right)^2 + \binom{4}{3}\left(\frac{1}{4}\right)\left(\frac{3}{4}\right)^3 + \binom{4}{4}\left(\frac{3}{4}\right)^4$

2. (a) 6 (b) 1 (c) 0 (d) 4

3. (a) $\binom{11}{2}$ (b) $\binom{11}{8}$ (c) $\binom{11}{0}$ (d) $\binom{11}{r}$

4. (a) $(a + b)^4$ (b) $(x^2 + \frac{1}{x})^6$ (c) $(-3 + 2)^5$

5. (a) $8a^3 + 12a^2b + 6ab^2 + b^3$
(b) $a^4 - 8a^3b + 24a^2b^2 - 32ab^3 + 16b^4$
(c) $1 - 5x + 10x^2 - 10x^3 + 5x^4 - x^5$
(d) $1 + 6x^2 + 15x^4 + 20x^6 + 15x^8 + 6x^{10} + x^{12}$
(e) $1 + \dfrac{4}{x} + \dfrac{6}{x^2} + \dfrac{4}{x^3} + \dfrac{1}{x^4}$
(f) $x^5 - 5x^3 + 10x - \dfrac{10}{x} + \dfrac{5}{x^3} - \dfrac{1}{x^5}$

6. (a) $x^5 - 10x^2 + \dfrac{40}{x} - \dfrac{80}{x^4} + \dfrac{80}{x^7} - \dfrac{32}{x^{10}}$
(b) $16x^{12} + 32x^9\sqrt{y} + 24x^6y + 8x^3\sqrt{y^3} + y^2$
(c) $a^8 + 12a^5b + 54a^2b^2 + \dfrac{108b^3}{a} + \dfrac{81b^4}{a^4}$
(d) $x^3 - 12x^2 + 60x - 160 + \dfrac{240}{x} - \dfrac{192}{x^2} + \dfrac{64}{x^3}$

7. (a) $a^{10} + 10a^9b + 45a^8b^2 + 120a^7b^3 + \ldots$
(b) $1 - 12x^2 + 66x^4 - 220x^6 + \ldots$
(c) $x^{18} + 18x^{14} + 144x^{10} + 672x^6 + \ldots$
(d) $256x^8 - 3072x^5 + 16\,128x^2 - \dfrac{48\,384}{x} + \ldots$
(e) $x^{18} - 12x^{13} + 60x^8 - 160x^3 + \ldots$
(f) $x^{11} + 11\sqrt{x^{23}} + 55x^{12} + 165\sqrt{x^{25}} + \ldots$

8. (a) 1 (b) 1 (c) -8

9. $(a + b)^n = \sum\limits_{r=0}^{n} \binom{n}{r} a^{n-r}b^r$

10. (a) $\frac{1}{32} + \frac{5}{32} + \frac{10}{32} + \frac{10}{32} + \frac{5}{32} + \frac{1}{32}$ (b) 1
(c)

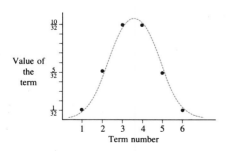

Value of the term

Term number

11. (a) $0.0016 + 0.0256 + 0.1536 + 0.4096 + 0.4096$ (b) 1

(c)

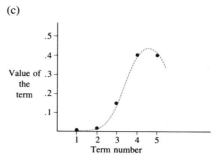

Value of the term

Term number

13. $\sum\limits_{r=10}^{n} (-1)^r \binom{n}{r} = 0, n \neq 0$ **14.** $n = 9, x = -2$

15. $n = 5, a = \frac{1}{3}$ **16.** $\frac{4}{5}$

EXERCISE 3.4

1. (a) 10 (b) 19 (c) 34 (d) $n + 1$

2. (a) 0 (b) 5 (c) no such term (d) 8 (e) $k - 1$
(f) 6

3. (a) $\binom{7}{r}x^{7-r}y^r$ (b) $\binom{13}{r}p^{13-r}q^r$
(c) $\binom{11}{r} 1^{11-r}(-x)^r$ (d) $\binom{12}{r} x^{12-r}\left(-\dfrac{1}{x}\right)^r$

4. (a) $\frac{21}{4} x^{12}$ (b) $252a^5b^5$ (c) $\dfrac{16\,896}{x^8}$ (d) $126x^6$
(e) $\frac{135}{1024}$ (f) $1120x^4y^4$

5. (a) $\binom{11}{r} a^{11-r}b^r$ (b) $(-1)^r\binom{10}{r} x^{20-r}$
(c) $(-1)^r\binom{13}{r} a^{13-2r}$ (d) $\binom{7}{r} x^{14-3r}$
(e) $(-1)^r\binom{9}{r} 2^{9-r} x^{\frac{18-r}{2}}$ (f) $\binom{5}{r} \dfrac{5^{5-r}}{7776}$
(g) $\binom{8}{r} (0.3)^{8-r}(0.7)^r$ or $\binom{8}{r} \dfrac{3^{8-r}7^r}{10^8}$ (h) $\binom{6}{r} \dfrac{1}{64}$

6. (a) $-6x^4$ (b) $15x^{-2}$

7. (a) 1120 (b) 0 **8.** 540

9. (a) 36 (b) -126 (c) 0

10. (a) $10y$ (b) no such term **11.** 970

EXERCISE 3.5

1. $8x^4 - 4x^3 - 18x^2 - 11x - 2$

2. $8a^5 + 32a^4 + 44a^3 + 28a^2 + \frac{17}{2}a + 1$

3. $x^6 - 3x^4 + 2x^2 + 2 - \dfrac{3}{x^2} + \dfrac{1}{x^4}$

4. $x^{16} + 11x^{15} + 39x^{14} + \ldots$

5. $1 + 5a^2 + 5a^4 + \ldots$

6. $x^{30} + x^{28} - 7x^{26} + \ldots$

7. $4320x^5$ **8.** $-8x$ **9.** $-35a^8$

10. $a^4 + 4a^3b + 4a^3c + 6a^2b^2 + 12a^2bc + 6a^2c^2$
$+ 4ab^3 + 12ab^2c + 12abc^2 + 4ac^3 + b^4$
$+ 4b^3c + 6b^2c^2 + 4bc^3 + c^4$

11. -8

12. (a) $\dbinom{m+n}{k}$ (b) $\dbinom{m}{0}\dbinom{n}{k}, \dbinom{m}{1}\dbinom{n}{k-1},$
$\dbinom{m}{2}\dbinom{n}{k-2}, \ldots, \dbinom{m}{k}\dbinom{n}{0}$
(c) $\dbinom{m}{0}\dbinom{n}{k} + \dbinom{m}{1}\dbinom{n}{k-1} + \dbinom{m}{2}\dbinom{n}{k-2}$
$+ \ldots + \dbinom{m}{k}\dbinom{n}{0} = \dbinom{m+n}{k}$ or
$\displaystyle\sum_{r=0}^{k} \dbinom{m}{r}\dbinom{n}{k-r} = \dbinom{m+n}{k}$

3.6 REVIEW EXERCISE

1. (a) $\dbinom{9}{4}$ (b) $\dbinom{19}{6}$ (c) $\dbinom{101}{50}$ (d) $\dbinom{n}{k}$

2. (a) 32   (b) 0   (c) 70

3. (a) 13   (b) 11

4. (a) 9   (b) 0   (c) 3

5. (a) $\dbinom{10}{r} (2x^2)^{10-r} \left(-\dfrac{3}{x}\right)^r$ (b) $\dbinom{19}{r}\left(\dfrac{1}{a^2}\right)^{19-r}(a^2)^r$

6. 1 999 000   **7.** (a) 6   (b) 8

8. 4   **9.** 0   **10.** 512

11. (a) 286   (b) 66   (c) 220

12. (a) 40   (b) 56   **13.** 48   **14.** yes

15. (a) $64x^6 - 192x^4 + 240x^2 - 160 + \dfrac{60}{x^2}$
$- \dfrac{12}{x^4} + \dfrac{1}{x^6}$

(b) $x^8 + 4x^4 + 6 + \dfrac{4}{x^4} + \dfrac{1}{x^8}$

(c) $a^5 - \dfrac{10a^4}{b} + \dfrac{40a^3}{b^2} - \dfrac{80a^2}{b^3} + \dfrac{80a}{b^4} - \dfrac{32}{b^5}$

(d) $\dfrac{x^3}{8} + 3\sqrt{x^3} + 24 + \dfrac{64}{\sqrt{x^3}}$

16. (a) $x^8 - 8x^6 + 28x^4 - \ldots$
(b) $a^{14} + 7a^{10} + 21a^6 + \ldots$
(c) $x^6 - 12x^3 + 60 - \ldots$

17. (a) $\dbinom{12}{r} a^{12-r}b^r$ (b) $(-1)^r\dbinom{7}{r} x^{14-r}$

(c) $(-1)^r\dbinom{13}{r} x^{13-3r}$ (d) $\dbinom{6}{r} 2^{6-2r}x^{\frac{3r-12}{2}}$

18. 1   **19.** (a) $45x^6$ (b) -252

20. (a) 35   (b) 0   **21.** $\frac{40}{243}$ **22.** 64

23. (a) $0.4096 + 0.4096 + 0.1536 + 0.0256$
$+ 0.0016$ (b) 1

(c)

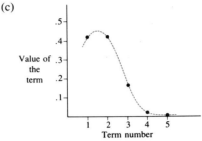

24. $n = 6, b = -\frac{1}{2}$ **25.** $1 + 8x + 29x^2 + \ldots$

26. $1 + x - 2x^2 + \ldots$

27. 36   **28.** (b) $\displaystyle\sum_{r=0}^{n} (-3)^r \dbinom{n}{r} = (-2)^n$

3.7 CHAPTER 3 TEST

1. (a) $\dbinom{20}{3} = 1140$ (b) 0   (c) $2^8 = 256$

(d) $\dbinom{10}{5} = 252$

2. 25 250   **3.** 42   **4.** $\displaystyle\sum_{r=0}^{n} (-1)^r \dbinom{n}{r}^2$

5. (a) $x^5 - 5x^3 + 10x - \dfrac{10}{x} + \dfrac{5}{x^3} - \dfrac{1}{x^5}$

(b) $16a^8 + 32a^4 + 24 + \dfrac{8}{a^4} + \dfrac{1}{a^8}$

6. $x^{20} - 30\sqrt{x^{37}} + 405x^{17} + \ldots$

7. 1   **8.** $\frac{256}{625}$

9. (a) $(-1)^r \dbinom{8}{r} 2^{8-r}x^{8-2r}$ (b) 1792

10. (a) $\dbinom{10}{r} x^{\frac{40-5r}{2}}$ (b) 45

11. $-30x^4$ **12.** (b) $\displaystyle\sum_{r=0}^{n} 2^r \dbinom{n}{r} = 3^n$

CHAPTER 4 FINITE SERIES

REVIEW AND PREVIEW TO CHAPTER 4

EXERCISE 1

1. (a) 5, 8, 11, 14, 17; $a = 5$, $d = 3$
(b) 5, 3, 1, -1, -3; $a = 5$, $d = -2$
(c) 1, 4, 7, 10, 13; $a = 1$, $d = 3$
(d) 3, -1, -5, -9, -13; $a = 3$, $d = -4$

2. (a) $5 + 120(n - 1)$ (b) $1 + \frac{1}{2}(n - 1)$
(c) $-9 + 1(n - 1)$ (d) $3 - 4(n - 1)$

3. $a = 8$, $d = -4$

EXERCISE 2

1. (a) 1, 2, 4, 8, 16; $a = 1$, $r = 2$
(b) 3, 6, 12, 24, 48; $a = 3$, $r = 2$
(c) 6, 18, 54, 162, 486; $a = 6$, $r = 3$
(d) $1, \frac{1}{3}, \frac{1}{9}, \frac{1}{27}, \frac{1}{81}$; $a = 1$, $r = \frac{1}{3}$

2. (a) $5(2^{n-1})$ (b) $5(3^{n-1})$ (c) $7^4(-\frac{1}{7})^{n-1}$
(d) $3(5^{n-1})$ or $3(-5)^{n-1}$

3. $a = 9$, $r = \frac{1}{3}$ **4.** $t_n = 10$ for all n

EXERCISE 3

1. (a) 28 (b) $\frac{7}{81}$ **2.** -135

EXERCISE 4

1. (a) $698.92 (b) $701.38 (c) $704.96
(d) $711.78   **2.** $83 000

EXERCISE 4.1

1. b   **2.** (a) 9 (b) 8 (c) 3   **3.** a

4. (a) $1 + 2 + 3 + 4 + 5$
(b) $(2^2 - 6) + (3^2 - 6) + (4^2 - 6)$
(c) $(5 - 6) + (6 - 6) + (7 - 6) + (8 - 6)$
(d) $(7 - \frac{4}{2^2}) + (7 - \frac{4}{3^2}) + (7 - \frac{4}{4^2})$
$+ (7 - \frac{4}{5^2}) + (7 - \frac{4}{6^2}) + (7 - \frac{4}{7^2})$

5. (a) $\binom{12}{10} + \binom{12}{11} + \binom{12}{12}$
(b) $t_1 + t_3 + t_5 + t_7 + t_9 + t_{11} + t_{13}$
(c) $t_6 + t_5 + t_4 + t_3 + t_2 + t_1$
(d) $\dfrac{1}{4 - 3} + \dfrac{1}{5 - 3} + \dfrac{1}{6 - 3} + \dfrac{1}{7 - 3} +$
$\dfrac{1}{8 - 3} + \dfrac{1}{9 - 3}$

6. (a) $\displaystyle\sum_{k=1}^{7} k^2$ (b) $\displaystyle\sum_{k=1}^{9} k^3$ (c) $\displaystyle\sum_{i=1}^{7} \left(\frac{1}{2}\right)^{i-1}$
(d) $\displaystyle\sum_{i=1}^{10} \frac{1}{10 + i}$ (e) $\displaystyle\sum_{k=1}^{8} \frac{1}{(k - 1)!}$

(f) $\displaystyle\sum_{k=1}^{7} \frac{1}{k(k + 1)}$ (g) $\displaystyle\sum_{i=1}^{7} i3^{i-1}$ (h) $\displaystyle\sum_{j=1}^{6} \binom{5}{j - 1}$
(i) $\displaystyle\sum_{k=1}^{8} \left(-\frac{1}{3}\right)^{k-1}$ (j) $\displaystyle\sum_{k=1}^{7} (-1)^{k-1}t_k$ (k) $\displaystyle\sum_{i=1}^{6} iu_i$
(l) $\displaystyle\sum_{j=1}^{6} t_j^2$ (m) $\displaystyle\sum_{k=1}^{6} \left(\frac{x + k - 1}{x + k}\right)$

7. (a) 303 (b) 115 (c) 311 (d) 397

8. (a) $30 500 (b) $81 000
(c) $(24 500 + 2000n)$
(d) $\displaystyle\sum_{i=1}^{n} \$[25\,000 + (i - 1)2000]$

9. (a) $24 478.07 (b) $66 301.20
(c) $20 500 (1.03)^{2n}$ (d) $\$\dfrac{20\,500}{2} \displaystyle\sum_{i=1}^{2n} (1.03)^{i-1}$
or $\displaystyle\sum_{i=1}^{n} \$20\,500(1.015)(1.03)^{2(i-1)}$

EXERCISE 4.2

1. (a) geometric, $a = 1$, $r = -1$
(b) arithmetic, $a = 1$, $d = -3$
(c) arithmetic, $a = 1$, $d = 0$ *and*
geometric, $a = 1$, $r = 1$
(d) geometric, $a = 1$, $r = 0$

2. (a) 39 (b) 153 (c) 52 (d) 512

3. (a) 495 (b) 1350 (c) 350 (d) -1512

4. 348   **5.** 24 550

6. (a) 12 (b) 30 (c) 15 (d) 13

7. $a = 17$, $d = -3$

8. (a) 2550 (b) 11 718 (c) -3280
(d) $1457\frac{1}{3} = \frac{4372}{3}$

9. (a) 797 160 (b) 0.999 023 (c) 12.483 418
(d) 2 096 128

10. 925   **11.** 2046   **12.** 4 551 048   **13.** 3

14. $2^{11} - 1 = 2047$ **15.** $2^{17} - 1 = 131\,071$

16. n^2 **17.** 816

EXERCISE 4.3

1. (a) $a = 1$, $d = 1$, $r = 3$
(b) $a = 4$, $d = 1$, $r = 2$
(c) $a = 1$, $d = 0$, $r = 1$
(d) $a = 1$, $d = 0$, $r = 4$
(e) $a = 2$, $d = 2$, $r = \frac{1}{2}$
(f) $a = 1$, $d = 1$, $r = -1$

2. (a) 1.988 281 25   (b) 1.020 304
(c) 1.321 178   (d) 75 376.486

3. (a) 2.867 187 5   (b) 257 253.696
(c) 305 086.333   (d) $-0.499\ 060\ 102$

5. (a) $\dfrac{n[2a + (n-1)d]}{2}$ (b) $a\left(\dfrac{1 - r^n}{1 - r}\right)$

(c) $d\left(\dfrac{1 - r^n}{(1 - r)^2}\right) + \dfrac{a - d - [a + (n-1)d]\, r^n}{1 - r}$

EXERCISE 4.4

1. The formula only applies if the common ratio, r, satisfies $|r| < 1$.

2. The formula only applies if the common ratio, r, satisfies $|r| < 1$.

3. (a) 1   (b) $\frac{2}{3}$ (c) 4   (d) 50   (e) $\frac{4}{3}$ (f) 10

4. (a) $\frac{7}{11}$ (b) $\frac{37}{55}$ (c) $\frac{926}{4995}$ (d) $\frac{17}{35}$

6. (a) $\frac{1}{2^9}$ **7.** s^{-1}

8. $27\frac{3}{11}$ minutes after five o'clock

9. $38\frac{2}{11}$ minutes after one o'clock

10. 4.8 minutes after noon   **11.** 7.5 km

EXERCISE 4.5

1. \$142 319.61   **2.** \$136 739.71
3. \$133 771.20   **4.** \$19 022.05
5. (a) 10.8, 9.72, 8.75, 7.87, 7.09, 6.34, 5.74, 5.17
(b)

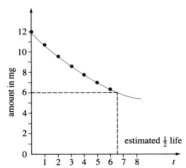

(c) 6.5 days

6. (a) $\dfrac{(1 + r + rn)}{n}\, A - \dfrac{rA}{n}\, k = A_k$

(b) $P_k = \dfrac{A_k}{(1 + i)^k}$ (c) $P = \dfrac{nri - r + i}{n\, i^2}\, A$
$+ \dfrac{(r - i)\, A}{n\, i^2}\, \dfrac{1}{(1 + i)^n}\ (i > 0)$

EXERCISE 4.6

1. (a) $n^2 + 2n$ (b) $n^4 + 4n^3 + 6n^2 + 4n$
(c) $n^5 + 5n^4 + 10n^3 + 10n^2 + 5n$

2. (a) $\dfrac{n}{2n + 1}$ (b) $\dfrac{n}{3n + 1}$ (c) $\dfrac{n}{4n + 1}$

3. $\dfrac{n(n + 3)}{4(n + 1)(n + 2)}$ **4.** $(n + 1)! - 1$

6. (a) $\left(\dfrac{n(n + 1)}{2}\right)^2$ (b) $\frac{1}{5}n^5 + \frac{1}{2}n^4 + \frac{1}{3}n^3 - \frac{1}{30}n$

EXERCISE 4.7

13. (a) $\frac{1}{2}, \frac{5}{6}, \frac{23}{24}, \frac{119}{120}$ (b) $S_n = 1 - \dfrac{1}{(n + 1)!}$

4.8 REVIEW EXERCISE

1. $\displaystyle\sum_{k=1}^{17} x^{k-1}$

2. $\dfrac{2}{2 + 1} + \dfrac{3}{3 + 1} + \dfrac{4}{4 + 1} + \dfrac{5}{5 + 1} + \dfrac{6}{6 + 1}$
$+ \dfrac{7}{7 + 1} + \dfrac{8}{8 + 1}$

3. $\displaystyle\sum_{k=1}^{30} \dfrac{1}{13 + k}$ **4.** 57.14

5. (a) \$(38\ 000 + 4000n)$

(b) $\displaystyle\sum_{k=1}^{n} \$[39\ 500 + (k - 1)4000]$

6. About 35%   **7.** $\displaystyle\sum_{k=1}^{64} 2^{k-1} = 2^{64} - 1$

8. $\frac{1}{4}L^2$ **9.** 280 483   **10.** 39

11. 955 710   **12.** 28   **13.** $\frac{3}{2}$ **14.** $\frac{1439}{1665}$

15. $21\frac{9}{11}$ minutes after four o'clock

16. \$14 034   **17.** $\frac{3}{2} - \dfrac{2n + 3}{(n + 1)(n + 2)}$

19. $1 - \dfrac{1}{(n + 1)^2}$

4.9 CHAPTER 4 TEST

1. $\dfrac{1^2}{1^3 + 1} + \dfrac{2^2}{2^3 + 1} + \dfrac{3^2}{3^3 + 1} + \dfrac{4^2}{4^3 + 1}$

$+ \dfrac{5^2}{5^3 + 1} + \dfrac{6^2}{6^3 + 1} + \dfrac{7^2}{7^3 + 1}$

2. $\displaystyle\sum_{k=1}^{8} \dfrac{1}{8 + 3k}$ **3.** 2   **4.** $\dfrac{1 - r^n}{1 - r}$

5. $\dfrac{n(t_1 + t_n)}{2}$ **6.** $\frac{1}{13}$ **7.** x^{-1}

CUMULATIVE REVIEW FOR CHAPTERS 1 TO 4

1. (a) 120   (b) 734   (c) 122   (d) 5049   (e) 0
   (f) 72 576   (g) 105   (h) 120 960   (i) 27 720

3. (a) $9 \times \dfrac{9!}{3!}$ (b) 8!   (c) $\dfrac{8!}{3!\,2!}$ (d) $\dfrac{8!}{3!\,5!}$

   (e) $\dfrac{7!}{2!\,3!\,2!}$

4. 20   **5.** 336   **6.** 15   **7.** 40 320

8. 7203   **9.** 2880   **10.** 168 168   **11.** 36

12. 35   **13.** 359   **14.** 7999

15. (a) 1540   (b) 350

16. (a) $A \subseteq B$ (b) $B \subseteq A$ (c) $A \cap B = \varnothing$

17. 18   **18.** (a) $\dbinom{16}{9}$ (b) $\dbinom{22}{10}$ (c) $\dbinom{n-2}{k+2}$

   (d) $\dbinom{11}{6}$

19. (a) 128   (b) 0   (c) 252

20. 103   **21.** 252   **22.** (a) 12   (b) 64

23. (a) 10   (b) 5   **24.** $n \in N$ **25.** 24

26. (a) 22   (b) 16   (c) 11

27. (a) $a^6 + 6a^5b + 15a^4b^2 + 20a^3b^3 + 15a^2b^4$
   $+ 6ab^5 + b^6$
   (b) $32x^5 - 80x^4y + 80x^3y^2 - 40x^2y^3 + 10xy^4$
   $- y^5$ (c) $x^8 + 4x^5 + 6x^2 + \dfrac{4}{x} + \dfrac{1}{x^4}$
   (d) $8x^3 - 6\sqrt{x^3} + \frac{3}{2} - \dfrac{1}{8\sqrt{x^3}}$

28. (a) $a^{13} + 13a^{12}b + 78a^{11}b^2 + \ldots$
   (b) $x^{16} - 8x^{13} + 28x^{10} - \ldots$
   (c) $128a^7 + 896a^4 + 2688a + \ldots$

29. (a) $\dbinom{9}{r} a^{9-r}b^r$ (b) $\dbinom{6}{r} x^{6-2r}$

   (c) $(-1)^r \dbinom{5}{r} 2^{5-2r}x^{2r-5}$

30. 165   **31.** $-56x^{-1}$, 28   **32.** -20

33. -128 **34.** $n = 8$, $a = \frac{3}{2}$

35. $1 - 4x + 11x^2 + \ldots$

36. 66   **37.** (b) $\displaystyle\sum_{r=0}^{n} \dbinom{n}{r} (-5)^r = (-4)^n$

38. (a) $[1^2 - 1] + [2^2 - 2] + [3^2 - 3]$
   $+ [4^2 - 4] + [5^2 - 5] + [6^2 - 6]$
   (b) $\dbinom{7}{3} + \dbinom{7}{4} + \dbinom{7}{5} + \dbinom{7}{6} + \dbinom{7}{7}$
   (c) $t_5 + t_7 + t_9 + t_{11} + t_{13} + t_{15} + t_{17}$

39. (a) $\displaystyle\sum_{k=1}^{8} (-\frac{1}{2})^{k-1}$ (b) $\displaystyle\sum_{i=1}^{6} \dfrac{x + 1 - i}{x - i}$

   (c) $\displaystyle\sum_{k=1}^{8} [1 + 4(k-1)]$ or $\displaystyle\sum_{k=1}^{8} (4k - 3)$

40. -74

41. (a) \$30 000   (b) \$136 250
   (c) \$$(25\,000 + 1000n)$
   (d) $\displaystyle\sum_{k=1}^{n}$ \$$[25\,250 + 1000(k-1)]$

42. (a) 351   (b) 649   **43.** (a) 720   (b) -1185

44. 315   **45.** (a) 20   (b) 35

46. $a = -2$, $d = 3$

47. (a) 19 682   (b) $\frac{215}{32}$ **48.** (a) 6138   (b) $\frac{728}{729}$

49. 510   **50.** (a) 6015   (b) $-\frac{243}{128}$

51. 797 161

52. (a) 5   (b) $\frac{1}{4}$ (c) $\frac{9}{4}$

53. (a) $\frac{79}{90}$ (b) $\frac{371}{990}$ (c) $\frac{41\,111}{333\,000}$

54. $5\frac{5}{11}$ minutes after one o'clock

55. \$112 756.08

56. (a) 90 mg, 81 mg, 72.9 mg, 65.61 mg,
   59.05 mg, 53.14 mg, 47.83 mg, 43.05 mg
   (b) 6.58 days   (Note: Final answers were
   rounded to two decimal places.)

57. $2n^3 + 9n^2 + 15n$

58. (a) $\dfrac{n}{2(3n + 2)}$ (b) $\dfrac{n}{5n + 1}$

CHAPTER 5 PROBABILITY THEORY

REVIEW AND PREVIEW TO CHAPTER 5
EXERCISE 1

1.

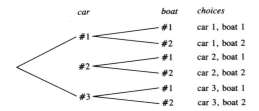

5.

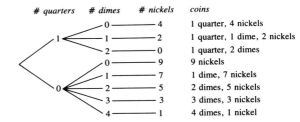

2.

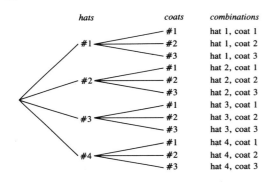

3. Winning tree:

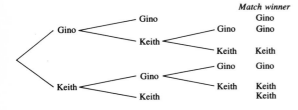

4.

top	sides	colour combination
orange	orange	orange, orange
	black	orange, black
	white	orange, white
black	orange	black, orange
	black	black, black
	white	black, white
white	orange	white, orange
	black	white, black
	white	white, white

EXERCISE 2

1. (a) 60   (b) 120

(c) $\dfrac{k!}{(k-3)!}$, $k \geqslant 3$

(d) $\dfrac{k!}{(k-c)!}$, $k \geqslant c$

2. 6   **3.** 1.007×10^{10} **4.** 800

5. 3.114×10^9

EXERCISE 3

1. (a) 10   (b) 1   (c) $\dfrac{k!}{2!\,(k-2)!}$, $k \geqslant 2$

(d) $\dfrac{k!}{c!\,(k-c)!}$, $k \geqslant c$

2. 56   **3.** 792   **4.** 1.378×10^{11} **5.** 10

EXERCISE 5.1

1. (a) $\{00, 0, 1, 2, 3, \ldots, 35\}$. Yes.   (b) $\{1, 2, \ldots, 20\}$. Yes.   (c) {applicant#1, applicant#2, ... , applicant#10}. No.   (d) {polka dots, striped, plain}. No.   (e) {rough, smooth}. Yes.   (f) {ticket#1, ticket#2, ... , ticket#n}. Yes.   (g) $\{1, 2, \ldots, 75\}$. Yes.

2. (a) 0.4   (b) 0.1   (c) 0.001   (d) 0.3   (e) 0.01   (f) 0.00001   (g) 0.00001

3. (a) $\frac{2}{5}$ (b) $\frac{1}{2}$ (c) $\frac{5}{26}, \frac{21}{26}$

4. (a) $\frac{1}{2}$ (b) $\frac{67}{100}$ (c) $\frac{3}{13}$ **5.** $\frac{5}{12}$

6. (a) $\frac{1}{3}$ (b) $\frac{1}{6}$ (c) $\frac{1}{2}$ (d) $\frac{5}{6}$ (e) $\frac{1}{3}$

7. (a) $\frac{1}{2}$ (b) $\frac{1}{2}$ (c) $\frac{4}{25}$ (d) $\frac{2}{25}$ (e) $\frac{1}{10}$ (f) $\frac{3}{50}$

(g) $\frac{43}{50}$ (h) $\frac{43}{50}$ (i) $\frac{4}{5}$

8. (a) $\frac{1}{3}$ (b) $\frac{5}{17}$

9. (a) $\frac{1}{2}$ (b) $\frac{1}{3}$ (c) $\frac{1}{3}$ (d) $\frac{1}{3}$

10. (a) $\frac{47}{100}$ (b) $\frac{53}{100}$

EXERCISE 5.2

1.

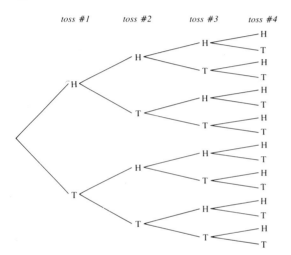

(a) $\frac{1}{16}$ (b) $\frac{5}{16}$ (c) $\frac{1}{4}$ (d) $\frac{1}{16}$ (e) $\frac{3}{8}$ (f) $\frac{1}{2}$

2.

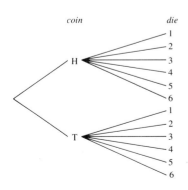

(a) $\frac{1}{4}$ (b) $\frac{1}{6}$ (c) $\frac{1}{12}$ (d) $\frac{1}{6}$

3. (a)

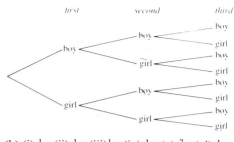

(b) (i) $\frac{1}{4}$ (ii) $\frac{1}{2}$ (iii) $\frac{1}{8}$ (iv) $\frac{1}{2}$ (v) $\frac{7}{8}$ (vi) $\frac{1}{2}$

4.

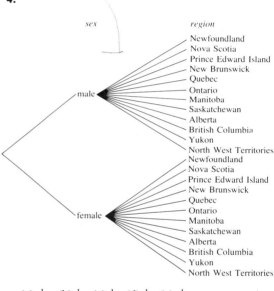

(a) $\frac{1}{12}$ (b) $\frac{1}{3}$ (c) $\frac{1}{6}$ (d) $\frac{1}{2}$ (e) $\frac{1}{12}$

5. (a) **Winning tree:**

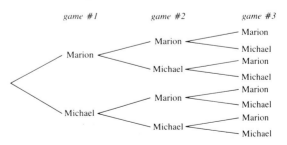

(b) (i) $\frac{1}{8}$ (ii) $\frac{1}{4}$ (iii) $\frac{1}{2}$ (iv) $\frac{3}{8}$

6. Winning tree:

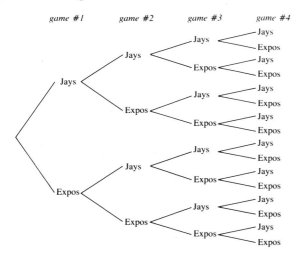

game #1   *game #2*   *game #3*   *game #4*

(a) $\frac{1}{16}$ (b) $\frac{1}{4}$ (c) $\frac{1}{2}$ (d) $\frac{3}{8}$

7. $\frac{1}{1296}$ **8.** $\frac{1}{6}$

9. (a) $\frac{1}{49}$ (a) $\frac{1}{2352}$ (c) 9.932×10^{-11}

10. (a) $\frac{1}{120}$ (b) $\frac{1}{5}$ (c) $\frac{1}{20}$ **11.** $\frac{3}{2197}$ **12.** $\frac{1}{4}$

13. (a) 0.44   (b) $\frac{7}{12}$ (c) $\frac{1}{792}$ **14.** $\frac{1}{11}$

15. (a) 0.012   (b) $\frac{10}{3553}$ (c) 0.52   (d) 0.42

16. (a) 0.26   (b) 0.33   (c) 0.29   (d) 0.03
    (e) 0.97   (f) 0.13   (g) $\frac{1}{148\ 005}$

17. $\frac{1}{13\ 983\ 816}$

EXERCISE 5.3

1. (a) not mutually exclusive
    (b) not mutually exclusive
    (c) mutually exclusive
    (d) not mutually exclusive
    (e) not mutually exclusive
    (f) mutually exclusive
    (g) not mutually exclusive
    (h) mutually exclusive

2. (a) 0.8   (b) 0.7   (c) 1   (d) (i) $\frac{5}{6}$ (ii) $\frac{5}{6}$ (iii) $\frac{2}{3}$
    (e) (i) $\frac{11}{26}$ (ii) $\frac{4}{13}$ (iii) $\frac{4}{13}$

3. 0.8   **4.** 0.6

5. (a) 0.371   (b) 0.628   (c) 0.966   (d) 0.395
    (e) 0.044   (f) 0.267   (g) 0.109

EXERCISE 5.4

1. (a) $\frac{5}{7}$ (b) 0.03   (c) (i) $\frac{1}{3}$ (ii) $\frac{4}{7}$ (iii) $\frac{3}{4}$ (iv) $\frac{2}{3}$
    (d) (i) 0.05   (ii) $\frac{2}{3}$

2. (a) $\frac{1}{3}$ (b) $\frac{1}{3}$ (c) (i) $\frac{1}{3}$ (ii) $\frac{1}{2}$

3. (a) $\frac{3}{11}$ (b) $\frac{1}{3}$

4. (a) $\frac{1}{120}$ (b) $\frac{1}{30}$

5. (a) 0.17   (b) $\frac{17}{60}$

6. $\frac{1}{2}, \frac{3}{8}, \frac{1}{8}$

8. (a) $\frac{1}{16}$ (b) $\frac{17}{32}$

EXERCISE 5.5

1. (a) independent   (b) not independent
    (c) independent   (d) independent
    (e) independent   (f) not independent

2. (a) $\frac{1}{60}$ (b) $\frac{3}{4}$ (c) $\frac{1}{4}$

3. $\frac{2}{25}$ **4.** $\frac{1}{46\ 656}$ **5.** yes

6. (a) 0.543   (b) 0.324   (c) 0.133

7. 0.891   **8.** 0.827   **9.** 0.777

10. approximately 1   **11.** 0.8488

12. $1 - \dfrac{m!}{(m-n)!\ m^n}$

EXERCISE 5.6

1. (a) 7 : 29   (b) 2 : 1   (c) $\frac{4}{9}$ (d) (i) $\frac{13}{18}$
    (ii) 13 : 5   (e) 3 : 17

2. \$4.29   **3.** 2 : 3   **4.** \$12.78

6. 1 : 23   **7.** 4 : 1   **8.** 3 : 1

9. (a) 3 : 10   (b) 3 : 7   (c) \$0.58   **10.** \$33.33

12. No; the probability of Mrs. Liu winning is close to one.

13. No; the sum of the probabilities is greater than one.

14.

Number of People, A	P(A)	Approximate odds	Winnings \$
10	0.117	117 : 883 ≐ 13 : 100	7.70
20	0.411	411 : 589 ≐ 7 : 10	1.43
30	0.706	706 : 294 ≐ 12 : 5	0.42
40	0.891	891 : 109 ≐ 8 : 1	0.12
50	0.970	970 : 30 ≐ 32 : 1	0.03
60	0.994	994 : 6 ≐ 166 : 1	0.001

15. (a) Trez (b) $190.00 (c) Trez, Ace, Deuce
(d) 0.006, 497 : 3

EXERCISE 5.7

1. (a) **Winning tree:**

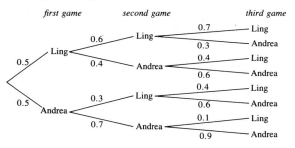

(b) 0.44 (c) 0.245

2. (a) 37.5% (b) 56%

3.

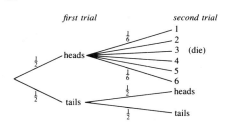

(a) 1 : 11 (b) 1 : 3 (c) 1 : 3

4.

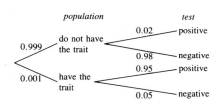

(a) 0.02 (b) 0.000 95 (c) 0.0475

5. (a) 0.21 (b) 0.27 (c) 0.507

6. (a) $\frac{5}{8}$ (b) $\frac{13}{32}$

7. (a)

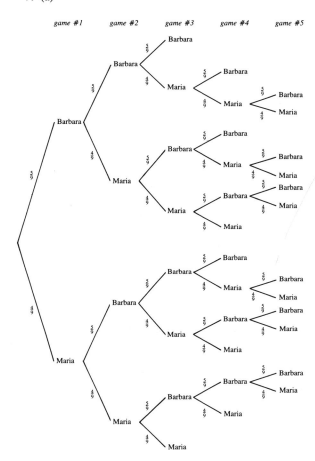

(b) 0.088 (c) 0.603

5.8 REVIEW EXERCISE

2. (a) $\frac{1}{3}$ (b) $\frac{4}{13}$

3. (a) (i) $1\frac{5}{18}$ (ii) $\frac{1}{18}$ (iii) $\frac{1}{4}$

(b) (i) $\frac{2}{3}$ (ii) $\frac{4}{5}$ (iii) $\frac{1}{8}$ (iv) 3 : 7 (v) 1 : 4

4. (a) $\frac{1}{5}$ (b) $\frac{3}{5}$ **5.** (a) $\frac{1}{4}$ (b) $\frac{1}{2}$

6. (a)

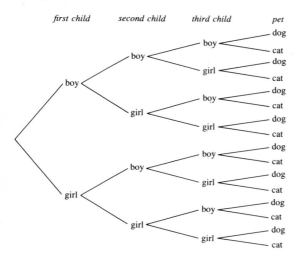

first child   second child   third child   pet

(b) $\frac{1}{2}$ **7.** (a) $\frac{1}{14}$ (b) $\frac{1}{2}$ **8.** $\frac{1}{358\,800}$

9. (a) $\frac{1}{2}$ (b) $\frac{2}{3}$ (c) $\frac{4}{9}$ **10.** (a) 0.8 (b) 0.2

11. (a) $\frac{1}{13}$ (b) $\frac{1}{10}$ **12.** $\frac{1}{3}, \frac{7}{18}, \frac{5}{18}$

13. 0.463   **14.** (a) $\frac{1}{52}$ (b) $\frac{1}{624}$

15. \$70.00   **16.** 3 : 1   **17.** 0.397

18. 0.528

5.9 CHAPTER 5 TEST

1. (a) (i) $\frac{1}{6}$ (ii) 1 : 5 (b) $\frac{1}{36}$

2. (a)

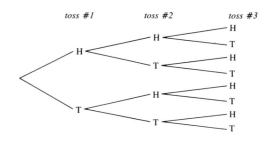

toss #1   toss #2   toss #3

(b)

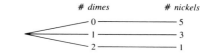

dimes   # nickels

3. 0.618   **4.** $\frac{1}{5}$ **5.** $\frac{11}{51}$ **6.** 0.333

CHAPTER 6 PROBABILITY MODELS

REVIEW AND PREVIEW TO CHAPTER 6
EXERCISE 1

1. (a) $\sum_{i=1}^{6} a_i$ (b) $\frac{1}{9}\sum_{i=1}^{9} x_i$ (c) $\sum_{i=1}^{5} x_i f_i$

(d) $\sqrt{\dfrac{\sum_{i=1}^{n}(x_i - k)^2}{n}}$

2. (a) $x_1 + x_2 + x_3 + x_4$ (b) $x_1 f_1 + x_2 f_2 + \ldots + x_n f_n$

(c) $\dfrac{x_1 + x_2 + \ldots + x_n}{n}$

(d) $(x_1 - k)^2 f_1 + (x_2 - k)^2 f_2 + \ldots + (x_n - k)^2 f_n$

(e) $\binom{n}{0} p^0 q^n + \binom{n}{1} p^1 q^{n-1} + \binom{n}{2} p^2 q^{n-2} + \ldots$

$+ \binom{n}{n} p^n q^0$

EXERCISE 2

1. (a) $x^4 + 8x^3 + 24x^2 + 32x + 16$

(b) $\frac{1}{27} + \frac{2}{9} + \frac{4}{9} + \frac{8}{27}$

(c) $0.6561 + 0.2916 + 0.0486 + 0.0001$

(d) $\frac{32}{3125} + \frac{48}{625} + \frac{144}{625} + \frac{216}{625} + \frac{162}{625} + \frac{243}{3125}$

(e) $\binom{n}{0} p^n + \binom{n}{1} p^{n-1}q^1 + \binom{n}{2} p^{n-2}q^2 + \ldots$

$+ \binom{n}{n} q^n$

EXERCISE 6.1

2. (a) (i)

x	$p(x)$
1	$\frac{1}{6}$
2	$\frac{1}{6}$
3	$\frac{1}{6}$
4	$\frac{1}{6}$
5	$\frac{1}{6}$
6	$\frac{1}{6}$

(ii)

x	$p(x)$
1	$\dfrac{1}{n}$
2	$\dfrac{1}{n}$
3	$\dfrac{1}{n}$
...	...
n	$\dfrac{1}{n}$

3. (a)

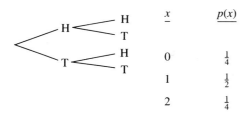

x	$p(x)$
0	$\frac{1}{4}$
1	$\frac{1}{2}$
2	$\frac{1}{4}$

(b) 1

4. (a) 4.95   (b) $\frac{480}{7}$

5. (a)(b)(c)

first coin		second coin	probability	coin value ¢
penny $\frac{4}{10}$		penny	20/110	2
	$\frac{2}{10}$	nickel	10/110	6
	$\frac{3}{10}$	dime	15/110	11
	$\frac{1}{10}$	quarter	5/110	26
nickel $\frac{5}{10}$		penny	10/110	6
	$\frac{1}{10}$	nickel	2/110	10
	$\frac{3}{10}$	dime	6/110	15
	$\frac{1}{10}$	quarter	2/110	30
dime $\frac{5}{10}$		penny	15/110	11
	$\frac{2}{10}$	nickel	6/110	15
	$\frac{3}{10}$	dime	6/110	20
	$\frac{1}{10}$	quarter	3/110	35
quarter $\frac{5}{10}$		penny	5/110	26
	$\frac{2}{10}$	nickel	2/110	30
	$\frac{3}{10}$	dime	3/110	35

(d) 12.7¢   **6.** $25.00

7. (a) no; the expectation is $0.28   (b) lose $22.22

8. (a) 0   (b) $7.00

9. less than one cent; approximately $\underline{0.8\ \text{¢}}$.

10. 1.71   **11.** 1.54

12. (a) $1100   (b) $1463

13. (a)

x	$p(x)$
1	0.1
2	0.2
3	0.3
4	0.4

(b) 3

14. 3.44 minutes or 3 minutes and 26 seconds.

EXERCISE 6.2

1. (a) (i) uniform   (ii) uniform   (iii) not uniform
(iv) uniform   (v) uniform

(b) (i) $p(x) = \frac{1}{52}$ (ii) $p(x) = \frac{1}{100}$

(iv) $p(x) = \frac{1}{n}$ where n is the number of names

(v) $p(x) = \dfrac{1}{n}$ where n is the number of tickets in
the lottery

2. (a) $p(x) = \frac{1}{6}$ where $x \in \{10, 11, \ldots, 15\}$

(b) $p(x) = \dfrac{1}{j - i + 1}$ where $x \in \{i, i+1, \ldots, j\}$

3. yes; $5.00   **4.** $1.50

5. (a) (i) 3.5×3.5 units   (ii) 14 units

(iii) $\frac{91}{6}$ units^2

(b) (i) 73.5 units^3 (ii) 91 units^2

6. 18.33 m^2 **7.** 9   **8.** $0.39   **9.** $\dfrac{n+1}{2}$

EXERCISE 6.3

1. (a)

x	$p(x)$
0	0.590
1	0.328
2	0.073
3	0.008
4	0
5	0

(b)

x	$p(x)$
0	0
1	0
2	0.008
3	0.073
4	0.328
5	0.590

(c)

x	$p(x)$
0	0.240
1	0.412
2	0.265
3	0.076
4	0.008

(d)

x	$p(x)$
0	0.058
1	0.198
2	0.296
3	0.254
4	0.136
5	0.047
6	0.010
7	0.001
8	0

(e)

x	$p(x)$
0	0.335
1	0.402
2	0.201
3	0.054
4	0.008
5	0
6	0

2. (a) $(0.1+0.9)^5 \doteq (0.590+0.328+0.073+0.008 +0+0)$

(b) $(0.9+0.1)^5 \doteq (0+0+0.008+0.073+0.328 +0.590)$

(c) $(0.3+0.7)^4 \doteq (0.240+0.412+0.265+0.076 +0.008)$

(d) $(0.3+0.7)^8 \doteq (0.058+0.198+0.296+0.254 +0.136+0.047+0.010+0.001+0)$

(e) $(\frac{1}{6}+\frac{5}{6})^6 \doteq (0.335+0.402+0.201+0.054 +0.008+0+0)$

4. (a) 0.205   (b) 0.989   (c) 0.055

5. (a) 0.033   (b) 0.980

6. (a) 0.125   (b) 0.969

7. 90   **8.** (a) 0.998   (b) 0.99999

9. (a) 20   (b) 2.04×10^{-10}

10. 0.636   **11.** 0.803   **12.** 0.481

13. 0.823   **14.** 0.994

15. (a) $\frac{11}{36}$ (b) $\frac{5}{9}$ (c) $\frac{3}{4}$ (d) $\frac{8}{9}$ (e) $\frac{35}{36}$ (f) 1

EXERCISE 6.4

1. (a) uniform   (b) binomial   (c) geometric

2. (a)

x	$p(x)$
0	0.5
1	0.25
2	0.125
3	0.0625

(b)

x	$p(x)$
0	0.2
1	0.16
2	0.128
3	0.1024

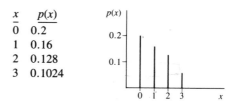

(c)

x	p(x)
0	0.7
1	0.21
2	0.063
3	0.0189

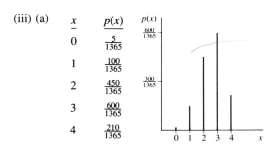

3. $\frac{8}{81}$ **4.** 0.274   **5.** 125 : 91   **6.** 364

7. 10   **8.** 0.017   **9.** 0.556

10. (a) 0.24   (b) 0.936

11. (a) 32   (b) 0.141

EXERCISE 6.5

1. (a) hypergeometric   (b) geometric
(c) hypergeometric   (d) binomial

2. $a = 10$, $b = 8$, $n = 4$, $x = 2$

3. (i) (a)

x	p(x)
0	$\frac{5}{210}$
1	$\frac{50}{210}$
2	$\frac{100}{210}$
3	$\frac{50}{210}$
4	$\frac{5}{210}$

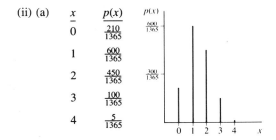

(b) 2

(ii) (a)

x	p(x)
0	$\frac{210}{1365}$
1	$\frac{600}{1365}$
2	$\frac{450}{1365}$
3	$\frac{100}{1365}$
4	$\frac{5}{1365}$

(b) $\frac{4}{3}$

(iii) (a)

x	p(x)
0	$\frac{5}{1365}$
1	$\frac{100}{1365}$
2	$\frac{450}{1365}$
3	$\frac{600}{1365}$
4	$\frac{210}{1365}$

(b) $\frac{8}{3}$

4. (a) 0.257   (b) 0.687   (c) 0.0047

5. 0.848   **6.** (a) 0.253   (b) 0.019

7. (a) 0.215   (b) 0.063

8. 0.115   **9.** 0.018   **10.** 0.288

11. 0.026

12. 0.000 394

13. (a) 0.0026   (b) 0.181   (c) 0.087

14. 2500   **15.** 2000   **16.** 36%

6.6 REVIEW EXERCISE

3. (a)

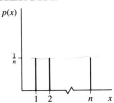

(b)

(c)

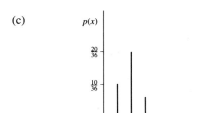

(d)

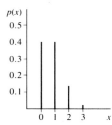

4. (a) $\frac{3}{4}$ (b) 12.96   **5.** $7.00   **6.** $3.39

7. (a) 0.220 (b) 0.912

8. 0.035   **9.** (a) $\frac{12}{105}$ (b) 3.6

10. 0.576   **11.** (a) 0.139 (b) 3

12. 9999   **13.** (a) 35 (b) 0.107

6.7 CHAPTER 6 TEST

1.

3. (a) 0.057 (b) $\frac{4}{27}$ (c) 3

4. (a) 0.377 (b) 0.108 (c) 0.412

5. 3000

CHAPTER 7 STATISTICS

REVIEW AND PREVIEW TO CHAPTER 7
EXERCISE 1
1. (a) 4.2 (b) 3.6 (c) 1 (d) 12 (e) 1.2

2. (a) 3 (b) 6 (c) 2

EXERCISE 2
1. (a) (i) 2 (ii) 6 (iii) $\frac{2}{3}$

2. (a) (i) $55 - 72$ (ii) $43 - 57$ (iv) $12 - 15$
(v) 1985 (vi) less than (vii) 4
(b) (i) 2.52 per 100 000
(ii) 1974, 1979, 1981, 1983, 1984
(iii) 64–66, 74–76, 77–80, 83–84
(iv) 1979 (v) increase
(c) (i) 3885 (ii) February, March (iii) 36.3
(iv) 6 (v) August, July

EXERCISE 7.1
2. (i)

Age	Frequency	Relative Frequency	Relative Frequency %	Cumulative Frequency
12	15	$\frac{15}{570}$	2.6	15
13	25	$\frac{25}{570}$	4.4	40
14	123	$\frac{123}{570}$	21.6	163
15	136	$\frac{136}{570}$	23.9	299
16	101	$\frac{101}{570}$	17.7	400
17	87	$\frac{87}{570}$	15.3	487
18	71	$\frac{71}{570}$	12.4	558
19	12	$\frac{12}{570}$	2.1	570

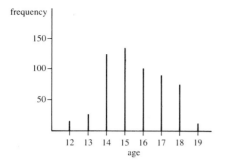

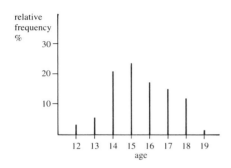

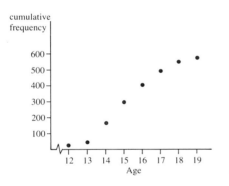

(ii)

Score	Frequency	Relative Frequency	Relative Frequency %	Cumulative Frequency
66	2	$\frac{2}{97}$	2.1	2
67	0	0	0	2
68	3	$\frac{3}{97}$	3.1	5
69	9	$\frac{9}{97}$	9.3	14
70	16	$\frac{16}{97}$	16.5	30
71	13	$\frac{13}{97}$	13.4	43
72	24	$\frac{24}{97}$	24.7	67
73	17	$\frac{17}{97}$	17.5	84
74	6	$\frac{6}{97}$	6.2	90
75	5	$\frac{5}{97}$	5.1	95
76	2	$\frac{2}{97}$	2.1	97

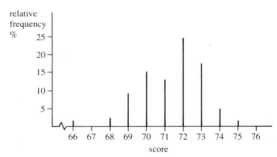

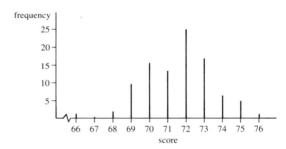

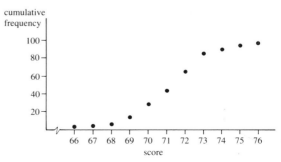

(iii)

Bill ($)	Frequency	Relative Frequency	Relative Frequency %	Cumulative Frequency
29.50–39.50	7	$\frac{7}{425}$	1.7	7
39.50–49.50	11	$\frac{11}{425}$	2.6	18
49.50–59.50	18	$\frac{18}{425}$	4.2	36
59.50–69.50	47	$\frac{47}{425}$	11.1	83
69.50–79.50	33	$\frac{33}{425}$	7.8	116
79.50–89.50	67	$\frac{67}{425}$	15.8	183
89.50–99.50	82	$\frac{82}{425}$	19.3	265
99.50–109.50	51	$\frac{51}{425}$	12.0	316
109.50–119.50	40	$\frac{40}{425}$	9.4	356
119.50–129.50	32	$\frac{32}{425}$	7.5	388
129.50–139.50	16	$\frac{16}{425}$	3.8	404
139.50–149.50	7	$\frac{7}{425}$	1.6	411
149.50–159.50	9	$\frac{9}{425}$	2.1	420
159.50–169.50	4	$\frac{4}{425}$	0.9	424
169.50–179.50	1	$\frac{1}{425}$	0.2	425

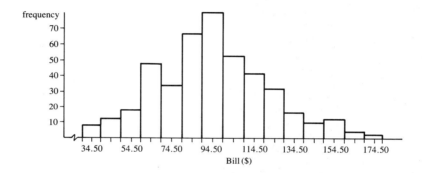

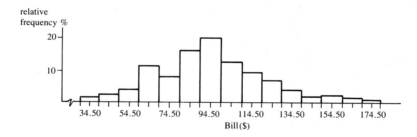

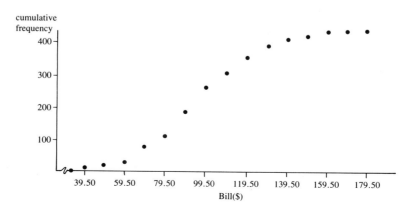

3. (a)

Shoe size	Frequency	Relative Frequency %	Cumulative Frequency
5	3	9.4	3
6	2	6.3	5
7	5	15.6	10
8	7	21.9	17
9	8	25.0	25
10	4	12.5	29
11	2	6.3	31
12	1	3.1	32

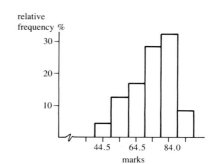

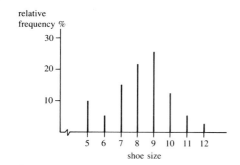

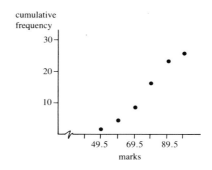

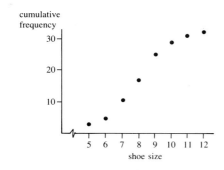

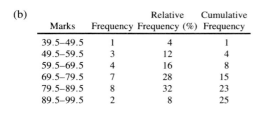

4. From a cumulative frequency diagram, less than 50% of students attend concerts at least twice a year.

7.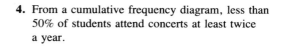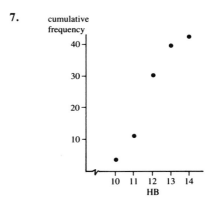

(b)

Marks	Frequency	Relative Frequency (%)	Cumulative Frequency
39.5–49.5	1	4	1
49.5–59.5	3	12	4
59.5–69.5	4	16	8
69.5–79.5	7	28	15
79.5–89.5	8	32	23
89.5–99.5	2	8	25

9. (a)

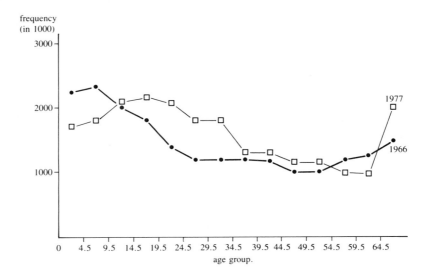

10.

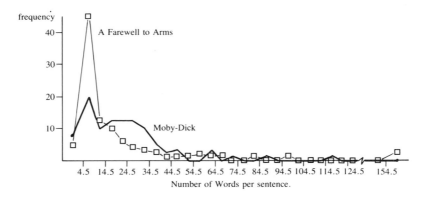

11.

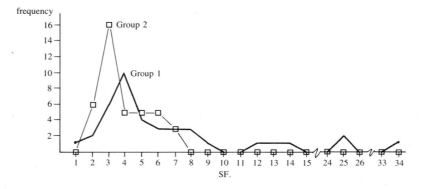

EXERCISE 7.2

1. (a) 5   (b) 34   **3.** (a) 39.23   (b) 36.5

4. (a) $28 300   (b) $14 500   (c) labour–median; management–mean.

5. the modal intervals

6. (a) Tobias 11; Louise 20.7; Lulu 17.2; Orlon 18.4

(b)

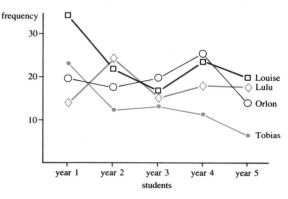

(c) Louise

7. 67.7%

8. (a) (i) 9.9   (ii) suitable to the average reader
(b) 38.8—good luck!

10. 364.7

EXERCISE 7.3

1.

	interquartile range	mean deviation
(a)	0.45	0.248
(b)	9.3	5.29
(c)	15	7.1
(d)	10	6.9

2. (a) mean 12.3; mean deviation 0.49   (b) 55.5%
(c) 88.8%

4. (a) 993   (b) 24

5. (a) 17   (b) 89–92   (c) 115+

6. (b) 325.8

EXERCISE 7.4

1.

	mean	standard deviation
(a)	33.625	0.296
(b)	11.73	6.03
(c)	59.53	8.7
(d)	10.9	8.3

2. (a) 55.5%   (b) 19   (c) $\sqrt{2}$ standard deviations
(d) 35

3. (a) $\bar{x} = 12.3$; s = 0.615   (b) 75% or 13.5

4. (a) 1   (b) $\dfrac{|c - 65|}{7}$

5. (a) Maureen
(b) David: 2.8, 2.57, 3.25, 2.25, 2.83, 2.3
Maureen: 2.64, 2.89, 2.33, 3.00, 1.82, 2.75
(c) David

EXERCISE 7.5

1. (a) 0.5000   (b) 0.8413   (c) 0.1587
(d) 0.6826   (e) 0.9546   (f) 0.1178
(g) 0.5098

2. (a) 0.2660   (b) 0.2266   (c) 0.3721
(d) 0.3085   (e) 0.0227   (f) 0.8413
(g) 0.6826

3. (a) 2.27%   (b) 0.26%   **4.** 0.62%

5. (a) 10.6%   (b) 0.19%

6. 2.27%   **7.** earth, 4.54%; space, 0

8. (a) 2.5   (b) 5.0   (c) 9.4   (d) 66.25
(e) $\mu = 75.05$, $\sigma = 3.81$
(f) $\mu = 12.33$, $\sigma = 3.33$
(g) 0.5793   (h) 0.1401

9. 252 h

10. (a) mean 121.67; standard deviation 16.67
(b) 53.9%   **11.** 45.4

12. mean 68.3; standard deviation 16.6

13. (a) $f(x) = \dfrac{10x + 360}{13}$ (b) 100   **14.** (b) 75%

EXERCISE 7.6

1. (a) NO   (b) YES   (c) NO   (d) NO

2. (a) $P(2.5 < X < 3.5)$ (b) $P(X > 4.5)$
(c) $P(X < 5.5)$ (d) $P(X < 114.5)$
(e) $P(11.5 < X < 15.5)$
(f) $P(50.5 < X < 74.5)$

3. (a) 0.09   (b) 0.0001

4. 0   **5.** (a) 0.146   (b) 0.139

6. 0.11   **7.** 0.25   **8.** 0.405

EXERCISE 7.7

1. (a) 1.96   (b) 1.28   (c) 1.65   (d) 3.10

2. (a) $z_t = 1.5$, accept H_0
(b) $z_t = 2.93$, reject H_0

(c) $z_t = 0.75$, accept H_0
(d) $z_t = 1.39$, accept H_0
(e) $z_t = 6.5$, reject H_0

3. $H_0 : p = \frac{2}{7}$; $z_t = 0.096$; accept H_0 at $\alpha = 0.05$

4. $H_0 : p = 0.5$; $z_t = 0.8$; accept H_0 at $\alpha = 0.05$

5. $H_0 : p = 0.09$; $z_t = 1.46$; accept H_0 at $\alpha = 0.05$

6. $H_0 : p = 0.0001$; $z_t = 0.47$; accept H_0 at $\alpha = 0.05$

7. $H_0 : p = 0.995$; $z_t = 1.94$; reject H_0 at $\alpha = 0.05$

8. $H_0 : p = 0.30$; $z_t = -3.02$; reject H_0 at $\alpha = 0.05$

7.8 REVIEW EXERCISE

1. (a) (i)

Shoe size	Frequency	Relative Frequency
6	5	0.147
7	8	0.235
8	6	0.176
9	9	0.265
10	3	0.088
11	2	0.059
12	1	0.029

(ii)

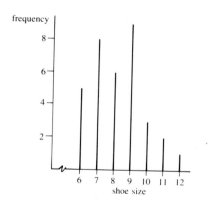

(iii)

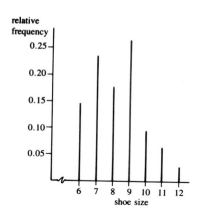

(iv) $\bar{x} \doteq 8.2$; median $= 8$; mode $= 9$
(v) $s \doteq 1.5$; mean deviation $\doteq 1.3$; interquartile range $= 1.0$

(b) (i)

Mark	Midpoint	Frequency	Relative Frequency
0–19.5	9.5	1	0.023
19.5–39.5	29.5	2	0.045
39.5–59.5	49.5	7	0.159
59.5–79.5	69.5	23	0.523
79.5–99.5	89.5	11	0.250

(ii)

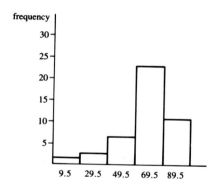

(iii)

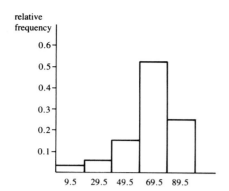

relative frequency

(iv) $\bar{x} \doteq 68.9$; median $= 69.5$;
modal interval: 60–79
(v) $s \doteq 17.12$; mean deviation $\doteq 12.11$
interquartile range $= 10.0$

3. (a) mean $= \dfrac{w + x + y + z}{4}$; median $= \dfrac{x + y}{2}$

4. 84%
5. (i) first test   (ii) $\bar{z} = 0.29$; $s_z = 1.12$
6. 2.9
7. (a) 0.0227   (b) 0.3050   (c) 0.500   (d) 0.1360
8. (a) 3.1   (b) 14.4   (c) $\mu \doteq 76.8$; $\sigma \doteq 2.5$
   (d) $\mu \doteq 7.7$; $\sigma \doteq 1.0$
9. 0.25   **10.** 0.8 kg
11. (a) $\mu = 6$; $\sigma = 1.73$ (b) $\mu = 115$; $\sigma = 9.41$
12. 0.0047
13. (a) approximately 0   (b) approximately 0
14. $H_0 : p = 0.50$; $z_t = 0.55$; accept H_0 at
    $\alpha = 0.05$
15. $H_0 : p = 0.10$; $z_t = 4.10$; reject H_0 at $\alpha = 0.01$

7.9 CHAPTER 7 TEST

1. (a) (i) $\bar{x} = 53.4$; median 52.5; bimodal : 50 and
   53.   (ii) 3.5

(iii)

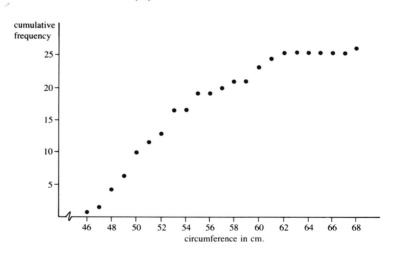

cumulative frequency

circumference in cm.

(b) mean deviation $= \frac{1}{16}(|\, 3w - x - y - z\,|$
$+\ |\, 3x - w - y - z\,| + |\, 3y - w - x - z\,|$
$+\ |\, 3z - w - x - y\,|)$
standard deviation $=$

$\frac{1}{8}\sqrt{\begin{array}{l}(3w - x - y - z)^2 + (3x - w - y - z)^2 \\ +\ (3y - w - x - z)^2 + (3z - w - x - y)^2\end{array}}$

(b) (i) 5.28   (ii) 65%
2. (a) 0.9332   (b) 0.2420   (c) 0.6449
   (d) $\mu \doteq 16.6$ (e) $\mu \doteq 72.5$; $\sigma \doteq 5$
3. (a) 0.0668   (b) 1.6 mm
4. 0.6554
5. $H_0 : p = 0.5$; $z_t = 0.346$; accept H_0

CUMULATIVE REVIEW FOR CHAPTERS 5 TO 7

1.

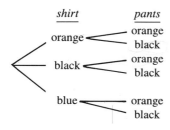

shirt	pants
orange	orange
	black
black	orange
	black
blue	orange
	black

P(orange and black) $= \frac{1}{3}$

2. (a) $\frac{5}{12}$ (b) $\frac{1}{2}$

3. (a) $\frac{1}{15}$ (b) $\frac{2}{37}$

4. 0.167 **5.** $9.86

6. (a) 0.21 (b) 0.50

7. (a) 0.137 (b) 0.824

8. $\frac{1}{42}$

9. 433

10. (a) 0.108 (b) 6

11. (a)

x	Frequency	Cumulative Frequency
2	10	10
4	15	25
6	30	55
8	20	75
10	5	80
12	35	115
14	15	130
16	5	135

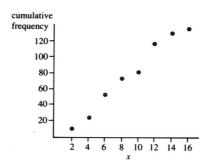

(b) $\bar{x} = 8.7$; median 8; mode 12 (c) 6

12. (a) $\bar{x} \doteq 196.6$; $s \doteq 26.3$

13. (a) $34\ 000 (b) $36\ 200

14. 10.96% **15.** 0.5793

16. $H_0 : p = \frac{1}{6}$; $z_t = 0.76$; accept H_0 at $\alpha = 0.05$. No further investigation is warranted.

17. $H_0 : p = 0.20$; $z_t = 0.530$; accept H_0 at $\alpha = 0.05$. The claim is refuted.

CHAPTER 8 MATRICES

REVIEW AND PREVIEW TO CHAPTER 8

EXERCISE 1

1. (a) $\frac{1}{64}$ (b) $\frac{15}{64}$ (c) $\frac{21}{32}$

2. (a) $\frac{1}{2}$ (b) $\frac{1}{8}$ (c) $\frac{11}{16}$

3. (a) 0.216 (b) 0.663 04

4. $\frac{16}{6561}$

EXERCISE 2

1. (a)

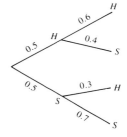

(b) 0.3   (c)

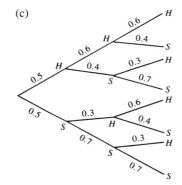

(d) 0.245   (e) 0.45

2. (a) 35%   (b) 27.8%

3. (a) 0.8075 or 80.75%   (b) 0.1745 or 17.45%

4. (a) 0.216   (b) 0.317 44

EXERCISE 8.1

1. (a) (i) no such entry   (ii) 4   (iii) no such entry
   (b) (i) − 14   (ii) 6   (iii) no such entry
   (c) (i) no such entry   (ii) no such entry
   (iii) 250

2. (a) 4×2 (b) 3×3 (c) 1×4

3. (a) a_{32} (b) a_{23} (c) a_{12} (d) a_{31}

4. (a) Individual 2   (b) Individual 4

5. (a) Beatrice   (b) Toru
   (c) Toru has low self-esteem

6. (a) 220   (b) 640   (c) 600   (d) 670   (e) 1450

7.

		Destination Zone			
		I	II	III	IV
Origin Zone	I	257	120	217	35
	II	312	295	315	27
	III	56	38	97	16
	IV	387	410	560	355

8. (a)

		To			
		1	2	3	4
From	1	0	0	2	1
	2	0	0	1	0
	3	0	1	1	0
	4	1	1	1	0

(b)

		To		
		A	B	C
From	A	0	2	1
	B	1	0	2
	C	0	1	0

9.

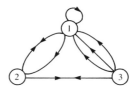

10.   row matrices   column matrices
   $[2 \quad 3]$ or $[1 \quad -2 \quad 4]$ $\begin{bmatrix} 1 \\ 3 \end{bmatrix}$ or $\begin{bmatrix} -2 \\ 3 \\ 5 \end{bmatrix}$

11. $\begin{bmatrix} 1 & 2 \\ 3 & 4 \end{bmatrix}$ or $\begin{bmatrix} 1 & -2 & 3 \\ -4 & 5 & 7 \\ 3 & 0 & -1 \end{bmatrix}$

12. (a) $\begin{bmatrix} 216 \\ -156 \\ 114 \end{bmatrix}$ (b) $\begin{bmatrix} -157 & 117 \\ -29 & -143 \end{bmatrix}$

(c) $\begin{bmatrix} 1 & 2 & \frac{19}{6} \\ 13 & -\frac{35}{6} & -\frac{20}{3} \end{bmatrix}$ (d) $\begin{bmatrix} 3.75 & 5.1 \\ 0.6 & 5.58 \\ -9.69 & 0.9 \\ 5.01 & -4.2 \end{bmatrix}$

13. (a) $\begin{bmatrix} 7.1 & 2.8 & 3.1 \\ -6.1 & 7.3 & -1.5 \end{bmatrix}$

(b) $\begin{bmatrix} -8.8 & 10.1 & -10.8 \\ -4.2 & -7.4 & 1 \end{bmatrix}$ (c) not possible

(d) $\begin{bmatrix} 6.48 & -0.43 & 4.36 \\ -2.98 & 6.3 & -1.18 \end{bmatrix}$

(e) not possible

14. (a)

JANUARY	Zenith	Sony	Elect.	RCA
Henri	10	8	7	14
Tran	7	9	11	6
Anya	15	12	13	10

FEBRUARY	Zenith	Sony	Elect.	RCA
Henri	8	14	10	9
Tran	13	17	9	13
Anya	0	0	0	0

(b)

TOTAL	Zenith	Sony	Elect.	RCA
Henri	18	22	17	23
Tran	20	26	20	19
Anya	15	12	13	10

(c)

MONTHLY AVERAGE	Zenith	Sony	Elect.	RCA
Henri	9	11	8.5	11.5
Tran	10	13	10	9.5
Anya	7.5	6	6.5	5

15. (a)

	30 Days	60 Days	90 Days
0 to 10 000	108	−235	−242
10 000 to 20 000	136	−108	−83
over 20 000	184	60	−109

(b)

	30 Days	60 Days	90 Days
0 to 10 000	812	449	269
10 000 to 20 000	520	205	207
over 20 000	367	201	71

[Answers are rounded to the nearest whole number.]

(c)

	30 Days	60 Days	90 Days
0 to 10 000	860	475	285
10 000 to 20 000	551	217	220
over 20 000	324	177	63

[Answers are rounded to the nearest whole number.]

16. (a)

	Hard Drives	Printers	Monitors	Keyboards
Toronto	35	28	37	26
St. Catharines	23	22	29	24
Hamilton	32	38	25	29

(b)

	Hard Drives	Printers	Monitors	Keyboards
Toronto	13	8	19	5
St. Catharines	11	4	6	8
Hamilton	13	19	2	7

(c)

	Hard Drives	Printers	Monitors	Keyboards
Toronto	44	36	44	34
St. Catharines	28	29	38	30
Hamilton	40	46	34	38

[Answers are rounded to the nearest whole number.]

17.

	P	Q	R	S
P	0	1	$\sqrt{2}$	1
Q	1	0	1	$\sqrt{2}$
R	$\sqrt{2}$	1	0	1
S	1	$\sqrt{2}$	1	0

18.

	P	Q	R	S	T	U	V	W
P	0	1	$\sqrt{2}$	1	1	$\sqrt{2}$	$\sqrt{3}$	$\sqrt{2}$
Q	1	0	1	$\sqrt{2}$	$\sqrt{2}$	1	$\sqrt{2}$	$\sqrt{3}$
R	$\sqrt{2}$	1	0	1	$\sqrt{3}$	$\sqrt{2}$	1	$\sqrt{2}$
S	1	$\sqrt{2}$	1	0	$\sqrt{2}$	$\sqrt{3}$	$\sqrt{2}$	1
T	1	$\sqrt{2}$	$\sqrt{3}$	$\sqrt{2}$	0	1	$\sqrt{2}$	1
U	$\sqrt{2}$	1	$\sqrt{2}$	$\sqrt{3}$	1	0	1	$\sqrt{2}$
V	$\sqrt{3}$	$\sqrt{2}$	1	$\sqrt{2}$	$\sqrt{2}$	1	0	1
W	$\sqrt{2}$	$\sqrt{3}$	$\sqrt{2}$	1	1	$\sqrt{2}$	1	0

EXERCISE 8.2

1. (a) yes   (b) yes   (c) no   (d) yes   (e) yes
(f) no   (g) yes   (h) yes

2. (a) 1×3 (b) 2×2 (c) 2×1 (d) 2×3
(e) not defined   (f) 4×1

3. (a) (i) yes   (ii) 3×4 (b) (i) yes   (ii) 1×3
(c) (i) yes   (ii) 3×2 (d) (i) yes   (ii) 1×1
(e) (i) yes   (ii) 3×3 (f) (i) not defined
(g) (i) yes   (ii) 2×2

4. (a) (i) not defined   (b) (i) not defined
(c) (i) not defined   (d) (i) yes   (ii) 4×4
(e) (i) yes   (ii) 1×1 (f) (i) yes   (ii) 3×2
(g) (i) yes   (ii) 2×2

5. (a) $[-34]$ (b) $[-402]$ (c) not possible
(d) $[-1274]$ (e) $\begin{bmatrix} -132 & 96 \\ 176 & -128 \end{bmatrix}$
(f) $[2x - 3y + 5z]$

6. (a) $[-23 \quad 5]$ (b) $\begin{bmatrix} -30 & 3 \\ 12 & 31 \end{bmatrix}$
(c) $\begin{bmatrix} -9 & 10 & 42 \\ -6 & 4 & 18 \\ 12 & 0 & -6 \end{bmatrix}$ (d) $\begin{bmatrix} 3 & -20 \\ -12 & 7 \end{bmatrix}$
(e) $\begin{bmatrix} -56 \\ 55 \\ 118 \end{bmatrix}$ (f) $\begin{bmatrix} 30 & 100 & -204 \\ -99 & -146 & 260 \\ -41 & -13 & 1 \end{bmatrix}$
(g) not possible   (h) $\begin{bmatrix} \frac{3}{4} \\ \frac{5}{4} \end{bmatrix}$ (i) $\begin{bmatrix} 5x - 8y \\ 2x + 11y \end{bmatrix}$
(j) $\begin{bmatrix} 3x - y - 4z \\ 6x + 2y - 5z \end{bmatrix}$

7. (a) $\begin{bmatrix} -58 & -2 & 15 \\ 133 & 70 & -49 \end{bmatrix}$ (b) not possible
(c) not possible   (d) $\begin{bmatrix} -38 & -16 & 12 \\ 93 & 82 & -15 \\ -6 & 40 & -32 \end{bmatrix}$

8. (a) $\begin{bmatrix} 5 & -27 \\ -32 & -24 \end{bmatrix}$ (b) $\begin{bmatrix} -136 & 153 \\ 280 & -192 \end{bmatrix}$
(c) $\begin{bmatrix} -74 & 59 \\ -6 & 8 \\ -64 & 57 \end{bmatrix}$ (d) $\begin{bmatrix} -136 & 153 \\ 280 & -192 \end{bmatrix}$

9. (a) $\begin{bmatrix} 3 & -8 \\ 7 & 9 \end{bmatrix}$ (b) $\begin{bmatrix} 3 & -8 \\ 7 & 9 \end{bmatrix}$

10. (a) $\begin{bmatrix} 2 & -3 & 1 \\ 0 & -2 & 4 \\ 3 & 5 & 2 \end{bmatrix}$ (b) $\begin{bmatrix} 2 & -3 & 1 \\ 0 & -2 & 4 \\ 3 & 5 & 2 \end{bmatrix}$

11. (a)

$$\text{From } \begin{array}{c} \\ 1 \\ 2 \\ 3 \end{array} \begin{array}{ccc} \overset{\displaystyle\text{To}}{1\ \ 2\ \ 3} \\ \begin{bmatrix} 0 & 1 & 1 \\ 1 & 0 & 0 \\ 0 & 1 & 0 \end{bmatrix} \end{array} = A$$

(b) $A^2 = \begin{bmatrix} 1 & 1 & 0 \\ 0 & 1 & 1 \\ 1 & 0 & 0 \end{bmatrix}$

(d) $A^3 = \begin{bmatrix} 1 & 1 & 1 \\ 1 & 1 & 0 \\ 0 & 1 & 1 \end{bmatrix}$

(e) The three-step paths in the network

12. (a)

$$\text{From } \begin{array}{c} \\ 1 \\ 2 \\ 3 \end{array} \begin{array}{ccc} \overset{\displaystyle\text{To}}{1\ \ 2\ \ 3} \\ \begin{bmatrix} 0 & 1 & 2 \\ 2 & 0 & 1 \\ 1 & 0 & 1 \end{bmatrix} \end{array} = A$$

(b) $A^2 = \begin{bmatrix} 4 & 0 & 3 \\ 1 & 2 & 5 \\ 1 & 1 & 3 \end{bmatrix}$

13. (a)

$$\text{To } \begin{array}{c} \\ \text{Vancouver} \\ \text{Winnipeg} \\ \text{Toronto} \\ \text{Halifax} \end{array} \begin{array}{c} \overset{\displaystyle\text{From}}{\text{Vancouver Winnipeg Toronto Halifax}} \\ \begin{bmatrix} 0 & 1 & 1 & 0 \\ 1 & 0 & 1 & 1 \\ 1 & 1 & 0 & 1 \\ 0 & 1 & 1 & 0 \end{bmatrix} \end{array}$$

(b) $A^2 = \begin{bmatrix} 2 & 1 & 1 & 2 \\ 1 & 3 & 2 & 1 \\ 1 & 2 & 3 & 1 \\ 2 & 1 & 1 & 2 \end{bmatrix}$ $A^3 = \begin{bmatrix} 2 & 5 & 5 & 2 \\ 5 & 4 & 5 & 5 \\ 5 & 5 & 4 & 5 \\ 2 & 5 & 5 & 2 \end{bmatrix}$

(c) 2   (d) 7

14. $A^2 = \begin{bmatrix} 0.48 & 0.52 \\ 0.39 & 0.61 \end{bmatrix}$ $A^3 = \begin{bmatrix} 0.444 & 0.556 \\ 0.417 & 0.583 \end{bmatrix}$

$A^4 = \begin{bmatrix} 0.4332 & 0.5668 \\ 0.4251 & 0.5749 \end{bmatrix}$

15. $A^2 = \begin{bmatrix} 0.25 & 0.58 & 0.17 \\ 0.07 & 0.82 & 0.11 \\ 0.28 & 0.46 & 0.26 \end{bmatrix}$

$A^3 = \begin{bmatrix} 0.169 & 0.664 & 0.167 \\ 0.091 & 0.784 & 0.125 \\ 0.238 & 0.58 & 0.182 \end{bmatrix}$

16. (a) $\begin{bmatrix} 7 & 1 \\ 13 & 11 \end{bmatrix}$ (b) $[-81 \quad 10 \quad -20]$

(c) $\begin{bmatrix} 10 \\ -36 \\ 32 \end{bmatrix}$

17. $x = \frac{43}{11}, y = \frac{3}{11}$

18. $x = -11, y = -26, z = 3$

19. (A) ACDC   (b) GENESIS   (c) WHITNEY HOUSTON   (d) COUNTRY AND WESTERN

20. (a) $\begin{bmatrix} 3 & -2 \\ -7 & 5 \end{bmatrix}$ (b) CONGRATULATIONS

EXERCISE 8.3

1.

A	B	C
[22.26	21.48	22.94]

Store B is the cheapest.

2. $\begin{array}{l} \text{Anderson N.} \\ \text{Anthony D.} \\ \text{Bellavia D.} \\ \text{Curic A.} \end{array} \begin{bmatrix} 64 \\ 78 \\ 52 \\ 90 \end{bmatrix}$ (Answers are rounded to the nearest mark.)

3.

Anderson N.	Anthony D.	Bellavia D.	Curic A.
[64	78	52	90]

4. (a)   Raw Material

A	B	C	D
[367	371	358	398]

(b) $\begin{array}{l} \text{Laser} \\ \text{Graphics} \\ \text{High Quality} \\ \text{Budget} \end{array} \begin{bmatrix} 232 \\ 306 \\ 169 \\ 143 \end{bmatrix}$ (Entries in dollars)

5.

Under $20 000	$20 000–$40 000	Over $40 000
[360	420	220]

6. (a)

Material (m^2)	Labour (h)
[1475	2485]

(b) $\begin{array}{l} \text{Small} \\ \text{Medium} \\ \text{Large} \\ \text{Extra-Large} \end{array} \begin{bmatrix} 32.70 \\ 36.09 \\ 51.31 \\ 54.70 \end{bmatrix}$ (Entries in dollars)

(c) $43 257.00

EXERCISE 8.4

1. (a) yes   (b) yes   (c) no   (d) no   (e) no
(f) no

2. (a) no   (b) yes   (c) no   (d) yes

3. (a) 0.2   (b) 0   (c) 0.3

4. (a) $\begin{array}{cc} & \text{A}\ \ \text{B} \\ \begin{array}{c} \text{A} \\ \text{B} \end{array} & \begin{bmatrix} 0.6 & 0.4 \\ 0.1 & 0.9 \end{bmatrix} \end{array} = P$

(b) $S^{(0)} = \begin{array}{c} \text{A}\ \ \text{B} \\ [\ 0.7 \ \ 0.3\ ] \end{array}$

(c) $P^2 = \begin{bmatrix} 0.4 & 0.6 \\ 0.15 & 0.85 \end{bmatrix}$ $P^3 = \begin{bmatrix} 0.3 & 0.7 \\ 0.175 & 0.825 \end{bmatrix}$

(d) 0.45 or 45% for calculator A,
0.55 or 55% for calculator B

(e) 0.325 or 32.5% for calculator A,
0.675 or 67.5% for calculator B

(f) 0.2625 or 26.25% for calculator A,
0.7375 or 73.75% for calculator B

5. (a)

	sun	cloud	rain
sun	0.5	0.35	0.15
cloud	0.3	0.45	0.25
rain	0.15	0.45	0.4

(b) 0.4 or 40%   (c) 0.3225 or 32.25%

6. (a)

	city	suburban	rural
city	0.86	0.12	0.02
suburban	0.08	0.89	0.03
rural	0.15	0.06	0.79

(b) 0.86 or 86%   (c) 0.505 441 or about 50.5%

7. (a)

$$\begin{array}{c c} & \begin{matrix} 1 & 2 & 3 & 4 \end{matrix} \\ \begin{matrix} 1 \\ 2 \\ 3 \\ 4 \end{matrix} & \begin{bmatrix} 0 & \frac{1}{2} & 0 & \frac{1}{2} \\ \frac{1}{2} & 0 & \frac{1}{2} & 0 \\ 0 & \frac{1}{2} & 0 & \frac{1}{2} \\ \frac{1}{2} & 0 & \frac{1}{2} & 0 \end{bmatrix} = P \end{array}$$

(b) $P^2 = \begin{bmatrix} \frac{1}{2} & 0 & \frac{1}{2} & 0 \\ 0 & \frac{1}{2} & 0 & \frac{1}{2} \\ \frac{1}{2} & 0 & \frac{1}{2} & 0 \\ 0 & \frac{1}{2} & 0 & \frac{1}{2} \end{bmatrix}$ $\begin{matrix} P^3 = P \\ P^4 = P^2 \end{matrix}$

(c) $\frac{1}{2}$, 0   (d) 0, 0

8. (a)

$$\begin{array}{c c} & \begin{matrix} 1 & 2 & 3 & 4 \end{matrix} \\ \begin{matrix} 1 \\ 2 \\ 3 \\ 4 \end{matrix} & \begin{bmatrix} 0 & 1 & 0 & 0 \\ \frac{1}{3} & 0 & \frac{2}{3} & 0 \\ 0 & \frac{2}{3} & 0 & \frac{1}{3} \\ 0 & 0 & 1 & 0 \end{bmatrix} = P \end{array}$$

(b) $P^2 = \begin{bmatrix} \frac{1}{3} & 0 & \frac{2}{3} & 0 \\ 0 & \frac{7}{9} & 0 & \frac{2}{9} \\ \frac{2}{9} & 0 & \frac{7}{9} & 0 \\ 0 & \frac{2}{3} & 0 & \frac{1}{3} \end{bmatrix}$

$$P^3 = \begin{bmatrix} 0 & \frac{7}{9} & 0 & \frac{2}{9} \\ \frac{7}{27} & 0 & \frac{20}{27} & 0 \\ 0 & \frac{20}{27} & 0 & \frac{7}{27} \\ \frac{2}{9} & 0 & \frac{7}{9} & 0 \end{bmatrix}$$

$$P^4 = \begin{bmatrix} \frac{7}{27} & 0 & \frac{20}{27} & 0 \\ 0 & \frac{61}{81} & 0 & \frac{20}{81} \\ \frac{20}{81} & 0 & \frac{61}{81} & 0 \\ 0 & \frac{20}{27} & 0 & \frac{7}{27} \end{bmatrix}$$ (c) $\frac{2}{3}$, 0   (d) 0, 0

9. (a)

$$\begin{array}{c c} & \begin{matrix} \text{on time} & \text{late} \end{matrix} \\ \begin{matrix} \text{on time} \\ \text{late} \end{matrix} & \begin{bmatrix} 0.7 & 0.3 \\ 0.9 & 0.1 \end{bmatrix} = P \end{array}$$

(b) $P^2 = \begin{bmatrix} 0.76 & 0.24 \\ 0.72 & 0.28 \end{bmatrix}$ $P^3 = \begin{bmatrix} 0.748 & 0.252 \\ 0.756 & 0.244 \end{bmatrix}$

$P^4 = \begin{bmatrix} 0.7504 & 0.2496 \\ 0.7488 & 0.2512 \end{bmatrix}$

(c) 0.74 or 74% 0.752 or 75.2% 0.7496 or 74.96% 0.750 08 or about 75%

10. (a)

	degree	no degree
degree	0.75	0.25
no degree	0.33	0.67

(b) 0.4686 or about 47%

(c) 0.6009 or about 60%

11. (a)

	Northstar	Red Lake
Northstar	0.1	0.9
Red Lake	0.8	0.2

(b) $P^2 = P^3 = P^4 = P$

(c) o.4 or 40% in each case

12. (a) [0 1 0]   (b) [0 0 1]

(c) $P^2 = \begin{bmatrix} 0.51 & 0.34 & 0.15 \\ 0.46 & 0.36 & 0.18 \\ 0.43 & 0.37 & 0.2 \end{bmatrix}$

$P^3 = \begin{bmatrix} 0.487 & 0.349 & 0.164 \\ 0.474 & 0.354 & 0.172 \\ 0.466 & 0.357 & 0.177 \end{bmatrix}$

$P^4 = \begin{bmatrix} 0.481 & 0.3513 & 0.1677 \\ 0.4776 & 0.3526 & 0.1698 \\ 0.4755 & 0.3534 & 0.1711 \end{bmatrix}$

(d) 0.4   (e) 0.164   (f) 0.3526

EXERCISE 8.5

1. (a) yes   (b) no   (c) yes   (d) yes   (e) no
(f) no

2. (a) [0.5 0.5]   (b) [0.75 0.25]

3. (a)

	A	B
A	0.8	0.2
B	0.5	0.5

(b) Company A: $\frac{5}{7}$ or 71%

Company B: $\frac{2}{7}$ or 29%

4. (a)

	Natural	Poco's
Natural	0.9	0.1
Poco's	0.4	0.6

(b) Natural Foods: $\frac{4}{5}$ or 80%

Poco's: $\frac{1}{5}$ or 20%

5. Machine B

6. (c) 34% at location A, 46% at location B, 20% at location C

7. (a)

	A	B	C
A	0	0.4	0.6
B	0.6	0	0.4
C	0.4	0.6	0

(d) $\begin{bmatrix} \frac{1}{3} & \frac{1}{3} & \frac{1}{3} \end{bmatrix}$

8.6 REVIEW EXERCISE

1. (a) (i) 17   (ii) 9   (iii) -3
(b) (i) 1.9   (ii) 1.0   (iii) 5.1
(c) (i) 0   (ii) no such entry   (iii) no such entry

2. (a) 4×4 (b) 4×3 (c) 2×3

3. (a) a_{12} (b) a_{32} (c) a_{34} (d) a_{23}

4. (a) Individual 4   (b) Individual 3
(c) They are the same age

5. (a)

$$\begin{array}{c} \\ 1 \\ 2 \\ 3 \\ 4 \end{array} \begin{array}{cccc} 1 & 2 & 3 & 4 \\ \begin{bmatrix} 0 & 1 & 0 & 0 \\ 1 & 0 & 1 & 0 \\ 1 & 2 & 0 & 0 \\ 1 & 0 & 1 & 0 \end{bmatrix} \end{array} = A$$

(b) $A^2 = \begin{bmatrix} 1 & 0 & 1 & 0 \\ 1 & 3 & 0 & 0 \\ 2 & 1 & 2 & 0 \\ 1 & 3 & 0 & 0 \end{bmatrix}$

6. (a) $\begin{bmatrix} -37 & 66 \\ -76 & 34 \\ 55 & -12 \end{bmatrix}$

(b) $\begin{bmatrix} -6 & 6.4 & -1.2 \\ -6.4 & 15.2 & -5.6 \end{bmatrix}$

(c) $\begin{bmatrix} -23 & 44 & -2 \end{bmatrix}$

(d) $\begin{bmatrix} -2 & 40 & -10 \\ -63 & 56 & -21 \\ -22 & -76 & 16 \end{bmatrix}$ (e) not possible

(f) $\begin{bmatrix} -34 \\ -82 \\ 20 \\ 74 \end{bmatrix}$ (g) $\begin{bmatrix} 5 & 32 \\ -1 & 1 \\ -32 & -16 \end{bmatrix}$

7. (a) $\begin{bmatrix} -8 & 10 \\ 9 & -3 \end{bmatrix}$ (b) $\begin{bmatrix} 14 & 30 \\ 20 & -111 \end{bmatrix}$

(c) $\begin{bmatrix} 454 & -1018 \\ -1987 & 4513 \end{bmatrix}$

(d) $\begin{bmatrix} 52 & -148 \\ -294 & 654 \\ 45 & 9 \end{bmatrix}$

(e) $\begin{bmatrix} 12\ 032 & -17\ 984 \\ -45\ 803 & 68\ 513 \end{bmatrix}$ (f) not possible

8. (a)

Regular Hours

	Oct. 9	Oct. 10	Oct. 11	Oct. 12	Oct. 13
Worker 1	8	8	8	8	8
Worker 2	8	8	8	8	8
Worker 3	8	8	8	8	8

Overtime Hours

	Oct. 9	Oct. 10	Oct. 11	Oct. 12	Oct. 13
Worker 1	0	0.5	0.5	0	1
Worker 2	0	0	0.5	0	0.5
Worker 3	0	0.5	1	0.5	1

(b)

Daily Pay (entries in dollars)

Worker					
1	84.00	91.88	91.88	84.00	99.75
2	84.00	84.00	91.88	84.00	91.88
3	84.00	91.88	99.75	91.88	99.75

9.

Company

	I	II	III
0–100 g	7.15	7.70	8.25
100–200 g	8.25	8.25	8.80
200–300 g	9.35	8.80	8.80
300–400 g	10.45	9.35	9.35

10. (a) TGIF   (b) ONLY TWO CHAPTERS LEFT

11. (a)

Raw Material

I	II	III
3200	2550	2150

(b) VCR

A	191
B	125
C	107

(entries in dollars)

12.

Adderly L.	70
Campbell U.	87
Denton T.	52
Lee F.	60

(Answers rounded to the nearest mark)

13. (a) yes, yes   (b) no   (c) no   (d) yes, no

14. (a)

	Nancy	Kevin
Nancy	0.6	0.4
Kevin	0.3	0.7

(b) 0.45 for Nancy and 0.55 for Kevin

(c) 0.61   (d) $\begin{bmatrix} \frac{3}{7} & \frac{4}{7} \end{bmatrix}$

15. (a)

	A	B	C
A	0.6	0.2	0.2
B	0.25	0.5	0.25
C	0.1	0.1	0.8

(b) $S^{(1)} = [0.295 \quad 0.25 \quad 0.455]$
   $S^{(2)} = [0.285 \quad 0.2295 \quad 0.4855]$

(c) 0.26 or 26%

16. (c) $\begin{bmatrix} \frac{1}{3} & \frac{1}{3} & \frac{1}{3} \end{bmatrix}$

8.7 CHAPTER 8 TEST

1. (a) $\begin{bmatrix} 24 & -49 \\ -40 & 10 \\ 51 & -3 \end{bmatrix}$ (b) $\begin{bmatrix} -30 & -11 \\ -58 & 34 \end{bmatrix}$

(c) not possible

2. (a) $\begin{bmatrix} -25 & 10 \\ 21 & -8 \\ 42 & -3 \end{bmatrix}$ (b) $\begin{bmatrix} 9 & -18 & 8 \\ 9 & 13 & -10 \\ -15 & 10 & 5 \end{bmatrix}$

(c) not possible

3. (a)

Paper Type	Riverside	Holbrook	Westview
216mm × 279mm	18	12	15
216mm × 279mm (punched)	21	15	18
216mm × 356mm	12	7	6

(b)

Paper Type	Riverside	Holbrook	Westview
216mm × 279mm	156	104	130
216mm × 279mm (punched)	132	80	106
216mm × 356mm	204	144	202

(c) no

4. MATRICES

5. (a) $\begin{matrix} \text{Mechanic} \\ \text{Inspector} \end{matrix} \begin{bmatrix} 12\,500 \\ 1250 \end{bmatrix}$ (b) \$243 750

6. (a)

	sun	cloud	rain
sun	0.6	0.3	0.1
cloud	0.3	0.4	0.3
rain	0.2	0.4	0.4

(b) 0.47 or 47%   (c) 0.255 or 25.5%

7. (a)

	Hillside	Garden
Hillside	0.8	0.2
Garden	0.4	0.6

(b) 0.72 or 72%   (c) $\begin{bmatrix} \frac{2}{3} & \frac{1}{3} \end{bmatrix}$

CHAPTER 9 SYSTEMS OF LINEAR EQUATIONS

REVIEW AND PREVIEW TO CHAPTER 9
EXERCISE 1

1. (a)

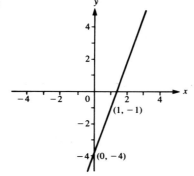

(b)

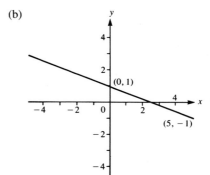

(c)

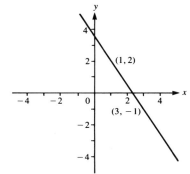

(b)

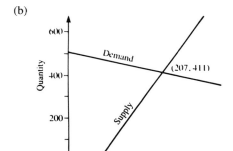

2. (a) The equilibrium price is $240 and 480 items would be produced at this price.
(b)

(d)

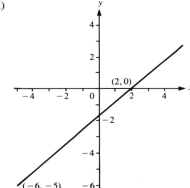

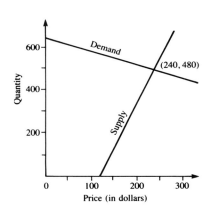

3. (a) The equilibrium price is $450 and 220 items would be produced at this price.
(b)

2. (a) $\begin{cases} x = 3 \\ y = 3 \end{cases}$

(b) $\begin{cases} x = -2 \\ y = 1 \end{cases}$

(c) The graphs of the two equations are the same; therefore any point satisfying $2x - y = 6$ is a solution to the system.

(d) no solution   (e) $\begin{cases} x = -1 \\ y = 2 \end{cases}$ (f) no solution

EXERCISE 2
  1. (a) The equilibrium price is $207 and 411 items would be produced at this price.

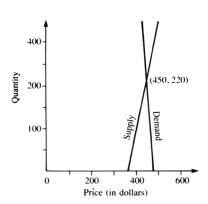

4. (a) The equilibrium price is \$336 and 188 items would be produced at this price.

(b)

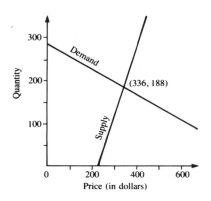

2. $\begin{cases} x = -\frac{50}{39} \\ y = -\frac{98}{39} \end{cases}$

3. Inconsistent

4. $\begin{cases} x = \dfrac{-3k - 5}{2} \\ y = k \end{cases}$ $\begin{cases} x = -\frac{5}{2} \\ y = 0 \end{cases}$ $\begin{cases} x = -4 \\ y = 1 \end{cases}$

5. Inconsistent

6. $\begin{cases} x = 2 \\ y = 1 \end{cases}$

7. $\begin{cases} x = \dfrac{-3k - 8}{7} \\ y = \dfrac{8k + 5}{7} \\ z = k \end{cases}$ $\begin{cases} x = -\frac{8}{7} \\ y = \frac{5}{7} \\ z = 0 \end{cases}$ $\begin{cases} x = -\frac{11}{7} \\ y = \frac{13}{7} \\ z = 1 \end{cases}$

8. Inconsistent

9. $\begin{cases} x = 1 \\ y = 1 \\ z = -1 \end{cases}$

10. $\begin{cases} x = k - 2 \\ y = 2k - 7 \\ z = k \end{cases}$ $\begin{cases} x = -2 \\ y = -7 \\ z = 0 \end{cases}$ $\begin{cases} x = -1 \\ y = -5 \\ z = 1 \end{cases}$

11. $\begin{cases} x = 2 \\ y = -1 \\ z = 2 \end{cases}$

12. $\begin{cases} x = k - 2 \\ y = -2k + 3 \\ z = k \end{cases}$ $\begin{cases} x = -2 \\ y = 3 \\ z = 0 \end{cases}$ $\begin{cases} x = -1 \\ y = 1 \\ z = 1 \end{cases}$

13. $\begin{cases} x = \dfrac{-19k + 50}{2} \\ y = k \\ z = 5k - 10 \end{cases}$ $\begin{cases} x = 25 \\ y = 0 \\ z = -10 \end{cases}$ $\begin{cases} x = 6 \\ y = 2 \\ z = 0 \end{cases}$

14. $\begin{cases} w = -3k - 2m - 4 \\ x = m \\ y = 5k + 6 \\ z = k \end{cases}$ $\begin{cases} w = -4 \\ x = 0 \\ y = 6 \\ z = 0 \end{cases}$

15. $\begin{cases} w = -6 \\ x = 1 \\ y = 6 \\ z = 0 \end{cases}$ $\begin{cases} w = 1 \\ x = -1 \\ y = 2 \\ z = 3 \end{cases}$

16. $\begin{cases} w = k - 3 \\ x = k - 2 \\ y = k - 1 \\ z = k \end{cases}$ $\begin{cases} w = -3 \\ x = -2 \\ y = -1 \\ z = 0 \end{cases}$ $\begin{cases} w = -2 \\ x = -1 \\ y = 0 \\ z = 1 \end{cases}$

EXERCISE 9.1

1. (a) $\begin{cases} x = -2 \\ y = -2 \end{cases}$ **(b)** $\begin{cases} x = -3 \\ y = -\frac{14}{3} \end{cases}$ **(c)** $\begin{cases} x = -\frac{30}{41} \\ y = \frac{94}{41} \end{cases}$

(d) $\begin{cases} x = -\frac{44}{17} \\ y = \frac{23}{34} \end{cases}$

2. (a) $\begin{cases} x = 2 \\ y = -2 \\ z = 1 \end{cases}$ **(b)** $\begin{cases} x = 1 \\ y = -1 \\ z = 3 \end{cases}$ **(c)** $\begin{cases} x = 3 \\ y = -2 \\ z = 1 \end{cases}$

(d) $\begin{cases} x = 4 \\ y = -3 \\ z = -5 \end{cases}$ **(e)** $\begin{cases} x = 7 \\ y = 3 \\ z = -2 \end{cases}$ **(f)** $\begin{cases} x = 3 \\ y = -4 \\ z = 6 \end{cases}$

3. (a) $\begin{cases} w = 1 \\ x = -1 \\ y = 2 \\ z = -2 \end{cases}$ **(b)** $\begin{cases} w = 2 \\ x = -1 \\ y = 3 \\ z = 1 \end{cases}$

(c) $\begin{cases} w = 2 \\ x = -1 \\ y = 3 \\ z = -2 \end{cases}$

4. (a) $\begin{cases} x = 4 \\ y = -5 \\ z = 8 \end{cases}$ **(b)** $\begin{cases} w = 1 \\ x = -1 \\ y = 2 \\ z = -3 \end{cases}$ **(c)** $\begin{cases} w = 1 \\ x = 2 \\ y = 3 \\ z = 4 \end{cases}$

EXERCISE 9.2

1. $\begin{cases} x = \dfrac{3k - 4}{7} \\ y = k \end{cases}$ $\begin{cases} x = -\frac{4}{7} \\ y = 0 \end{cases}$ $\begin{cases} x = -\frac{1}{7} \\ y = 1 \end{cases}$

17. $\begin{cases} w = 2 - k \\ x = k \\ y = 2 - k \\ z = k \end{cases}$ $\begin{cases} w = 2 \\ x = 0 \\ y = 2 \\ z = 0 \end{cases}$ $\begin{cases} w = 0 \\ x = 2 \\ y = 0 \\ z = 2 \end{cases}$

18. $\begin{cases} w = m \\ x = k \\ y = -m - 4k - 7 \\ z = m - 7k - 13 \end{cases}$ $\begin{cases} w = 0 \\ x = 0 \\ y = -7 \\ z = -13 \end{cases}$

$\begin{cases} w = 1 \\ x = 0 \\ y = -8 \\ z = -12 \end{cases}$

EXERCISE 9.3

1.

Coefficient Matrix   Augmented Matrix

(a) $\begin{bmatrix} 2 & -4 \\ 1 & 3 \end{bmatrix}$ $\begin{bmatrix} 2 & -4 & | & 18 \\ 1 & 3 & | & -4 \end{bmatrix}$

(b) $\begin{bmatrix} 2 & -5 & 7 \\ -3 & 0 & -4 \end{bmatrix}$ $\begin{bmatrix} 2 & -5 & 7 & | & 23 \\ -3 & 0 & -4 & | & 12 \end{bmatrix}$

(c) $\begin{bmatrix} 2 & -4 & 6 \\ 0 & 3 & 2 \\ -1 & -3 & 0 \end{bmatrix}$ $\begin{bmatrix} 2 & -4 & 6 & | & -12 \\ 0 & 3 & 2 & | & 6 \\ -1 & -3 & 0 & | & 9 \end{bmatrix}$

(d) $\begin{bmatrix} 2 & 1 \\ 4 & -5 \\ 1 & 1 \end{bmatrix}$ $\begin{bmatrix} 2 & 1 & | & 0 \\ 4 & -5 & | & 0 \\ 1 & 1 & | & 0 \end{bmatrix}$

(e) $\begin{bmatrix} 2 & 5 & -2 \\ -3 & -2 & 1 \\ 1 & 1 & 1 \\ -9 & 0 & -3 \end{bmatrix}$ $\begin{bmatrix} 2 & 5 & -2 & | & 4 \\ -3 & -2 & 1 & | & 18 \\ 1 & 1 & 1 & | & 21 \\ -9 & 0 & -3 & | & 13 \end{bmatrix}$

(f) $\begin{bmatrix} 2 & -1 & 7 & -4 \\ 1 & 3 & -5 & 3 \\ -6 & 0 & 9 & 0 \\ 2 & 0 & 0 & 7 \end{bmatrix}$ $\begin{bmatrix} 2 & -1 & 7 & -4 & | & 24 \\ 1 & 3 & -5 & 3 & | & 16 \\ -6 & 0 & 9 & 0 & | & 10 \\ 2 & 0 & 0 & 7 & | & 28 \end{bmatrix}$

2. (a) $\begin{cases} 3x + 8y = -4 \\ 4x = 7 \end{cases}$ (b) $\begin{cases} -2x + 4y = 6 \\ 7y = 14 \\ 3x - 5y = 12 \end{cases}$

(c) $\begin{cases} 4x - 3y + z = 0 \\ 3x - z = 6 \end{cases}$

(d) $\begin{cases} y + 2z = -4 \\ 2x + y = 3 \\ 3x - 3y + z = 10 \\ x - z = 12 \end{cases}$

3. (a) $\begin{bmatrix} 1 & 2 & | & -4 \\ 0 & 1 & | & -7 \\ 0 & -3 & | & 5 \end{bmatrix}$ (b) $\begin{bmatrix} 1 & -3 & | & 5 \\ 0 & 4 & | & -19 \end{bmatrix}$

(c) $\begin{bmatrix} 1 & -8 & 4 & | & -1 \\ 0 & 2 & -5 & | & 6 \\ 0 & -13 & 6 & | & -1 \end{bmatrix}$ (d) $\begin{bmatrix} 1 & -3 & | & 7 \\ 0 & 1 & | & -\frac{3}{2} \end{bmatrix}$

4. (c) $\begin{bmatrix} 1 & -4 & | & 2 \\ 0 & 1 & | & -1 \end{bmatrix}$ **5.** (f) $\begin{bmatrix} 1 & 1 & 1 & | & 5 \\ 0 & 1 & 1 & | & 1 \\ 0 & 0 & 1 & | & -2 \end{bmatrix}$

6. (c) $\begin{bmatrix} 1 & \frac{3}{2} & 2 & | & 3 \\ 0 & 1 & \frac{8}{3} & | & \frac{44}{9} \end{bmatrix}$ **7.** (i) $\begin{bmatrix} 1 & 0 & | & 0 \\ 0 & 1 & | & 0 \\ 0 & 0 & | & 1 \end{bmatrix}$

8. (i) $\begin{bmatrix} 1 & 0 & 1 & | & 0 \\ 0 & 1 & -1 & | & 0 \\ 0 & 0 & 0 & | & 1 \end{bmatrix}$

9. (g) $\begin{bmatrix} 1 & 3 & 1 & -4 & & 3 \\ 0 & 1 & -\frac{2}{9} & -\frac{7}{9} & | & -\frac{4}{9} \\ 0 & 0 & 0 & 0 & | & 0 \\ 0 & 0 & 0 & 0 & | & 0 \end{bmatrix}$

10. (g) $\begin{bmatrix} 1 & -6 & 3 & 3 & & 7 \\ 0 & 1 & -\frac{2}{9} & -\frac{7}{9} & | & -\frac{4}{9} \\ 0 & 0 & 0 & 0 & | & 0 \\ 0 & 0 & 0 & 0 & | & 0 \end{bmatrix}$

11. Interchange row 1 with row 2
Multiply row 1 by -1
Subtract four times row 1 from row 2
Multiply row 2 by one-seventh

12. Subtract row 3 from row 1
Add three times row 1 to row 2
Subtract row 1 from row 3
Multiply row 2 by $-\frac{1}{11}$
Add five times row 2 to row 1
Subtract seven times row 2 from row 3

13. Interchange row 1 with row 2
Subtract three times row 1 from row 2
Subtract 13 times row 1 from row 3
Multiply row 2 by $-\frac{1}{10}$
Add 30 times row 2 to row 3

14. Interchange row 1 with row 3
Subtract two times row 1 from row 2
Subtract three times row 1 from row 3
Multiply row 2 by $-\frac{1}{5}$
Subtract row 2 from row 1
Add row 2 to row 3
Multiply row 3 by $\frac{1}{9}$
Add three times row 3 to row 1

EXERCISE 9.4

1. (a) no (b) no (c) yes (d) yes (e) yes
(f) yes (g) yes (h) yes

2. (a) Independent (b) Dependent (1 parameter)
 (c) Dependent (1 parameter) (d) Inconsistent
 (e) Dependent (1 parameter)
 (f) Dependent (1 parameter)

3. [Note: Other answers are possible.]

(a) $\begin{bmatrix} 1 & -7 & | & 5 \\ 0 & 1 & | & -\frac{11}{16} \end{bmatrix}$ (b) $\begin{bmatrix} 1 & 9 & | & -10 \\ 0 & 1 & | & -\frac{22}{19} \end{bmatrix}$

(c) $\begin{bmatrix} 1 & 4 & | & -3 \\ 0 & 1 & | & -\frac{19}{14} \end{bmatrix}$ (d) $\begin{bmatrix} 1 & \frac{3}{2} & -\frac{7}{2} & | & \frac{1}{2} \\ 0 & 1 & -\frac{5}{3} & | & \frac{1}{7} \end{bmatrix}$

(e) $\begin{bmatrix} 1 & -3 & | & -9 \\ 0 & 1 & | & 4 \\ 0 & 0 & | & 1 \end{bmatrix}$ (f) $\begin{bmatrix} 1 & -2 & 6 & | & -3 \\ 0 & 1 & \frac{5}{2} & | & -\frac{5}{2} \\ 0 & 0 & 1 & | & -\frac{9}{7} \end{bmatrix}$

(g) $\begin{bmatrix} 1 & 1 & -1 & | & -2 \\ 0 & 1 & -\frac{7}{5} & | & -\frac{4}{5} \\ 0 & 0 & 1 & | & -\frac{63}{11} \end{bmatrix}$

(h) $\begin{bmatrix} 1 & 1 & 0 & -1 & | & 0 \\ 0 & 1 & 0 & -1 & | & 1 \\ 0 & 0 & 1 & -1 & | & 0 \\ 0 & 0 & 0 & 1 & | & -1 \end{bmatrix}$

4. (a) $\begin{cases} x = 14 \\ y = 2 \end{cases}$

(b) $\begin{cases} x = 2k + 3 \\ y = k \end{cases}$ $\begin{cases} x = 3 \\ y = 0 \end{cases}$ $\begin{cases} x = 5 \\ y = 1 \end{cases}$

(c) $\begin{cases} x = -4 \\ y = -1 \\ z = -1 \end{cases}$

(d) $\begin{cases} x = 13k + 33 \\ y = 2k + 4 \\ z = k \end{cases}$ $\begin{cases} x = 33 \\ y = 4 \\ z = 0 \end{cases}$ $\begin{cases} x = 46 \\ y = 6 \\ z = 1 \end{cases}$

(e) Inconsistent

(f) $\begin{cases} w = 6m - 2k - 5 \\ x = m \\ y = 3k + 1 \\ z = k \end{cases}$ $\begin{cases} w = -5 \\ x = 0 \\ y = 1 \\ z = 0 \end{cases}$

$\begin{cases} w = 1 \\ x = 1 \\ y = 1 \\ z = 0 \end{cases}$

5. (a) $\begin{cases} x = 5 \\ y = 2 \end{cases}$ (b) $\begin{cases} x = \frac{4}{3} \\ y = -\frac{5}{9} \end{cases}$ (c) $\begin{cases} x = \frac{31}{22} \\ y = -\frac{7}{22} \end{cases}$

(d) $\begin{cases} x = \dfrac{4k + 9}{3} \\ y = k \end{cases}$

6. (a) $\begin{cases} x = 2 \\ y = -2 \\ z = 3 \end{cases}$ (b) $\begin{cases} x = 2 \\ y = 3 \\ z = -1 \end{cases}$

(c) $\begin{cases} x = \dfrac{12 - 5k}{7} \\ y = \dfrac{8 - k}{7} \\ z = k \end{cases}$ (d) $\begin{cases} x = 2k - 4 \\ y = \dfrac{17 - 5k}{2} \\ z = k \end{cases}$

(e) $\begin{cases} x = 2 \\ y = -2 \\ z = -2 \end{cases}$ (f) $\begin{cases} x = 1 \\ y = 1 \\ z = 1 \end{cases}$ (g) $\begin{cases} w = 2 \\ x = 1 \\ y = -1 \\ z = 2 \end{cases}$

(h) $\begin{cases} w = 2k + 3 \\ x = 2k + 3 \\ y = -k \\ z = k \end{cases}$ (i) Inconsistent

(j) $\begin{cases} w = \frac{4}{3} \\ x = \dfrac{3m - 3k + 4}{3} \\ y = m \\ z = k \end{cases}$

EXERCISE 9.5

1. (a) yes (b) no (c) yes (d) yes (e) no
 (f) no

2. (a) Independent (b) Inconsistent
 (c) Dependent (1 parameter) (d) Dependent
 (1 parameter) (e) Independent (f) Dependent
 (1 parameter) (g) Dependent (1 parameter)
 (h) Dependent (2 parameters)

3. (a) $\begin{bmatrix} 1 & 0 & | & \frac{1}{5} \\ 0 & 1 & | & -\frac{7}{5} \end{bmatrix}$ (b) $\begin{bmatrix} 1 & 0 & | & -7 \\ 0 & 1 & | & -18 \end{bmatrix}$

(c) $\begin{bmatrix} 1 & 0 & 0 & | & \frac{13}{10} \\ 0 & 1 & 0 & | & \frac{9}{10} \\ 0 & 0 & 1 & | & \frac{3}{2} \end{bmatrix}$ (d) $\begin{bmatrix} 1 & 0 & | & 0 \\ 0 & 1 & | & 0 \\ 0 & 0 & | & 1 \end{bmatrix}$

(e) $\begin{bmatrix} 1 & 0 & -\frac{4}{5} & | & -1 \\ 0 & 1 & -\frac{4}{5} & | & 1 \\ 0 & 0 & 0 & | & 0 \end{bmatrix}$ (f) $\begin{bmatrix} 1 & 0 & 0 & 0 & | & 0 \\ 0 & 1 & 0 & 0 & | & 0 \\ 0 & 0 & 1 & 1 & | & 0 \\ 0 & 0 & 0 & 1 & | & 1 \end{bmatrix}$

4. (a) $\begin{cases} x = 2 \\ y = -\frac{1}{3} \end{cases}$ (b) $\begin{cases} x = -\frac{3}{2} \\ y = \frac{1}{2} \end{cases}$

(c) $\begin{cases} x = 2k + 4 \\ y = k \end{cases}$ (d) $\begin{cases} x = 3k - 4 \\ y = k \end{cases}$

(e) Inconsistent

5. (a) $\begin{cases} x = 4 \\ y = 3 \\ z = -2 \end{cases}$ (b) $\begin{cases} x = \dfrac{k + 13}{7} \\ y = \dfrac{-9k - 12}{7} \\ z = k \end{cases}$

(c) $\begin{cases} x = \dfrac{7 - 3k}{4} \\ y = \dfrac{1 - k}{4} \\ z = k \end{cases}$ (d) $\begin{cases} x = 0 \\ y = 0 \\ z = 0 \end{cases}$

(e) Inconsistent (f) $\begin{cases} x = -1 \\ y = -2 \\ z = 5 \end{cases}$

6. (a) $\begin{cases} w = 1 \\ x = -2 \\ y = 1 \\ z = -2 \end{cases}$ (b) $\begin{cases} w = 2 \\ x = 1 \\ y = -1 \\ z = -2 \end{cases}$

(c) $\begin{cases} w = \dfrac{17 - m - 2k}{6} \\ x = \dfrac{-4 + k - m}{3} \\ y = m \\ z = k \end{cases}$

7. (a) $\begin{cases} x = \dfrac{10 - 2k}{5} \\ y = \dfrac{11k}{5} \\ z = k \end{cases}$

(b) $\begin{cases} w = \dfrac{16 - 2k}{3} \\ x = \dfrac{-14 + k + 3m}{3} \\ y = m \\ z = k \end{cases}$ (c) $\begin{cases} w = \dfrac{k}{7} \\ x = -\dfrac{4k}{7} \\ y = \dfrac{2k}{7} \\ z = k \end{cases}$

(d) $\begin{cases} x = 3 \\ y = -1 \end{cases}$ (e) $\begin{cases} w = \dfrac{25 + 3k - 2m}{5} \\ x = \dfrac{25 + 4k - m}{5} \\ y = m \\ z = k \end{cases}$

(f) $\begin{cases} w = \dfrac{12 - 2m}{3} \\ x = \dfrac{3 - 3k - m}{3} \\ y = m \\ z = k \end{cases}$

8. (a) $\begin{cases} x = \frac{202}{275} \\ y = \frac{369}{275} \\ z = -\frac{119}{275} \end{cases}$ (b) $\begin{cases} x = \dfrac{-17k + 216}{89} \\ y = \dfrac{32k - 171}{89} \\ z = k \end{cases}$

EXERCISE 9.6

1. (a) $\dfrac{80\ 000 - 4k}{3}$ dollars in fund A, $\dfrac{40\ 000 + k}{3}$ dollars in fund B, and k dollars in fund C; where $0 \leqslant k \leqslant 20\ 000$

(b) Yes, by investing the remaining \$20 000 in fund C and nothing in fund A.

2. 5000 hectares supplying the furniture manufacturers and 15 000 hectares supplying the construction companies

3. 200 mL of Solution 1 and 800 mL of Solution 2

4. 339 species I and 722 species II; species I appears to be dying out

5. 120 g of food I, 120 g of food II, and 60 g of food III

6. (a) $\dfrac{30 - k}{4}$ Truck 1's, $\dfrac{30 - k}{4}$ Truck 2's, $\dfrac{30 - k}{4}$ Truck 3's, and k Truck 4's; where $k = 2, 6, 10, 14, 18, 22, 26, 30$ (Note: other values for k lead to fractional or negative numbers of trucks.)

(b) Solution 1: 5 Truck 1's, 5 Truck 2's, 5 Truck 3's, and 10 Truck 4's
Solution 2: 6 Truck 1's, 6 Truck 2's, 6 Truck 3's, and 6 Truck 4's

Solution 3: 7 Truck 1's, 7 Truck 2's, 7 Truck 3's, and 2 Truck 4's

(c) Solution 1: 0 Truck 1's, 0 Truck 2's, 0 Truck 3's, and 30 Truck 4's

Solution 2: 1 Truck 1, 1 Truck 2, 1 Truck 3, and 26 Truck 4's

Solution 3: 2 Truck 1's, 2 Truck 2's, 2 Truck 3's, and 22 Truck 4's

Solution 4: 3 Truck 1's, 3 Truck 2's, 3 Truck 3's, and 18 Trucks 4's

Solution 5: 4 Truck 1's, 4 Truck 2's, 4 Truck 3's, and 14 Truck 4's

Solution 6: 5 Truck 1's, 5 Truck 2's, 5 Truck 3's, and 10 Truck 4's

Solution 7: 6 Truck 1's, 6 Truck 2's, 6 Truck 3's, and 6 Truck 4's

7. 10 console televisions, 20 portable televisions, and 20 stereos

9.7 REVIEW EXERCISE

1. (a) $\begin{cases} x = \frac{73}{39} \\ y = -\frac{19}{39} \end{cases}$ (b) Inconsistent

(c) $\begin{cases} x = 3 \\ y = -2 \\ z = -1 \end{cases}$ (d) $\begin{cases} x = \dfrac{-5k + 1}{14} \\ y = \dfrac{4k - 26}{7} \\ z = k \end{cases}$

(e) $\begin{cases} x = 1 \\ y = -1 \\ z = 1 \end{cases}$ (f) $\begin{cases} x = -3 \\ y = 1 \end{cases}$

(g) $\begin{cases} w = \dfrac{-273 - 16k}{31} \\ x = \dfrac{128 - 21k}{31} \\ y = \dfrac{-11 + 19k}{31} \\ z = k \end{cases}$ (h) $\begin{cases} w = \frac{3}{2} \\ x = -\frac{1}{2} \\ y = \frac{1}{2} \\ z = \frac{1}{2} \end{cases}$

(i) $\begin{cases} w = 1 \\ x = 2 \\ y = 3 \\ z = 4 \end{cases}$ (j) $\begin{cases} w = 3 - m + k \\ x = m \\ y = k \\ z = -1 - 3m + 3k \end{cases}$

2. (a) $\begin{bmatrix} 1 & 0 & | & \frac{19}{9} \\ 0 & 1 & | & -\frac{2}{9} \end{bmatrix}$ (b) $\begin{bmatrix} 1 & 0 & -1 & | & 0 \\ 0 & 1 & -1 & | & 0 \\ 0 & 0 & 0 & | & 1 \end{bmatrix}$

3. (a) yes (b) yes (c) no (d) no (e) no
(f) yes

4. (a) no (b) no (c) no (d) no (e) no (f) yes

5. (Note: other answers are possible)

(a) $\begin{bmatrix} 1 & 4 & | & 6 \\ 0 & 1 & | & \frac{14}{13} \end{bmatrix}$ (b) $\begin{bmatrix} 1 & -2 & | & -\frac{3}{2} \\ 0 & 1 & | & \frac{19}{10} \end{bmatrix}$

(c) $\begin{bmatrix} 1 & 0 & -2 & 1 & | & -5 \\ 0 & 1 & 3 & 0 & | & 9 \\ 0 & 0 & 1 & 1 & | & 13 \end{bmatrix}$

(d) $\begin{bmatrix} 1 & -6 & -1 & | & 2 \\ 0 & 1 & \frac{2}{19} & | & -\frac{1}{19} \end{bmatrix}$

6. (a) $\begin{bmatrix} 1 & 0 & | & 0 \\ 0 & 1 & | & 0 \\ 0 & 0 & | & 1 \end{bmatrix}$ (b) $\begin{bmatrix} 1 & 0 & 0 & | & -\frac{23}{6} \\ 0 & 1 & 0 & | & -\frac{29}{6} \\ 0 & 0 & 1 & | & -\frac{1}{6} \end{bmatrix}$

(c) $\begin{bmatrix} 1 & | & 0 \\ 0 & | & 1 \\ 0 & | & 0 \\ 0 & | & 0 \end{bmatrix}$ (d) $\begin{bmatrix} 1 & 0 & 0 & | & \frac{8}{7} \\ 0 & 1 & 0 & | & \frac{4}{7} \\ 0 & 0 & 1 & | & -\frac{2}{7} \\ 0 & 0 & 0 & | & 0 \end{bmatrix}$

7. (a) $\begin{cases} x = 31 \\ y = 19 \end{cases}$ (b) Inconsistent

(c) $\begin{cases} x = \dfrac{4 - 5k}{7} \\ y = \dfrac{4k - 6}{7} \\ z = k \end{cases}$ (d) $\begin{cases} x = 3 \\ y = -\frac{41}{14} \\ z = \frac{2}{7} \end{cases}$

(e) $\begin{cases} x = 2 \\ y = 2 \\ z = -1 \end{cases}$ (f) $\begin{cases} x = \dfrac{5 - 2k}{3} \\ y = \dfrac{5k + 1}{6} \\ z = k \end{cases}$

8. (a) $\begin{cases} w = \dfrac{143 - 5k}{32} \\ x = \dfrac{13 + k}{8} \\ y = \dfrac{-89 + 19k}{32} \\ z = k \end{cases}$

(b) $\begin{cases} w = \dfrac{16 + k + m}{4} \\ x = \dfrac{7m - 5k}{4} \\ y = m \\ z = k \end{cases}$ (c) $\begin{cases} w = 2 \\ x = -\frac{2}{3} \\ y = 3 \\ z = \frac{2}{3} \end{cases}$

(d) $\begin{cases} w = k + 2 \\ x = k \\ y = -2k - 1 \\ z = k \end{cases}$ (e) Inconsistent

(f) $\begin{cases} w = \dfrac{29 - 5k - 3m}{3} \\ x = \dfrac{7 - 4k}{3} \\ y = m \\ z = k \end{cases}$

9. 937.5 mL of the 50% solution with 562.5 mL of the 10% solution

10. This gives an inconsistent system of equations; thus all the nutritional needs cannot be met exactly.

11. (a) $\dfrac{100\ 000 - 4k}{3}$ dollars in stock A,

$\dfrac{50\ 000 + k}{3}$ dollars in stock B, and k dollars in stock C; where $0 \leqslant k \leqslant 25\ 000$

(b) $20 000 in stock A and $10 000 in stock C

9.8 CHAPTER 9 TEST

1. $\begin{cases} x = 4 \\ y = -2 \\ z = -3 \end{cases}$

2. $\begin{bmatrix} 1 & 1 & 4 & | & -5 \\ 0 & 1 & 13 & | & -15 \\ 0 & 0 & 1 & | & -\frac{21}{22} \end{bmatrix}$

3. (a) yes (b) no
4. (a) yes (b) no

5. $\begin{bmatrix} 1 & 0 & 0 \\ 0 & 1 & 0 \\ 0 & 0 & 1 \\ 0 & 0 & 0 \end{bmatrix}$

6. (a) $\begin{cases} x = k + 1 \\ y = k - 2 \\ z = k \end{cases}$ $\begin{cases} x = 1 \\ y = -2 \\ z = 0 \end{cases}$ $\begin{cases} x = 2 \\ y = -1 \\ z = 1 \end{cases}$

(b) $\begin{cases} x = 3 \\ y = -1 \end{cases}$

(c) $\begin{cases} w = -k \\ x = k \\ y = -k \\ z = k \end{cases}$ $\begin{cases} w = 0 \\ x = 0 \\ y = 0 \\ z = 0 \end{cases}$ $\begin{cases} w = -1 \\ x = 1 \\ y = -1 \\ z = 1 \end{cases}$

7. 1875 mL of the 90% solution with 3125 mL of the 50% solution

8. (a) $(120\ 000 - 4k)$ dollars in fund A, $(3k - 60\ 000)$ dollars in fund B, and k dollars in fund C; where $20\ 000 \leqslant k \leqslant 30\ 000$
(b) $20 000 in fund A and $15 000 in fund B
(c) $30 000

CHAPTER 10 LINEAR PROGRAMMING

REVIEW AND PREVIEW TO CHAPTER 10
EXERCISE 1
1. (a)

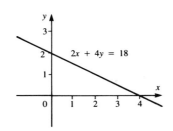

(b)

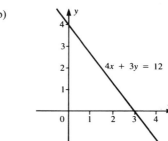

(c)

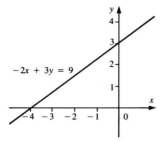

$-2x + 3y = 9$

(g)

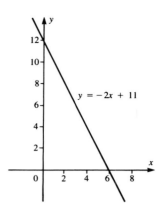

$y = -2x + 11$

(d)

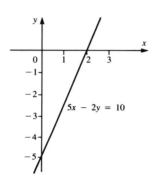

$5x - 2y = 10$

(h)

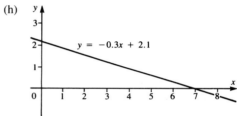

$y = -0.3x + 2.1$

(e)

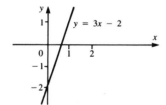

$y = 3x - 2$

EXERCISE 2

1. (a)

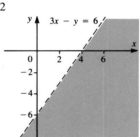

$3x - y = 6$

(f)

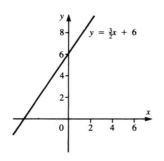

$y = \frac{3}{2}x + 6$

(b)

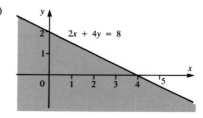

$2x + 4y = 8$

(c)

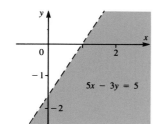

$5x - 3y = 5$

(g)

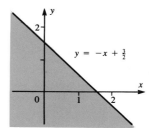

$y = -x + \frac{3}{2}$

(d)

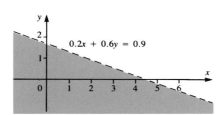

$0.2x + 0.6y = 0.9$

2. (a)

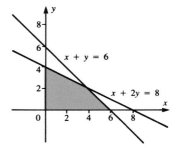

$x + y = 6$

$x + 2y = 8$

(e)

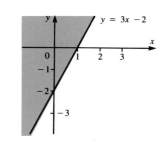

$y = 3x - 2$

(b)

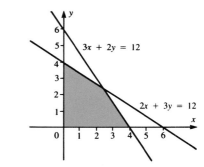

$3x + 2y = 12$

$2x + 3y = 12$

(f)

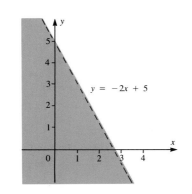

$y = -2x + 5$

(c)

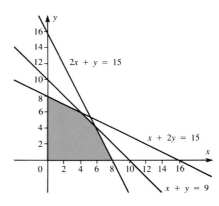

$2x + y = 15$

$x + 2y = 15$

$x + y = 9$

EXERCISE 3

1. (a)

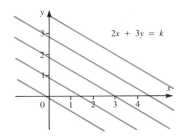

(b)

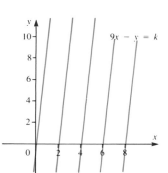

(c)

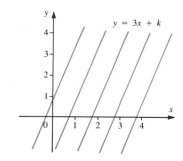

(d)

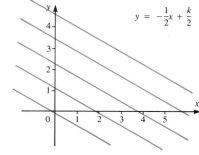

(e)

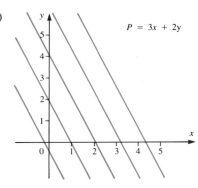

EXERCISE 10.1

1. (a) $s + t < 500$ (b) $s > t$ (c) $t < s$

(d) $s \geq 2t$ (e) $0.75s + \dfrac{2.95}{3}t \leq 100.00$

2. (a) let c be the number of dozens of corn
let b be the number of bunches of beets
Maximize: $P = 0.50C + 0.35b$
(b) let n be the number of novels
let t be the number of textbooks
Maximize: $P = 0.75n + 2.25t$
(c) let a be the number of hectares of apples
let p be the number of hectares of peaches
Maximize: $P = 300a + 250p$
(d) let s be the number of short articles
let l be the number of long articles
Maximize: $P = 250s + 400l$
(e) let b be the number of km by bus.
let t be the number of km by train
Minimize: $C = 0.10b + 0.15t$

3. Maximize: $P = 1.20b + 1.75h$
Subject to: $10b + 15h \leq 600$
$5b + 3h \leq 240$
$b \geq 0$
$h \geq 0$

4. Maximize: $O = 250p + 175s$
Subject to: $400p + 500s \leq 4000$
$8p + 4s \leq 44$
$p \geq 0$
$s \geq 0$

5. Maximize: $A = w + r$
Subject to: $2.25w + 0.50r \leq 900.00$
$\frac{1}{6}r - w \leq 0$
$w \geq 0$
$r \geq 0$

6. Maximize: $P = 175p + 140c$
    Subject to: $p + c \leqslant 20$
                  $3p + 2c \leqslant 42$
                      $p \geqslant 0$
                      $c \geqslant 0$

7. Maximize: $M = 3o + 7n$
    Subject to: $o + n \leqslant 30$
                  $n - o \leqslant 0$
                     $o \geqslant 0$
                     $n \geqslant 0$

8. Maximize: $P = 500t + 900r + 150w$
    Subject to: $3t + \frac{1}{2}r + 2w \leqslant 22$
                 $2t + 8r + w \leqslant 30$
                 $t + 2r + 4w \leqslant 26$
                         $t \geqslant 0$
                         $r \geqslant 0$
                        $w \geqslant 0$

9. Maximize:
$$f = \sum_{i=1}^{n} a_i x_i$$
    Subject to:
$$\sum_{i=1}^{n} a_{ki} x_i \leqslant c_k, \text{ for } k = 1, \dots, m$$
    and $x_i \geqslant 0$, for $i = 1, \dots, n$

10. Maximize:
    $P = 12p_1 + 9p_2 + 15p_3 + 9p_4 + 12p_5 + 18p_6$

    Subject to:
    $5p_1 + 3p_2 + 8p_3 + 2p_4 + 6p_5 + 6p_6 \leqslant 120$
      $3p_1 + 6p_2 + p_3 + 2p_4 + 5p_5 \leqslant 70$
  $2p_1 + 5p_2 + 3p_3 + 4p_4 + p_5 + 4p_6 \leqslant 80$
  $0.22p_1 + 0.07p_2 + 0.15p_3 + 0.04p_4$
               $+ 0.11p_5 + 0.22p_6 \leqslant 3.70$
        and $p_1, p_2, p_3, p_4, p_5, p_6 \geqslant 0$

EXERCISE 10.2

1. (a) (i) B   (ii) C   (iii) D   (iv) B
    (b) (i) B   (ii) C

2. (a) (i) B   (ii) A   (iii) B   (iv) B
    (b) (i) C   (ii) D

3. (a) $m = 3, n = 0, K = 9$
    (b) $h = \frac{6}{5}, k = \frac{6}{5}, R = 8.4$
    (c) $s = 3, t = 4, R = 21$
    (d) $u = \frac{5}{2}, v = 0, M = \frac{15}{2}$
    (e) $w = \frac{20}{7}, z = \frac{12}{7}, N = 18.29$
    (f) $x = 5, y = 2, W = 20$
    (g) $p = 11, q = 0; V = 132$
    (h) $r = 6, s = 5, P = 196$

4. let the slope of the objective function be m
    (a) $m > m_1$ (b) $m_2 < m < m_1$ (c) $m < m_2$

EXERCISE 10.3

1. real estate: \$10 000, stocks: \$10 000, return: \$3000

2. Nutrifood: 5.25 kg, Omnidiet: 1.875 kg, cost: \$24.94

3. bats: 40, sticks: $13\frac{1}{3}$; profits: \$71.33

4. punches: $\frac{5}{2}$; shears: 6; output 1675.

5. windows: 171.4 m², roof and walls: 1028.6 m²; surface area: 1200.0 m²

6. potatoes: 2 ha; corn: 18 ha; profit: \$2870

7. old songs: 15, new songs: 15; success index: 160

EXERCISE 10.4

1.

	pivot column	pivot
(a)	2nd	5
(b)	1st	35
(c)	1st	4
(d)	2nd	19
(e)	2nd	4
(f)	3rd	12
(g)	3rd	4

2. (a) $x = 7, y = 4, R = 23$
    (b) $x = \frac{7}{2}, y = 9, A = 53$
    (c) $x = 7, y = \frac{5}{2}, z = 24, w = 13, M = 123$
    (d) $x = 5, y = 11, z = \frac{9}{2}, w = 23, P = 201$

3. (a) $x = 5.6, y = 2.4, P = 32.8$
    (b) $x = 4, y = 7, P = 29$
    (c) $x = 9, y = 4.5, z = 13.5, P = 139.5$

4. (a) $x = 24, y = 0, z = 0, C = 1200$
    (b) $x = 7.75, y = 8.08, z = 8.83, P = 73.25$

5. dimension: $(m + 1)$ by $(n + m + 2)$

EXERCISE 10.5

1. (a) normal tapes: 3000; chromium dioxide tapes: 3000; profits: \$2700

(b) normal tapes: 500; chromium dioxide tapes: 3000; metal: 2500; profits $2950

2. compact discs: 4.8; turntables: 0; cassette decks: 4.8; profit $288

3. Option 1: $5000; Option 2: $20 000; Option 3: $25 000; Return $7400

4. grade X: 0t; grade XX: 100t; grade XXX: 0t; profit $5000

10.6 REVIEW EXERCISE

1. (a) B   (b) B
2. (a) $x = 6, y = 0, G = 54$
   (b) $x = 5, y = 3, W = 44$
3. (a) $x = 6, y = 0, P = 54$
   (b) $x = 18, y = 0, z = 9, P = 144$
4. (a) $x = 0, y = 450, C = 22\ 500$
   (b) $x = 0, y = 9, z = 6.5, P = 424$
5. regular tires: 100; radials: 125; profit $7950
6. product X: 15.67; product Y: 0; product Z: 2.67; product W: 10.17; profit $319.50

10.7 CHAPTER 10 TEST

1. Maximize: $P = 220w + 260c$
   Subject to: $w + c \le 400$
   $$\frac{w}{25} + \frac{c}{20} \le 18$$
   $$w \ge 0$$
   $$c \ge 0$$

2. (a) $x = 0, y = 2, K = 18$
   (b) $x = 0, y = \frac{7}{3}, M = 16\frac{1}{3}$

3. 10-gauge mufflers: 4; 12-gauge mufflers: 4; profit $76

4. economy seats: 3; deluxe: 0; executive: 3; profit $81

CUMULATIVE REVIEW FOR CHAPTERS 8 TO 10

1. (a) 3×4 (b) 1, 4   (c) a_{31}
2. (a)

To

		1	2	3	4
	1	0	1	2	1
From	2	1	0	0	2
	3	1	0	0	1
	4	1	0	0	0

$= A$

(b) $A^2 = \begin{bmatrix} 4 & 0 & 0 & 4 \\ 2 & 1 & 2 & 1 \\ 1 & 1 & 2 & 1 \\ 0 & 1 & 2 & 1 \end{bmatrix}$

(c) The entry a_{ij} in A^2 is the number of two-step paths from i to j.

3. (a) $\begin{bmatrix} 4.8 & 29.6 \\ 5.6 & 13.6 \\ -1.2 & -2.4 \end{bmatrix}$ (b) $\begin{bmatrix} 0 & -3 & \frac{1}{2} \\ \frac{1}{6} & \frac{1}{3} & -7 \end{bmatrix}$

(c) $[-15 \quad -44]$ (d) $\begin{bmatrix} -13 & -31 & 7 \\ -70 & -44 & 43 \end{bmatrix}$

(e) $\begin{bmatrix} 36 & -29 & -29 \\ 67 & -96 & -45 \\ 144 & -116 & -116 \\ -114 & 77 & 95 \end{bmatrix}$ (f) $\begin{bmatrix} 5 & 25 \\ 20 & -12 \end{bmatrix}$

(g) $\begin{bmatrix} 7 & 10 \\ -1 & -4 \end{bmatrix}$

4. (a) $\begin{bmatrix} 0.32 & -0.95 & 6.15 \\ 0.46 & 3.53 & -3.07 \end{bmatrix}$

(b) $\begin{bmatrix} 16 & -27 \\ -36 & 61 \end{bmatrix}$ (c) not possible

(d) $\begin{bmatrix} 13.9 & 10.8 & -8.7 \\ -29.8 & -27.3 & 12.7 \end{bmatrix}$

5. JANET JACKSON

6. (a)

Regular Hours

Worker

	1	2	3	4
Mon	8	8	8	8
Tues	8	8	8	8
Wed	8	8	8	8
Thur	8	8	8	8
Fri	8	8	8	8

Overtime Hours

Worker

	1	2	3	4
Mon	0.5	0	0.5	1
Tues	0.5	0.5	0.5	1
Wed	0	0	0.5	0.5
Thur	1	1	1.5	2
Fri	0	0	0	0.5

(b)

Weekly Pay

Worker

1	2	3	4
516	507	534	570

(entries are in dollars)

7.

Final Marks

Anchors, J.	70
Bettram, T.	86
Gallo, B.	49
Hutton, B.	60

(marks are rounded to the nearest percent)

8. (a) yes   (b) no   (c) yes   (d) no

9. (a) yes (b) no (c) yes (d) no

10. (a) $P^2 = \begin{bmatrix} 0.73 & 0.27 \\ 0.72 & 0.28 \end{bmatrix}$ $P^3 = \begin{bmatrix} 0.727 & 0.273 \\ 0.728 & 0.272 \end{bmatrix}$

(b) $S^{(1)} = [0.75 \quad 0.25]$ $S^{(2)} = [0.725 \quad 0.275]$

$S^{(3)} = [0.7275 \quad 0.2725]$ (c) $\left[\frac{8}{11} \quad \frac{3}{11} \right]$

11. (a)

	Provincial	Private
Provincial	0.8	0.2
Private	0.4	0.6

$= P$

(b) $P^2 = \begin{bmatrix} 0.72 & 0.28 \\ 0.56 & 0.44 \end{bmatrix}$ $P^3 = \begin{bmatrix} 0.688 & 0.312 \\ 0.624 & 0.376 \end{bmatrix}$

(c) 66%, 66.4% (d) 44% (e) $\left[\frac{2}{3} \quad \frac{1}{3} \right]$

12. (a)

		To			
		1	2	3	4
	1	0	$\frac{1}{3}$	0	$\frac{2}{3}$
From	2	$\frac{1}{2}$	0	$\frac{1}{2}$	0
	3	0	$\frac{1}{3}$	0	$\frac{2}{3}$
	4	$\frac{1}{2}$	0	$\frac{1}{2}$	0

$= P$

(b) $P^2 = \begin{bmatrix} \frac{1}{2} & 0 & \frac{1}{2} & 0 \\ 0 & \frac{1}{3} & 0 & \frac{2}{3} \\ \frac{1}{2} & 0 & \frac{1}{2} & 0 \\ 0 & \frac{1}{3} & 0 & \frac{2}{3} \end{bmatrix}$ $\begin{array}{l} P^3 = P \\ P^4 = P^2 \end{array}$

(c) $\frac{1}{2}$ (d) $\frac{1}{2}$ (e) $\frac{1}{3}$

13. (b) $\left[\frac{4}{9} \quad \frac{1}{3} \quad \frac{2}{9} \right]$

14. (a) $\begin{cases} x = 4 \\ y = -1 \\ z = 2 \end{cases}$ (b) $\begin{cases} x = \dfrac{-5k - 8}{9} \\ y = \dfrac{7k + 58}{9} \\ z = k \end{cases}$

15. (f) $\begin{bmatrix} 1 & 3 & | & 4 \\ 0 & 1 & | & \frac{5}{7} \\ 0 & 0 & | & 1 \end{bmatrix}$

16. (a) no (b) no (c) yes

17. (a) $\begin{bmatrix} 1 & -14 & | & 16 \\ 0 & 1 & | & -\frac{12}{11} \end{bmatrix}$

(b) $\begin{bmatrix} 1 & 2 & -1 & | & 1 \\ 0 & 1 & \frac{1}{6} & | & \frac{1}{6} \\ 0 & 0 & 1 & | & -\frac{1}{3} \\ 0 & 0 & 0 & | & 1 \end{bmatrix}$ (c) $\begin{bmatrix} 1 & -1 & | & 2 \\ 0 & 1 & | & -2 \\ 0 & 0 & | & 1 \\ 0 & 0 & | & 0 \end{bmatrix}$

18. (a) $\begin{cases} x = \frac{27}{17} \\ y = \frac{103}{34} \end{cases}$ (b) $\begin{cases} x = 1 \\ y = -3 \\ z = 2 \end{cases}$

(c) $\begin{cases} x = k - 4 \\ y = 3k - 12 \\ z = k \end{cases}$ (d) $\begin{cases} w = \dfrac{3m - 5k + 12}{8} \\ x = \dfrac{-m - k - 4}{8} \\ y = m \\ z = k \end{cases}$

(e) $\begin{cases} w = 1 \\ x = 2 \\ y = 1 \\ z = 2 \end{cases}$

19. 937.5 mL of the 50% solution with 562.5 mL of the 90% solution

20. 100 g of food I, 150 g of food II, 50 g of food III

21. (a) $(2k + 3m - 10\,000)$ dollars in fund A, $(30\,000 - 3k - 4m)$ dollars in fund B, k dollars in fund C, and m dollars in fund D

(b) $3750 in fund A and $1250 in fund D

22. (a) $B(\frac{11}{2}, 4)$

(b) any point on the line segment BC

23. (a) S has a maximum value of 54 which occurs at the point (6, 6).

(b) T has a maximum value of 57 which occurs at the point (4, 11).

24. (a) P has a maximum value of 62 when $x = -14$ and $y = 26$.

(b) P has a maximum value of -200 when $x = 100$, $y = -60$, and $z = -10$.

25. P has a maximum value of 43 when $x = 5$, $y = 2$, and $z = 5$.

26. $6666.67 in Stock A, $8000.00 in Stock B, and $5333.33 in Stock C

INDEX